Manufacturing

Materials and Processes

THE IRWIN SERIES IN MANAGEMENT

Consulting Editor   JOHN F. MEE, *Indiana University*

MOORE   *Manufacturing Management*   3d ed.

NIEBEL   *Motion and Time Study*   3d ed.

ROSCOE   *Organization for Production*   3d ed.

JUCIUS   *Personnel Management*   5th ed.

CRUICKSHANK & DAVIS   *Cases in Management*   3d ed.

FILIPETTI   *Industrial Management in Transition*   rev. ed.

SPRIEGEL & MYERS (Editors)   *The Writings of the Gilbreths*

TERRY   *Principles of Management*   4th ed.

VORIS   *Production Control: Text and Cases*   rev. ed.

SIMONDS & GRIMALDI   *Safety Management: Accident Cost and Control*   rev. ed.

JONES   *Executive Decision Making*   rev. ed.

NIEBEL & BALDWIN   *Designing for Production*   rev. ed.

PATTON, LITTLEFIELD, & SELF   *Job Evaluation: Text and Cases*   3d ed.

SHULL (Editor)   *Selected Readings in Management*   First Series

SHULL & DELBECQ (Editors)   *Selected Readings in Management: Extensions and Modifications*   Second Series

BRENNAN   *Wage Administration: Plans, Practices, and Principles*   rev. ed.

LAITALA   *Engineering and Organization*

JUCIUS & SCHLENDER   *Elements of Managerial Action*   rev. ed.

HANEY   *Communication: Patterns and Incidents*

JOHNSON   *Personnel and Industrial Relations*

DEPHILLIPS, BERLINER, & CRIBBIN   *Management of Training Programs*

MORRIS   *The Analysis of Management Decisions*   rev. ed.

THAYER   *Administrative Communication*

ROSCOE   *Project Economy*

EELLS & WALTON   *Conceptual Foundations of Business*

HOUSTON   *Manager Development: Principles and Perspectives*

SEIMER   *Cases in Industrial Management*

REED   *Plant Layout: Factors, Principles, and Techniques*

AMMER   *Materials Management*

BROOM   *Production Management*

SCOTT   *Human Relations in Management: A Behavioral Science Approach*

SIEGEL   *Industrial Psychology*

TIMMS   *The Production Function in Business: Fundamentals and Analysis for Management*

NADLER   *Work Design*

FOX   *The Management Process: An Integrated Functional Approach*

CHAMPION & BRIDGES   *Critical Incidents in Management*

MOORE & KIBBEY   *Manufacturing: Materials and Processes*

MANUFACTURING

MATERIALS AND PROCESSES

by

HARRY D. MOORE

and

DONALD R. KIBBEY

DEPARTMENT OF INDUSTRIAL ENGINEERING
THE OHIO STATE UNIVERSITY

1965

RICHARD D. IRWIN, INC.

HOMEWOOD, ILLINOIS

First Printing, March, 1965

Library of Congress Catalog Card No. 65–12419

PRINTED IN THE UNITED STATES OF AMERICA

Preface

THIS BOOK has been written with the intention that it be used as an assignment and reference text for use with a single introductory, comprehensive
course concerned with manufacturing. Such courses are mostly offered
at the second or early third year level of college for students in engineering who have had little or no previous work with either engineering materials or manufacturing processes. The greatest value can be provided by
the subject matter if it is taught immediately before the majority of tech-
nical courses by which abstract decision making ability is developed. This
presentation, because of its broad coverage and use of every day language,
should be of value also to nonengineering students who wish to gain
knowledge of the manufacturing field.

In the past, a number of different courses were used to cover the subject matter included in this book. Each phase was treated separately in
great depth with emphasis on how things were done and little attention
given to why work was done in certain ways. Since World War II, the
trend has been to treat all manufacturing processes together as a single
integrated subject. This has been due, in part, to the great increase of all
knowledge, and the resulting decrease of learning time available for each
individual field and, in part, to the increase in fundamental information
that permits broad treatment with understanding.

Although there have been many new developments in recent years, and
all of them, such as chemical milling, electrospark machining, and explosive forming are important, or even indispensable in certain areas, they
all supplement rather than replace the standard methods that have been
the backbone of manufacturing for many decades. The major emphasis in
a text of this type must continue to be on the standard methods, and the
difference between texts is largely on emphasis, balance, and detail.

An attempt has been made here to establish a logical sequence and balanced treatment of the subject matter as an aid to understanding. Materials, which are essential to all manufacturing, become a common tie
between the processes. Fundamental information regarding materials and
their properties is provided in Chapters 2 through 6. Additional discussion
of materials occurs in relation to specific processes. Chapters 7 through 24
cover processes grouped roughly according to the state in which the
material is treated. The primary emphasis is with the processes. Secondary
emphasis on facilities is necessarily concerned mainly with job shop type
equipment. Most of the concepts and subject matter of Chapters 25 and

v

26 are common to all processing. Line drawings are used for a large majority of the illustrations since they usually depict the principles of interest better than photographs.

It is felt by the authors that a laboratory taught in conjunction with classroom discussion is highly desirable in this subject to convey the concept of relationship between theory and physical objects. At The Ohio State University, complete laboratories for Foundry, Heat Treating, Welding, and Machine Tools, as well as some press equipment, are used concurrently with classroom discussions. It is recommended that when laboratories are used, chapters containing fundamental information concerning materials and processes to be covered in laboratory work, be assigned and discussed as early in the program as possible. The best order will be dependent on the laboratory facilities, but proper scheduling will insure maximum learning and understanding from both experiences.

The following material is a regrouping of much old knowledge, together with some more recent information, particularly of fundamental type, concerning basic processes. It is hoped that this presentation will aid in promoting a better understanding of the general manufacturing processes and the relations between them as they are used today. It is also hoped that students, who although they may not at a later date be connected directly with manufacturing, will nevertheless be better equipped to make decisions and perform their work because of information or interest gained through use of this book.

The authors gratefully acknowledge the aid, encouragement, and support given by their colleagues, and the cooperation of the publisher, all of which have been essential to the completion of this book.

Harry D. Moore
Donald R. Kibbey

Columbus, Ohio
March, 1965

Table of Contents

Introduction

WEBSTER DEFINES "manufacture" as "to make by hand, by machinery, or by other agency; to produce by labor, especially now with division of labor and usually by machinery."

Such a definition is all-inclusive and covers the making of foods, drugs, textiles, chemicals, and in fact, everything made usable or more usable by the conversion of shape, form, or properties of natural materials.

Special interests have developed in the mechanical and industrial phases of industry concerned with the making of durable goods of metals and plastics. The majority of metals and some other materials fall in a class that is often referred to as *engineering materials*. Characteristic of this group are the properties of relatively high hardness, strength, toughness, and durability. Although they may compete with metals in many applications, glass, ceramics, wood, concrete, and textiles have usually been excluded from these structural materials because of a difference in the combination of properties, difference in processing requirements, and difference in type of goods produced. The list of so-called engineering materials continues to grow with the addition of new metallic combinations, plastics, and even materials that have been previously excluded from the list, as they are developed with better properties or used in new applications.

Present interpretation of the term "engineering materials" includes most of the metals and those plastics that are solids and have reasonable strength at room temperature. This book will be concerned with these materials and the processes that are used to shape them or change their properties to a more usable form. Obviously, these restrictions eliminate consideration of many important fields of manufacturing, such as drugs, textiles, chemicals, and assembled structures, such as buildings, highways, and bridges, even though such structures frequently make use of some products of engineering materials.

HISTORY

Growth. The growth of industry in the United States starting with colonial times is typical of industrial development throughout history.

1

Early settlers were concerned primarily with the growing and storage of food, and those manufactured goods that could not be produced within the family unit were, of necessity, imported. As the economy developed, family specialization occurred and excess production was made available for trade and sale. As specialization increased, so did efficiency, and the increased demand for cheaper products resulted in the growth of industry to factory form, although early industries were still controlled by single families. Some family-controlled businesses are still in operation, even though the majority of goods produced at the present time is made by corporate enterprises under the ownership and ultimate control of many individuals.

Early manufacture was dictated largely by the needs of the times. Agricultural and military requirements set up a demand for specific types of products. The DuPont Company, which started in Revolutionary War times to manufacture gunpowder for the Continental Armies, has continued in existence and grown to include a wide variety of products.

One of the earliest industrial operations to develop was the reduction of ore to metal. By its very nature, this process is not adaptable to very small operations, particularly for ferrous metals. The trend of increasing size in this industry has continued to the present. A few very large corporations produce nearly all of the basic metals, even though there are many small fabricators.

Following revolutionary times in the United States, development of industry continued to be controlled by the predominantly agricultural economy. Major developments were tied frequently to new inventions, such as the reaper, the cotton gin, and to the use of steam power for rail and water transportation. The Civil War and the development of the West provided much incentive for industrial developments in the manufacture of firearms, and the first example of true interchangeable manufacture was in the production of rifles for the government by Eli Whitney.

Following the Civil War, developments in transportation and higher efficiency in the production of agricultural products freed a larger proportion of the population for work other than farming. The resulting growth in the production of goods, which at the time were considered luxuries, caused an increase in the standard of living which has continued to the present. Many manufactured items, such as the automobile, may start as luxury items but become necessities at a later date.

The modern period of our economy as identified with manufacturing began with the development of facilities for producing inexpensive steel during the middle of the nineteenth century. Since that time, improvements in production have been largely the result of increased knowledge of materials and people, and many small improvements in machines, processes, and techniques. The social and economic climate possible under the United States political system has made these results possible. It is interesting to note that in the United States and other areas of the world, mainly western Europe, industrial development has proceeded most rapidly under systems of free enterprise.

It is difficult to assess the importance of manufacturing processes in today's economy. Manufactured products are an integral part of everyone's life, to the extent that most persons do not realize the amount of investment and labor necessary to make these products possible. Consider, for example, a few of the essential manufactured products a person might come into contact with or depend on at the beginning of an average day. Giving thought only to articles made of metals and plastics, the list would include alarm clock, bedside lamp, radio, bed and mattress springs, bed hardware, drawer pulls on chest and dresser, glides on furniture feet and fastening hardware, bathroom fixtures and plumbing, clothing fasteners, toothbrush, electric razor, the complex of transmission and generating facilities necessary to furnish power for the razor, and similar systems for water, sewage, and natural gas. After making use of the stove, coffee pot, tableware, including possibly even plastic dishes, and other kitchen items, a person might be ready to use his automobile. Many of these items are assemblies of large numbers of parts constructed of many different materials. The average automobile is made of over 25,000 individual parts involving the use of over thirty different metals and alloys and over twenty different plastics.

Over sixty million persons are employed in the United States in manufacturing, wholesale and retail trade, agriculture, business and finance, professional services, and other service industries. Of these, over 25 per cent are employed in manufacturing, where they make goods for themselves and others. Of our gross national income approximately 25 per cent goes for the purchase of manufactured goods.

INDUSTRIAL RELATIONSHIPS

Competition in Industry.   In the American way of life, the profit motive is the root of most business, including manufacturing. The system presumes direct competition, so that if a number of companies are engaged in the manufacture of similar products, the sales volume will be in proportion to the product quality, promotional activities, service policies, and price. The cost of manufacturing therefore becomes of prime importance, for the company that can produce at the lowest cost and maintain quality can spend more for sales activities, can sell at a lower cost, or can make a larger profit per sale than competitors in a less fortunate position. For this reason industry is continually engaged in a battle to lower production costs and to gain this favored position.

Because of the complexity of the over-all manufacturing operation, many decisions are of necessity rather arbitrary. For nearly all products there are many alternatives of design, materials, and processing that will satisfy the function the product is to have. For many products direct sales price comparisons are not adequate, for different demands for similar products made of different materials or having different designs may exist. Most frequently, the purchaser is the final decision-maker, which makes advertising and sales promotion a most important phase of the business. Adequate time is often not available to study the effect of a design on the market, or to investigate all the possible processes of manufacture, particularly for new products. In many cases to determine the exact material that would serve best even for a fixed design is too time consuming. In any case, reasonable decisions must be made and when absolute knowledge is not available, they are based on past experiences of similar nature. Because of the interrelationships existing in manufacturing, accurate decisions will depend not only on exact knowledge of a specific area but also on knowledge of related areas.

Personnel.   Two kinds of workers are needed in any kind of manufacturing operation: those who work directly with the product, and those who are only indirectly connected with the product but are more concerned with the organization producing the goods. Those directly connected with the product include the designer and those responsible for choosing the processes, establishing control over the operation, and supervising all of the manufacturing. The designer must not only know the functional requirements of the product but also have some knowledge of the probable market demands for various levels of quality and appearance. He certainly must be familiar with the mechanical properties of the various materials he might choose. Less obvious at times is the importance of the part the designer plays in the selection of manufacturing processes. If the designer designates a sheet metal housing for a radio, obviously it cannot be a plastic molded part or a die casting. If he specifies certain tolerances, these may not only dictate that a certain dimension be achieved by machining but the tolerance may even dictate the specific type of machine to be used. Clearly, then, in nearly every case, the designer's choices of materials, shapes, finishes, tolerances, and other factors restrict the possible choices to be made in the manufacturing processes.

The choice of a manufacturing process within the limitations set by the designer is dependent on the availability of equipment, the condition and design of the equipment permitting it to meet the required specifications, the relationship between the quantity to be produced and the cost of production by various methods, and even knowledge of the operating personnel. Manufacturing supervision is responsible for turning out a specified quantity of product with a satisfactory quality and cost. This can be done only with complete knowledge of the product, the alternative methods of manufacture, and familiarity with the available facilities. A constant campaign for cost reduction by improved efficiency of manufacture is necessary for all directly connected personnel in order for a company to maintain a competitive position.

It would seem that knowledge of materials and processes is of minor importance to indirectly connected personnel, but even when true it is only a matter of degree. The salesman of many products may have to be as familiar with the design as the designer himself in order to compare the product with competitive makes. He may also have to be completely familiar with the installation problems and know what modifications the production department can make in order to meet specific customer needs. Although not directly connected with the product, the purchasing department has a strong influence on the manufacturing operation by reason of its responsibility for supplying materials and equipment of suitable type and quantity at suitable times. Substitution of materials is often necessary and may be left to the discretion of the purchasing department, but unless properly performed may lead to increased cost of manufacture or may even prevent satisfactory results with its use. For example, one steel substituted for another may satisfy the functional requirements of the product but may lead to increased machining costs, thus decreasing or eliminating the margin of necessary profit.

In general, the administration of a company has the responsibility for setting up the policies and rules for the operation of that company. This can be done only with the knowledge of the effect of those policies and rules on all of the operating departments of the company. The inner relationships that exist between all supervisory levels of a manufacturing operation make universal knowledge of the areas important and consultation between areas mandatory. A change in tolerances may be desirable from a processing standpoint, but its effect on quality and life must be fully investigated. Ultimately most decisions become a compromise between the most desirable from a design, life, and function standpoint and the most practical from a production and cost standpoint.

Nomenclature. The ability of personnel from one area of manufacturing to discuss and understand problems with people from some other area will depend directly on their knowledge of the nomenclature used in the area of concern. In order for a designer to discuss intelligently with a production man the effects of various design changes on the method and cost of production, he must be able to understand and to use the language of the production man. In most cases, he needs to know at least the names of the various machines and tools that might be used and have some understanding of their capabilities. In the final analysis, the problems of the production of a product become the problems of the machine and equipment operators. The loyalty, cooperation, and respect of these people for supervision, necessary for the proper solution of these problems, can be gained only when a full understanding exists between the two groups. Of necessity, this understanding must be based on suitable language, including proper terminology, even to the point of using local terms and nicknames when appropriate.

SUBJECT MATTER

Even with the limitations that have been placed on the term "manufacturing processes" for use in this text, many possible variations of content and organization of subject matter exist. Each subject mentioned could be expanded into complete book length. In fact, at some time or other most have been discussed in fine detail and expanded to large volume. The principal objective of this text will be to present a broad discussion of the materials used in manufacturing and the principal processes by which these materials are made into usable products, with emphasis such that the reader obtains a comprehensive, balanced picture of manufacturing. The subject of "materials and manufacturing processes" is truly a single subject when the orientation of discussion is toward the end product that must be manufactured to fulfill some function. Although the attempt has been made in this book to show this singleness of subject matter, it is still necessary to treat specific areas as specific topics. In order to make efficient use of specialization, manufacturing plants are normally divided into areas in which the equipment and personnel concentrate on particular manufacturing operations. In some cases this is carried to the extreme. For example, a foundry may produce only iron castings of a certain weight range because of specialized experience and equipment. This product would normally be a raw material for other manufacturing operations and would be processed in another plant to give it the properties required by the final consumer.

Materials.   An understanding of materials is important to any kind of manufacturing procedure. One or more materials are required for any product, and most can be processed in a number of different ways. However, for many materials, the processing possibilities are very limited, and the process may be dictated by the particular material chosen.

The practical difference between various materials is in their *properties* or combinations of properties. Compared to many other materials, steel is hard and strong and may be chosen as a manufacturing material for these reasons. Steel is elastic to some extent. However, if elasticity is the important property of interest, it may be necessary to choose a material like rubber for the application. An intelligent comparison of materials depends on precise meanings of the terms used and an understanding of how properties are defined and measured. Some properties are defined by tests, such that the results may be used directly as design data. For example, from a standard tensile test the modulus of elasticity of a material may be determined, and a designer can use this value to predict accurately the deflection of a certain size beam under known loads. On the other hand, many properties are defined no less specifically but in a more arbitrary manner, making the use of the results obtained by tests difficult or impossible for calculation. However, they still provide the opportunity for accurate comparisons with data obtained from similar tests from other materials. For example, hardness measurements may give an indication of relative wear resistance for different materials, or hardness numbers may correlate with tensile strength for a given material, but the number values can seldom be used directly in computation for design loads.

Each elemental material has at least some properties different from those of all other elemental materials. Some or all of the properties of an element may be changed by the addition of even small parts of another element, and in many cases the properties obtained from the combination will be better than those of either element alone. In a similar manner, the properties of elements or combinations can be varied by the type of treatment given the material. The treatments that affect properties are often intentional for this purpose. However, the properties are no less affected, often in an undesirable way, by the processes being used with the objective of shaping the material. Sufficient knowledge of the relationship between the properties and the processing of materials may permit the improvement of the properties as a natural result of the processing for a different main objective. Reducing the cross-sectional size during the shaping of most metals results in an increase in hardness and strength that may be undesirable if the metal must undergo further deformation processing. In many cases, this increase in hardness and strength that occurs as a result of the processing can be beneficial and part of the product design.

Processes. Manufacturing consists in converting some raw material, which may be in rough, unrefined shape, into a usable product. The selection of material and processes seldom can be separated. Although in a few cases some unusual property requirements dictate a specific material, generally a wide choice exists in the combination of material and processing that will satisfy the product requirements, and the choice usually becomes one of economic comparison. In any case, a material is usually selected first, sometimes rather arbitrarily, and a process must then be chosen. Processing consists of one or many separate steps producing changes in shape, properties, or both.

Shape changing of most materials can be accomplished with the material in one of several different forms or states: liquid, solid, or plastic. Melting of a material and control of its shape while it solidifies is referred to as casting. Reshaping of the material in the plastic or semi-solid form is called molding, forging, pressworking, rolling, or extrusion. Shaping by metal removal or separation in the solid state is commonly performed to produce product shapes. If the removed material is in chipped form, the process is machining. Other methods which remove material in larger sections are classified differently. The joining of solid parts by welding usually involves small localized liquid areas which are allowed to solidify to produce a complete union between solid parts.

The material condition and energy form used to effect these shape changes may vary. As noted, the material may be in a liquid, solid, or plastic form. The energy may be supplied in the form of heat, mechanical power, chemical reaction, electrical energy, or, as in one of the newest procedures, in the form of light. In nearly every instance, one of the principal objectives is shape-changing, but usually part of the energy is consumed in change of properties, particularly in those processes involving changes of state or solid deformation. Different materials react differently to the same energy system, and the same materials react differently to different energy systems.

Many concepts and fundamentals in reference to materials are common to different kinds of processes. When studied in connection with the material, these concepts, then, can be applied regardless of the kind of process by which the material is treated. The metallurgical changes that take place during solidification during casting are of the same nature as those that take place in fusion welding.

The completion of a product for final use generally includes the various finishing procedures apart from basic shape-changing processes. The dimensions and properties that are produced by any process are subject to variation, and in practically all cases some *inspection* procedure is necessary for controlling the process and for assuring that the final product meets certain specifications as to size and other properties. As one of the final steps or sometimes at an intermediate stage, control of properties by *heat treatment* or other means is necessary. The final steps may also require surface changes for appearance, wear properties, corrosion protection, or other uses. These steps may involve only the base material or may require the addition of paints, platings, or other coatings.

Few finished products are constructed of single pieces of material because of the impracticality of producing them at reasonable cost. Also, it is frequently necessary that properties that can be obtained only from different materials be combined into a single unit. The result is that most manufactured articles consist of *assemblies* of a number of separate parts. The joining of these parts can be accomplished in a great number of ways, with the best method being dependent on all the factors of shape, size, and material properties involved in the particular design.

Order.   The enormous quantity of knowledge available about manufacturing processes can be discussed in varying degrees of depth and coverage. The following chapters of this book have been chosen with the hope that the order will seem logical and conducive to maximum learning. The discussion does not go into great detail in the belief that for the purpose of this book broad knowledge of the over-all manufacturing system is more important than the development of depth in any special but restricted area. As has been indicated in this chapter, the properties of materials are very important and cannot be divorced from the manufacturing processes. The first topic of discussion will therefore be properties, with their definitions, which generally consist of a description of the test procedure used to measure the property, followed by the fundamentals of metallurgy as they apply to the commonly used manufacturing materials and processes. The properties of specific materials will be discussed only as they affect the process choice and as the process affects them.

The major processes of casting, deformation shaping, welding, machining and finishing will be discussed in that order, with an emphasis in length and depth commensurate with their use and importance in industry. The experiences of many individuals frequently leads to a belief that one area of manufacturing is more important than others, but the interrelationships are such that no one area can exist alone and the importance of any process in an individual case is entirely dependent upon its relation to the product with which it is associated.

QUESTIONS

1. What are the principal characteristics of engineering materials?
2. Why does specialization increase efficiency?
3. What conditions in the post Civil War period led to larger, centralized manufacturing organizations?
4. How does "free enterprise" benefit industry?
5. Discuss the importance of manufactured products to the individual.
6. Is it true that if you build a better mouse trap, the world will beat a path to your door? Why?
7. Describe the functions of the two different kinds of workers needed in a manufacturing operation, once a design has been established.
8. Why should a product designer be familiar with manufacturing processes?
9. Why are most quality tolerances set at values above those most desirable from the design or product life point of view?
10. Why should sales engineers have knowledge of manufacturing processes?
11. Why are most manufacturing plants divided into a number of distinct operating divisions?
12. By what criteria are materials chosen for a product?
13. Discuss briefly the interrelation of material properties and manufacturing processes.
14. What are the two main objectives of manufacturing processes?
15. What factors lead to the use of composite structures instead of single materials for many applications?

CHAPTER 2

Properties of Materials

INTRODUCTION

As INDICATED in Chapter 1, the qualities of materials that are of practical interest to manufacturing are measured quantities called *properties*, as distinguished from the physical make-up of materials called atomic *structure*. Science in recent years has made great strides in determining the atomic structure of materials. Fig. 2–1 shows that an atom of iron contains

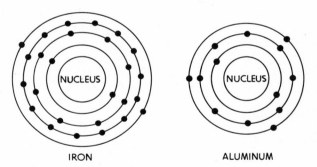

IRON　　　　　　　ALUMINUM

FIG. 2–1. Atomic structure.

twenty-six electrons and an atom of aluminum contains thirteen electrons, arranged in definite order. The number and arrangement of particles in each atom actually determine all the properties of any material, and it should be theoretically possible to predict the properties of a material from the structure of the atoms. Physicists and chemists can make some predictions of properties, particularly chemical and electrical, based on structure, but the mechanical properties of greatest interest to a study of manufacturing processes must still be defined and measured by empirical test for each material.

Classes of Properties. The application to which a material is put determines which of its properties are most important. The chemical properties (reaction with other materials) are of interest for all materials mainly because of the almost universal need for resistance to corrosion. Although aluminum is chemically more active than iron, it happens that in most atmospheres the corrosion by-products from aluminum form a denser coating which acts as a shield to further corrosion than do the by-products formed in a similar way with iron.

While the atomic and crystalline structure of all metals gives them high electrical and thermal conductivity compared to nonmetals, individual metals still differ considerably. Aluminum is among the best electrical conductors, while iron, although much more conductive than nonmetals, is a poor conductor compared to aluminum. On the other hand, the magnetic properties of iron make it much more desirable for some electrical uses than aluminum.

All metals are opaque to visible light, and the structure of all metals permits them to be polished to have a highly light-reflective surface. When the combination of all properties is considered, however, individual metals become preferred for specific types of mirrors. Back surfacing on a glass mirror is normally silver, front surfacing is aluminum, a camp mirror may be stainless steel (an iron-base alloy), and a reflector in a slide projector subjected to excessive heat may be chromium plated.

Physical properties for each material are constants associated with the atomic structure. These include density (weight per unit volume), crystalline type, atomic spacing, specific heat, cohesive strength (theoretical), melting point, and others. Iron has a much higher melting point and density than aluminum. Iron can exist in several different crystalline structures as opposed to aluminum, which makes possible control of properties by heat treatment of iron-based alloys not possible with aluminum. Some aluminum-based alloys may be heat treated, but by entirely different procedures.

Of most interest for manufacturing are the mechanical properties of hardness, strength, and others which are of prime importance in design considerations in determining sizes and shapes necessary for carrying loads. These qualities will also determine the work loads for any deformation type of manufacturing process. Neither iron nor aluminum in the pure state have many applications in manufacturing because their strengths are low, but their alloys, particularly of iron, are the most commonly used of all metals. Both of these materials can be strengthened over their weakest forms by factors of almost ten by suitable alloying and treatment, with alloys of iron being approximately five times as strong as those of aluminum on a volume basis.

As pointed out at the beginning of the chapter, the properties that have been discussed are actually dependent on the atomic structure of a material, but in practice these properties must be separately measured. In a similar way, different properties which are related to hardness, strength, ductility, and other physical and mechanical properties and which are frequently of even greater importance to manufacturing must in practice be defined by separate tests. These include tests for *castability*, *weldability*, *machinability*, and others describing the ability of the material to be processed in definite ways. Tests of this type may be developed at any time there is need for determining the ability of the material to meet critical needs of processing, and they are usually performed under conditions very similar to those under which the process is performed.

Material cost is not a functional property as are strength, density, and the others discussed previously, but is an extremely important variable quality that is often the principal influencing factor in the material choice. To be usable a material must be in a given form, at the proper place, at the right time. Form might be anything from a metallic ore to a semifinished product and the cost will be dependent not only on previous processing but also on abundance or scarcity, difficulty of mining and transporting, availability of processing facilities, supply and demand, and quantity or lot sizes purchased. It is evident that many influences affect material prices and frequent changes can be expected.

Significance of Properties. A designer is necessarily interested in properties since he must know material strengths, before he can calculate sizes and shapes required to carry loads, chemical properties to meet corrosive conditions, and other properties to satisfy other functional requirements. Knowledge of processing properties is likely to be of more importance to manufacturing personnel than to the designer, although even he must be able to choose material that can be manufactured in a reasonably economical manner. Many manufacturing problems arise from choice of materials based only on functional requirements without consideration for which is the most suitable for the processing required.

Most products can be manufactured from a number of different possible materials that will satisfy the functional requirements. However, some are more desirable from the product standpoint than others and one particular material may have the best possible combination of properties. Likewise, all materials can be manufactured by some means, although costs of manufacturing will vary and there will likely be one single material from which a usable product could be manufactured at lowest cost. It is seldom that a material can be chosen that has both optimum properties for the product and optimum properties for manufacturing, so the majority of material choices turn out to be compromises. The final choice may be a result of trial and error tests between several possible best materials and processes. New choices may be required with changes of design, material availability, processes, or market demand.

LOADING SYSTEMS AND MATERIAL FAILURE

Loading Systems. Physical loading of material is a result of applying force under one or more simple, basic loading systems. In nearly all cases, even when a piece is loaded by only a single set of outside forces, the internal loads developed are more complex than those applied. However, in many testing procedures this complexity is disregarded and the forces are treated as though they were uniform throughout the material.

Internal forces, acting upon imaginary planes cutting the body being loaded, are called stresses. For purposes of ease in understanding and comparison, stresses are usually reduced to unit stress by assuming that the force acts uniformly over the cross-sectional area under consideration. The load-per-unit area can then be calculated by dividing the total load or force by the area on which it acts. The common units used for measurement and description in the United States are pounds for force and square inches for area, so unit stress becomes pounds per square inch, psi, or when dealing with large figures, thousands of pounds per square inch, kips/in².

Fig. 2–2 represents a bar subjected to a pulling force of P pounds. If

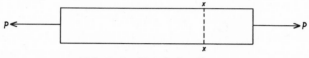

FIG. 2–2. Simple loading.

the load P is uniformly distributed over the ends of the bar, it can be assumed that the internal loads are uniformly distributed. Examination at any plane $x - x$ perpendicular to the line of applied force will show that the crystals along one side of the plane are trying to separate from the adjacent crystals along the plane. This internal force tending to separate the material is known as stress. If the surface area cut by the imaginary plane $x - x$ is A, then the unit stress (s) is P/A, or written as a formula, s =P/A. Since in this case the applied force is a pulling force or tensile force, the internal loads are tensile stresses (S_t) and the formula may be written $S_t = P/A$.

Reversal of the external load P would cause the internal stress to be compressive instead of tensile. The unit stress on any plane $x - x$, perpendicular to the line of force would then be calculated from the formula $S_c = P/A$.

Tension and compression forces and their resulting stresses are always considered to act normally, or perpendicular, to a plane. A third term, shear stress, is used to describe the effect of forces that act along, or parallel, to a plane. No provision has been made for describing forces meeting a plane at an angle for the purpose of studying stresses. Since, however, an infinite number of planes may be of interest, it becomes necessary to resolve the stresses to various angles to determine critical values and positions. Fig. 2–3 illustrates a bar similar to that of Fig. 2–2 with tensile load being applied to the end. As already illustrated, tensile stresses and tensile stresses only are set up on any imaginary plane, $x - x$, perpendicular to the line of force. If, however, a plane not perpendicular to the line of force is examined, it can be seen that a different situation exists. The imaginary plane, $z - z$, is at any angle ϕ. The area cut by the imaginary plane, $z - z$, is equal to the area of the plane $x - x$ multiplied by the secant of the angle ϕ. Therefore, the unit shear stress is:

$$S_s = \frac{P \sin \phi}{A \sec \phi} = \frac{P}{A} \sin \phi \cos \phi$$

$$= \frac{P}{2A} \sin 2\phi.$$

Substitution of the values for ϕ in this formula shows that for zero or 90°, the shear stress is equal to zero, but that the maximum shear stress occurs when ϕ is 45° and the sin of 2 ϕ equals 1, in which case the shear stress, S_s, equals $P/2A$, reaching a maximum value which is one half the tensile stress,

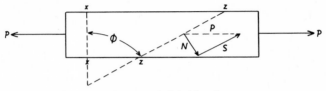

FIG. 2–3. Resolved loading.

S_t, established on a plane that is perpendicular to the applied force.

If, in the above case, the external load were compression instead of tension, shear stress would have been developed to the same magnitude and in the same way but opposite in direction and combined with compressive stress instead of tensile stress. Shear stress exists alone only in a bar subjected to pure torsion, that is, a bar being twisted with no tension, compression, or bending present. Shear stresses are important to our manufacturing processes because these are the forces that cause material to shift in plastic flow and permit shape changing by deformation processes.

Bending loads create a combination of stresses. The concave side of a bent body will be in compression and the convex side in tension with transverse shear occurring along the axis between them. The maximum unit stress will be in the outer fibers of the bent body and is represented by the formula $S_b = Mc/I$ where M equals bending moment, in lbs., c equals distance from neutral axis, in in., and I equals moment of inertia of body, in in^4.

The principal point to be made in this discussion of forces and stresses is that structural designs must be of suitable size and shape and made of material with proper strength values to withstand the loads imposed upon them. When a structural member (almost any object) is physically loaded by weight, by pressure from mechanical, hydraulic, or pneumatic sources, by thermal expansion or contraction, or by other means, internal stresses are set up in the member. The size, direction, and kind of stresses are dependent upon the loading system. The magnitude of the unit stresses will be dependent not only upon the applied force but upon the area of material resisting the stresses. As loads are increased, unit stresses will increase to the point where, in some direction, one or more reach critical values in relation to the material. Failure by plastic flow or by fracture can then be expected, depending upon which critical values are reached first. In nearly all cases of fracture failure, the separation of material is preceded by at least a small amount of plastic flow. In those cases where plastic flow occurs to a large degree, fracture failure will finally result.

TESTING

Testing of material is essential to gain practical knowledge of how materials react under various situations. The ultimate goal of any test is to enable the making of decisions which provide the best economic results. In practice two general methods of testing are used. The only test that supplies absolute information about a workpiece or a material is a test of the particular property of interest conducted on that part itself. In this *direct* method of testing, an attempt is made to use the materials under the exact conditions of practical use, and the test may be concerned with a product, a process, or both.

Direct testing is usually time consuming and, for the results to have statistical significance, often requires compilation of data from many test samples. The procedure is necessary, however, for those cases where simpler methods are not available and where sufficient historical information has not been accumulated to permit correlation between the attribute about which information is desired and some other measurable factor. *Indirect testing* involves the use of such a correlation, such that accurate knowledge of the relationship between the two factors must exist.

The ability of grinding wheels to resist the centrifugal forces imposed in use is directly tested by rotating them at higher speeds than those of actual use. Such a test indicates that the wheel strength is sufficient for normal use with some safety margin. An indirect test which is sometimes used for the same purpose can be performed by rapping a suspended wheel to cause mechanical vibrations in the sonic range. A clear tone indicates no cracks. A danger of indirect testing exists as conclusions depend on the assumption that correlation between the measured factor and the critical factor exists under all conditions. The rapping test for grinding wheels does not give any real indication of strength, unless knowledge of the wheel's history permits the assumption that with no cracks it has sufficient strength for use.

A large number of direct tests are destructive. These also are dangerous because the assumption that those not tested are like the ones for which test information has been obtained must be made. A portion of weld bead may be examined for quality by sectioning it to look for voids, inclusions, penetration, bond, and metallurgical structure by visual examination. By this operation, this portion of the bead has been destroyed; regardless of the quality that was found, the only knowledge acquired about the remaining portion of the weld comes from an assumption that it is similar to that examined because it was made under the same conditions.

Over the years a number of tests have been standardized for checking of material properties. Some of these provide data that is useful for design calculation while others have the primary purpose of aiding in material choices by supplying comparative information. Many properties are defined only by the test procedure which has been developed for its measurement. In order to cover the wide range of values occurring with different materials, shapes, and sizes, different sets of conditions have been established for some of the tests. For any test for which this is true it is necessary that the test conditions used be indicated as part of the measurement.

The Tensile Test. One of the more important tests for determination of mechanical properties of materials is the tension test. Material specimens are fastened between a fixed table and a movable table on a machine designed specifically for this purpose. A weighing scale is attached to the tables so that as they are moved apart (together for compression testing) the load imposed on the specimen can be measured. Some machines are fitted with auxillary equipment which takes into account the loads imposed and the resulting elongation of the specimen to actually plot a stress-strain diagram of the test. The same results can be accomplished without this special equipment by measuring the elongation as the loads are increased and plotting the individual points to develop the curve.

In order that these standard tests can be accurately reproducible and be of value for comparison with other tests, test specimens are made to one of several standard designs. Fig. 2–4 shows the dimensions for a standard tension test bar with eight-inch gage length for rolled, flat stock. The radii outside the gage-length portion to the increased section size at the ends are designed, in this and other test bars, to minimize stress direction effects from clamping loads on the end of the bar. Round test bars with the same eight-inch gage length are standard for testing rod and bar materials, but since it is often impossible to produce test samples of this length from castings and forgings and other material sources, a two-inch gage length as shown in Fig. 2–5 is frequently used. The diameter of the parallel section of round, tensile test bars is made to .505 inches (.2 square inches cross-sectional area) to facilitate calculations.

An understanding of a tensile test can best be acquired from a stress-strain diagram made by plotting the unit tensile stress against the unit strain (elongation), as shown in Fig. 2–6. The illustration displays data from a tensile test on ductile steel and is representative of this kind of material only. Curves for other materials take on slightly different shapes.

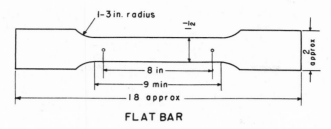

FLAT BAR

ROUND BAR

FIG. 2–4. Tension test bars 8-inch gage length.

The straight line from *A* to *B* represents loads and deformations in the elastic range, and as long as the load at *B* is not exceeded, the material would resume its original position and shape after removal of the load. *B* is the elastic limit for this particular material and loads above that at this point will cause permanent deformation (plastic flow) that cannot be recovered by removal of the load. At the load represented by the point at *C*, plastic flow is occurring at such a rate that stresses are being relieved faster than they are formed and strain increases with no additional, or even with a reduction of, stress. The unit stress at *C* is known as the yield point.

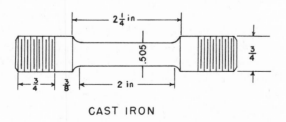

CAST IRON

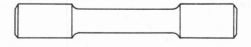

STEEL

FIG. 2–5. Tension test bars 2-inch gage length.

Plastic flow occurring at normal temperature is called cold working, regardless of the kind of loading system under which it is accomplished. As plastic flow takes place, the crystals and atoms of the material rearrange internally to take stronger positions resisting further change. The material becomes stronger and harder and is said to be work-hardened. At the point *D* in Fig. 2–6 the curve suddenly turns upward, indicating that the material has become stronger because of work-hardening and that

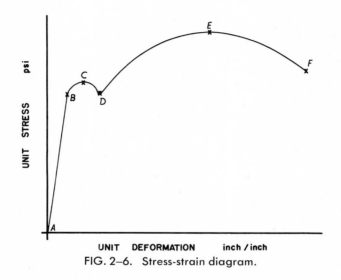

FIG. 2–6. Stress-strain diagram.

higher loads are required to continue deformation. The deformation rate, however, increases until at point *E* the ultimate strength is indicated.

The ultimate tensile strength of a material is defined as being the highest strength in pounds per square inch, based on the original cross-sectional area. By this definition, ductile materials that elongate appreciably and neck down with considerable reduction of cross-sectional area, rupture at a load lower than that passed through previous to fracture. The breaking strength or rupture strength for this material is shown at *F*, considerably below the ultimate strength. This is typical of ductile materials, but as materials become less ductile, the ultimate strength and the breaking strength get closer and closer together until there is no detectable difference.

Many materials do not have a well-defined or reproducible yield point. Plotting of tensile stress-strain values produces a curve of the type shown in Fig. 2–7. For these materials, an artificial value similar to the yield point, called yield strength, may be calculated. The yield strength is defined as the amount of stress required to produce a predetermined amount of permanent strain. A commonly used strain or deformation is .002 inches per inch, or .2 per cent offset, which must be necessarily indicated with

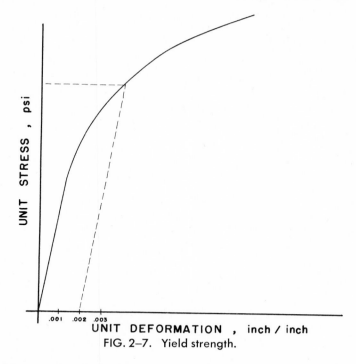

FIG. 2–7. Yield strength.

the yield strength value. The yield strength is the stress value indicated by the intersection point between the stress-strain curve and the offset line drawn parallel to the straight portion of the curve.

In the stress range below the elastic limit the ratio of unit stress to unit deformation, or the slope of the curve, is referred to as the modulus of elasticity or Young's modulus and is represented by E. E, therefore, equals s divided by δ. Following are listed the values of E for some of the more common structural materials:

Aluminum alloys................10 to 11 million psi
Copper alloys...................14 to 19 million psi
Gray iron......................12 to 19 million psi
Steel and high strength irons......28 to 30 million psi
Cemented carbides.............approx. 50 million psi

The gross values of the modulus of elasticity are important to the design of members where deflection or deformation in the elastic range must be given consideration. The relative stiffness or rigidity of different materials can be ascertained merely by comparing their moduli. By rearrangement of the formula for E, the unit deformation δ becomes equal to the unit stress divided by E. If a bar of steel of 1 square inch cross-sectional area and with a modulus of elasticity of 30 million pounds per square inch is subjected to a tensile pull of 1,000 pounds, each inch of length of the bar will be stretched $\frac{1}{30,000}$ of an inch. A steel bar of this cross section 30 inches long would then be elongated $\frac{1}{1,000}$ (.001) of an inch over-all with a 1,000 pound tensile load.

The tension test provides two measures of ductility. One is called per cent elongation, represented by the formula:

$$\text{per cent elongation} = \frac{(L_f - L_o)}{L_o} \times 100$$

where:

L_f = final gage length
L_o = original gage length .

For ductile material the major portion of the elongation will occur over a relatively small portion of the gage length after the specimen begins to neck as it approaches the breaking point. Since much of the elongation is localized, a variation of gage length would cause a difference in calculated per cent elongation.

Another measure, per cent reduction of area, is calculated by comparing the original area of the specimen to the smallest area of the neck at rupture.

The area under a curve is influenced by both of the factors which are used to make that curve. In a stress-strain diagram the area under any portion of the curve is the energy required to deform the material. Up to the elastic limit this energy is recoverable and is called *resilience*. *Toughness* is defined as the ability of a material to absorb energy without fracture. For the tension test the total area under the curve is a measure of toughness.

True Stress—True Strain. In the tensile test just described, stresses were calculated as though the original specimen size did not change. More precisely, the vertical axis of the diagram should be labeled load/original area rather than stress. If each time a load reading were made, the smallest diameter of the specimen were found and the calculation for stress based on this actual diameter, this axis could be labeled true stress. The definition of true strain is somewhat more complex, and in any case true strain does not differ greatly from elongation normally plotted. The greatest difference between the diagram of Fig. 2–6 and a true stress–true strain diagram would be in the plastic flow region. True stress would continue to increase throughout the test, as shown in Fig. 2–8, and maximum stress would occur at the final break. The test of Fig. 2–6 is usually called an engineer's stress-strain diagram. This curve is shown as a dotted line in Fig. 2–8. Not only is it easier to prepare than a true stress–true strain diagram, but the value for ultimate strength obtained from it is more useful for design than the maximum true stress which occurs when the specimen breaks. The true concern of a designer is the maximum load that can be supported, not the maximum stress.

Compression Testing. Up to the elastic limit, most metals are approximately equal in properties under either tensile or compressive loading. Cast iron, however, has a tensile strength of only about one half its compressive strength and is therefore used mostly in applications where the principal loads are of the compressive type. Many nonmetals such as timber, concrete, and other aggregates are also used almost entirely for supporting compressive or compactive loads. This is due in part to higher

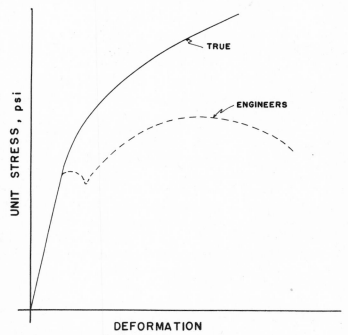

FIG. 2–8.   True stress–true strain diagram.

compressive strength but also is true because with these materials there is high incidence of flaws and faults that might cause sudden failure in tension but produce relatively small effect under compressive loading.

The testing of materials in compression is conducted in much the same manner as in testing under tension. Specimens are placed between tables of a testing machine which are brought together to subject the specimen to compressive loads. Compression specimens must be short compared to their diameter so that column effect will not cause bending with eccentric, unequal loading.

Transverse Rupture Testing. In a number of cases a substitute for the standard tensile test is necessary. With some materials that are difficult to shape or very brittle in nature, it is impractical to produce a specimen for tension testing. This condition occurs particularly with ceramics. With most materials that are very brittle in character, even though a tensile specimen might be produced, the results from the standard tensile test would have only limited significance. It is almost impossible to insure in the tension test that the applied load will be precisely centered in the specimen and will be exactly parallel to the axis of the specimen. If this is not the case, bending moments are introduced in the specimen. With a ductile material, small amounts of plastic flow take place in the specimen, particularly where the load is applied, the specimen aligns itself properly with the load, and the stresses are uniform across the tested area. With a brittle material where this alignment cannot take place, the bending moments result in higher stresses on one side of the specimen than the other. The specimen fails when the highest stress reaches some critical value but the observed stress at this time, based on the assumption of uniformity, is somewhat lower. As a consequence, the results from testing a number of similar brittle specimens exhibit wide variations and are not representative of the true strength of the material.

The transverse rupture test, while it gives less complete information than the tension test, is a fast and simple test, making use of more easily prepared specimens, and especially well suited to brittle materials. In many instances the specimen can be an actual workpiece. The test is particularly well suited for those materials that are to be used in beam applications. It is really the only meaningful type of strength test for reinforced concrete.

The test consists of loading a simple beam as illustrated in Fig. 2–9. While some standards have been set for particular materials, there are no universal standards for specimen sizes and shapes as there are for the tension test.

The modulus of rupture or beam strength is calculated by the formula:

$$S_r = \frac{3PL}{2bd^2}.$$

While this formula is the formula that is used to calculate the maximum actual stress in the outer fibres in a beam, it is based on the assumption that stress remains proportional to strain. This is not the case for most materials when highly loaded, with the result that the calculated "stress" is higher than the actual stress in the outer fibres at rupture, and direct comparison cannot be made with ultimate tensile strength values taken from a tension test, nor can the values of modulus of rupture be used as design tensile strength values. The values are useful for comparing materials and they are useful in design where the material is to be used as a beam.

Shear Testing.   In the section dealing with material failure it was pointed out that when a bar is subjected to a tension load as in the tension test, the value of shear stress existing in the bar at failure can be calculated from the load and the dimensions of the bar. The term *shear*, however, has a broader meaning than shear stress only and is used to describe loading

systems which subject a material to a shearing action. Actually, the stress
distribution in such loading systems is quite complex, but a rather simple
shear strength test has been developed which simulates the conditions of
actual loading and provides information which may be used in design
where the loading situation is similar to that of the test. Such loading

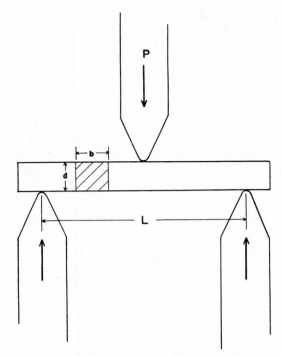

FIG. 2–9. Transverse rupture test.

occurs in the use of bolts or rivets and in shearing operations where
material is being separated. In the test indicated in Fig. 2–10, the bar with
cross-sectional area A is made to fail simultaneously in two places so that
the area of failure is $2A$, and the shear strength is defined as: shear
strength $= P/2A$.

Fatigue Testing. A metal may fail under sufficient cycles of repeated
stress, even though the maximum stress applied is considerably less than
the strength of the material determined by static test. Failure will occur at
a lower stress level if the cyclic loading is reversed, alternating tension and
compression, than if the cycles are repeated in the same direction time
after time. Structural members subject to vibration, repeated variation of
load, or any cyclic disturbance causing deflection must be designed to
have low enough stress levels that fatigue phenomenon will not cause
failure.

Fatigue failure starts at some imperfection in the metal or at some spot where stress concentration is high because of the shape of the member. Holes through the material, notches in the surface, internal flaws, such as voids, cracks, or inclusions or even minor scratches and faults caused by corrosive attack on the grain boundaries, may be sources of fatigue failure. With repeated stressing, a crack starts at one of these fatigue nuclei and grows until insufficient solid metal remains to carry the load and complete

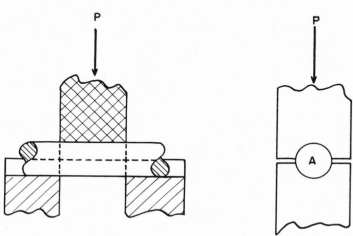

FIG. 2–10. Shear strength test.

failure in a sudden, brittle manner results. Examination of the exposed surface of a fatigue failure shows part of the surface to be smooth and polished while the rest exhibits a well-defined grain structure. The crystalline-appearing portion was separated in the sudden, final break. The smooth part was polished and burnished by the movement of the material with repeated deflection as the crack developed and grew.

Since a material may fail under conditions of a great many repeated loads at a stress level far below that determined by the standard strength test, it is important for a designer to know how different materials stand up under these conditions. The conclusion from one comprehensive study of service failures was that in over 90 per cent of such failures where fracture occurred, fatigue was involved. Tests have been developed with special machines which bend plate-shaped test specimens or subject a rotating beam to a bending load for large numbers of cycles. From data collected from such tests, the endurance limit of a material can be determined.

The *endurance limit* is the highest completely reversed stress whose repeated application can be endured for an indefinitely large number of cycles without failure. Fig. 2–11 shows a typical *S-N* or endurance limit curve. The material represented by this curve would have an endurance limit of 42,000 pounds per square inch since the curve has flattened out and stressing at this level could be continued indefinitely without failure.

Endurance limits correlate fairly closely with tensile strength and for most materials are from about one third to one half the stress required to break a tensile specimen.

For some materials the curve does not flatten even after several hundred million cycles. When the endurance limit cannot be determined, or it is

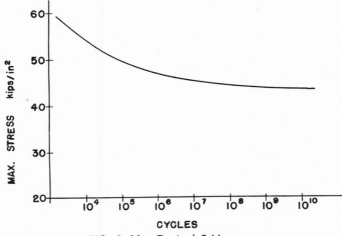

FIG. 2–11. Typical *S-N* curve.

impractical to carry on a test long enough for this determination, it is common practice to use another value, fatigue strength, as the evaluation of the ability of a material to resist fatigue failure. *Fatigue strength* is the stress which can be applied for some arbitrary number of cycles without failure. The number of cycles for which a fatigue strength is valid must always be specified, since the operating stress chosen may be at a level where the *S-N* curve still slopes and indefinite cyclic operation could cause fatigue failure.

Creep.   The term "creep" is used to describe the continuous deformation of a material under constant load, producing unit stresses below those of the elastic limit. At normal temperature, the effect of creep is very small and can be neglected. As operating temperatures increase, however, this deformation by slow plastic flow becomes very important in the design and use of material. Recognition of this phenomenon is most important for the higher-strength materials that are to be used at elevated temperatures.

Creep tests are conducted by applying a constant load to a material specimen held at the desired temperature and measured periodically for deformation over a long period of time. The results may be plotted on a graph of elongation against time, as in Fig. 2–12, with an indication of the maintained temperature and stress level under which the test was conducted. Most creep tests are carried on for periods of at least one thousand hours, so this is a time-consuming test. The *creep strength* of a material is the stress required to produce some predetermined creep rate (the slope of the straight portion of a curve) for a prolonged period of time. Commonly, the stress required to produce a creep rate of 1 per cent in ten thousand hours is used as creep strength. *Stress rupture strength* is defined as the stress required to produce failure at prescribed values of time and temperature.

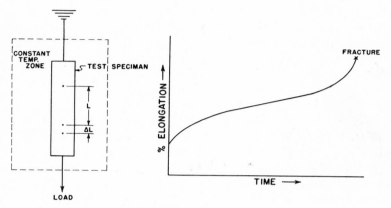

FIG. 2–12.   Creep test.

Notched Bar Test.   Materials are often used in situations where dynamic loads are suddenly applied to produce impact which increases the effective load far above that which would be expected from gradual application of the same load or a similar static load. Tests designed to check the ability of a material to withstand this kind of loading are energy absorption tests that seldom can be used to give information that can be used directly in design, but primarily provide data for comparison of different materials. While such tests are frequently called impact tests, the energy required to cause failure does not differ greatly from that required if the load were applied slowly. True impact failure, in which the energy-absorbing capacity of a material is greatly reduced, occurs only at much higher speeds.

The most commonly conducted tests are bending impact tests, using one of two kinds of specimens, Fig. 2–13, both of which are notched. The Charpy specimen is supported at both ends by a standard impact testing machine and struck on the side opposite that of the notch. The testing machine is constructed with a weighted pendulum, which is lifted to start the test. Upon its release, the pendulum swings past the specimen, breaking it. As it swings on past, the remaining energy can be measured by the height of swing and the absorbed energy determined.

The Izod specimen is supported in the testing machine by one end only and is loaded as a cantilever beam with a notch on the side of impact. Energy absorption is measured in the same way as with the Charpy specimen.

Two kinds of notches are used on bending impact specimens. The Izod specimen is usually made with a 45° angular notch with a .010 inch radius at the bottom. The specimen is extremely sensitive to variation of notch size or change of radius and extreme care in manufacture of the test specimen is necessary for reproducibility of test results. The keyhole notch shown on the Charpy specimen can be duplicated more accurately but is limited in the smallness of the hole producing the notch effect by the size of the smallest drill that will not "drift" in making the hole. The notches in the test specimens act as points of stress concentration and the smaller the notch radius, the more severe is the stressing at this point. These notched test specimens actually provide only information regarding material that is to be used in a similar notched condition, but are often practical because materials are frequently

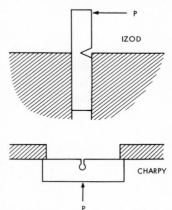

FIG. 2–13. Impact specimens.

used with design shapes or structural imperfections, that cause a structural member to be, in effect a notched beam.

Greater reproducibility and greater similarity between the test and some use conditions can be provided by tensile impact tests. The specimens for these tests are not notched and are supported so that uni-axial tensile impact loads may be applied. The standard impact testing machine with pendulum weight can be tooled for testing small specimens of this type. For larger specimens a special machine with a variable speed flywheel to store energy can be obtained.

Bend Testing. Materials that are to be deformation processed by being subjected to bending loads and materials that may have been affected by localized heating, such as in welding, are sometimes tested by bend tests to provide comparative data. Free bends are accomplished by prebending a flat specimen slightly to produce eccentricity, then loading the specimen in compression (column) until failure occurs or a 180° bend is produced. Normally, the loads to accomplish this are so variable that they are of little value and are not recorded. Instead, the angle of bend at failure is compared with results of other tests.

Guided bend tests bend the test specimen about a fixed radius to 180°. The bend angle of a failure before 180° bending usually cannot be satisfactorily compared with other test results because of nonuniform plastic flow of material in the specimen caused by pressures set up by the guided

bend fixture. Multiple radius guided bends may be used for rating specimens by comparing the smallest radius about which a standard specimen
will bend 180°.

Hardness Testing. The most frequently used test of all for determining
material properties are hardness tests. With sufficient knowledge of material composition and previous processing, hardness tests can be used as
indirect measures for properties entirely different from hardness. For
example, hardness can sometimes be used to separate raw materials of
different composition, to determine whether or not satisfactory heat
treating or other processing has been accomplished, or to measure the
strength and wear resistance properties of a product. Hardness measurements, therefore, are frequently made on raw material, on parts in process,
and on finished goods ready for use.

Most hardness tests result in some kind of a measure of the ability of a
material to resist penetration of the near surface material. Penetration of
material with any kind of indentor requires the use of force and involves
plastic flow of the tested material. The work-hardening qualities of a
material, therefore, become part of most hardness measurements and
partially explain the difficulty of converting from one type of hardness
measure to another because different methods of measuring hardness do
not measure exactly the same thing. They are, however, well enough
standardized to provide useful and practical information.

One of the first standardized systems of measuring hardness made use of
Mohs scale of hardness, which specifies ten standard minerals arranged in
order of their increasing hardness and numbered according to their position. Starting with number 1 as the softest, the standard Mohs scale is:

1 . . . . Talc	6 . . . . Orthoclase (Feldspar)
2 . . . . Gypsum	7 . . . . Quartz
3 . . . . Calcite	8 . . . . Topaz
4 . . . . Fluorite	9 . . . . Corundum
5 . . . . Apatite	10 . . . . Diamond

If a material can be noticeably scratched with the mineral topaz (number 8) but cannot be by quartz (number 7), it would have a hardness
value between 7 and 8 on the Mohs scale. The Mohs scale of hardness has
little value for hardness testing of metals but is still widely used in the
field of mineralogy.

Another abrasion or scratch method of measuring hardness that does
have some practical use in metal working is the file test. Standard test files
can be used to gage quickly the approximate hardness of a material and,
although not very accurate, can be used in many shop situations with
satisfactory results. Experiences and comparison with standard test blocks
will permit a fair degree of accuracy to be attained.

In 1900, a Swedish engineer by the name of Brinell introduced a new

universal system for hardness measurement. The method involves impressing a hardened steel ball into the material to be tested with a definite load
and calculation of a *Brinell* hardness number from the impression size, Fig.
2–14. A wide range of hardnesses can be tested by varying the size of the
ball and the loads imposed, but in the hardness range most frequently
tested, a ball 10 millimeters in diameter is impressed into the material under
a load of 3,000 kilograms for ten seconds in checking steel and with a load
of 500 kilograms for thirty seconds to check nonferrous materials. The
numerical value of the Brinell hardness number is obtained by dividing the
load in kilograms by the area of the spherical impression in millimeters. In

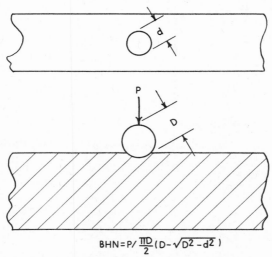

$$BHN = P / \frac{\pi D}{2} (D - \sqrt{D^2 - d^2})$$

FIG. 2–14. Brinell hardness measurement.

practice, the average diameter of the impression is usually read with a
measuring microscope and the Brinell hardness number determined directly from a table.

The Brinell hardness method has the advantage over most other measuring methods of determining a hardness value over a relatively large area,
thus reducing the inconsistencies caused by flaws, imperfections, and
nonhomogeneity in the material, likely to be introduced with small area
measurement that includes only a few metallic grains. With plain carbon
and low alloy steels, the relation between tensile strength and Brinell
hardness is so consistent in the medium hardness range that the tensile
strength of the steel can be closely approximated by multiplying the
Brinell hardness number (BHN) by 500. The principal disadvantages of
the Brinell method are that the machine to supply the load for impressing
the ball in the material is often cumbersome and cannot always produce
the impression where desired. The ball cannot be impressed in very thin

materials and, of course, cannot be used to examine extremely small samples, and the impression is of such size that it may harm the appearance or use of finished surfaces.

Because of its convenience and the fact that only small marks are left in the work tested, one of the most frequently used tests is the *Rockwell* hardness test, Fig. 2–15. This also is an impression test, but the hardness number is determined by a differential depth measurement which can be read directly on a dial indicator of the machine used to impose the load. To obtain a Rockwell hardness reading, the equipment is used to first place a minor load of 10 kilograms on the penetrator to reduce the effect of dirt,

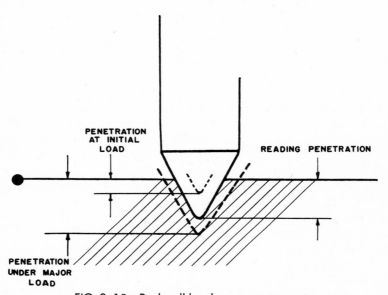

FIG. 2–15. Rockwell hardness measurement.

oil films, scale, and other surface conditions that might affect the reading. A major load of 60,100, or 150 kilograms, depending upon the type of penetrator and scale being used is then imposed to force the penetrator into the work material. After the penetrator has seated to its full depth— the time usually being controlled by a dash pot built in the equipment—the major load is removed and the permanent differential depth between the minor and major loads is read directly as a Rockwell Hardness Number.

Although provision has been made for use of a ⅛ inch diameter ball as a penetrator, almost all hardness testing with the Rockwell equipment is done with one of two standard penetrators. The one used for softer materials is a 1⁄16 inch diameter hardened steel ball supported in a special chuck which permits easy replacement should the ball become damaged. The testing of harder materials that would cause excessive deformation of the hardened steel ball is performed with a diamond-tipped penetrator with 120° conical point and spherical tip of .200 millimeter radius. The diamond penetrator or indentor is known as a brale.

Which of the two penetrators used and the size of load impressing it into the test material are defined by a letter which becomes part of the Rockwell reading. The accompanying table shows the relationship between the scale designation, the loads, and the penetrators.

Scale	Load Kilograms	Penetrator
A	60	Brale
B	100	$\frac{1}{16}''$ Ball
C	150	Brale
D	100	Brale
F	60	$\frac{1}{16}''$ Ball
G	50	$\frac{1}{16}''$ Ball

The letter designating the test conditions is a very important part of a hardness notation since the number alone could represent a number of different hardness conditions. For example, a Rockwell hardness reading of B 60 would represent a relatively soft material such as a medium hard copper alloy, while a Rockwell hardness reading of C 60, sometimes written R_c 60, would represent a hardness such as might be used for a hardened tool steel to cut metals.

Another machine, the Rockwell *Superficial* Hardness Tester, is constructed and used in much the same manner as the standard machine but is a special purpose tester designed to be used in work where only a very shallow impression is permissible or where measurement of hardness of material very close to the surface is the principal aim. The Superficial Hardness Tester makes use of the same penetrators, except that the Brale is of higher precision and is designated as **N** Brale. The loads used to cause penetration are lighter, being of 15, 30, and 45 kilograms. The following table shows the testing conditions for Superficial Rockwell Hardness Testing.

Scale	Load Kilograms	Penetrator
15N	15	N Brale
30N	30	N Brale
45N	45	N Brale
15T	15	$\frac{1}{16}''$ Ball
30T	30	$\frac{1}{16}''$ Ball
45T	45	$\frac{1}{16}''$ Ball

As in the previous case, the scale indication must be used as a prefix to the hardness number read from the dial.

The *Vickers* hardness tester operates on the same principle as the Brinell instrument, but makes use of a diamond penetrator shaped as a four-sided pyramid. The impression made by the penetrator is accurately measured by swinging a microscope into position without moving the test piece in the machine. As in the Brinell method, the Vickers hardness number is the ratio of the force imposed on the indentor to the area of the pyramidal impression. In the lower range of hardness, under Brinell 300, Vickers and Brinell hardness numbers are almost identical, but above this range they separate as hardness increases, primarily because of distortion of the steel ball used for Brinell testing when forced against the harder materials.

It is frequently important, particularly in research or development work, to test the hardness of material that is very thin or very small in area. A number of special machines have been developed for determining "microhardness." One of the more commonly used pieces of equipment of this type is the *Tukon* Microhardness Tester. Normally, the machine is fitted with an elongated diamond-shaped penetrator. Microscopic measurement of the impression provides information which can be converted to *Knoop* numbers. Knoop hardness numbers often cannot be compared directly with Brinell or Vickers hardness measurement because the elongated impression is rather strongly affected by the directional properties of the material being tested. The use of a symmetrical, square-based, pyramid-shaped indentor will provide hardness data comparable with that of the other systems.

It should be self-evident that the lighter the indentor loads and the smaller the impressions made, the greater the care that must be used to perform a hardness test and the better must be the quality of surface on which it is made. In Brinell testing, small surface imperfections tend to be averaged out because of the large area covered, but in microhardness checks where the impression may be only a few thousandths of an inch long, small scratches and surface imperfections may contribute large errors. Microhardness testing is usually performed on a highly polished surface and in many cases, to obtain reproducibility, it is necessary to etch the surface to reveal the constituent structure in order to locate the impression properly.

Factor of Safety. No property, structural or otherwise, whether calculated from theoretical considerations or determined by test procedures, can be safely used at or very close to its ultimate (maximum) value. For one thing, tests are neither consistent enough nor accurate enough, particularly since they are not conducted under exact use conditions, to permit strong confidence to be placed in their results. Also, because of the complexity of stress-analysis problems, it is almost essential that simplifying assumptions be made during design to prevent design costs and time from becoming prohibitive. A factor of safety is therefore used to prevent working too close to maximum values. The factor of safety is the ratio between the maximum value and the working value and is determined by competent judgment, taking into consideration all of the conditions of use. Factors of safety vary from as low as one to as high as five or more. They may be applied to any quality but are most commonly used in connection with strengths.

As an example of its use, if the ultimate tensile strength of a certain grade of steel is 80,000 pounds per square inch and its elastic limit 60,000 pounds per square inch, an allowable stress, or working stress, of 20,000 pounds per square inch would provide a factor of safety of four, based on the ultimate strength, or of three based on the elastic limit.

The closer the factor of safety approaches one, the more the danger that an unforeseen fault or condition of use may cause failure. On the other hand, the larger the factor of safety, the greater the volume and weight of material needed, with a corresponding increase in cost and in storage problems. Factors of safety in the range of two to four are most common, but a satisfactory value depends upon a great number of conditions, some of which are as follows.

Allowances must be made for unexpected loads or conditions. This is particularly true if the human element is large in the use of the equipment, since the human mind is most unpredictable. It is common to include a factor of at least two in the factor of safety where a design is based on static tensile strength values but subjected in use to varying loads. This corresponds approximately to the ratio of static tensile strength to endurance limit.

Allowance must be made for environmental and time factors. Strengths of most materials are greatly reduced by corrosion and other chemical effects. Other materials lose strength or become brittle with age. The consistency of test data should influence the factor of safety choice. Test information should be of large enough volume to be statistically significant. Larger safety factors are necessary with materials varying widely in quality than with those that are quite uniform.

Whether or not the use of a material may affect human life has a large influence on the factor of safety. In the designing of hoists, cranes, and other lifting equipment, factors of safety of five or more are commonly used because failure could mean injury or loss of life. The same thing applies, of course, to aircraft design. Here, however, space and weight are very important, and large factors of safety could easily prevent a usable design, so the problem is handled in a different way. Extreme care is used in selecting and testing materials. Stresses are carefully calculated and, as far as possible, the structures built, so that they cannot be overloaded in use. Thus, by spending more care, time and money preceding and during manufacturing, it is possible to use a smaller factor of safety because of greater certainty of not exceeding the design condition.

QUESTIONS

1. Why has there been, up to the present time, only minor interest shown by manufacturing engineers in atomic structure of materials?
2. Upon what are the properties of any material dependent?
3. Why are chemical properties of a material often of interest in manufacturing?
4. What structural difference permits better control of properties by heat treatment for iron than for aluminum?
5. Why are the most common structural metals nearly always used in an alloyed form?
6. What major factors affect the cost of a material?
7. Why is it true that materials used for manufacturing are often compromises?
8. What is the meaning of the term "loading system"?
9. Describe the types of stresses that may occur in a material under load.
10. Name the two kinds of material failure that can result from excessive loads.
11. What is the difference between direct and indirect testing?
12. What is the principal danger of indirect tests?
13. What is the principal danger of direct tests?
14. What is the elastic limit of a material?
15. Why is the breaking strength of a ductile material less than its ultimate strength?
16. Why may the percentage elongation be different from two tensile test specimens that are identical except for gage length?
17. Why is the tensile test not suitable for brittle materials?
18. What test is substituted for the tensile test when checking brittle materials?
19. Describe fatigue failure.
20. What is the difference between endurance limit and fatigue strength?
21. Why is knowledge concerning creep more important today than in earlier times?
22. Izod and Charpy specimens are used in what kind of testing?
23. Why is it difficult to convert one type hardness reading to another accurately?
24. Name and describe the way hardness is determined by five different methods.
25. Why is it possible to use smaller factors of safety in design of aircraft than for railroad equipment?

CHAPTER 3

The Nature of Materials

THE CHEMIST ordinarily considers the smallest functional portion of matter to be the atom. The atom consists of a nucleus made up of positively charged protons and uncharged neutrons surrounded by electrons, which carry negative charges, moving in orbit at different levels. Each level of orbit can contain only a definite number of electrons, and the number of levels or shells is determined by the atomic number of the element. All the shells will usually be full except the outer one, which is short of the maximum possible number of electrons for most materials. All of the electrons are in constant motion, spinning about their own axis and traveling through their orbits about the nucleus with speeds dependent on their energy level, which in turn is strongly affected by the pressure and temperature conditions. The physicist's picture of an atom depicts it as a heavy nucleus containing most of the mass, surrounded by a cloud of moving electrons.

A number of different forces exist between the different atoms of a material, some of them attractive, some repulsive. The nature of any material depends primarily on the nature of these forces, which themselves depend not only on the type of atom, but also on the energy level of the atom. At high free energy levels, the repelling forces predominate and the atoms tend to move as far from each other as possible. This condition is called the *gaseous* state. If the free energy of the material is lowered, the forces change, and a condition of equilibrium is reached in which the atoms assume fixed average distances from each other, although still free to to move and not tied closely together. In this *liquid* state, the materials have fixed volume but assume the shape of the container in which they are placed.

As the free energy level is further decreased the mobility of the atoms decreases. There are at least four different mechanisms by which the atoms can assume positions well fixed enough that for practical purposes the material could be called *solid*. Of the materials of interest to manufacturing, all the metals occur as *crystalline* solids.

35

Metallic Structure. <u>Metals are usually defined as materials having some degree of plasticity, relatively high hardness and strength, good electric and thermal conductivity, crystallinity when solids, and opaqueness.</u> A definition based on atomic structure is more precise. A metallic solid is one that has free electrons available in the structure to carry a current and which has a negative coefficient of conductivity with increasing temperature.

Fig. 3–1 shows the relationship that exists between the three states of

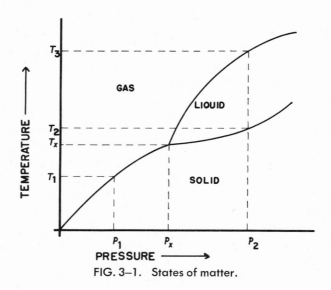

FIG. 3–1. States of matter.

matter for a crystalline material. At the intersection on the curve of temperature T_1, and pressure P_1, it will be noticed that an increase of temperature of a material for which this curve is valid would cause the material to change directly from solid to gas. Similarly, a reduction of pressure (shift toward the left) would also cause the same change. Such a change of state from solid directly to gas is known as *sublimation*. Arsenic is the only metallic material that acts in this way at atmospheric pressure. At pressure P_2, the atoms of the material will become sufficiently active when the temperature is raised to T_2 that a change is made from solid to liquid state. A further increase in temperature at this same pressure to point T_3 will cause a second change from liquid to gas. The intersecting point of the curves at the temperature T_x and pressure P_x is known as the *triple point* and occurs at the temperature and pressure conditions under which a material may exist as a solid, liquid, or gas, or partially all three at the same time. For most metals, this point occurs below normal temperatures and well below atmospheric pressure, so most metals upon being heated go through the changes from solid to liquid to gas as the temperature increases.

As the energy of a liquid metal is reduced by taking away heat, the

attraction between atoms increases until they arrange themselves in definite three-dimensional geometric patterns that are characteristic of the
metal. These structures are called *space lattices* and consist of network
groupings of identical *unit cells* which are aligned in parallel planes.

There are fourteen types of crystal lattices, but most of the common
and commercially important metals in the solid state exist in one of three
structures. These are, as shown in Fig. 3–2: body-centered cubic, face-

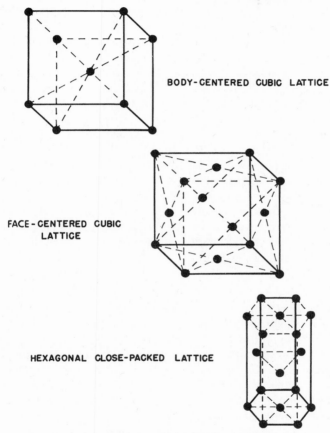

BODY-CENTERED CUBIC LATTICE

FACE-CENTERED CUBIC
LATTICE

HEXAGONAL CLOSE-PACKED LATTICE

FIG. 3–2. Common metallic space lattice.

centered cubic, and hexagonal close packed. In the illustrations of unit
cells the dots representing atoms should be considered as centers of activity for the atoms and not as graphic illustrations of the atoms themselves.

A single unit cell does not exist alone. In order to attain stability, it must
grow past some critical size by being joined with other cells which share
the atoms on the outer adjacent surface. For purposes of illustration, it has
been assumed that a unit cell can exist by itself and that all its atoms belong
to it alone.

The body-centered cubic cell is made up of nine atoms. Eight are located on the corners of the cube with the ninth positioned centrally between them. The body-centered cubic is a strong structure, and in general, the metals that are hard and strong are in this form at normal temperatures. These include chromium, iron, molybdenum, tantalum, tungsten, and vanadium.

Face-centered cubic cells consist of fourteen atoms with eight at the corners and the other six centered in the cube faces. This structure is characteristic of ductile metals and includes aluminum, copper, gold, lead, nickel, platinum, and silver. Iron, which is body-centered cubic at room temperature, is also of the face-centered structure in the temperature range from about 1670° Fahrenheit to 2550° Fahrenheit. This is a solid state change that will be discussed more thoroughly in the following chapter.

Seventeen atoms combine to make the hexagonal close-packed unit cell. Seven atoms are located in each hexagonal face with one at each corner and the seventh in the center. The three remaining atoms take up a triangular position in the center of the cell equidistant from the two faces. The metals made with this structure are quite susceptible to work hardening, which will be discussed in the following chapter. Some of the more commonly used metals that crystallize with this structure are cadmium, cobalt, magnesium, titanium, and zinc.

Tin is an exception to the other commonly used metals in that the atomic configuration is body-centered tetragonal, which is similar to the body-centered cubic, but has wider atomic spacing and an elongated axis between two of the opposite faces.

Solidification. As the temperature of the liquid metal is reduced and the atoms become less active, they are attracted to each other and take definite positions to form unit cells. Since cooling cannot be exactly the same for every atom, certain ones will assume their positions ahead of others and become a nucleus for crystal formation. In the process of assuming their positions, these first atoms will give up kinetic energy in the form of heat, which retards the slowing down of other atoms; but as heat removal is continued, other atoms will take their places along the sides of the already solidified unit cell, forming new cells that share atoms with the first and with others to come later. Orderly growth continues in all directions until the crystal, or as usually referred to for metals, the *grain,* runs into interference from other grains that are forming simultaneously about other nuclei.

Although with some metals and with special treatments it is possible to grow single crystals several inches in diameter, with most metals and at the usual cooling rates, great numbers of crystals are nucleated and growing at one time with different orientations. If two grains that have the same orientation meet, they will join to form a larger grain, but if they are forming about different axes, the last atoms to solidify between the growing grains will be attracted to each and must assume compromise positions in an attempt to satisfy a double desire to join with each. These misplaced atoms are in layers about the grains and are known as *grain boundaries*. They are interruptions in the orderly arrangement of the space lattices and offer resistance to deformation of the metal. A fine-grained metal with large numbers of interruptions, therefore, will be harder and stronger than a coarse-grained metal of the same composition and condition.

Grain Size.   The grain sizes produced during solidification are dependent both upon the rate of nucleation and the rate of growth of grains. For most materials the rate of growth is relatively low and the primary influence on grain size is by the rate of nucleation. Grain size can be used as an indication or measure of properties, and, for this reason, visual standards have been set up to aid accurate comparisons.

Grain size exerts an important influence on the mechanical properties of materials and, fortunately, can be controlled by methods much more precise than by manipulation of the factors that influence growth during solidification. In some processes though, particularly casting, the solidification grain size is important, because with some materials and some shapes, grain size cannot be readily changed after the first formation. In those cases where changes can be effected, additional processing costs will be added. The methods, other than by solidification, which can be used for grain-size control involve solid-state changes.

As has already been indicated, coarse grains in the harder materials have lower strength than fine grains; however, coarse grain materials machine more easily, requiring less power, although the quality of surface produced will not be as good with a finer-grained material. Coarse-grained material (irons and steels) is easier to harden by heat treatment than fine-grained material of the same composition but has increased susceptibility to cracking under the thermal loads. Coarse-grained material will case harden on the surface more readily than fine-grained. It is evident then, that coarse grains may sometimes be desirable during processing, but fine grains are usually necessary in the final product to provide the best mechanical properties. Some of the deformation processes of shaping materials can be used in such a way as to cause grain-size reduction automatically during the shaping process with little or no additional cost involved.

Cooling Curves.   When a metal is cooled from its molten condition to a temperature below its point of solidification, the temperature at various stages of cooling may be plotted against time to produce a cooling curve. The shape, position, and points of slope change indicating change of cooling rate will vary depending upon the metal or alloy being examined. The cooling curve shown in Fig. 3–3 is typical of those produced with data from studies of pure metals and certain alloys of specific composition. The line *a-b* shows the temperature change in the liquid metal. The vertical height of *a-b* represents the degrees superheat (temperature differential above the liquid to solid transformation temperature) at which the study is begun. The line *b-c* is approximately horizontal, indicating little or no temperature change for an appreciable length of time. It is during this period that solidification takes place, and even though heat is still being taken away, the temperature remains constant because of the balancing effect of heat being given up by the atoms as they take their

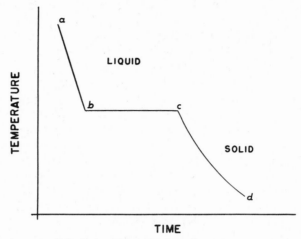

FIG. 3–3.   Pure metal cooling curve.

positions during solidification. The material becomes progressively more solid until at point *c* solidification is complete. The portion of the curve *c-d* represents normal cooling of the solid material.

The cooling curve shown in Fig. 3–4 is indicative of the combination of two metals which are soluble as liquids and as solids. A solid solution is a

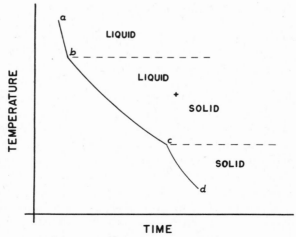

FIG. 3–4.   Solid solution cooling curve.

homogeneous crystalline structure in which the crystals or grains are made up of two or more dissimilar atoms or intermetallic compounds. The portion of the curve *a-b* shows the temperature change and the time required for that change while the metal is in the liquid state. Point *b* represents the time and temperature at which freezing begins, and the temperature continues to decrease at a somewhat slower rate than during the liquid state, cooling until at the point *c* complete solidification has taken place. During both the temperature range and the time from *b* to *c*, both liquid and solid material exist together; *c-d* again represents the cooling of the solid metal.

Fig. 3–5 shows the type of curve produced in a thermal study of a

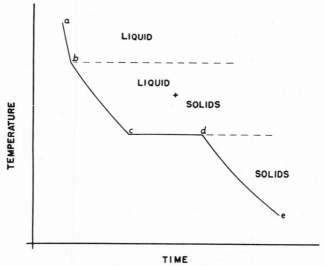

FIG. 3–5.　Insoluble alloy cooling curve.

combination of two metals that are soluble in the molten condition but are insoluble in the solid state. As in the other curves, *a-b* is the cooling of the liquid metal and point *b* is the temperature at which solidification starts. During the temperature change that occurs as the curve is followed from *b* to *c* however, only one of the metals freezes in the form of a pure metal. The solidification of the one metal during this period causes the remaining liquid solution to become richer in the other metal as the temperature decreases. At the temperature of point *c*, the remaining liquid solution solidifies with pure crystals of the two metals at a constant temperature for a period of time represented by the distance from *c* to *d*. Again at *d* complete solidification has occurred, and the solid material cools in the normal way. With an original composition of the liquid corresponding to that from *c* to *d*, the cooling curve would be similar to that of a pure metal shown in Fig. 3–3.

Equilibrium Diagrams. By combining a number of cooling curves for various compositions of an alloy system, an equilibrium diagram can be constructed. Illustration of the method is shown in Fig. 3–6, representing two metals, *A* and *B*, which are soluble as liquids, but totally insoluble as solids. The construction of the illustration has been greatly simplified.

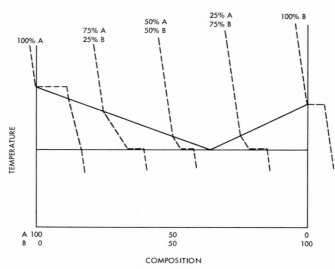

FIG. 3–6. Equilibrium diagram construction.

Since some of the lines are often curved, large numbers of cooling tests are necessary to establish the shapes and points of change. In effect, an equilibrium diagram consists of a series of transformation points from an infinite number of alloy composition variations. A diagram can be used to predict the solidification behavior of the metal for which it has been constructed. As temperatures are varied through their entire range, it is extremely important to remember, however, that it is an equilibrium diagram and its interpretation must be based on the assumption that temperature changes of the metal being studied occur slowly enough that equilibrium conditions will be attained. The effect of sudden temperature change cannot be predicted on the basis of this diagram alone.

Fig. 3–7 is a completed equilibrium diagram for the simple situation of metals *A* and *B* which are totally insoluble in the solid state. The line *C-E-F* is called the "liquidus" and represents the points labeled *b* in the previous temperature-time cooling curves. This line shows the temperature at which any particular composition will start to freeze. The straight line *D-E-H* is called the "solidus" and shows the temperature at which all solidification is complete. Between the liquidus and the solidus the metal exists in the form of solid particles of one of the two metals (which one depends upon the composition) surrounded by liquid composed of both metals. The solidification behavior of alloys of this type can be illustrated by examination of what happens to three different compositions as they are cooled from their molten state.

Referring again to Fig. 3–7 if the composition shown as number 1 is cooled from a liquid state, the liquidus line indicates that at temperature T_1 crystals of metal A will start to freeze. As A freezes out, the remaining liquid solution will become richer in B and with the change of liquid

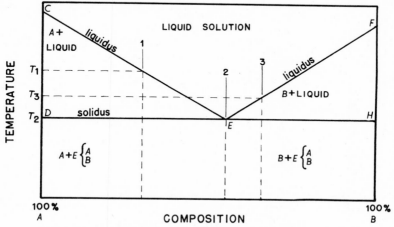

FIG. 3–7. Equilibrium diagram for two insoluble metals.

composition, the temperature at which more A will freeze becomes lower. The process of A crystals forming with further enrichment of the liquid solution will continue until the composition is that shown as number 2, which freezes at temperature T_2. This last metal to freeze is known as eutectic composition and freezes as a mixture of solid A and solid B crystals.

The eutectic is shown as the lowest freezing point on the diagram. The eutectic composition is that of this lowest point, and the eutectic temperature is the related temperature value. Composition number 2 of eutectic composition in liquid solution must be decreased in temperature to T_2 before any freezing takes place. At this temperature, freezing much the same as that of a pure metal will cause the liquid to change to a solid mixture of metal A and metal B crystals. The eutectic is even more important in melting procedures than in freezing since, with this composition, an alloy will have its lowest melting temperature.

With composition 3, behavior during freezing is similar to that of composition 1 except that the solid particles that freeze after reducing the temperature to that indicated by the liquidus line are crystals of metal B instead of A. The remaining liquid solution, therefore, is enriched with A particles and the composition moves toward the eutectic. The final metal to freeze again will be the eutectic composition and will be made up of interspersed crystals of *A* and *B*.

Only a few of the metals are totally insoluble in the solid state. Most are at least partially soluble with the solubility often varying as the temperature. The problem of behavior is less simple under these conditions. Fig. 3–8 shows an equilibrium diagram again for two metals *A* and *B*, each of

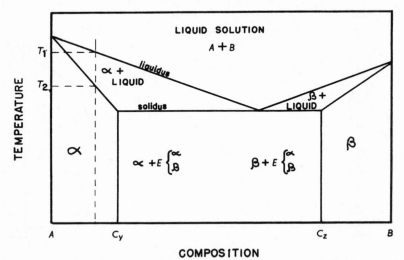

COMPOSITION

FIG. 3–8. Equilibrium diagram for two metals partially soluble in each other.

which is partially soluble in the other in the solid state. The areas a on the left of the diagram and β on the right represent solid solution material of *B* dissolved in *A* and *A* dissolved in *B* respectively. Because of the solubility exhibited in these areas, solidification behavior is different than when the two metals are completely insoluble as solids.

The alloy shown in the figure as number 1 composition will start to solidify as the liquidus line indicates at temperature T_1 with the formation of solid solution crystals which will have a composition lower in the metal *A* than that of the liquid. The liquid, therefore, is at least momentarily enriched with *A*. As the temperature falls, solid solution continues to form with increasing percentages of metal *A*, but reaching the original composition only as the last particles freeze at T_2. The freezing crystals and the unfrozen liquid are continuously changing in composition. There is, however, during the same time, a balancing action taking place called diffusion, providing the cooling rate is low enough that equilibrium can be established. Atoms of *A* from the enriched liquid diffuse into the already frozen crystals causing the solid composition to approach that freezing at the time. Diffusion can take place even in the solid state, so theoretically a completely homogeneous solid of the same composition as the beginning liquid can be formed. However, in many practical applications, slow, uniform cooling rates are impractical and the resulting solid, although of the same average composition as the beginning liquid will be nonhomogeneous. Such variations cause unstable structure, which in some cases has marked effect on the properties of the material.

Fig. 3–9 shows the left side only of the diagram illustrated in Fig. 3–8

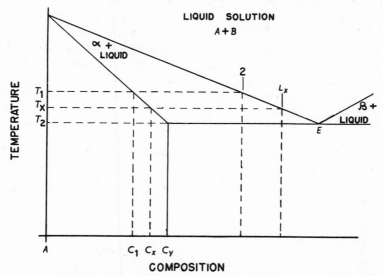

FIG. 3–9. Left portion of equilibrium diagram for two metals partially soluble in each other.

with a different alloy composition indicated by the line number 2. When cooled from the liquid state, freezing of solid solution crystals will start at T_1, which is of course a lower temperature than the starting temperature of the previous illustration because of the change in position along the liquidus line. The first solid solution crystals (α) will be of the composition C_1 which, as before, will be lower in metal A than the composition of the liquid. Further freezing at any lower temperature T_x results in crystal composition richer in the metal A as indicated by C_x. At the same time the liquid composition is L_x. Diffusion occurs as before to increase A in the first crystals frozen.

It will be noticed that the temperature of the last material to become solid, T_2, is the eutectic temperature. When the temperature T_2 is first reached, the composition has reached C_y which represents the maximum condition of solubility of metal B in metal A. Any further freezing of composition C_y tends to make the liquid super-rich in metal B and some component richer in metal B than C_y must freeze. In the case of the freezing of a eutectic where insolubility exists, this second component would be pure metal B. With limited solubility of A in B the composition of the new component is represented by composition C_z of Fig. 3–8. The eutectic then will consist of alternate layers of composition C_y (α) and C_z (β) and the final structure will consist of relatively large crystals of α surrounding crystals of eutectic which themselves consist of smaller crystals of α and β.

If the alloy is of eutectic composition in the liquid state before solidification begins, no crystals will form until the temperature drops to the eutectic temperature, T_2 in Figure 3–8. At this temperature, the entire mass will solidify into the eutectic mixture of α and β.

Alloys richer in B than the eutectic composition will solidify in similar manner to one of the first two cases, except that the first crystals will be solid solutions of metal A in B (β) instead of B in A (α).

Fig. 3–10 shows a third type diagram that is typical of two metals

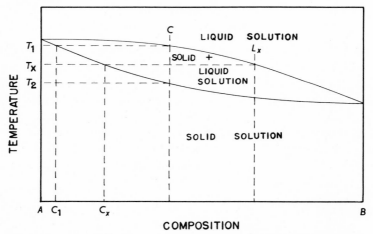

FIG. 3–10. Equilibrium diagram for two completely soluble metals.

that are mutually soluble in all proportions both as liquids and solids. Freezing will begin when the temperature of the molten alloy (composition C) decreases to T_1 when crystals of C_1 composition form in similar manner as with the partially soluble metals. As the temperature T_x continues to decrease, solid material closer to the original composition will form. As in the other case also, diffusion causes the early crystals to be enriched with B to approach the average composition and higher stability. Homogeneity of the final solid will be attained only under conditions of slow, uniform cooling to maintain equilibrium conditions throughout the cooling cycle.

Examination of an equilibrium diagram will permit the calculation of the ratio of liquid to solid material at any particular temperature. The procedure makes use of the so-called "lever arm" relationship which states that the relative amounts of liquid and solid present are inversely proportional to the length of the horizontal temperature line sections between the

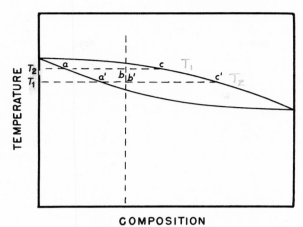

COMPOSITION
FIG. 3–11. Lever law.

composition and the solidus or liquidus intersections. In Fig. 3–11, $\overline{ab}/\overline{ac}$ represents the per cent of liquid and $\overline{bc}/\overline{ac}$ the per cent of solid at temperature T_1. At the lower temperature T_2 the ratio $\overline{a_1b_1}/\overline{a_1c_1}$ is much less, indicating much lower per cent of liquid and larger quantity of solid present.

The preceding illustration and discussion are typical of only the simplest of the binary alloy systems. Fig. 3–12 showing the equilibrium

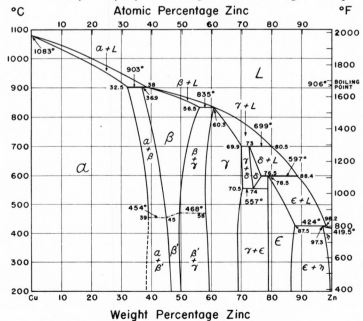

Weight Percentage Zinc
FIG. 3–12. Copper-zinc equilibrium diagram.

diagram for a copper-zinc alloy gives some indication of the complexity that can occur in a combination of only two metals. When three or more metals are combined into an alloy, the equilibrium diagram can become very complicated, requiring considerable training and experience for interpretation. These are far beyond the scope of this text. Equilibrium diagrams have been introduced at this point to aid in providing a better understanding of the behavior of metals during solidification from the molten state and under some of the conditions by which metals are processed. It should be emphasized by repetition that these diagrams are graphic illustrations of conditions of equilibrium and that exact interpretation can be accomplished only for metals whose temperature changes are at rates permitting equilibrium to take place.

QUESTIONS

1. Describe an atom.
2. Describe how variation of energy can affect atomic activity and material state.
3. What are the characteristic properties of metallic materials?
4. What is a space lattice?
5. Make schematic sketches of body centered cubic, face centered cubic, and hexagonal close packed unit cells.
6. Describe the solidification process of a metal from its liquid state.
7. What is the importance of grain size?
8. Sketch cooling curves representative of pure metals, alloys fully soluble in each other, and bimetal alloys which are insoluble as solids.
9. What is a solid solution?
10. What is the principal use for equilibrium diagrams?
11. What is the meaning of the "liquidus" and "solidus" lines on an equilibrium diagram?
12. What is the nature of a solid structure formed from two metals that are completely insoluble in each other?
13. Why are eutectic compositions often of importance?
14. Explain how faster than equilibrium cooling rates produce nonuniform solid structures.
15. What is the "lever arm" relationship?

Solid State Changes in Metals

In the previous chapter the process of metal solidification was briefly described. It was pointed out that the equilibrium diagram can be used to predict the behavior of the metals during their solidification period. It was implied that the properties of a material are derived from the crystalline structure, including the atomic arrangement and the grain sizes, and are affected by the boundary layers which join the grains together. The atomic arrangement is primarily a function of the material composition, which may consist of a single material or a combination of materials that are completely soluble, partially soluble, or totally insoluble in each other in the solid state. The structure and grain size also may be influenced by the operating temperature or by the level and rate of previous temperature changes and by mechanical loads which stress the material sufficiently to cause plastic flow in combination with time and heat effects.

Some materials, particularly those that are cast to shape, may be used with the structure in which they solidify, but some of the cast materials and nearly all metals processed by any other method are treated in some way in the solid state to obtain improved mechanical properties.

These treatments include work hardening, recrystallization, age hardening, and heat treating of allotropic materials to cause crystal transformations. In many cases, treatment may be inherent in the process. This may be beneficial as in many cases of deformation shaping with associated work hardening, or may be detrimental as in other cases where cold working develops directional properties in a material to make some kinds of further cold work difficult or impossible.

WORK HARDENING

The application of loads to a solid material in processing or in service can cause two kinds of deformation. If the load does not stress the material past its elastic limit, the deformation is "elastic" and the material returns to its original position upon removal of the load. If, however, the elastic limit is exceeded, the material does not return completely to its original position when the load is removed and is permanently deformed by plastic flow within its crystalline structure. When the elastic limit is passed, elastic properties are not lost, but instead are enhanced, providing the deformation is produced by cold work. The strength of metal is increased by plastic flow to resist further plastic flow and the elastic properties are improved by raising the elastic limit. Some of the deformation processes make use of this in shaping materials to produce improved properties at the same time the shaping is being performed.

Plastic Deformation.   Permanent deformation of metallic crystals occurs in three ways: slip, twinning, and rotational deformation. The degree

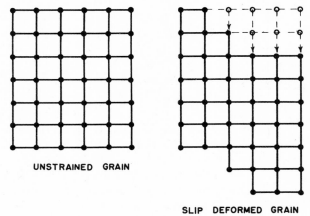

UNSTRAINED GRAIN

SLIP DEFORMED GRAIN

FIG. 4–1. Slip.

of each is dependent largely on the characteristics of the particular metal. *Slip* deformation is illustrated in Fig. 4–1 and occurs by translation or sliding between the atomic planes within a grain. If the deformation produced causes more than a very minor shift, a large number of atomic planes in each grain will slide over adjacent planes to occupy new locations with new neighbors. The planes through the crystal that are usually most subject to slip are those of the greatest atomic population and greatest distance between planes. The orientation of the planes along which slip takes place most easily will, of course, be different for different types of crystal lattices. Because of the usual random orientation of the crystals, the slip planes of many will not be in line with the direction of loading. When the best slip planes are completely out of alignment, slip may occur along other less preferred planes.

Fig. 4–2 shows a type of grain deformation referred to as *twinning*, which seems to occur most easily under loads applied suddenly rather than gradually. With twinning, the grain deforms by twisting or reorientation of a band of adjacent lattice forms, with each unit cell remaining in contact with the same neighbors it had before deformation took place.

A third type of shift in a grain is a kind of rotational deformation of portions of the crystal lattice. Stresses below the elastic limit cause the crystals to be temporarily bent and deformed, but when the elastic limit has been exceeded and slip has occurred on a number of different planes, sections of the lattice tend to bend and rotate to a new, preferred orientation. After a large per cent of grains have been reoriented by action of

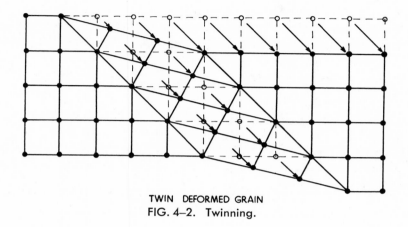

TWIN DEFORMED GRAIN
FIG. 4–2. Twinning.

considerable deformation work, the metal is likely to take on directional properties called *fibering*, which may be beneficial or harmful depending upon the use to which the material is put.

Dislocation Theory.   The above described failure mechanisms of slip, twinning, and crystal deformation can be seen by microscopic examination of crystals and even though only a two-dimensional crystalline plane can be observed at a time, seem to be a partial explanation of crystal failure. One of the more recent theories advanced independently in 1934 by G. I. Taylor of England and E. Orowan, then of Germany, appears to explain the discrepancies not covered by the above theories. The *Dislocation Theory* is at the present time the most widely accepted explanation for plastic deformation in metals.

Using the older theories alone, and based on known interatomic forces, calculation of the strength of the metals to resist plastic flow indicates that they should be many times stronger than they prove to be under test. Simply stated, the dislocation theory proposes that slip, instead of occurring across an entire crystalline plane, occurs only atom by atom as the dislocation moves through the material, as shown in Fig. 4–3. Except near the point of dislocation at the end of the slip region, the lattice arrangement is the same as before deformation with the same atomic pattern, although some cells have shifted to associate with new neighbors. By this theory, a dislocation may move across the plane from cell to cell with the result that much less force would be required to deform the crystal than if

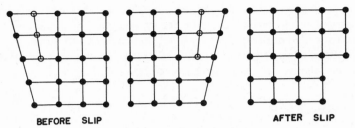

BEFORE SLIP   AFTER SLIP

FIG. 4–3. Dislocation slip.

it were necessary to shift the entire plane by breaking all the atomic bonds at one time. Under a deforming force, many of these dislocations are moving at one time. It has been estimated that in most metals there are from 10^8 to 10^{12} dislocations per cubic centimeter. If two of like kind encounter each other, as in Fig. 4–4, they obviously will offer resistance to more motion since their combination would increase the tension and compression stresses tending to cause localized atomic deformation. If, on the other hand, dislocations of opposite sign or reversed position meet each other on a slip plane, they are attracted to each other because their localized disturbances balance, and if they join, the atoms can take their

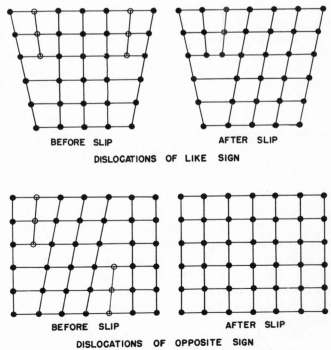

BEFORE SLIP   AFTER SLIP

DISLOCATIONS OF LIKE SIGN

BEFORE SLIP   AFTER SLIP

DISLOCATIONS OF OPPOSITE SIGN

FIG. 4–4. Reinforcement or cancellation of dislocations.

strongest and most stable positions. Interacting dislocalitions, therefore, regardless of their type, tend to become stationary and resist further deformation.

Cold Work. According to the dislocation theory, as plastic flow takes place, existing dislocations are reinforced and new dislocations are created to resist further plastic movement. Regardless of what the exact mechanisms may be by which plastic flow takes place in the metal grains, it is a proven fact that when metals are cold worked to produce plastic deformation they gecome harder and stronger. The word cold in this instance refers to different temperatures for different metals. Cold work is work accomplished below the recrystallization temperatures for the materials.

RECRYSTALLIZATION

Metals that are cold worked are left with their grains in a strained and unstable condition. The grains have a tendency to return to the equilibrium of a lower energy state by equalization of internal crystalline stress or by changing to new, unstrained grains. The greater the deformation strain, the greater the instability and the easier it is for the changes to take place although time and temperature have strong influence on its occurrence. Two kinds of changes, recovery and recrystallization, take place upon the heating of a cold worked metal.

Recovery. Recovery, sometimes referred to as stress relief, involves rearrangement of some of the more strenuous dislocations or imperfections with little or no effect on the external form of the crystals or grains. Although the changes that take place during recovery are rather minor in character, they have a marked effect in improving electrical properties and corrosion resistance, and in reduction of residual stresses to cut down distortion.

Although recovery occurs completely for some metals at room temperature, and partially for most others over a long period of time without increase of temperature, for most it is necessary to heat treat to a specific temperature which will depend upon the degree of recovery desired. The temperature chosen will, of course, be dependent upon the metal and to some extent on the amount of cold work that has been performed previously. The objective of recovery is usually to regain electrical and chemical properties without sacrifice of mechanical properties. If the temperature is raised too high or maintained for too long a time, hardness and strength of the metal will decrease but such high temperature treatment is sometimes necessary to remove completely residual stresses in forgings and steel weldments.

Recrystallization. Although some of the major distortions are eliminated by treatment for recovery, most of the distorted crystalline lattice remains as it was produced by cold work where it lost some or all of its ability to be deformed by plastic flow. In other words, the elastic limit for the material has been raised close to the ultimate strength and further deformation will cause fracture failure. Recovery of ductility to permit further change of shape by deformation can be obtained only by elimination of the deformed grains and this can be accomplished only as a result of recrystallization. By this heat treating process new, smaller, unstrained grains with fully recovered capacity for plastic flow can be formed by solid state change in the metal. It is important to note that in the absence of allotropic changes, which will be discussed later, no grain size changes by heating metal to any temperature below the melting point can be accomplished unless the strained condition of cold worked metal is present. Recrystallization is the nucleation and growth of new, strain-free crystals from the strained crystals of a cold worked material. The phenomenon occurs over a wide temperature range with the length of time required for complete recrystallization inversely related to the temperature and to the degree of strain present. For practical purposes, recrystallization temperatures, such as shown in Table 4–1, are temperatures which will permit complete recrystallization in a time period of approximately one hour for metals that have been fully hardened by previous cold work.

TABLE 4–1

Recrystallization Temperatures for Some Common Metals and Alloys

Material	Temperature, °F.
Aluminum (pure)	175
Aluminum alloys	600
Copper (pure)	250
Copper alloys	600
Iron (pure)	750
Low carbon steel	1000
Magnesium (pure)	150
Magnesium alloys	450
Zinc	50
Tin	25
Lead	25

The recrystallization table shows that zinc, tin, and lead all recrystallize at temperatures below room temperature. This means that these metals in the pure state cannot, at ordinary temperatures, maintain a work hardened condition. The normal use of deformation processes on these materials would be hot working rather than cold working since it would be performed above their recrystallization temperatures. Examination of the table also reveals that contamination of a pure metal with other elements makes it more difficult for recrystallization to occur and the temperatures must be increased for completion in a reasonable length of time.

It is believed that recrystallization takes place by the nucleation of new grains mainly about the high energy points of dislocation in a work hardened grain. They then appear to grow until they fill the old grain space and eliminate the existing strain by realignment of the atoms into a new crystal lattice. Recrystallization then, can be a grain refining process as well as a method for recovery of ductility, if it is discontinued as soon as complete recrystallization has taken place.

The new grains formed during recrystallization are likely to take positions with preferred orientations. Directional properties caused by preferred orientation are objectionable for most manufacturing operations. This tendency can be reduced and more random orientation obtained by the addition of small amounts of some alloying element or by recrystallizing before maximum work hardening has been performed.

In a few cases, recrystallization may be used as an end process to leave a product in its most ductile condition or with its best electrical and chemical properties, but more often it is an in-process treatment for improvement of ductility or for grain refinement purposes. In many cold deformation processes, such as deep drawing, the ductility of the material may be reduced by cold working to the point where fracture failure is imminent. Ductility may be returned to the material any number of times by repeated recrystallization between steps of the forming operation. In most cases the last forming operation will not be followed by recrystallization, in order that the higher hardness and strength of the cold worked material may be retained in the product.

Although heating for recovery is a stress relieving process, recrystallization at a higher temperature is sometimes also called stress relieving. The same process may be referred to as process annealing, particularly when performed in conjunction with deformation processes.

Grain Growth. If a metal is kept heated at or above its recrystallization temperature after the new, unstrained grains have formed, the tendency is for some of the new grains to absorb others and grow to larger size. Large grains are more stable than small grains because of the higher grain to boundary area ratio which is a lower energy state. If fine grain structure is desired after the recrystallization process, it is necessary to reduce the temperature quickly to prevent subsequent grain growth. This is usually performed by some kind of quench.

During processing, small grain size is not always wanted since large grains usually exhibit greater ductility, better machinability, and require less pressure to be deformed. The final product usually should be of relatively fine structure, though, in order that the material will exhibit its best properties. Grain size for materials that do not go through allotropic phase changes is controlled primarily during the solidification process for cast metals and by recrystallization for wrought (deformation worked) metals. Allotropic or polymorphic metal (metal existing in more than one crystalline form) grain size can be controlled by a more effective and satisfactory method discussed later in the chapter.

AGE HARDENING

In connection with equilibrium diagrams, it was pointed out that with alloys of two or more metals, fully soluble in each other, the composition of solid and liquid material during solidification will vary. Under conditions of equilibrium cooling diffusion of atoms from the liquid to the solid will continually change the composition until the completed solid will be the same throughout as the original liquid metal. With metals having only partial solubility, this is true only when the composition of the liquid is of a per cent within the solid solubility range.

Solubility of the solid phase can vary with the temperature, usually becoming less with decrease of temperature, as shown in Fig. 4–5 illustrat-

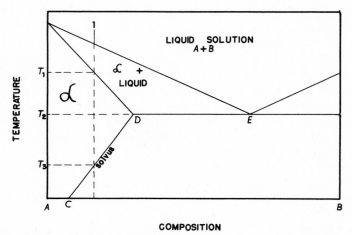

FIG. 4–5. Equilibrium diagram of two metals with variable solubility.

ing two metals, *A* and *B*, with *B* partially soluble in *A* in the solid state. In this illustration the solid solubility decreases with lowering temperature below the eutectic temperature of T_2 as indicated by the slope of the line *C-D*, referred to as the Solvus line. Study of a composition of the percentage indicated by the line 1 shows that the alloy becomes completely solid at temperature T_1 and, assuming complete equilibrium, is a homogeneous solid solution α in the temperature range T_1 to T_3. At T_3 the composition line crosses the Solvus line. Below this temperature the solubility of *B* in *A* is lower than the composition ratio, so to remain in equilibrium α must give up metal *B* in the form of a precipitate, an action that might be described as the opposite of enrichment by diffusion. The maximum amount of precipitant would be formed by a composition of the percentages of metals at point *D*. Under this slow cooling the metal is placed in its softest, most ductile condition and the process is referred to as annealing. With faster cooling the precipitant cannot appear and the excess *B* is retained in the form of a supersaturated solution. In this condition the metal is susceptible to *age hardening.*

Exact explanation of the hardening phenomena is not available with present knowledge, but by close study it has been theorized that the precipitant from this supersaturated solution first appears as a transition lattice widely dispersed and closely associated with the solid solution lattice. Close association causes lattice distortion with accompanying increase of hardness, much as the distortion by cold working increases hardness. With sufficient time, which decreases with higher temperature, the transition particles combine to form larger, more widely spaced, and the more stable equilibrium precipitant, as in the annealed structure. For hardening purposes, the intermediate phase must be present, and when it disappears because of the complete formation of the final phase, the material is considered to be overaged with loss of the special properties present during the intermediate or transition stage.

The need for hardness and strength is often not present at the time of metal solidification, so commercial practice handles age hardening, precipitation hardening, or solution hardening (all names used to describe the same process) in two steps as a treatment separate from solidification for development of hardness and/or strength properties.

The first step is solution treatment to dissolve a maximum amount of equilibrium precipitant in the solid solution and freeze it in place by sudden cooling to eliminate the necessary time at temperature for precipitation to reoccur. The solution temperature used should be low enough to prevent excessive grain growth but high enough to insure maximum diffusion of the precipitant to saturate the α phase in a minimum amount of time. Time required depends upon the metal alloy and may vary from a few minutes to several hours of soaking at the increased temperature. After saturation of the alpha phase, the metal is quenched in water to create the supersaturated solid solution at room temperature. High energy points in the crystal lattice set up by the nonequilibrium situation of supersaturation causes the alloy to be harder than its annealed condition.

The full hardness, however, is developed during the second stage of treatment when the excess metallic component is partially precipitated from the solid solution. This step is usually referred to as aging and may be natural or artificial. If the surplus material goes into the initial transition stage of precipitation of its own accord at room temperature, full hardness will develop naturally with the passage of time. If an increase of temperature is necessary, as is true with many alloys, to release the unnaturally held metal, this heat treating step is called artificial aging. Too high aging temperature and/or too much time with this stage causes the precipitant to reach its final equilibrium state where the hardness and strength properties are low and similar to those of the annealed alloy.

Most alloys of two or more components showing partial solubility, have a sloping Solvus line indicating the possibility of solution and precipitation treatment. Most, but not all, can be hardened by this treatment.

One of the greatest uses for precipitation hardening is for improvement of properties of some of the aluminum alloys. The system can be used for either cast or wrought shapes and can be of particular value in some instances because of the time that is necessary for full hardening to develop. For example, it has been common practice in the aircraft industry to solution treat aluminum rivets and hold them under refrigeration after their quench to retard precipitation. Before precipitation starts, they are relatively ductile and easy to form plastically. In this condition they can be headed to join riveted assemblies and develop their full strength by aging after being upset in place.

ALLOTROPIC CHANGES

A few metals change lattice structure upon heating and cooling to exist in different forms through various temperature ranges. Such metals are classed as *allotropic*. Although they occur completely in the solid state with a slower reaction, allotropic changes are very similar to the phase changes from liquid to solid. In addition to a significant change of properties, heat is given up or absorbed as the metal phase change occurs in the solid state but to a much lower degree than in freezing or melting. With some metals special methods are necessary to detect heat changes that accompany the solid state phase change.

Iron combined with carbon and sometimes small amounts of other elements is by far the most used metal for manufacturing. Iron is an allotropic material that changes upon heating to 1670°F. from a body-centered cubic lattice (BCC) to a face-centered cubic lattice (FCC). A second phase change occurs with further heating to 2552°F. where the lattice structure returns to the body-centered cubic form. The reverse transformation occurs on cooling through the same temperatures. Iron in the temperature range up to 1670°F. is called alpha iron, from 1670° to 2552° gamma iron, and above 2552° to 2802°F., the melting point, delta iron. Little attention is given to delta iron since the changes that occur here have little or no effect in commercial practice of treatment for properties. The changes that take place between alpha and gamma iron at 1670°F., however, are extremely important. The most effective change is the difference of carbon solubility in the two phases which serves as the basis for all heat treat hardening and most grain size control for steel.

Iron Carbon Equilibrium Diagram.   In order to understand the behavior of iron materials upon heating and cooling, it is important to have knowledge and understanding of the iron carbon equilibrium diagram as shown in Fig. 4–6. Even though the diagram is designed only for prediction under equilibrium conditions, some behavior patterns can be interpreted from it. Other design curves and methods will be necessary to explain and predict behavior under some of the dynamic and nonequilibrium situations. Examination of the iron carbon equilibrium diagram reveals that 4.3 per cent carbon in iron establishes a eutectic composition that freezes at 2066°F. to produce a solid mixture product known as ledeburite. Ledeburite is composed of cementite, an intermetallic compound which is the first carbide of iron (Fe_3C), and austenite, a solid solution of carbon in FCC iron. With decrease of temperature, this and other compositions of iron and carbon undergo diffusion and precipitation changes. Between 1670° and 1333° a crystal transformation takes place, the exact temperature or temperature range depending on composition.

It will be observed on the diagram that at 1333°F. and 0.8 per cent

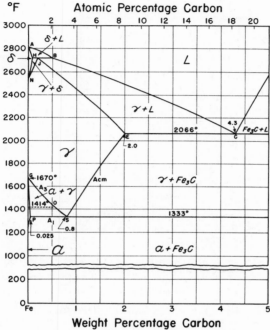

FIG. 4–6. Iron carbon equilibrium diagram.

carbon a point exists that is very similar to the eutectic point shown at 2066° F. and 4.3 per cent carbon. These points are in fact much alike with the principal difference being that the second point exists completely in solid metal while the eutectic is a point of change between liquid and solid. The two points are so much alike that the second is named the *eutectoid*, meaning "eutectic-like." An enlarged view of the eutectoid region is shown in Fig. 4–7. The maximum solubility of carbon occurs at the eutectic temperature of 2066°F. Some controversy exists over the exact amount of carbon that can be held in solid solution by the iron, and figures of 1.7 per cent and 2 per cent are authoritatively quoted. For purposes of discussion in this text, 2 per cent carbon, as shown in the illustrations, will be assumed to be the correct figure.

Referring to Fig. 4–7, it can be seen that a composition containing .8 per cent carbon and indicated by line 1 will exist above 1330°F. as 100 per cent austenite, the name given to the solid solution of carbon in gamma iron. Upon cooling to the eutectoid temperature, the equilibrium product of eutectoid decomposition consists of cementite (iron carbide) and ferrite. Ferrite is a solid solution of carbon in alpha iron with a maximum solubility of .025 per cent at the eutectoid temperature decreasing to about .006 per cent at room temperature. The cementite and ferrite form in lamellar

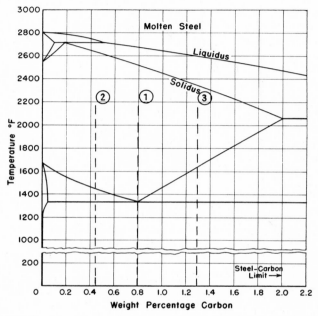

FIG. 4–7. A portion of the iron-carbon diagram (steel range).

structured crystals given the name of pearlite because of their resemblance, when magnified through a microscope, to mother-of-pearl.

Steels containing less than .8 per cent carbon are called hypoeutectoid steels. With this lower carbon composition as represented by line 2 in the figure, austenite first changes to a mixture of austenite and ferrite with continuously changing compositions as discussed in connection with solidification. The austenite remaining at the eutectoid temperature will contain .8 per cent carbon and will transform at this temperature as described above. The final structure will consist of pearlite (lamellar ferrite and cementite) in a matrix of ferrite.

Line number 3 represents an alloy with more carbon than the eutectoid value of .8. Such a steel is referred to as a hypereutectoid steel. The reaction is similar to that of the lower carbon material except that the first product is cementite (iron carbide) combined with varying composition austenite, finally resulting at the eutectoid temperature again in pearlite, but this time in a matrix of cementite.

Hypoeutectoid steels, therefore, when cooled slowly will be made up of various percentages of pearlite and ferrite with the ratio between the two depending on the over-all carbon content. Hypereutectoid steels will vary in the same way but the constituents will be pearlite and cementite. The crystalline relationship between these structures is shown in Fig. 4–8.

All of the preceding has been predicated on slow uniform cooling, producing what would be commercially known as fully annealed steel. Differences in properties will, of course, exist with variation of composition and the differences of reaction end-products in the decomposition of

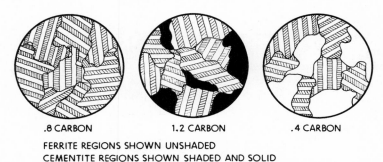

.8 CARBON   1.2 CARBON   .4 CARBON

FERRITE REGIONS SHOWN UNSHADED
CEMENTITE REGIONS SHOWN SHADED AND SOLID
FIG. 4–8. Structures obtained by slow cooling of plain carbon steels.

austenite. Presence of impurities or alloys in minute quantities may affect transformation temperatures with resulting differences in the crystal makeup and crystal sizes of pearlite which will have effect on the final properties. As will be seen later, the rates of cooling and, in particular, the temperatures at which decomposition of austenite is allowed to take place, will have definite influence on the products of decomposition and the associated properties.

HEAT TREATMENT OF STEEL

Steel has been treated by heating and cooling methods to vary its properties ever since its discovery, but even today the exact mechanism by which these variations take place cannot be completely explained by fully accepted theories. Most of the treatments have been developed empirically and various theoretical explanations have been used to describe the mechanism, but it has been only in recent years that the theory has advanced to the point that it is a prime source of new development of commercial heat treating methods.

Change of properties of steel can be accomplished by cold working, by precipitation hardening, and by allotropic changes. Cold working changes are important in most of the cold deformation processes and in some cases may be the only treatment received by the metal. Precipitation hardening is seldom used intentionally, except for stainless steels, although it may be an incidental occurrence with some of the processing treatments. Causing allotropic changes by heat treating procedures is the most effective and most easily accomplished method of varying mechanical properties of steel and therefore is the most frequently used way of obtaining the desired properties.

Heat treating is often defined as intentional heating and cooling for control of properties. Such a definition is perfectly good, but it must be remembered that the effects of temperature changes are no less important when they are caused by unintentional heat transfer during a process such as fusion welding or a service use in high environmental temperatures as in a furnace or gas turbine.

Approximate Equilibrium Heat Treatment Processes. Several heat treating processes place the material in either a complete or an approximate equilibrium energy condition. These include austenitizing, annealing, normalizing, and spherodizing. Except for the first, all are finalized at room temperature, but since austenitizing consists of diffusion of carbon into face-centered cubic iron which exists at a minimum temperature of 1333°F. (eutectoid composition only, all others higher), stability or equilibrium in this state can be maintained only at the higher temperatures. Austenitization is therefore not a final process but only a step in one of several heat treating procedures. For these approximate equilibrium processes, it is possible to predict the material behavior from the equilibrium phase diagrams.

Austenitization.   When steel is heated to or above its *critical temperature* (transformation temperature range), the value of which is dependent upon the alloy percentages, and held at temperature for some period of time, carbon unites in solid solution with iron in the gamma or face-centered cubic lattice form. In this phase, as much as 2 per cent carbon can dissolve at the eutectic temperature of 2066°F. where the widest range of gamma composition exists.

Fig. 4–9 shows the portion of the diagram which indicates the temperatures for austenitization. When the A_1 line at 1333°F. is reached, with increasing temperature austenite starts to form, but 100 per cent austenite cannot be formed until the A_3 line is crossed for hypoeutectoid steels. At or very close to the temperatures represented by these latter lines, considerable time is required for the formation of austenite that is homogeneous throughout the material, so commercial practice is usually to exceed these temperatures by approximately 100°. For hardening and annealing of hypereutectoid steels where complete austenitization is not required, sufficient austenite can be formed by exceeding only the A_1 line. The small amount of iron carbide that remains in the alloy with this lower temperature transformation has little effect on the final properties and may, in fact, even improve the wear resistance qualities of the steel.

It is important that the austenitization temperatures not be exceeded more than necessary to accomplish the work in a reasonable length of time because grain growth can occur rapidly as the temperature is increased. One of the important features of austenitization is grain refinement that occurs with the formation of the new face-centered cubic lattice. These new small grains are nucleated with the raising of the metal temperature through the austenite range and will remain small if the temperature is not raised too high or maintained too long. With lowering temperature and decomposition of austenite into the room temperature phase, the grain size

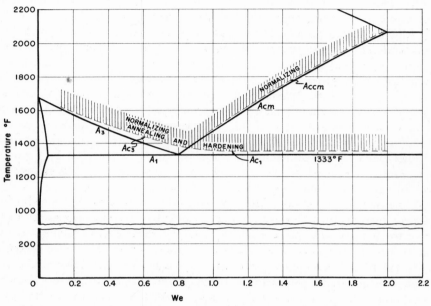

FIG. 4–9. A portion of the iron-carbon diagram (steel heat treating range).

changes little. Grain sizes are affected only by increasing temperature through this range and not by decreasing temperature. However, since metal grains must be of a certain critical size before they can maintain themselves alone, practically all the grain refinement that is possible can be acquired by one or two austenitization treatments, providing grain growth is not allowed at the higher temperature.

It was mentioned above that time is required for carbon to diffuse and take its position in the austenite crystal lattice. The time required is dependent on temperature as already mentioned, but other factors such as the mass of the steel, the original grain size, the rate of heating, and the degree of lattice distortion also affect the time required. A rule of thumb frequently used to determine the heating time decrees that the object being treated be placed in a furnace, previously heated to the austenitizing temperature, and held one hour for each inch of section thickness. This rule tends to be on the conservative side although most of the time is required to raise the metal to the temperature where austenite begins to form.

Annealing. The word "anneal" has been used before to describe heat treating processes for softening and regaining ductility in connection with cold working of material. It has a similar meaning when used in connection with the heat treating of allotropic materials. The purpose of full annealing is to decrease hardness and increase ductility, usually to improve machinability of steels that might otherwise be difficult to cut. The treatment is also used to relieve stresses, refine grain size, and promote uniformity of structure throughout the material.

Machinability, discussed in Chapter 18, is not always improved by annealing. The word *machinability* is used to describe several interrelated factors including the ability of a material to be cut with a good surface finish. Plain low carbon steels, when fully annealed, are soft and relatively weak, offering little resistance to cutting, but usually have sufficient ductility and toughness that a cut chip tends to pull and tear the surface from which it is removed, leaving a comparatively poor quality surface resulting in a poor machinability rating. The machinability of many of the higher plain carbon and most of the alloy steels can usually be greatly improved by annealing, since they are often too hard and strong to be easily cut at any but their softest condition.

The procedure for annealing hypoeutectoid steel is to heat slowly to approximately 100°F. above A_{c3} line, soak for a long enough period that the temperature equalizes throughout the material and homogeneous austenite is formed, and then allow the steel to cool very slowly by cooling it in the furnace or burying it in lime or some other insulating material. The slow cooling is essential to the precipitation of the maximum ferrite and the coarsest pearlite to place the steel in one of its softer, more ductile, and least strained conditions.

Shift of Arrest Lines. *The arrest lines, A_1, A_3, etc.,* shown on an equilibrium diagram often are written with additional subscripts of c or r. Briefly explained, these subscripts are used to indicate a shift of the temperatures at which transformation takes place because of the time required for diffusion or precipitation, and the fact that it is impractical to even approach infinitely slow heating or cooling. Fig. 4–10 shows the approximate relation of the A_c and A_r lines to the basic *arrest* lines which describe the temperature where transformation would theoretically take place with infinitely slow heat transfer. The letter c for *chauffage* denotes the line shift with temperature increase when heat is being added. The letter r for *refroidissement* denotes a shift in the opposite direction when the temperature is decreased. The position of the A_c and the A_r lines is dependent on the cooling or heating rate. The faster the rate the farther they will be separated from the basic arrest lines that apply only to complete equilibrium conditions.

The heating of a carbon steel with a .4 per cent carbon as represented by the line number one in Fig. 4–10 would produce 100 per cent austenite only after reaching the temperature represented by the intersection with A_{c3}. This temperature would be higher than the temperature for completion of equilibrium transformation by an amount dependent on the heating rate. It is evident from the diagram that even more difference in the temperature would exist for a higher carbon hypoeutectoid steel and the same rate of heating.

Similarly, with decreasing temperature, decomposition of austenite for the same alloy would start at the temperature of the intersection point with A_{r3} and finish at A_{r1}.

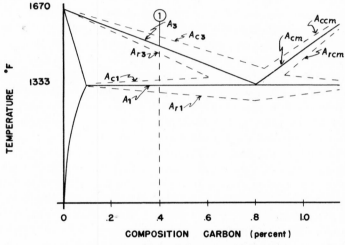

FIG. 4–10. Shift of the arrest lines.

The A_c and the A_r lines, therefore, take the place of the A lines to indicate the superheating or supercooling that takes place before transformation with the normal nonequilibrium conditions experienced in practice.

Normalizing. The purpose of *normalizing* is somewhat similar to that of annealing with the exceptions that the steel is not reduced to its softest condition and the pearlite is left rather fine instead of coarse. Refinement of grain size, relief of internal stresses, and improved structural uniformity together with recovery of some ductility provide high toughness qualities in normalized steel. The process in frequently used for improvement of machinability and for stress relief to reduce distortion that might occur with partial machining or aging.

The procedure for normalizing is to austenitize by slowly heating to approximately 150°F. above the A_{c3} or A_{ccm} temperature for hypoeutectoid or hypereutectoid steels respectively, providing soaking time for the formation of austenite, and cooling slowly in still air. Note that the steels with higher per cent carbon than the eutectoid composition are heated above the A_{ccm} instead of the A_{c1} used for annealing. The purpose of normalizing is to dissolve all the cementite during austenitization to eliminate, as far as possible, the settling of hard, brittle iron carbide in the grain boundaries. The desired decomposition products are small-grained, fine pearlite with a minimum of free ferrite and free cementite.

Spheroidizing. Minimum hardness and maximum ductility of steel can be produced by a process called *spheroidizing* which causes the iron carbide to form in small spheres or nodules in a ferrite matrix. In order to start with small grains which spheroidize more readily, the process is usually performed on normalized steel. Several variations of processing are used, but all require the holding of the steel near the A_1 temperature (usually slightly below) for a number of hours to allow the iron carbide to form in its more stable and lower energy state of small, rounded globules.

The main need for the process is to improve the machinability quality of high carbon steel and as a pretreatment for hardened steel to help produce greater structural uniformity after quenching. Because of the lengthy treatment time and therefore rather high cost, spheroidizing is not performed nearly as much as annealing or normalizing.

Isothermal Transformation Diagrams. Many heat treatments of steel, mostly involving hardening processes, are so different from equilibrium conditions that the equilibrium diagram has little value. Another group of curves known by various names: isothermal transformation diagram (I-T diagram), time-temperature transformation diagram (T-T-T diagram), or S-curve have been developed to take time element into account. These curves are developed by painstaking treatment and measurement of many small samples, sometimes a hundred or more for a single diagram. By use of isothermal (constant temperature) treatment at different temperatures and examination of the result, the amount and type of transformation for various times and temperatures can be determined and plotted.

I-T diagrams, such as shown in Fig. 4–11, have been constructed for most of the commonly used steels. Variations of composition, even small ones, cause changes in the shapes and in the positions of the curves. Sufficient knowledge has been acquired in this field so that even when an exact isothermal diagram is not available, consideration for the effect of differences from a similar material for which a diagram has been made will allow predictions accurate enough for most heat treatments.

The I-T diagram of Fig. 4–11 shows superimposed sketches of the austenite decomposition structure than can be expected with isothermal treatment at various temperatures. Fig. 4–12 shows cooling rate curves for some of the standard heat treating procedures. The time of the start of decomposition is the time of the meeting of the cooling curve with the first curve of the diagram and completion of the transformation occurs at the time when the second curve is reached, moving from left to right. It will be noted that the transformation for some products such as coarse pearlite is quite lengthy. This is, of course, reflected in treatments such as annealing and it becomes evident that cooling in the furnace or some other equally slow cooling is essential for obtaining the softest state of a steel material.

If the cooling curve passes through the diagram at a temperature lower than that required for annealing but still remains above the *nose* or *knee*, the product will still be pearlite but it will be made up of thinner plates, or laminations, which exhibit higher hardness and strength. The results would be characteristic of the normalizing treatment.

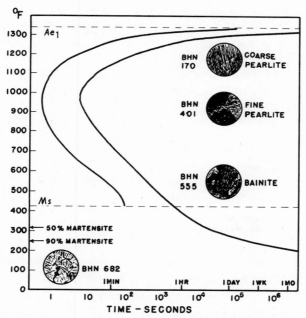

FIG. 4–11.   Structures obtained by isothermal transformation of eutectoid steel.

Cooling below the nose of the I-T curves produces a different kind of iron carbide and ferrite mixture known as *bainite*. Bainite takes on the form shown in Fig. 4–11. Feathery bainite, with its characteristic appearance, is formed with isothermal transformation at the higher temperature close to the nose, while at lower temperatures the structure is acicular or "needle-like." Bainite can be formed only by isothermal treatment with the exception of treatment of a few alloy steels for which the diagrams have two noses, one associated with pearlite and the other with bainite formation, for which a cooling curve that is practically vertical can enter the bainite region on the transformation diagram. Except for these few cases, the bainite product will result only if the slope of the cooling curve is lower than the slope of the transformation curve below the nose.

It can be observed from the I-T diagram that austenite, even though it is stable only above the A_1 temperature, can and usually is supercooled before transformation takes place. In fact, if the cooling can be accomplished without touching the nose of the curve, the austenite can be supercooled to a point where a need to change energy state becomes so great that the change to a different lattice structure will take place without diffusion of carbon. The result is a highly strained, distorted, and unstable structure called *martensite*, which is hard and brittle.

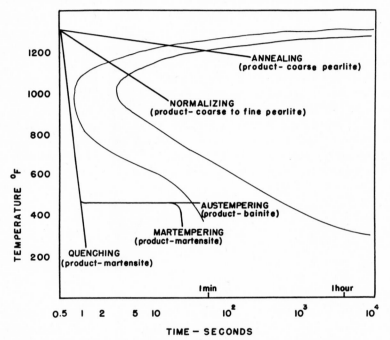

FIG. 4–12. Relationship of commercial heat treating processes to a typical TTT diagram.

Martensite forms only during cooling and starts at the temperature marked M_s on the diagram and completes at the temperature M_f. Any austenite that has not been transformed at higher temperatures will change to martensite in this temperature range. The formation of martensite is primarily dependent on temperature, and isothermal treatment in this range will direct the cooling curve to the right resulting in the formation of some martensite and some bainite.

As pointed out earlier, the shape and position of the curves representing transformation temperatures and time are different with each composition. It can be stated that in general, increase of carbon or alloying elements will cause the lines to shift toward the right and at the same time depress the M_s and M_f temperatures. This means that with higher carbon steels, and with most alloy steels, more time is available to cool past the nose of the curve in an attempt to produce martensite but that the temperature must be carried to a lower level before the formation of this structure occurs.

Hardening of Steel.   Although in some cases some of the other products of austenite decomposition are desirable for improved properties, most of the heat treatment hardening processes for steel are based on the production of high percentages of martensite. The first step, therefore, is that used for most of the other heat treating processes—treatment to produce austenite. Hypoeutectoid steels are heated to approximately 100°F. above the A_{c3} temperature and allowed to soak to obtain temperature uniformity and austenite homogeneity. Hypereutectoid steels are soaked at about 100°F. above the A_{c1} temperature, leaving some iron carbide present in the material.

The second step involves cooling rapidly in an attempt to avoid pearlite transformation by missing the nose of the I-T curve. The cooling rate is determined by the temperature and the ability of the quenching media to carry heat away from the surface of the material being quenched and the conduction of heat through the material itself. Table 4–2 shows some of the commonly used media and the method of application to remove heat, arranged in order of decreasing cooling ability.

TABLE 4–2

Heat Treating Quenching

Media	*Method*
1. Brine	1. Blast
2. Water	2. Violent agitation
3. Light oil	3. Slow agitation
4. Heavy oil	4. Still
5. Air	

High temperature gradients contribute to high stresses that cause distortion and cracking, so the quench should be only as extreme as is necessary to produce satisfactorily the desired structure. Care must be exercised in quenching that heat is removed uniformly to minimize thermal stresses that are due to nonuniform surface temperatures. For example, a long slender bar should be end-quenched, that is, inserted into the quenching medium end-wise so the entire section is subjected to temperature change at one time. If a shape of this kind were to be quenched in a way that caused one side to drop in temperature before the other, change of dimensions would likely cause stresses in some parts of the material to exceed the elastic limit for the material and thus, cause plastic flow and permanent distortion.

Several special types of quench are conducted to minimize quenching stresses and decrease the tendency for distortion and cracking. One of these, shown in Fig. 4–12, is called *martempering* and consists of quenching an austenitized steel in a salt bath at a temperature about that needed for the start of martensite formation (M_s). The steel being quenched is held in this bath until it is of uniform temperature but is removed before there is time for the formation of bainite to start. Completion of the cooling in air then causes the same hard martensite that would have formed with quenching from the high temperature, but the high thermal or "quench" stresses that are the primary source of cracks and warping will have been eliminated.

A similar process performed at a slightly higher temperature is called *austempering*. In this case the steel is held at the bath temperature for a longer period and the result of the isothermal treatment is the formation of bainite. The bainite structure is not as hard as the martensite that could be formed from the same composition, but in addition to reducing the thermal shock to which the steel would be subjected under normal hardening procedures, it is usually unnecessary to perform any further treatment to develop good impact resistance in the high hardness range.

A third step usually required to condition a hardened steel for service is *tempering*, or as it is sometimes referred to, *drawing*. With the exception of austempered steel, which is frequently used in the as-hardened condition, most steels are not serviceable "as quenched." The drastic cooling to produce martensite causes the steel to be very hard and to contain both macroscopic and microscopic internal stresses with the result that the material has little ductility and extreme brittleness. Reduction of these faults is accomplished by re-heating the steel to some point below the A_1 temperature. The structural changes caused by tempering of hardened steel are functions of both time and temperature, with temperature being the most important. It should be emphasized that tempering is not a hardening process, but is instead the reverse. A tempered steel is one that has been hardened by heat treatment and then stress relieved, softened, and provided with increased ductility by reheating in the tempering or drawing procedure.

The magnitude of the structural changes and the change of properties caused by tempering depend upon the temperature to which the steel is reheated. The higher the temperature, the greater the effect, so the choice of temperature will generally depend on willingness to sacrifice hardness and strength to gain ductility and toughness. Reheating to below 200°F. has little noticeable effect on hardened plain carbon steel. Between 200°F. and 400°F. the effect seems to be primarily that of stress relief, although at 400°F. there is evidence of some structural changes. Above 400°F. marked changes in structure and properties appear. Prolonged heating just under the A_1 temperature will result in a spherodized structure similar to that produced by the spherodizing process.

In commercial tempering the temperature range of 500°F. to 800°F. is usually avoided because of an unexplained enbrittlement or loss of ductility that often occurs with steels tempered in this range. Certain alloy steels also develop a "temper brittleness" in the temperature range of 800°F. to 1100°F., particularly when cooled slowly from or through this range of temperature. When high temperature tempering is necessary for these steels, they are usually heated to above 1100°F. and quenched for rapid cooling. Quenches from this temperature, of course, do not cause hardening since austenitization has not been accomplished.

Temper Colors. Steel with a roughly polished and clean surface when heated in the presence of air is subject to the formation of an oxide surface the thickness of which is dependent on the temperature. Different thicknesses of oxide reflect light to display a series of colors that are related to the causing temperature as shown below.

Color	*Approximate Temperature °F.*
Light straw	425
Straw	465
Yellow brown	495
Brown	515
Light purple	525
Purple	535
Light blue	550
Blue	600
Gray	700

These colors might better be called temperature colors instead of temper colors since they are indications of the temperature to which the steel has been exposed and have no direct relationship with the temper conditions of a hardened steel. They can be associated with hardness or ductility qualities only if it is known that the steel has previously been heat treat hardened to a martensitic structure. The colors are, however, produced by a range of temperatures where many tempering operations are carried on and may be used to estimate approximate tempering temperatures in the absence of any more reliable means. Since the colors are indications of surface temperature only, it is necessary that the heating to temperature be conducted slowly in order that the internal temperature will be closely related to the surface temperature. The use of temper colors is not highly recommended where close accuracies are desirable. The system does, however, permit the gauging of variable tempering temperatures such as might be desirable in a tool like a cold chisel. An application of this kind requires that the material of the cutting edge be hard and strong, but the end of the shank be ductile to prevent chipping when hit by a hard hammer. By supplying heat to the shank end the series of colors will move along the tool as the heat is conducted toward the tip, indicating the changes of tempering temperature. The process can be stopped when the colors related to suitable temperature reach the tip area by quenching to prevent further temperature increase. The result is a highly drawn ductile shank and a low-drawn hard cutting edge.

Hardenability. The term "hardenability" refers to the capacity of a steel to be hardened to depth and has no relation to hardness itself. The hardness of martensite is dependent on the amount of carbon present, but the hardenability of a steel depends on several different factors, principally the composition and the austenite grain size that influence the formation of martensite at something less than the ideal cooling rate. The presence of some alloying elements such as manganese and chromium tends to discourage pearlitic transformation from austenite and thus increase the possibility of supercooling for the production of martensite. Large austenite grain size also slows the pearlitic reaction and improves the hardenability of a steel.

Certain steels when quenched from the austenitization temperature will become hard for a considerable distance below the surface from which heat is being taken. These can be described as deep hardening steels that have high hardenability. Other fast reacting steels with exactly the same treatment will harden only a short distance below the surface, although

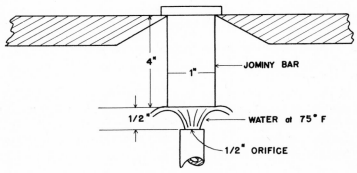

FIG. 4–13.   Jominy end quench.

the surface material may be as hard or even harder than the deep hardening steel. These are shallow hardening and have relatively low hardenability.

Hardenability is often defined in terms of the diameter in inches of a cylindrical bar that will form 50 per cent martensite at the center during an ideal quench. The ideal quench is one that would instantly cool the surface of the bar to room temperature. The 50 per cent martensite is an arbitrarily chosen value. Assignment of values to the various quenching methods permits the calculation of the critical diameter of a bar for steel of a particular composition. Determination of the critical diameter for any particular composition, therefore, establishes the maximum diameter that can be fully hardened to the center, with fully hardened being defined as 50 per cent martensite.

Hardenability is an important economic factor for applications requiring good use of steel hardened by heat treating. The alloys with high hardenability contain relatively large percentages of alloying elements, which increases the cost to a large degree. For any particular use where hardening ability is the principal consideration, the best choice is a steel for

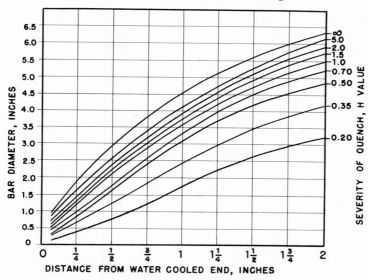

FIG. 4–14. Relation of end quench distance to round bar diameter.

which the minimum hardenability, considering the alloy and heat treating process tolerances, meets the use requirements. High hardenability permits the use of less drastic quenches.

The End Quench Test. A practical, easily performed test for determining the hardenability of steel is the *Jominy* or *End Quench Test*. A Jominy test bar, Fig. 4–13, after being heated to the proper temperature for austenitization is end quenched in a fixture by playing a stream of water on the end only. The result is a variable cooling rate that at 1300°F. varies from approximately 600°F. per second at a point 1/16 of an inch from the quenched end to approximately 4°F. per second two inches back along the bar. These different cooling rates can be related to other quenching media and the distance of hardening back along the bar can be related to the diameter of cylindrical bars as shown by Fig. 4–14 and Table 4–3.

After treatment a Rockwell Hardness traverse is made at specific distances along the sides of the Jominy Bar providing data for a hardness-

TABLE 4–3

Relation of Quenching Conditions

Quenching Condition	*H value*
Poor oil quench—no agitation	.20
Good oil quench—moderate agitation	.35
Very good oil quench—good agitation	.50
Strong oil quench—violent agitation	.70
Poor water quench—no agitation	1.00
Very good water quench—strong agitation	1.50
Brine quench—no agitation	2.00
Brine quench—violent agitation	5.00
Ideal quench	∞

distance curve to indicate the relation between hardnesses at various distances from the quenched surface. A curve such as shown in Fig. 4–15 can be developed from test information for any specific material and can be used for comparison to determine the relative hardenability with other materials. Direct comparison between the Jominy Test results and the anticipated results of heat treating service parts cannot be as accurately performed because of differences in quench effects and heat transfer from the variety of shapes and mass relationships of production parts.

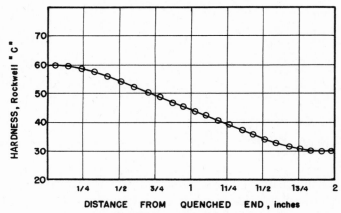

FIG. 4–15. Jominy hardness curve.

QUESTIONS

1. What are the most important solid state changes related to manufacturing processes?
2. Name the two possible benefits to be derived from deformation processing.
3. By what three mechanisms may permanent deformation occur?
4. What term is used to describe the directional properties developed by crystal orientation during deformation?
5. How does the dislocation theory explain the lower strengths of metals than those that could be predicted from the values of atomic bonds?
6. Name the three successive occurences that result from heating a cold worked metal.
7. How are recrystallization temperatures and degree of cold work related?
8. What is the usual reason for recrystallization heat treatment?
9. What is the significance of material recrystallization temperatures at, or below, room temperature?
10. For nonallotropic materials, how does cold working and recrystallization produce better properties than might be expected from cast materials?
11. What conflict exists in grain size desirability?
12. What is the fundamental requirement for an alloy in order that it can be age hardened?

13. What is meant by overaging of a precipitation hardened material and by what may it be caused?
14. Briefly explain the steps of solution hardening.
15. What is the difference between natural and artificial aging?
16. What is the meaning of "allotropic" as used in connection with metals?
17. Why is the allotropic change that takes place with iron-base alloys important?
18. Describe the differences between the eutectoid and the eutectic that appear on the iron-carbon equilibrium diagram.
19. What are the final equilibrium structures of hypoeutectoid, eutectoid, and hypereutectoid steels?
20. What will be the relative proportions of the components of 0.6 per cent carbon steel that has been slowly cooled from above its transformation temperature?
21. By what methods is it possible to harden steel?
22. Describe: Annealing, normalizing, conventional heat treat hardening, austempering, and martempering.
23. Why do the arrest lines on the iron-carbon diagram shift?
24. What is the usual purpose of spherodizing?
25. Why are isothermal-transformation curves more valuable than equilibrium diagrams for predicting processing results?
26. Why are various quenching media and methods necessary for cooling material from elevated temperatures?
27. On what basis is the choice of a tempering temperature made?
28. How are temper colors related to material hardness?
29. Why are steels containing some alloying elements frequently used when heat treat hardening is to be a step in the processing of large section parts?
30. What problem exists in using the results of a Jominy test to predict the heat treatment for hardening a service part?

CHAPTER 5

Ferrous Metals

FOR THE PURPOSES of manufacturing, a material could be defined as any substance having strength, weight, or other properties making it suitable for the construction of usable goods. For the purposes of this book, the discussion of materials will be limited to two general classes known as metals and plastics.

In Chapter 3, metals were discussed primarily on the basis of their atomic configurations. While it is true that this basis gives a more precise definition in the chemist's or physicist's terms, of greater practical interest in manufacturing are the metallic properties of relatively high hardness and strength, ability to undergo considerable plastic flow, high density, durability, rigidity, luster, and others. A distinction is sometimes made between the word *metal* as meaning a pure chemical element and the word *alloy* meaning a combination of materials, metals or non metals, the predominant one of which is a metal. The term "metal" in this text will be taken to mean any metallic material, whether pure or alloyed.

Among all the possible reasons for the choice and use of a material, one of very prime importance is availability. Table 5–1 shows the composition of the earth's crust.

Of the first twelve elements in occurrence, aluminum, iron, magnesium, and titanium are used as the base metals of alloy systems. For the other metals, although the total tonnage in the earth's crust may be considerable,

TABLE 5–1

Elements in the Earth's Crust

Element	Per Cent	Element	Per Cent
Oxygen	46.71	Magnesium	2.08
Silicon	27.69	Titanium	0.62
Aluminum	8.07	Hydrogen	0.14
Iron	5.05	Phosphorus	0.13
Calcium	3.65	Carbon	0.094
Sodium	2.75	Others	0.436
Potassium	2.58		

the potential use is much more restricted. Some of them, such as copper, are found in relatively pure deposits but frequently in remote locations, and the total use is dependent on relatively few of these rich deposits. Most other metals are recovered only in relatively small quantities either as by-products from the recovery of the more predominant metals or after extensive mining and concentration from low-yield ores where many tons of material must be handled for each pound of metal recovered. The United States has only marginal deposits of antimony, chromium, cobalt, manganese, and nickel, importing the major quantity of these metals in normal times, and is almost totally dependent on imports for its supply of mercury, tungsten, and tin. The location and availability of these materials has a marked influence on both the risk and cost of choosing these materials for large use applications.

Approximately seventy of the elements may be classed as metals, and of these about forty are of commercial importance. Historically, copper, lead, tin, and iron are metals of antiquity because they are either found free in nature or their ores are relatively easy to reduce. These four metals together with aluminum, magnesium, zinc, nickel, and titanium are presently the most important metals for use as base metals for structural alloy systems. Most of the other commercially important metals are either used primarily as alloying metals or are noble metals such as gold, silver, or platinum that are important only for special uses or because of their rarity.

The method of manufacture will frequently affect the alloy type to be used even when the base metal has been chosen. Although nearly all metals are cast at some time during their manufacture, those that are cast to approximate finished shape and finished without deformation are specifically referred to as *casting alloys*. When the metal is fabricated by deformation processes an alloy designed to have good ductility is specified and referred to as a *wrought alloy*. Some of the alloys can be either wrought or cast, and most of the wrought alloys can be cast, but many of the casting alloys have insufficient ductility for even simple deformation processing.

The choice of a material is usually a stepwise process. Sales requirements, raw material costs, equipment availability, or specific product requirements will frequently narrow the choice between the fields of metals and plastics. With the choice of either metals or plastics, some may be eliminated on the basis of properties, although a considerable number of plastics or metal alloys will still satisfy the functional requirements for the great majority of products. The life to be expected from the product may also eliminate some of the materials from consideration. Finally, however, the choice usually becomes one based on costs. From the various materials that would produce a functionally acceptable product with sufficient life and from the various processing means which are available to a manufacturer, the best combination must be found. Obviously, many combinations will be rather quickly eliminated, but of those remaining, costs of some may not be entirely predictable without actual experience in producing the product. Consequently the first choice is not always the final choice, and for this reason, as well as for reasons of sales appeal and product redesign, materials and processes frequently are changed on a trial and error basis.

Ferrous Materials.   The role that ferrous materials play in the economy is evident from annual production figures. Approximately one hundred million tons of ferrous products are made each year. The total for all nonferrous metals is less than ten million tons per year. Even allowing for the fact that much of the tonnage of steel goes into heavy products such as rails and structural steel shapes that have little secondary work done on them, ferrous metals are still the predominant materials of manufacturing. The wide variety of ferrous products is based largely on the economy of producing them, and in the section to follow an attempt will be made to discuss ferrous metals in the economic order of their production. Generally, as better properties are required, more costly processes are necessary.

Ore Reduction.   Both iron and steel have their start in the blast furnace. Even though other methods for reduction have been proposed and will likely be developed, the tremendous investment in equipment and trained personnel that would be required for the replacement of present facilities almost insures that the blast furnace method will remain for some time.

This device is a tall, columnar structure into which is fed, through a top opening, a mixture of iron ore (oxides of iron—Fe_3O_3, hematite or Fe_3O_4, magnetite), coke, and limestone. A blast of hot air is supplied through the mixture from near the bottom to provide oxygen for combustion of the coke. Temperatures in the neighborhood of 3000°F. are developed in the melting zone. The iron ore is reduced by chemical reaction with carbon monoxide gases and by high temperature contact directly with the carbon in the coke as well as other impurity elements in the mixture. Near the bottom of the furnace the iron, and slag made up of other metallic oxides combined with limestone, melt and accumulate in a well with the lighter slag floating on top of the melted iron. The molten iron and slag are tapped off periodically through separate holes. The slag is disposed of, either as trash or for by-product use and the iron is run into open molds to solidify as *pigs*, unless it is to be further processed immediately. In large installations the molten iron is frequently transported in large ladles to other equipment for carbon reduction in the manufacture of steel.

Pig Iron.   The product of the blast furnace is called *pig iron* whether liquid or solid. The distinction between the terms *pig* and *pig iron* should be noted. The term *pig* refers to a crude casting of any metal, convenient for transportation, storage, and remelting; the term *pig iron* refers to the composition of the metal tapped from the blast furnace, whether in liquid or solid state. Although this composition varies some with ore, coke, blast furnace conditions, and other factors, the blast furnace is controllable only within broad limits. Pig iron as a natural result of the conditions with the furnace always contains 3 to 4 per cent carbon and smaller amounts of silicon, sulfur, phosphorus, manganese, and other elements.

In the solid state, pig iron is weak, too hard to be machined, and has practically no ductility to permit deformation work. It must therefore be treated in some way to improve some of its properties by one of the methods shown in Fig. 5–1. The simplest of these treatments are those

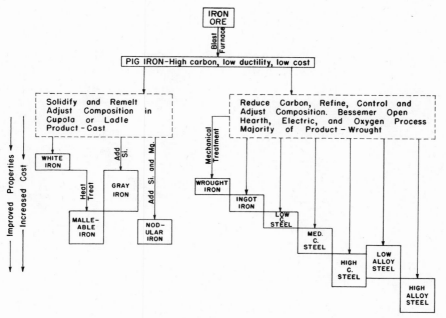

FIG. 5–1. General relationship of ferrous materials.

shown on the left of Fig. 5–1, involving remelting with only moderate control of composition, in particular without attempting to remove the carbon.

CAST IRONS

Under equilibrium or near equilibrium conditions, iron with 3 to 4 per cent carbon will solidify with a structure composed primarily of the eutectic *ledeburite*. The structure of this material is shown in Fig. 5–2. Of greatest significance in the structure of ledeburite are the large amounts of iron carbide formed. Iron carbide is a component of pearlite, and pearlite can have high strength and ductility. However, the large masses of iron carbide formed in ledeburite are not combined with the softer alpha ferrite as in pearlite. Consequently, so long as the iron carbide remains, the material will be hard and brittle.

White Iron. In a few cases these hard brittle characteristics are acceptable or even desirable, particularly where wear-resistant material of low strength and low cost is needed. With these qualities the structure is referred to as *white iron*. The name comes from the bright, silvery appearance of a fresh fracture. The maximum hardness of white iron is in the neighborhood of 500 BHN, which makes the material practically unmachinable except by grinding. White iron would be the natural result of solidification at normal cooling rates if the only constituents were iron

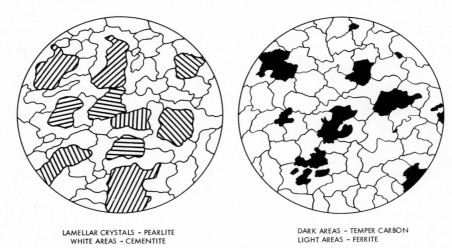

LAMELLAR CRYSTALS – PEARLITE
WHITE AREAS – CEMENTITE

DARK AREAS – TEMPER CARBON
LIGHT AREAS – FERRITE

FIG. 5–2. Structure of ledeburite.   **FIG. 5–3. Structure of malleable iron.**

and carbon as indicated on the diagram. In practice, other elements, particularly silicon, can lead to other structures, and close control of composition and cooling rate are normally necessary for the production of high quality white iron. Although a few products such as railway brake shoes, pulverizing mills, and welding bells may be made from white iron, the material is a necessary process step in the manufacture of *malleable iron*, and its principal importance stems from this use.

Malleable Iron. The iron carbide in the eutectic ledeburite is not in complete equilibrium. Suitable heat treatment of white iron causes most of the combined carbon to dissociate and reform as nodules of free graphite. The material formed by this procedure is malleable iron, which may be either of two general types depending upon the heat treatment it has been given.

The standard, or *ferritic*, malleable iron consists of nodules of graphite called *temper carbon* in a matrix of ferrite, as shown in Fig. 5–3. White iron castings are packed in annealing boxes with sand, millscale, or some similar granular material to reduce oxidation and provide support to cut down warpage during the heat treating process. The loaded boxes are then placed in a furnace and slowly heated (about twenty hours required) to a temperature in the neighborhood of 1600 to 1700°F. The castings are soaked at this temperature for a period of approximately forty hours to permit complete graphitization of the free cementite. At this temperature the austenite retains carbon in solution, so it is necessary, after soaking, to lower the temperature slowly to a range of 1100 to 1200°F., which is below the critical temperature for allotropic change of iron. During the slow cooling, secondary precipitation of graphite occurs as the austenite breaks down, with ferrite remaining as the matrix for the temper carbon. Faster cooling to room temperature below this point has little effect on mechanical properties of the material.

Malleable irons have strengths in the order of 40,000 to 50,000 psi, machinability better than that of most steels, and ductility that permits further processing by limited plastic deformation or provides a valuable safety feature in service use. The long, slow, heat treatment produces stress-free castings with extremely uniform structure.

The second kind of product is *pearlitic* malleable iron, which is made up of temper carbon distributed throughout a pearlite matrix. The annealing cycle is conducted in the same manner for all malleable irons. The cooling cycle may or may not be the same for pearlitic malleable iron since the pearlite can be produced in several ways. Pearlitic malleable iron can be made by preventing the secondary graphitization with alloying elements such as excess manganese, molybdenum, or chromium which tend to stabilize the carbides, by cooling the material faster to prevent full precipitation of carbon from the austenite, or by reheat treating standard malleable iron. The last two methods are, of course, similar in that they both depend upon moderately rapid cooling from above the critical temperature for the production of pearlite.

Pearlitic malleable irons are stronger and harder than the standard types, because this pearlitic matrix is effectively high carbon steel with similar properties and subject to the same control. Gains in hardness and strength are made only at a sacrifice of ductility. The tensile strengths of pearlitic malleable irons are of the order of 60,000 to 90,000 psi.

The lengthy heat treatment necessary in the production of malleable irons (Fig. 5–4) increases their cost above that for most of the other cast irons, but their ductility and resistance to impact stresses make them important materials in many structural applications. A large part of malleable production is used for automotive parts such as motor mounts, spring shackles, and running gear linkages. The properties of malleable iron make the material useful also for pipe fittings, road and farm machinery, and railroad equipment. Even though the weight-strength ratio may leave something to be desired, malleable iron is used for some aircraft parts. Ability to be deformed plastically is usually an important safety consideration for parts subject to failure under load, particularly when human life or safety may be concerned.

Nodular Iron. An iron of superior strength and ductility called *nodular* or *ductile* cast iron can be produced by ladle additions of a few hundredths of a per cent of magnesium or cerium. Reaction with the additives causes the carbon to assume nodular or spheroidal shapes similar to that of temper carbon in malleable iron. Spheroidal carbon does not have the weakening effect of the flake type found in gray iron. Strengths of nodular irons vary over a wide range depending upon whether the matrix is ferritic, pearlitic, or some heat treated structure such as tempered martensite, but strengths over 100,000 psi can be produced with ductilities comparable to those of malleable iron or steel.

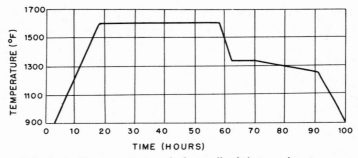

FIG. 5–4. Heat treating cycle for malleabilizing white iron.

Nodular iron was introduced to this country in the late 1940's and, in relation to the other cast irons, is new. Although this new material has been used for the making of many gears, crankshafts, and other machine or engine parts, its full potential has not yet been realized. The cost of manufacturing nodular iron has been somewhat restrictive because of the need for special equipment and the difficulty of treating the material with the additives to cause spheroidal graphitization. However, the cost advantage from elimination of expensive heat treating procedures required for malleable iron has led to experimentation that has developed simpler, less expensive production procedures.

Gray Iron. In the production of malleable iron, it is necessary to first produce white iron which is then suitably heat treated to promote the formation of spheroidal graphite. However, if during solidification, larger amounts of carbon or silicon are present and if the cooling rate is sufficiently low, the carbon will be precipitated as flakes of graphite. A cast iron having carbon in this form is called *gray iron*.

The name "gray iron" denotes a group of materials with a broad range of composition, structure, and properties characterized by a large portion of their carbon existing free in the form of graphite flakes. Except when they have been burnished, fractured surfaces exhibit a dull, grayish appearance.

Because the graphite flakes contribute no more to strength than the same number of voids, the tensile strength of gray cast iron is low, but the compressive strength is relatively high and may be as much as five times the tensile strength. The tensile strength, being of considerable importance in design, is frequently designated by a class number which is the first two figures of the minimum permissible tensile strength.

The machinability of gray cast iron is generally excellent. The most machinable irons are those in the softer hardness range, but finishability goes up as the hardness increases. Castings that have cooled too rapidly may contain heavy concentration of iron-carbide in thin sections or at chilled edges to make them almost nonmachinable except by grinding. Such results, however, are usually caused by poor foundry practice or poor design.

An important property of gray iron is its *damping* ability, which is much higher than that for steel and most other structural metals. This quality is the ability to absorb vibration energy and cause vibration to die out quickly in the same way that an automobile shock absorber reduces the amplitude of spring vibration. The ability of gray iron to damp vibration can be attributed to the internal structure of randomly located carbon particles which permit energy absorption by internal deformation.

In many applications, the lubricating property of free graphite causes gray iron to be an important material. Graphite particles exposed on machined surfaces, especially when aided by external lubrication, cause cast iron to be exceptionally resistant to wear from sliding friction. Cast iron bearings for low speed, rotating members are not unusual, and many kinds of machinery that operate with straight line sliding motion are designed with cast iron bearing surfaces. For uses where the bearing pressure is high, and indentation becomes a problem, the iron may be manufactured with greater amounts of the carbon in the combined state as iron carbide to sacrifice graphite lubrication but gain strength and hardness.

Nearly all gray iron castings are used as cast without post heat treating. Exceptions exist, however, when improvement of machinability, wear resistance, strength, or dimensional stability is desirable. Improvement of machinability and relief of stresses caused by unequal cooling can be accomplished by either annealing or normalizing. Subcritical annealing to cause some spheroidization of pearlite and some graphitization is performed by heating gray iron castings to about 900°F. to 1200°F., holding at temperature from one to four hours and cooling slowly. Full annealing requires heating to 1650° to 1700°F., followed by slow cooling after the temperature has had time to equalize. The normalizing treatment is similar to the full anneal except that the faster air cooling permits retention of some pearlite to provide higher hardness and strength in the treated casting.

In some few cases where high hardness and strength are extremely important, hardening and tempering may be employed by heating the material to above the critical range, quenching, and tempering. Gray iron is subject to cracking under the thermal stresses set up by this procedure, so its use is restricted. When wear resistance is the principal objective, flame and induction heat treatment procedures may be more satisfactorily employed to harden only the material near the wear surface.

Because of the properties mentioned above and the lower costs as compared to other cast materials, gray iron is the most common cast metal. Its high compressive strength, excellent machinability, good wear resistance, and vibration-damping characteristics combined with ease of casting intricate shapes make the material particularly suitable for construction of the main parts of machine tools, internal combustion engines, and other goods subject to vibration and wear.

Gray Iron Variations. A composition that ordinarily would freeze as a gray iron can be cooled fast enough in localized areas by the insertion of chills in the mold to form white iron near the surface. The product so made is called *chilled* iron and is used for castings needing a hard, wear-resistant surface with a soft inner core that is better for the absorption of impact loads. Examples of this use are crushing and forming rolls or railroad car wheels which need a hard surface on the periphery but a softer core. These items can be machined internally and are better able to absorb shock without fracture failure.

Some compositions under certain cooling rates freeze with a structure known as mottled iron, consisting of randomly distributed white and gray areas. Depending upon the material constituents and the solidification conditions, mottled iron will exist for varying depths below the white iron of a chilled casting as a transition zone and will have some of the characteristics of each of the adjacent structures.

Table 5–2 shows a comparison of some of the common cast irons.

TABLE 5–2

Common Cast Irons

Type Iron	How Produced	Characteristics	Relative Cost
White	Rapid cooling Low $C + Si$	Hard, brittle Unmachinable	1
Malleable	Heat treated White iron	T.S. 50–120,000 Good malleability and ductility	4
Nodular	Ladle addition	T.S. 60–150,000 Similar to malleable	4
Gray	Slow cooling High $C + Si$	T.S. 20–60,000 Good machinability Brittle	2
Chilled	Fast surface chill	Hard surface (white iron) Soft core (gray iron)	3

STEEL

One of the largest and most influential manufacturing operations today is the steel industry, which makes some finished products but is primarily concerned with the making of raw material for further processing. The annual production of over one hundred million tons exceeds by far the total production of all other metals and plastics combined. Pound for pound, cast irons are cheaper than steel, and for those products that can be made with suitable shapes and strengths as castings, the cost of the finished product will often be lower in this form. However, all of the cast irons, because of their high carbon content, are subject to the definite processing limitations of casting. Thin sections, good finishes, and dimensional control are obtained at reasonable cost only by deformation processing instead of casting. Deformation can be performed only on materials having relatively high ductility, and for ferrous materials this requires reduction of carbon from the cast iron range to the extent that a material with an entirely new set of properties is produced.

All of the cast irons are essentially pig iron with at most only minor modifications of composition. The essential component of pig iron in addition to the iron is 3 to 4 per cent carbon. When this carbon content is reduced to below 2 per cent, the resulting new material is called *steel*.

Wrought Iron. Previous to the introduction of presently used methods for making steel, a method of reducing the carbon content of pig iron had been used since before 1600. The product, although called *wrought iron,* was actually the first low carbon steel to be manufactured in quantity.

In the early manufacture of wrought iron, molten pig iron was subjected to oxidizing agents, normally air and iron oxide, and the silicon and carbon content of the melt was reduced. The furnaces used were incapable of maintaining the iron at temperatures above about 2700°F. Reference to the iron carbon equilibrium diagram will show that at this temperature pig iron would be well above the liquidus line. However, as the carbon content was reduced, at constant temperature, the iron began to solidify, so in order to keep the reaction proceeding within the melt it was necessary to stir or *puddle* the material in the furnace. Since this material included slag, which floated on top as long as the metal was liquid, the slag was mixed with the purified iron. The resulting product was withdrawn from the furnace as a pasty ball on the end of the stirring rod and, while low in carbon and silicon, contained from 3 to 4 per cent slag, mostly SiO_2. These balls were then deformation processed by repeated rolling, cutting, stacking, and rerolling in the same direction with a resulting product that consisted of relatively pure iron with many very fine slag stringers running in the direction of rolling.

Although cheaper methods have been developed for reducing the carbon from pig iron, without incorporating the slag in the product, a demand for wrought iron continues, based primarily on its reputation for corrosion and fatigue resistance. It is presently manufactured by pouring molten refined iron into separately manufactured slag with subsequent rolling.

Wrought iron has a tensile strength of about 50,000 psi and good ductility, although the material is quite *anisotropic* (properties vary with orientation or direction of testing) because of the slag stringers. Its principal use is for the manufacture of welded pipe. While *wrought iron* originally referred to this product or to its composition, the term has frequently been extended to refer to any *worked* low carbon steel product, particularly when shaped or worked by hand, as in ornamental iron railings and grillwork.

Steelmaking. The oldest known method of making higher carbon steel consisted of reheating wrought iron and powdered charcoal together in the *cementation* process. According to the iron carbon equilibrium dia-

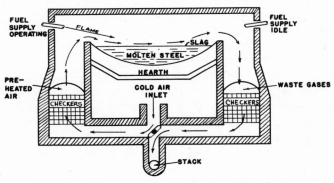

FIG. 5–5. Cross-section of open hearth furnace.

gram, at 2000°F. carbon is soluble in iron up to 2 per cent. At this temperature the carbon slowly diffused into the solid material, requiring a total cycle time, including heating, of about two weeks for the process. Much of the slag in the wrought iron migrated to the surface, forming surface blisters resulting in the term *blister* steel. Even after this lengthy treatment the carbon was not uniformly dispersed throughout the material and multiple cutting and rerolling procedures were required to produce a high quality product.

Further reduction of the slag, greater uniformity of the carbon, and closer control was later achieved by a secondary operation known as the *crucible* process. Bars made by the cementation process were remelted in a clay or graphite crucible where the slag floated to the surface. This crucible process produced steel of very high quality and modifications of the method are still used today, but it was made possible only by furnace developments which permitted higher temperatures to be achieved than were needed in the manufacture of wrought iron.

Both the modern open hearth furnace and the Bessemer converter were developed in the 1850's. These two developments greatly increased the speed with which pig iron could be refined. The modern era of industry can be tied to these developments which led to the production of large quantities of high quality, low cost steel.

Fig. 5–5 shows the construction of an open hearth furnace as is used for the majority of steel produced today in the United States. Various proportions of pig iron, either solid or molten, steel scrap, limestone for flux, and iron ore are charged on the hearth of the furnace. The principal reducing action takes place between the iron ore and the carbon of the pig iron, the final carbon content of the steel being controllable by the proper proportions of the charged materials. The principal difference between this furnace and that used previously in the manufacture of wrought iron lies

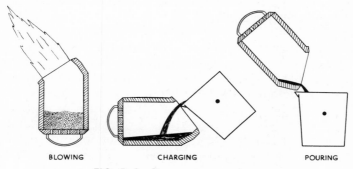

BLOWING   CHARGING   POURING

FIG. 5–6. Bessemer converter.

in the preheating of the entering combustion air. In the open hearth furnace for steelmaking, the air enters through a brick checkerwork which has been previously heated by the exhausting flue gases. Two similar checkerworks are used, one for the exhaust side and one for the entering air side of the furnace. After a relatively short period of operation in this manner, the air flow through the checkerworks is reversed. Preheating of the air permits higher temperatures to be developed in the furnace, and the bath of metal may be kept molten as the carbon content is reduced.

The Bessemer converter is shown in Fig. 5–6. The charge consists of molten pig iron. Steel scrap may be added to help control the temperature. After charging in the horizontal position, the air blast is turned on through the *tuyeres* and the converter turned upright so the air bubbles through the melt, oxidizing and burning out first silicon, then carbon. The process can be used to reduce the carbon content to about 0.05 per cent. Although less expensive to operate than the *basic*-lined open hearth furnace, the inability of the *acid*-lined Bessemer converter to reduce the phosphorus content of the metal has restricted its use to the production of only about 5 per cent of the steel made in the United States. Some steel is produced by initial refining in the Bessemer converter followed by further refining in the open hearth furnace.

Electric furnace steel is produced in a variation of the older crucible process with the furnace heated by electric arc or induction. The atmosphere can be well controlled in the electric furnace and careful control of composition may be maintained. Steel of the highest quality is produced by this method.

The most recent developments in steelmaking both by the open hearth and Bessemer methods involve the use of pure oxygen rather than air for oxidation of the carbon. The principal advantage of this method is shorter cycle time, which provides greater efficiency of equipment use.

Plain Carbon Steel. Any of the steelmaking processes is capable of producing a product which has .05 carbon or less. With this small amount of carbon the properties approach those of pure iron with maximum ductility and minimum strength. Maximum ductility is desirable both from the standpoint of ease in deformation processing and for service use. Minimum strength is desirable for deformation processing. However, higher strengths than that obtainable with this low carbon are desirable from the product design standpoint. The most practical means of increasing the strength is by the addition or retention of some carbon. However, it should be fully understood that any increase of strength over that of pure iron can be obtained only at the expense of some loss of ductility, and the final choice is always a compromise of some degree. Fig. 5–7 shows typical ferrous material applications in relation to carbon content.

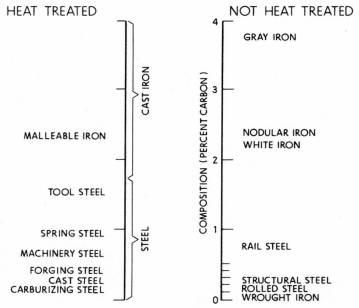

FIG. 5–7. Ferrous materials.

Because of the difficulty of composition control or the additional opera-tion of increasing carbon content, the cost of higher carbon, higher strength steel is greater than that with low carbon.

Because of their low cost, the majority of steels used are of the plain carbon variety. These consist of iron combined with carbon concentrated in three ranges classed as low carbon, medium carbon, and high carbon. With the exception of manganese used to control sulphur, other elements are present only in small enough quantities to be considered as impurities, though in some cases they may have minor effect on properties of the material.

Plain steels with approximately six to twenty-five *points* of carbon (.06 to .25 per cent) are rated as low carbon steels and are rarely hardened by heat treatment since the low carbon content permits so little formation of hard martensite that the process is relatively ineffective. Enormous ton-nages of these low carbon steels are processed in structural shapes, sheet, strip, rod, plate, pipe, and wire. A large portion of the material is cold worked in its final processing to improve its hardness, strength, and surface finish qualities. The grades containing twenty points or less of carbon are susceptible to considerable plastic flow and are frequently used for deep drawn products or may be used as a ductile core for case hardened material. The low plain carbon steels are readily brazed, welded, and forged.

The medium carbon steels, .25 to .5 per cent, contain sufficient carbon that they may be heat treated for desirable strength, hardness, machina-bility, or other properties. The hardness of plain carbon steels in this range cannot be increased sufficiently for the material to serve satisfacto-rily as cutting tools, but the load carrying capacity of the steels can be raised considerably, while still retaining sufficient ductility for good toughness. The majority of the steel is furnished in the hot rolled condi-tion and is often machined for final finishing. It can be welded, but is more difficult to join by this method than the low carbon steel because of structural changes caused by welding heat in localized areas.

High carbon steel contains from 50 points to as high as 160 points of carbon, .5 to 1.6 per cent. This group of steels is classed as tool and die steel where hardness is the principal property desired. Because of the fast reaction time and resulting low hardenability, plain carbon steels nearly always must be water quenched. Even with this drastic treatment and its associated danger of distortion or cracking, it is seldom possible to develop fully hardened structure in material more than about one inch in thickness. In practice the ductility of heat treat hardened plain carbon steel is low compared to that of alloy steels for the same strength, but even so carbon steel is frequently used because of its lower cost.

Free Machining Steels. Bessemer steel, which is normally high in sulphur, and resulphurized open hearth steels are called free machining or free cutting steels. These steels are much like plain carbon steels except that they contain sulphur and phosphorus above that considered a mere impurity concentration. Sulphur in amounts over 0.05 per cent combines with iron in plain carbon steel to form iron sulphide, which softens at temperatures where hot work is usually carried out, causing embrittlement which may result in cracks. A material with this characteristic is termed *hot short.* The bad effects of sulphur in free machining steel can be counteracted by the addition of extra quantities of manganese.

Phosphorus in small quantities tends to improve the strength of steel but in quantities over 0.05 per cent may cause cold shortness (brittleness at low temperatures).

The free machining steels are poor in impact resistance, can undergo only limited plastic deformation, are difficult to weld satisfactorily, and are not suitable for use in high temperature applications. Their use is therefore limited to those applications where impact loading is nonexistent or very low, and where machining ease has a significant effect on the over-all cost of manufacturing.

Another type of free machining steel which does not have the faults of the high sulphur type is produced by the addition of lead in the melt.

Alloy Steels.   Although plain carbon steels work well for many uses and are the cheapest of the steels and therefore the most used, they cannot completely fulfill the requirements for some work. Individual or groups or properties can be improved by addition of various elements in the form of alloys. Even plain carbon steels are alloys of at least iron, carbon, and manganese, but the term *alloy steel* refers to steels containing elements other than these in controlled quantities greater than impurity concentration or, in the case of manganese, greater than 1.50 per cent.

Table 5–3 shows the general effects of the more commonly used elements on some of the properties of steels. Some of the effects noted in the chart are independent but most of them are based on the influence the element has on the action of carbon. The hardness and strength of any steel, alloy or otherwise, depend primarily on the amount and form of the iron carbide or other metal carbides present. Even in unhardened steel, carbon produces an increase in hardness and strength with a consequent loss of ductility. The improvement in machinability and loss in weldability are based on this loss of ductility.

Interest in hardenability is indirect. Hardenability itself has been discussed earlier and is usually thought of most in connection with depth hardening ability in a full hardening operation. However, with the isothermal transformation curves shifted to the right, the properties of a material can be materially changed even when not fully hardened. After hot rolling or forging operations, the material usually air cools. Any alloy generally shifts the transformation curves to the right, which with air cooling results in finer pearlite than would be formed in a plain carbon steel. This finer pearlite has higher hardness and strength, which has an effect on machinability and may lower ductility.

TABLE 5-3

Effect of Some Alloying Elements on Properties of Steel

	Low Carbon .1–.2 Per Cent	Med. Carbon .2–.6 Per Cent	Manganese 2.0 Per Cent	Phosphorus .15 Per Cent	Sulfur .3 Per Cent	Silicon 2.0 Per Cent	Chromium 1.1 Per Cent	Nickel 5.0 Per Cent	Molybdenum .75 Per Cent	Vanadium .25 Per Cent	Copper 1.1 Per Cent	Aluminum .1 Per Cent	Boron .003 Per Cent
Hardenability	N	G	VG	G	B	G	VG	VG	VG	G	N	N	VG
Strength	G	VG	G	G	B	VG	G	G	G	N	N	G	G
Toughness	B	VB	G	VB	VB	B	VB	VG	G	G	N	G	?
Wear resistance	N	VG	VG	N	N	G	VG	G	VG	G	N	N	G
Machinability annealed	G	G	B	G	VG	B	B	VB	B	N	B	N	?
Weldability	B	VB	VB	VB	B	B	VB	VB	VB	G	B	N	VB
Corrosion resistance	B	VB	N	VG	VB	G	N	VG	G	N	VG	G	?

Very Good VG
Good G
Little or None N
Bad B
Very Bad VB

The generally bad influence of any alloys on weldability is a further reflection of the influence on hardenability. With alloys present during the rapid cooling taking place in the welding area, hard, nonductile structures are formed in the steel which frequently lead to cracking and distortion.

Nickel in particular has a very beneficial effect by retarding grain growth in the austenite range. As with hardenability, it is the secondary effects of grain refinement which are noted in properties. A finer grain structure may actually have less hardenability, but it has its most pronounced effect on toughness, where for two steels with equivalent hardness and strength, the one with finer grain will have better ductility that is reflected in the chart as improved toughness. This improved toughness, however, may be detrimental to machinability.

Most pure metals have relatively good corrosion resistance, which is generally lowered by impurities or small amounts of intentional alloys. In steel, carbon in particular lowers the corrosion resistance very seriously. In small percentages copper and phosphorus are beneficial in reducing corrosion. Nickel becomes effective in percentages of around 5 per cent, and chromium is extremely effective above 10 per cent, leading to a separate class of alloy steels called stainless steels. Many tool steels, while not designed for the purpose, are in effect stainless steels because of the high percentage of chromium present.

Not shown in Table 5–3 but of importance in many applications are the electrical properties of a steel, particularly the property of magnetic hysteresis. Pure iron has the lowest hysteresis of any ferrous material, and for the highest quality transformer laminations electrolytically refined iron is sometimes used. However, electrolytic refining is an expensive process. Most steel made for electrical use, particularly where alternating currents are involved, is steel containing as little carbon as is practical by open hearth refining but with up to 5 per cent silicon. The silicon graphitizes most of the carbon and the resulting material when annealed has low hysteresis and high permeability.

Low Alloy Structural Steels.   Certain low alloy steels sold under various trade names have been developed to provide a low cost structural material with higher yield strength than plain carbon steel. The addition of small amounts of some alloying elements can raise the yield strength of hot rolled sections without heat treatment to as high as seventy-five or eighty thousand psi as compared to forty-five to sixty thousand psi for plain carbon steels. Designing to higher working stresses may reduce the required section size by 25 to 30 per cent at increased cost of from 15 to 50 per cent, depending upon the amount and kind of alloy.

The low alloy structural steels are sold almost entirely in the form of hot rolled structural shapes. These materials have good weldability, ductility, impact strength better than that of plain carbon steel, and good corrosion resistance, particularly to atmospheric exposure. Many building codes are based on the more conservative use of plain carbon steels, and the use of alloy structural steel has no economic advantage in many cases.

Low Alloy AISI Steels. The low alloy AISI (American Iron and Steel Institute) steels are alloyed primarily for improved hardenability. They are more costly than plain carbon steels and their use can generally be justified only when needed in the heat treat hardened and tempered condition. Compared to plain carbon steels, they can have 30 to 40 per cent higher yield strength and 10 to 20 per cent higher tensile strength. At equivalent tensile strengths and hardnesses they can have 30 to 40 per cent higher reduction of area and approximately twice the impact strength.

The low alloy AISI steels are those containing less than approximately 8 per cent total alloying elements, although most commercially important steels contain less than 5 per cent. The carbon content may vary from very low to very high, but for most it is in the medium range where effective heat treatment may be employed for property improvement at minimum costs. The steels are used widely in automobile, machine tool, and aircraft construction, especially for the manufacture of moving parts that are subject to high stress and wear.

Stainless Steels. Tonnage-wise, the most important of the higher alloy steels are a group of high chromium steels with extremely high corrosion and chemical resistance compared to any of the lower alloy steels, and for most of them much better mechanical properties at high temperatures. This group was first called *stainless steel* but more recently, with the emphasis on high temperature use, are frequently called heat and corrosion resistant steels.

With lower amounts of chromium or with silicon or aluminum added to some of the higher chromium steels, the material responds to heat treatment much as any low alloy steel. The gamma to alpha transformation in iron occurs normally and the steel may be hardened by heat treatment similar to that used on plain carbon or low alloy steels. Steels of this class are called *martensitic* and the most used ones have 4 to 6 per cent chromium.

With larger amounts of chromium, up to 30 per cent or more, the austenite region of the iron carbide equilibrium diagram is suppressed and the steel loses its ability to be hardened by normal steel heat treating procedures. Steels of this type are called *ferritic* and are particularly useful where high corrosion resistance is necessary in cold worked products.

With high chromium and the addition of 8 per cent or more of nickel or combinations of nickel and manganese, the ferrite region of the diagram is suppressed. These steels, the most typical of which contains 18 per cent chromium and 8 per cent nickel, are referred to as *austenitic* stainless steels. They are not hardenable by normal steel heat treating procedures, but the addition of small amounts of other elements makes some of them hardenable by a solution-precipitation reaction.

In any of the stainless steels, serious loss of corrosion resistance can occur if large amounts of chromium carbide form. Consequently, the ferritic and austenitic grades are generally made with low amounts of carbon and even then may need special heat treatments or the addition of *stabilizing* elements such as molybdenum or titanium to prevent chromium carbide formation. With the martensitic grades where the hardness and strength depend on the carbon, the steels must be fully hardened with the carbon in a martensitic structure for maximum corrosion resistance.

The austenitic steels are the most expensive but possess the best impact properties at low temperatures, the highest strength and corrosion resistance at elevated temperature, and generally have the best appearance. They are used for heat exchangers, refining and chemical processing equipment, gas turbines, and other equipment exposed to severe corrosive conditions. The austenitic steels are paramagnetic (practically unaffected by magnetic flux).

Both the ferritic and martensitic stainless steels are magnetic. Most are not as corrosion resistant at high temperature as the austenitic type but offer good resistance at normal temperatures. They are used for such things as cutlery, surgical instruments, automobile trim, ball bearings, and kitchen equipment.

The stainless steels are more difficult to machine and weld than most of the other ferrous materials. In no case can stainless steels be classed as the easiest to work, but they can be processed by all of the normal procedures, including casting, rolling, forging, and pressworking.

Tool and Die Steels. The greatest tonnage of tools (other than cutting tools, which are discussed in Chapter 18) and dies are made from plain, high carbon tool steels. This is true only because of the low cost of these materials since their use has a number of disadvantages. These high carbon steels have low hardenability, low ductility associated with high hardness, and do not hold their hardness well at elevated temperature.

Manganese tool and die steels are oil hardening and have a reduced tendency to deform or crack during heat treatment. They contain from 85 to 100 points of carbon, $1\frac{1}{2}$ to $1\frac{3}{4}$ per cent manganese to improve hardenability, and small amounts of chromium, vanadium, and molybdenum to improve hardness and toughness qualities.

High chromium tool and die steels are usually quenched in oil for hardening, but some have sufficient hardenability to develop hardness with an air quench. One group of the high chromium steels called high speed steel has substantial additions of tungsten, vanadium, and sometimes cobalt to improve the hardness in the red heat range.

Cast Steels. Compared to the tonnage of cast iron produced and to wrought steel, the quantity of cast steel is small. The high temperatures necessary make melting and handling more difficult than for cast iron and also create problems in producing sound, high quality castings. The mechanical properties of cast steel tend to be poorer than those of the same material in wrought form, but certain shape and size relationships, together with property requirements that can be supplied only by steel, may favor the manufacture of a product as a steel casting. Steel castings may be produced with greater ductility than even malleable iron, and this quality may be needed in the product though not necessary for the process of casting.

The principal advantages of steel as a structural material, mainly the ability to control properties by composition and heat treatment, apply for both the wrought and cast material. One advantage of cast steel over its wrought counterpart is its lack of directional properties. Wrought steel and other materials tend to develop strength in the direction of working when deformed by plastic flow but at the same time become weaker and more brittle in the perpendicular directions. Steel that is cast to shape loses the opportunity for gain in properties by plastic work but by the same token is not adversely affected by weakness in some directions.

As far as composition is concerned, no real difference exists between wrought and cast steel. It was pointed out earlier that steel is a combination of mostly iron with carbon in amounts from just above that soluble at room temperature (0.008 per cent) to as high as 2 per cent, the maximum soluble in austenite at the eutectic temperature. Other elements may also be part of the composition in small enough quantities to be negligible or sufficiently large to have influence on the heat treating of the alloy or even of exerting effects of their own as in wrought alloy steels. The carbon content can be in any of the three ranges, low, medium, or high, but the majority of steel castings are produced with the medium carbon range since nearly all are heat treated to develop good mechanical properties.

MATERIAL IDENTIFICATION SYSTEMS

During earlier times in our economy, there was less need for material identification systems. A manufacturer generally had complete charge of the entire operation from raw material to finished product. There were relatively few materials to choose from in any event. More recently specialization has led to more division of the manufacturing procedure. Fabricators seldom produce their own raw materials and the number of material choices has grown tremendously and continues to grow yearly. Reliable and universally accepted systems of material specification are essential to permit designers to specify and fabricators to purchase materials and be assured of composition and properties.

The first group of materials for which standardization was needed were ferrous materials. The automotive industry set up the first recognized standards but with even broader use and more classes of steels, the present most universally recognized standards are those of the American Iron and Steel Institute (AISI).

The number of possible combinations of iron, carbon, and alloying elements is without limit. Some of these, for example the low alloy high strength structural steels, are not covered by any standard specification system, or designation. However the majority of commonly used steels in the plain carbon and low alloy categories can be described by a standardized code system consisting of a letter denoting the process by which the steel was manufactured, followed by four, or in a few cases, five

TABLE 5–4

AISI Basic Classification Numbers

AISI No.	Average Per Cent Alloy Content
10XX	None
11XX	0.08–0.33 S.
13XX	1.8–2.0 Mn.
23XX	3.5 Ni.
31XX	0.7–0.8 Cr., 1.3 Ni.
41XX	0.5–1.0 Cr., 0.2–0.3 Mo.
43XX	0.5–0.8 Cr., 1.8 Ni., 0.3 Mo.
51XX	0.8–1.1 Cr.
61XX	0.8–1.0 Cr., 0.1–0.2 V.
86XX	0.6 Ni., 0.5–0.7 Cr., 1.2 Mo.
87XX	0.6 Ni., 0.5 Cr., 0.3 Mo.

numbers. The first two number digits refer to the quantity and kind of principal alloying element or elements. The last two, or three in the case of some of the high carbon steels, refer to the carbon content in hundredths of a per cent. The letter prefix is used to describe the process as follows:

A—Basic open hearth alloy steel
B—Acid Bessemer carbon steel
C—Basic open hearth carbon steel
D—Acid open hearth carbon steel
E—Electric furnace alloy steel

Table 5–4 shows the average alloy content associated with some of the most frequently used classes of steels. The exact specified quantity varies with the carbon content of each steel and even steels with exactly the same number throughout will vary slightly from heat to heat because of necessary manufacturing tolerances. Exact composition can therefore be determined only from chemical analysis of individual heats.

A steel noted as AISI-B 1113 would be one that had been produced in an acid lined Bessemer converter (B *11XX*). The first two digits of the four figure number denote that the steel, although fundamentally a plain carbon steel, contains from 0.08 to 0.33 per cent sulphur which is more than the 0.05 per cent permitted as a maximum impurity concentration in plain carbon steel. The actual content of sulphur for the particular steel indicated falls in the tolerance range of 0.24 to 0.33 per cent. The last two digits (BXX*13*) indicate an average carbon content of 0.13 per cent. The permissible range of carbon included in the manufacturing tolerance is 0.11 to 0.16 per cent.

In a similar way the percentage of constituents making up a composition can be determined for steels identified by any AISI classification

TABLE 5–5

Some Stainless Steels and Properties

	Composition			Ten. St. 1000 psi.	Per Cent Elong. (2 in.)	Characteristics and Uses
Material	*Ni*	*Cr*	*Other*			
302	9	18				Austenitic—Work harden only.
Annealed				85	60	Excellent corrosion resistance to atmosphere and foods. Machinability fair. Welding not recommended. General purpose. Kitchen and chemical applications.
430		16	C. 0.12			
Annealed				75	30	Ferritic—Work harden only. Excellent corrosion resistance to weather and water exposure and most chemicals. Machinability fair. General purpose. Kitchen and chemical equipment. Automobile trim.
Cold worked				90	15	
420		13	C. 0.15			Matensitic—Heat treatable. Good corrosion resistance to weather and water exposure. Machinability fair. Cutlery, surgical instruments, ball bearings.
Annealed				95	25	
Hardened and tempered				230	8	
17-4PH	4	17	Cu 4			Age hardening. Good corrosion resistance. Maintains strength at elevated temperature. Machinability poor. Air frame skin and structure.
Room temp.				195	13	
1200°F.				59	15	

number. Values thus determined are average values only. More exact information showing the manufacturing tolerance range for each element can be obtained from steel handbooks. The general properties of machinability, weldability, strength, ductility, and others associated with these classified steels are also available from handbooks, but, as with composition, are subject to variation depending on actual composition and prior processing including heat treatment.

Table 5–5 gives compositions and properties for some typical stainless steels, and Table 5–6 gives similar information for tool steels.

TABLE 5–6

Some Tool Steels and Properties

Symbol	Composition					Temperature of Tempering	Hardness Rc	Characteristics and Uses
	C	Cr	Mo	W	V			
W1	0.6–1.4					300–650	65–50	Water hardening. Subject to distortion. Tools and short run dies.
S1	0.5	1.5		2.5		400–1200	58–40	Oil hardening. Toughness very good. Subject to distortion. Punching, shearing, trimming dies.
O1	0.9	0.5		0.5		300–500	62–47	Oil hardening. Toughness fair. Less distortion than W. All type dies.
A2	1.0	5.0	1.0			350–1000	62–57	Air hardening. Toughness fair. Little distortion. All type dies.
D1	1.0	12.0	1.0			400–1000	61–54	Air hardening. Toughness fair. Little distortion. Very good wear resistance. Long run tools and dies.
H11	0.35	5.0	1.5		0.4	1000–1200	54–38	Air hardening. Hot working 900°F. Toughness good. Little distortion. Casting, forging, extrusion dies.
H22	0.35	2.0		11.0		1100–1250	52–39	Air or oil hardening. Toughness good. Some distortion. Use to 1700° F. Casting, forging, extrusion, and punching dies.
H41	0.65	4.0	8.0	1.5	1.0	1050–1200	60–50	Similar to H22 but harder and not as tough.
T1	0.7 1.05	4.0		18	1.0	1000–1100	66–60	Air or oil hardening. Toughness poor. Cutting tools.
M1	0.8	4.0	8.0	1.5	1.0	1000–1100	65–60	Similar to T1. One of the most common HSS cutting tool materials.

QUESTIONS

1. Why is the metal beryllium, with desirable design properties, not likely to ever become a large tonnage competitor of steel?
2. Why has the United States Government made a practice of stockpiling tungsten, mercury, and tin?
3. Why were copper, tin, lead, and iron the first metals to be used in large quantities by man?
4. What are the principal factors to be considered in choosing a material for a product?
5. What is the function of the limestone charged into an iron reduction blast furnace?

6. Distinguish between a "pig" and "pig iron."
7. List the principal types of cast iron and give their principal properties.
8. How is each of the cast irons obtained?
9. What is the difference between "pearlitic" and "ferritic" malleable iron?
10. What mechanical property does gray iron have that makes its use especially desirable for machine tools in preference to steel?
11. What relationships exist among the amount of carbon and silicon present, the rate of solidification and cooling, and the ease of graphitization in the production of gray iron castings?
12. What is the principal difference in composition between cast iron and steel?
13. What is the principal property difference between cast iron and steel that has a major effect on processing?
14. Why would it be impossible to cast material having the composition of wrought iron?
15. Why is wrought iron anisotropic?
16. What is the function of the iron ore charged into an open hearth steel-making furnace?
17. What compromise is involved in the choice of carbon content for a steel?
18. How is Bessemer steel generally inferior to open hearth steel?
19. When is the higher sulphur content of Bessemer steel compared to open hearth steel of some advantage?
20. How is steel made free machining without the disadvantages of high sulphur content?
21. Explain the usual effect of alloys in hot worked steel that is not subsequently heat treated.
22. What will be the principal property difference between two steels of equal hardness and strength but different grain size?
23. Why are few of the AISI alloy steels produced with low carbon content?
24. What are the three classes of stainless steels and why are they so named?
25. What is the purpose of a stabilizing element such as titanium added to stainless steel?
26. What disadvantages has plain high carbon steel as a tool material?
27. Describe briefly the standard AISI identification system for steel.

Nonferrous Metals

THE FERROUS METALS, particularly steel and gray iron, hold such a predominant place in the economy that, for discussion, metals are usually divided into ferrous and nonferrous groups. On either a weight or a volume basis, pig iron is the cheapest refined metal form available today. Consequently the use of nonferrous metals can generally be justified only on the basis of some special property that ferrous metals do not have or some processing advantage that a nonferrous metal offers.

Nonferrous metals have a number of property advantages over steel and cast iron although not all nonferrous metals have all the advantages. Aluminum, magnesium, and beryllium (one of the more rare metals) have densities of from one fourth to one third that of steel. Although strength rather than weight is more frequently the basis of design, in many cases, particularly in casting, the process limits the minimum section thickness and products made of ferrous metals are made much stronger than required by the design. The same product made from even a weaker but less dense nonferrous metal may still have adequate strength and weigh much less. Even though the per pound cost of the nonferrous metal may be greater, the final costs of the products may be comparable. On a strength to weight basis, hardened steel is still superior to all but a few very high cost nonferrous metals, but some nonferrous alloys of only slightly less strength per unit weight may offer much greater ductility than the hardened steel and may be processed more economically. For the alloys shown in Fig. 6–1, those classed as light alloys have one fourth to one third the density of iron or steel. Those called heavy alloys have densities approximately one to one and one-half times that of steel.

The corrosion resistance of most of the nonferrous metals is generally superior to all the ferrous metals except stainless steel, and stainless steel does not offer the cost advantage of plain carbon and low alloy steels. This increased corrosion resistance is the most frequent reason for the choice of nonferrous metals.

Corrosion resistance is important for a number of reasons. Not only may the mechanical properties of the material be affected by corrosion but

100

the appearance of a metal is dependent on its corrosion resistance. Where appearance is important, the commonly used ferrous metals nearly always require some kind of finishing and protective surface treatment. With many nonferrous metals protective finishes are not needed, even under conditions that would be severely corrosive to steel. The distinctive appearance of many of the nonferrous metals as well as stainless steel is highly desirable in many products.

Although iron is the most frequently used magnet material, having high permeability and low magnetic hysteresis, pure iron is a poor permanent magnet material. The best permanent magnets are alloys high in nickel, aluminum, and cobalt. Silver, copper, and aluminum have much greater

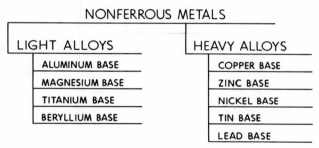

FIG. 6–1. Nonferrous metals.

electrical and thermal conductivities than any of the ferrous materials, and are usually used instead of steel where these properties are important.

Zinc is a typical example of a metal whose use in relatively large tonnages, depends not so much on mechanical properties, or even on its superior corrosion resistance, but on a special processing advantage. Zinc is weak, costs over twice as much per pound as pig iron or low carbon steel, and even with good corrosion resistance usually needs plating for good appearance, but its low melting point permits its use in die casting with longer die life than any other commonly cast metal.

ALUMINUM ALLOYS

Aluminum and copper are the most important of the nonferrous metals, being produced in approximately equal tonnages. However about three fourths of all the copper produced is used for electrical conductors, so aluminum is left as the most important structural nonferrous metal. Aluminum is potentially very available, large ore deposits being found at many places, but the most economical reduction process yet found still requires eight kilowatt hours of electrical energy per pound of metal refined. Even so, the only cheaper metals on a weight basis are lead, zinc, and iron. Lead is seldom used as a structural metal, and zinc is limited mostly to low strength applications so aluminum is a principal competitor with iron and steel. On a volume basis, only iron is cheaper.

General Properties.   Aluminum alloys have tensile strengths that range from twelve to eighty thousand psi. These values compare favorably with other nonferrous alloys and with many steels, although some steels may have strengths as high as three hundred thousand psi. Nevertheless, the low density of aluminum, about one third that of iron, steel, and brass, places the material in a favorable position when the strength-weight ratio is more important than space considerations.

The excellent ductility of aluminum permits it to be readily formed into complicated shapes and allows plastic flow instead of fracture failure under shock and other overload conditions. Pure aluminum has excellent corrosion resistance but is limited in use to those applications where strength requirements are low. The corrosion resistance of the high strength aluminum alloys is generally good except when exposed to some alkaline environments. Additional protection may be provided for these conditions by cladding with a thin layer of the pure metal. Plate produced in this form is called *Alclad.*

The endurance limit even for hardened alloys is in the range of from five to twenty thousand psi. This weakness prohibits the use of aluminum in some applications where vibration is combined with high stress levels and it is often necessary to observe special precautions to eliminate the occurrence of stress risers such as notches, scratches, and sudden section changes. Another deficiency is the loss of strength that occurs with increased temperature. Both work hardened and heat treat hardened alloys lose strength rapidly at temperatures above about 300 degrees F. This loss of strength at elevated temperatures not only restricts the design of parts made of aluminum, but because it is combined with a loss of ductility near the melting point (a condition called *hot-shortness*), the processes of casting and welding are made more difficult.

All of the metals and alloys, both ferrous and nonferrous, have some combination of properties which make them preferred for some applications. While aluminum is exceeded in any individual property by some other metal and while it has deficiencies which limit its use, the combination of properties it possesses, particularly good corrosion resistance, conductivity, lightness, good strength to weight ratio and good ductility, when combined with easy fabrication and moderately low cost, account for its importance as a structural metal second only to iron and steel.

Wrought Aluminum Alloys.   Aluminum alloys designed to be used with some deformation process, where ductility and strain hardening properties are of greatest importance, are referred to as wrought alloys. Any pure metal, including aluminum, generally has greater ductility, higher conductivity, and better corrosion resistance than any alloyed form of the metal. The purest readily available form of aluminum has especially high conductivity and is designated as EC or electrical grade. Compared to copper, its conductivity is 68 per cent on a volume basis and 200 per cent on a weight basis.

Highest purity is necessary only for electrical use. Commercially pure aluminum has sufficient impurities present to impair its electrical conductivity significantly but retains excellent corrosion resistance and ductility. In the fully softened condition the tensile strength is twelve to thirteen thousand psi. When fully work hardened the strength is twenty-four to twenty-seven thousand psi. The combination of high ductility and low strength generally results in poor machinability, particularly from the standpoint of surface finish.

Neither electrical grade nor commercially pure aluminum is susceptible to hardening by heat treatment. Likewise, a number of aluminum alloys contain alloying elements which remain in solid solution at all temperatures do not respond to heat treat hardening procedures. The effect of the alloys is to increase the strength at the expense of some ductility. Tensile strengths in the range of sixteen to forty thousand psi when annealed and twenty-nine to sixty thousand psi when fully work hardened may be obtained by additions of manganese, chromium, magnesium, and iron. Alloys of this type offer advantages over pure aluminum by compromising

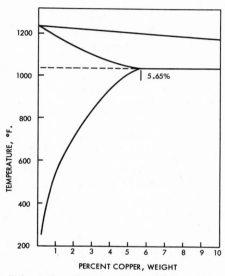

FIG. 6–2. Portion of equilibrium diagram for aluminum-copper.

with a reduction of forming properties to gain in mechanical properties. The additional strength is obtained only by the presence of the alloy in solid solution and not because of heat treatment. However, the alloys are subject to work hardening and recrystallization treatments as are all metals. The term "annealing" when used with reference to pure aluminum or one of the solid solution alloys can only be interpreted to mean "recrystallization."

As was discussed in Chapter 4, the possibility of heat treat hardening exists even in metals that undergo no allotropic changes when an alloying element is more soluble at elevated temperature than at room temperature. Fig. 6–2 shows the equilibrium diagram for aluminum and copper. The sloping solvus line below 5.65 per cent copper is evidence of the possibility of obtaining a supersaturated structure at room temperature. Depending on the heat treatment, three different structures may be actually obtained. With slow cooling, equilibrium conditions are approximated and the alloy is placed in its softest or annealed condition. With rapid cooling the fully supersaturated structure of intermediate hardness and ductility is obtained. Following the establishment of this supersaturated structure, the alloy is subject to aging, either natural with time at room temperature or artificial at slightly elevated temperature. The hardest structure is obtained only by heating to the solution temperature to allow the copper to form a solid solution, followed by quenching and aging.

Besides copper-aluminum, two other reactions of this type are used in commercial aluminum alloys. Above 4 per cent, magnesium forms heat treatable alloys with aluminum and the combination of magnesium and

TABLE 6–1
Aluminum Temper and Heat Treat Symbols

—F	As fabricated
—O	Annealed (recrystallized) temper of wrought material
—H 1	Strain hardened only. Degree of hardening designated by second digit through 8. Number 9 used to designate extra hard temper
—H 2	Strain hardened and partially annealed. Second digit 2 through 8 used in same manner as for H1 series
—H 3	Strain hardened and stabilized. Second digit to designate degree of residual strain
—T 2	Annealed temper of cast material
—T 3	Solution treat and strain harden
—T 4	Solution treat and natural age
—T 5	Artificial age only after cooling from elevated processing temperature
—T 6	Solution treat and artificial age
—T 7	Solution treat and stabilize
—T 8	Solution treat, strain harden, and artificial age
—T 9	Solution treat, artificial age, and strain harden

Note: The above symbols follow the number designating the aluminum alloy type and become part of the material identification.

silicon forms the compound MgSi which acts in the same way as copper or pure magnesium. Strengths of these alloys range from thirteen to thirty-five thousand psi in the annealed condition and from thirty-five to eighty thousand psi when fully hardened.

The fabricator of aluminum products may obtain the alloys in a number of different heat treated and work hardened conditions. Table 6–1 shows the standard symbols that are used to denote these conditions. The terms *solution treated, aged, annealed,* and *cold worked* have been discussed in connection with heat treatments. *Stabilizing* is an additional treatment used with aluminum alloys to control growth and distortion. In an alloy naturally or artificially aged to the maximum hardness level, a period of time follows during which the natural relieving of stresses will result in uncontrolled dimensional changes. If the aging process is carried slightly past that required for maximum hardness, the structure is dimensionally *stabilized* and no further significant changes will occur.

Cast Aluminum Alloys.   Aluminum castings could be made from any of the alloys intended for plastic deformation. These alloys do in fact have their beginning as cast ingots, but certain alloys have been developed specifically for castings. As a cast metal, pure aluminum is subject to the same drawbacks that are characteristic of the wrought alloys. In addition, the relatively high melting point leads to excessive oxidation and the entrapment of gases in the molten metal. The fluidity of the liquid metal is sometimes too poor for flow into thin sections and the metal is subject to high shrinkage and cracking while solidifying and cooling in the mold. By proper alloying all of these conditions may be improved.

As with the wrought alloys, some of the casting alloys may be heat treat hardened and some may not. Principal among the casting alloys that are not heat treatable are those containing silicon only. Used in amounts up to 11 per cent, silicon improves fluidity and decreases shrinkage. Tensile strengths of eighteen thousand psi for sand castings and thirty thousand psi for die castings are typical. Magnesium improves not only the casting characteristics but also the machinability of the cast metal.

Alloys subject to hardening by heat treatment are produced when copper only, magnesium plus silicon, or copper plus magnesium plus silicon are used as alloying elements. When subjected to a complete solution, quenching, and aging heat treatment, alloys of these types may have strength up to forty-eight thousand psi. Many aluminum castings are made of heat treatable alloys and used as cast without heat treatment. The casting process itself generally provides rapid enough cooling to constitute a degree of quenching sufficient to give some supersaturation and natural aging will provide some hardening. The use of the heat treatable casting alloys is restricted to applications requiring high strength to weight ratios since they are somewhat more difficult to cast. Shrinkage is generally higher than with the nonhardenable types and the metal is more subject to cracking and tearing during the cooling period in the mold. (Table 6–2 shows some typical wrought and cast alloys.)

COPPER ALLOYS

While the total tonnage of copper has not decreased, the importance of this metal relative to ferrous metals and to other nonferrous metals has decreased throughout recent history. However, copper is the metal which has been of greatest importance during the longest period of man's history. The "Bronze Age" refers to the period of history during which man fashioned tools from copper and copper alloys as they were found to occur naturally in the free state. The copper used today is reduced from ores as are other metals and the continued use depends on the properties which make it useful either as a pure or alloyed metal.

General Properties. Copper is one of the heavier structural metals with a density about 10 per cent greater than that of steel. Tensile strengths range from 30 to 125 thousand psi depending on alloy content, degree of work hardening, and heat treatment. The ductility is excellent and most

TABLE 6–2

Some Aluminum Alloys and Properties

Type	Composition Cu	Si	Mn	Mg	Other	Ten. St. 1000 psi	Per Cent Elong (2 in.)	Hardness Brinell	Characteristics and Uses
Wrought									
EC					.055	12 (O) 27 (H19)	23 (O) 1.5 (H19)		Good electrical conductor. Work harden only. Electrical conductors.
1100		1.0				13 (O) 24 (H18)	35 (O) 5 (H18)	23 (O) 44 (H18)	Good formability. High Corrosion Resistance. Work harden only. Cooking utensils, chemical equipment, reflectors.
3003			1.2			16 (O) 29 (H18)	30 (O) 4 (H18)	28 (O) 55 (H18)	Good corrosion resistance. Slightly less ductility. Work harden only. Extrusions, forgings, hardware.
5052	2.5				Cr 0.25	28 (O) 42 (H38)	25 (O) 7 (H38)	47 (O) 77 (H38)	Good corrosion resistance. Good machinability. Work harden only. Good weldability. Truck bodies, kitchen cabinets.
2017	4.0	0.7	0.5			26 (O) 62 (T4)	22 (O) 22 (T4)	45 (O) 105 (T4)	Corrosion resistance to rural atmosphere; poor corrosion to marine atmosphere. Machinability good when hard. Screw machine products.
6061	0.28	0.6		1.0	Cr 0.25	18 (O) 45 (T6)	25 (O) 12 (T6)	30 (O) 95 (T6)	Excellent corrosion resistance to rural atmosphere, good for industrial and marine. Good weldability. Structures, marine use, pipes.
7075	1.6			2.5	Zn 5.6 Cr 0.29	33 (O) 83 (T6)	17 (O) 11 (T6)	60 (O) 150 (T6)	Good corrosion resistance to rural atmosphere but poor for others. Frequently clad. Good machinability. Poor weldability. Aircraft structure.

TABLE 6–2 (Continued)

Type	Cu	Si	Mn	Mg	Other	Ten. St. 1000 psi	Per Cent Elong (2 in.)	Hardness Brinell	Characteristics and Uses
						Cast			
43		5.25				19 as cast	8	40	Good corrosion resistance. Only fair machinability. Sand and permanent mold castings, marine fittings, thin sections.
214				4.0		25 as cast	9	50	Good corrosion resistance. Excellent machinability. Sand castings, dairy and food handling, hardware.
355	1.25	5.0		0.5		42 Sol Treat Age	4	90	Good corrosion resistance. Good machinability. Sand and permanent mold castings.

alloys are easy to work by deformation processes, either hot or cold. The machinability ranges from only fair for some of the cast materials to excellent for some of the wrought materials. The most machinable are those containing lead or tin additives for the purpose of improving machinability.

If these were the only properties of note that copper had, it would probably be little used. However, copper has outstanding electrical and thermal conductivity and excellent corrosion resistance particularly when compared to ferrous metals. As noted before, three fourths of the copper produced is used in pure form because of its conductivity. While aluminum has higher conductivity than copper on a weight basis, and is displacing copper for some electrical applications, copper continues to be the principal metal for electrical use. This is partially due to the higher strength to weight ratio of copper in pure drawn form as is generally used for electrical conductors.

For other than electrical use copper and its alloys compete with steel primarily because of better corrosion resistance. Copper alloys have excellent resistance to atmospheric corrosion, particularly under marine conditions. The combination of corrosion resistance and high thermal conductivity makes them useful for radiators and other heat exchangers.

In the United States copper ores are mined principally from two areas.

TABLE 6–3

Properties of Some Brasses and Bronzes

Name	Composition (Balance Cu.)			Ten. St. 1000 psi	Per Cent Elong.	Characteristics and Uses
	Zn	Sn	Other			
Electrolytic copper	99.9 pure			32–50	6–45	Excellent workability. Good electrical properties and corrosion resistance. Electrical conductors, contacts, switches, automobile radiators, chemical equipment.
Commercial bronze	10.0			37	5–45	Good corrosion resistance. Excellent workability. Marine hardware, costume jewelry.
Red brass	15.0			39–70	5–48	Good corrosion resistance to atmosphere. Good workability. Fair machinability. Weatherstrip, heat exchangers, plumbing.
Yellow brass	35.0			46–74	8–65	Good corrosion resistance to atmosphere. Poor hot workability. Fair machinability. Grillwork, lamp fixtures, springs.
Naval brass	39.0	1.0		25–53	20–47	Corrosion resistance generally good. Seldom used full hard. Aircraft and marine hardware, valve stems, condenser plates.
Phosphor bronze		10.0		66–128	3–68	Good atmospheric corrosion resistance. Poor machinability. Good wear qualities. Bearing plates, springs.
Aluminum bronze			7.0 Al	85–90	20–40	Excellent atmospheric corrosion resistance. Excellent hot workability. Good machinability. Gears, nuts, bolts.
Beryllium copper			0.3 Co. 2.0 Be	185	3–50	Good atmospheric corrosion. Poor machinability. Good workability. Springs, valves, diaphragm, bellows.

Ore from the Great Lakes area is refined by first roasting the copper sulphide ore to copper oxide then reducing in a blast furnace and further refining in an open hearth furnace. Ores from the western states are high in phosphorus and require additional electrolytic refining following the open hearth treatment. The cost of pig or ingot copper generally runs from five to ten times that of low carbon steel.

Brasses and Bronzes. For many years copper alloys were rather simply divided into two groups. Those containing zinc as the principal alloying element were known as *brass* and those containing tin as the principal alloying element were known as *bronze*. More recently the names have become confusing. "Brasses" generally contain from 5 to 40 per cent zinc but even one of these alloys is known as "commercial bronze." "Bronzes" contain a principal alloying element other than zinc and tin is still the most common. While the conductivity and ductility of any of the alloys is less than that of pure copper, strength, corrosion resistance to some media, machinability, appearance or color, and casting properties may be improved by alloying. Pure zinc is cheaper than pure copper and the cost of their alloys becomes lower as the amount of zinc is increased. Bronzes generally have better properties than brass but the high cost of tin has limited their use. The low friction and excellent antiwear properties of bronze makes it preferred for many journal bearing applications.

A few of the copper alloys are hardenable by a solution-precipitation treatment similar to that used for aluminum. However the high cost has confined their use to applications where the combinations of high strength with high corrosion resistance or high strength with high conductivity are necessary. Most interesting of these alloys is one containing 98 per cent copper and 2 per cent beryllium. After proper heat treatment this alloy has a tensile strength of 185 thousand psi with a Rockwell "C" hardness of forty. It is useful not only for applications such as electrical relay springs where high endurance limit must be combined with high conductivity but also for chisels, hammers, and other tools for use in mines and other hazardous locations where sparks must be avoided.

Copper alloys intended for casting usually contain some tin and lead to improve machinability and to reduce the formation of voids in the castings. The properties which make the wrought alloys useful apply also to the cast alloys so that a large number of small castings are used in plumbing fixtures, marine hardware, pump impellers and bodies, electrical connectors, and statuary. Table 6–3 gives the compositions and properties of some typical brasses and bronzes.

NICKEL ALLOYS

Nickel and manganese are metals which both have mechanical characteristics similar to those of iron. However neither is subject to alloying with carbon and control of hardness by heat treatment as is steel. Also the ores of both metals are much less plentiful than iron ore and the price is therefore higher. While manganese is little used except as an alloying element, nickel has sufficiently better corrosion and heat resistance than iron or steel to justify its use where these qualities are of enough importance. Nearly three quarters of all the nickel produced is used either as a plating material for corrosion resistance or as an alloying element in steel. However its use in steel has decreased in recent years with the discovery that other elements in lower percentages may have the same effects as nickel.

As a structural metal by itself, or as the basis of alloys, the properties of nickel and its alloys are indicated in Table 6–4. Nickel and copper are

TABLE 6–4

Properties of Some Nickel Alloys

Name	Composition Balance Nickel				Ten. St. 1000 psi	Per Cent Elong.	Characteristics and Uses
	Mn.	*Fe*	*Cu*	*Other*			
A Nickel	0.25	0.15	0.05		55–130	55–2	Corrosion resistant at high temperature. Vacuum tube parts, springs, chemical equipment.
Monel	0.90	1.35	31.5		70–140	50–2	Good corrosion resistance combined with high strength at normal and medium temperature. Pump shafts, valves, springs, food handling equipment.
Inconel	0.20	7.20	0.10	Cr. 15	80–170	55–2	Similar to Monel but better high temperature strength.
Nickel 36		64.0			70–90	36–20	Corrosion resistant to atmospheres and salt water. Low thermal expansion. Length standards, thermostatic bimetals.
Cast Monel	0.75	1.5	32.0	Si. 1.6	65–90	50–20	Good corrosion resistance to salt water and most acids. Valve seats, turbine blades, exhaust manifolds.

completely soluble in the solid state and many different compositions are available. Those rich in copper compete with brass but have higher cost, corrosion resistance, and temperature resistance. Those richer in nickel have superior heat and corrosion resistance at even higher cost and are used in many applications where stainless steel is used. The composition of Monel metal is determined largely by the composition of the ores found in the Sudbury district of Canada.

MAGNESIUM ALLOYS

Although beryllium is the lightest metal available, its extremely high cost restricts its use to very special applications. Magnesium is therefore the lightest metal commercially available, with a density two thirds that of aluminum. Magnesium alloys have good strength, ranging up to fifty thousand psi for wrought alloys and up to forty thousand psi for cast alloys. Corrosion resistance is good in ordinary atmosphere but for more severe conditions, including marine atmospheres, some surface protection is necessary.

Wrought and cast alloys have similar compositions. Aluminum, zinc, and manganese improve strength and forming properties. With 8 per cent or more aluminum, a solution precipitation hardening treatment is possible. Thorium, zirconium, and certain rare earth elements produce alloys useful at temperatures up to 900°F.

The principal drawbacks of magnesium, other than the relatively high cost of recovery from sea water, are related to its crystalline structure. Magnesium is one of the few important metals having a close packed hexagonal structure. Characteristic of these metals is a high rate of strain hardening. This property has two practical consequences. The amount of cold working which can be done without recrystallization is quite limited so most forming operations must be done hot. This causes no great difficulty in rolling, forging, and extrusion operations which are normally performed hot with any metal, but secondary press operations on flat sheet may require heating of the dies and the magnesium sheet. Most press working equipment is not designed for this type of operation.

The high rate of strain hardening also results in the fault called "notch sensitivity." At a stress concentration point such as the base of the notch in an impact test specimen, the load carrying ability of a material depends on its ability to permit some plastic flow to enlarge the radius and relieve the stress concentration. The high rate of strain hardening in magnesium lessens its ability to do this, lowering its impact test values and making it subject to failure at such imperfections as grinding marks, small shrinkage cracks from welding or casting, or at sharp internal corners permitted as part of a design.

Some problems are introduced in the processing of magnesium because of its inflammability. Reasonable care is necessary to prevent the accumulation of dust or fine chips where they might be subject to ignition from sparks, flames, or high temperatures.

ZINC ALLOYS

Zinc has the lowest cost per pound of any of the nonferrous metals. However its use has been restricted by a combination of factors. The strength of even the best alloys (tensile strength forty-seven thousand psi, endurance limit eight thousand psi) when combined with the density which is about the same as that of iron results in a fairly low strength to weight ratio. The recrystallization temperature of about 70 degrees for pure zinc simplifies tooling and drawing operations but results in a very low creep strength. Precipitation reactions with even small amounts of iron, lead, cadmium, or tin present as impurities can result in gradual dimensional change and loss of shock resistance with time. With artificial aging the precipitation reaction that takes place with copper can be used to improve the mechanical properties of some alloys.

In addition to the relatively low cost, zinc has a number of other properties which make it desirable. It has good corrosion resistance when used as a coating on ferrous materials. The zinc is attacked in preference to the base metal even though there are interruptions in the coating. Plating or coating with zinc is called *galvanizing* and accounts for the use of over 50 per cent of all the zinc produced.

Pure or slightly alloyed wrought zinc has high formability. It is an excellent roofing material and is frequently used for flashing on roofs of other materials. Its chemical properties make it useful for dry cell battery cases and for photoengraving plates.

As a structural material zinc is used almost exclusively because of its excellent casting properties in metal molds. With pouring temperatures ranging from 740 to 800 degrees, zinc alloys used in die casting give much greater die life than magnesium, aluminum, or copper alloys. The higher density of zinc than of aluminum or magnesium is offset to some extent in die casting by the fact that zinc can be die cast in thinner sections than other metals. Although zinc has good natural corrosion resistance, this property can be improved along with appearance by appropriate platings, which are easy to apply.

SPECIAL GROUPS OF NONFERROUS ALLOYS

Heat and Corrosion Resistant Alloys.   Several different groups of materials, some including certain ferrous alloys, have traditionally been grouped on the basis of property requirements rather than base metal or alloy content. Of special importance and increasing interest recently have been alloys designed for use under high stress conditions at elevated temperatures in such applications as jet turbine engines, high temperature steam piping and boilers, and rocket combustion chambers and nozzles. The efficiency of many such devices depends on the maximum temperature at which they can be operated and they frequently involve highly oxidizing, corrosive, or erosive conditions. Most of the special materials that have been developed for these uses are difficult to process into usable products by some or all of the standard procedures. The high cost of such products is due both to the generally high cost of the materials themselves (rarity and cost of refining) and cost of special processing. Hot working involves extra high temperatures with high forces resulting in short equipment life; casting frequently must be done by investment or other high cost techniques; cold working is difficult or impossible; welding involves elaborate procedures to avoid contamination with nondestructive testing to insure reliability; and machining requires low cutting speeds with short tool life even under the best conditions.

These alloys may be divided into three rather roughly defined groups. Stainless steels which were discussed earlier have better strength and corrosion resistance than plain carbon or low alloy steels at temperatures above 1200°F. A number of alloys of the same general composition as standard stainless steels have been developed with larger amounts of nickel and generally larger amounts of the stabilizing elements such as titanium or molybdenum for better high temperature properties. Aluminum or copper may be used to provide a precipitation reaction which makes the alloys hardenable by heat treatment. Such heat treatment usually involves solution temperatures above 2000°F. and artificial aging at above 1400°F.

Nickel base alloys form a second group of high temperature materials. They normally contain chromium or cobalt as the principal alloying element with smaller amounts of aluminum, titanium, molybdenum, and iron. These alloys have better properties at high temperatures than the stainless steel types but cost more and are even more difficult to process.

Alloys having cobalt as the principal element form a third group. They are generally referred to as cobalt base alloys although they may not contain as much as 50 per cent of any single element. Other elements are generally nickel, chromium, tungsten, columbium, manganese, molybdenum, and carbon. Alloys of this type are useful structurally at temperatures as high as 2000°F. where they have good corrosion resistance and tensile strengths as high as thirteen thousand psi.

Bearing Alloys. Problems of friction and wear always exist where rolling or sliding contact between members must be provided for. The rolling contact provided by "anti-friction" ball and roller bearings makes them preferred from a functional standpoint for most applications, but anti-friction bearings have cost and space limitations and regardless of their name, do not always, particularly at high speeds, provide the lowest possible friction. The alternative is to use a *journal* bearing where sliding contact may take place between mating surfaces. The majority of journal bearings consist of steel shafts supported by a material with entirely different characteristics, usually referred to as the bearing material.

Journal bearing materials always have some combination of the following properties. They must be strong enough to support the load to be carried but soft enough to give under slight misalignment; where lubrication is used they must have the ability to be "wet" by the lubricant; where insufficient lubrication is present to maintain a fluid film or where no film exists during starting conditions, they must resist bonding with the shaft to prevent galling or seizing; the coefficient of friction with the shaft must be low to reduce power losses and heating. The last two conditions depend to some extent on the mutual alloying tendency of the materials involved. Because of its insolubility in steel, lead is frequently a large part of a bearing material composition.

High leaded tin bronzes are best suited for small bearings where light loads and high speeds are involved. Plain copper-tin alloys, with up to 20 per cent tin, will stand higher pressures. High strength aluminum bronze may be used with very high bearing loads but is restricted to low speeds.

Tin or lead base alloys are commonly called *babbit* metal and are generally better than copper base materials for high speeds but will not stand impacts or overloads as well. Tin base bearings are the most resistant to corrosion but the lead base type is cheaper. Automotive engine bearings

TABLE 6-5

Characteristics of Most Nonferrous Metals

Metal	Principal Characteristics	Applications		
		Pure or as Base Metal	As Alloying Constituent	
Antimony	Hard, brittle	None	1–12 per cent hardens lead Fusible alloys	
Beryllium	Lightest structural metal High strength/weight ratio Brittle, transparent to X-rays	Aircraft and rocket structures, X-ray tube windows	2 per cent hardens copper	
Bismuth	Soft, brittle. High negative coefficient of resistivity	Use restricted by cost Special resistance elements	Fusible alloys	
Cadmium	Higher temperature strength than tin or lead base alloy Corrosion resistance	Plating, especially on steel Bearing alloys Solders	Bearing alloys, solders	
Cerium	Soft, malleable, ductile	Rare	Lighter flints. Raises creep strength of Al, Mg, Ni, Cr. Nodular iron	
Cobalt	Weak, brittle, high corrosion resistance	Rare	High temperature alloys, permanent magnets, hard facing tool steels	
Columbium (Niobium)	High melting point Corrosion resistant	Nuclear reactors, missiles, rockets, electron tubes	High temperature alloys, stainless steels, nitriding steels	
Germanium	Brittle, corrosion resistant, semi-conductor	Diodes, transistors	Rare	
Gold	Ductile, malleable, weak, corrosion resistant	Monetary standard, plating, jewelry, dental work, electrical contacts	Rare	
Indium	Soft, low melting point	None	Hardener for silver and lead Corrosion resistance in bearings	
Iridium	Most corrosion resistant metal	None	Hardener for platinum Jewelry, contact alloys	
Lead	Weak, soft, malleable, corrosion resistant	Chemical equipment, storage batteries, roof flashing plumbing	Improves machinability of steel and most nonferrous alloys, solders, bearing alloys	
Manganese	Moderate strength ductile	Rare	To 2 per cent low alloy steels 12 per cent abrasion resistant steel Stainless steels	

| | | Applications | |
Metal	Principal Characteristics	Pure or as Base Metal	As Alloying Constituent
Mercury	Liquid at room temperature	Thermometer, switches	Low melting point alloys; Amalgam with silver for dental use
Molybdenum	High melting point, high strength at elevated temperature, oxidizes rapidly at high temperature	High temperature wire, structural use with surface protection, mercury switch contacts	Low alloy steels, high temperature alloys, stainless steel, tool steels
Palladium	Ductile; Corrosion resistance	Electrical contacts; Chemical catalyst	Jewelry, dental alloys
Platinum	High melting point, chemically inert, corrosion resistance	Chemical equipment, glass working equipment, chemical catalyst	Jewelry, dental alloys, spark plug electrodes
Rhodium	High reflectivity, free from oxidation films, chemically inert	Mirrors, plating	With platinum and palladium
Selenium	Special electrical and optical properties	Rectifiers, photocells	Machinability of stainless steel
Silver	Highest electrical conductivity, corrosion resistance to nonsulphur atmospheres	Coinage, jewelry, tableware, electrical contacts, plating, catalyst, reflectors	Brazing and soldering alloys; Bearing alloys
Silicon	Semi-conductor, special electrical and optical properties	Rectifiers, transistors, photocells	Electrical steel, cast iron, cast nonferrous
Tantalum	High melting point, ductile, corrosion resistance	Surgical implants, capacitors, chemical hardware electronic tubes	Tantalum carbide cutting tools
Tin	Soft, weak, malleable, corrosion resistant	Plating, collapsible tubes	Bronzes, solders, bearing alloys
Titanium	Density between steel and light alloys, high strength resistance	Marine, chemical, food processing equipment; Aircraft, rockets, orthopedic and orthodontic equipment	High temperature alloys, stainless steel, aluminum alloys, titanium carbide tools
Tungsten	Highest melting point of metals; strong, high modulus of elasticity; corrosion resistance	Lamp filaments, contacts, X-ray targets, nuclear reactors	Alloy steels, tool steels, high temperature alloys, tungsten carbide tools
Vanadium	Moderate strength, ductile	Rare	Alloy steel, tool steel; Nonferrous deoxidizer
Zirconium	Moderate strength, ductile corrosion resistance	Structural parts in nuclear reactors	Stainless steels

acquire the surface qualities of babbit metal with higher load carrying ability and impact strength by using a relatively thin film of bearing alloy on a steel backing.

Copper base or iron base *lifetime* or *oilless* bearings are produced by pressing and sintering powdered metal in such a manner as to leave up to 30 per cent voids in the material. The voids are then filled with oil which gives the bearing some self-lubricating properties for as long as the oil lasts.

Many other bearing materials are used, depending on corrosive conditions, economic factors, and compatibility with the processing and design requirements. Cast iron works reasonably well with steel where low speeds are involved, where some wear can be permitted, and where life requirements are not great. In recent years plastics have grown in importance as bearing materials especially for light loads where lubrication will be intermittent or nonexistant as in toys or many home appliances.

Other Nonferrous Metals.   Of the many other potential base metals, most are used under special conditions. Many of these metals have properties that are equal to or better than those of iron and the more common nonferrous metals but their use is restricted by economic consideration. Gold, platinum, and other *noble* metals have high chemical inertness but their rarity and high cost restrict their use. Beryllium has the highest strength to weight ratio of any known metal but the difficulty of obtaining pure metal and the rarity of the ore make the cost almost as high as that of gold. Titanium ores are abundant and titanium has extremely useful properties but the cost of reduction is approximately one hundred times that of iron. Titanium could easily be the most important nonferrous metal if low cost production methods could be developed. Table 6–5 gives the principal characteristics and uses for most of the nonferrous metals that are available commercially.

QUESTIONS

1. What is the most common advantage nonferrous materials have over iron-base alloys?
2. List at least three metals that serve as a base in each of the two general divisions of nonferrous alloys.
3. What property of zinc makes it one of the most used (tonnage wise) of the nonferrous metals?
4. Why has aluminum, even though it has many excellent properties, been relatively slow in its use development?
5. Why is aluminum highly polished for use as structural members in many mechanical devices such as aircraft?
6. What is "hot shortness" and how does it create processing problems?
7. List the combination of properties of aluminum which cause it to be an important structural material.

8. What elements may be combined with aluminum to form commercial alloys subject to hardening by heat treatment?

9. Explain the method and purpose of stabilization in connection with aluminum.

10. Why is silicon usually present in aluminum casting alloys?

11. For what is copper primarily used?

12. Where are the two main sources of copper ores and why are they refined differently?

13. What is the usual interpretation of the difference between brass and bronze?

14. Disregarding cost factors, discuss the main fault found in magnesium alloys?

15. What safety hazard exists in connection with the processing of magnesium and how may it be controlled?

16. For what purpose is approximately one half of all zinc produced used?

17. Name three groups of alloys suitable for use in high temperature environments.

18. What properties are important in a journal bearing material?

▶▶▶ CHAPTER 7

The Nature of Manufacturing

THE HEIGHT reached and the progress made by any past civilization is judged by many factors. In some cases a civilization is most remembered for cultural advances in the areas of art and literature. More commonly however, the degree of advancement is measured by the quality and quantity of durable goods produced. The use of the terms, "Stone Age," "Bronze Age," and "Iron Age" is based on the extent of man's knowledge and ability in the areas of materials and processing during these periods of history. A similar situation continues today. The United States is envied throughout the world for its ability to produce and distribute durable goods in large quantities.

Regardless of whether or not it is justified, present day evaluations of individuals, organizations, and countries are most frequently based on the goods used by them. Even the production of food is dependent on the manufacture of modern farm machinery and chemicals.

Early man must have been faced with many problems. Even as in some areas of the world today, he must have spent the major portion of his time satisfying basic needs for food and shelter. All he had for tools and raw materials were those that were immediately at hand. It is reasonable to assume however, that even at a bare subsistence level some men were better food gatherers than others, some were better weapon makers, and some were better cave diggers. While the transition from an individual existence to one of specialization undoubtedly occurred only after long periods of time, it is the idea of specialization that has been basic to man's progress throughout history.

Obviously if each worker performs where he is best qualified, the over-all work efficiency will be high and the product output maximum for any given technology. Such specialization however, can be accomplished only under some organizational control. In order for individuals to be willing to become specialists it is essential that a system of exchange and distribution be established. A control system of some type is necessary to balance the various speciality outputs, and set the values of service and product output.

118

The control organization may be based on undelegated authority (master and slave), delegated authority (elected officials), or on natural controls as the result of supply and demand in a free enterprise system. Our system today is based on the latter two in which elected officials and supply and demand are the principal controls.

MODERN MANUFACTURING

Markets.   Manufacturing in any period of history has been characterized by certain essential features. One requirement is that a market exist for any goods produced. A natural market exists for those things that are deemed essential to life such as food, but for most manufactured goods a market must be created by a requirement which is sometimes based on an expected standard of living rather than on any basic biological need of man.

Few "durable" goods have truly unlimited life. Because of the economics of manufacturing or the requirements of a design, the life of most products is limited. For all practical purposes an auto body made of titanium would have unlimited life so far as corrosion is concerned but the cost would be prohibitive for a mass market and the life of the body would be limited by design changes and wear out of other parts of the auto. The blades in a jet turbine have limited life not because it is desirable but because of design considerations of weight and the limited properties of the available materials.

In addition to wearout, a market for replacement exists because of obsolescence. New designs, new materials, or new features may make replacement desirable either for convenience, as with many new automobiles, or for economic reasons. Machine tools are generally replaced while they are still in working condition but their replacement is justified on the basis of lower maintenance, higher productivity, and higher accuracies of newer designs.

For nearly all durable goods growth has created an expanding market in the world and especially in the United States. This growth has occurred in two forms. Not only has the population been continually increasing, but also the rising standard of living has made a greater percentage of the population able to buy most durable consumer goods. More leisure time and increased purchasing power have caused large increases in the sale of many products. This has been particularly noticeable in automobiles, housing, household appliances, and recreational equipment. A part of the increase in per capita consumption must be attributed to the improved sales and advertising techniques that have developed in this country based to a large extent on the better communications that exist today.

The greatest increase in markets, particularly in the last fifty years, is due to new inventions and to new applications of older products and materials. In many cases the new products have been made economically possible primarily by improved processing machinery and techniques. Many of the presently used plastics have been known to chemists for over a hundred years, but the development of the plastics industry to its present state depended on the development of economical methods of raw material production and fabrication as well as the development of a product demand.

Other new products are based on basic concepts or discoveries that did not exist fifty years ago. The whole electronics industry, especially that depending on the transistor and solid state physics, falls in this category. The increased complexity, cost, and specialization of modern industry have led to an increased need for knowledge of expected demand prior to the time sales are actually made. In the production of goods sold seasonly it is necessary that the proper inventories be built up with a relatively constant level of production or that the work be balanced with other products in order that plant investment may be kept reasonable. Accurate forecasts of future demand are essential when increases in plant capacity or new plants for the production of new goods are anticipated, for the investment in a single new plant may be over one hundred million dollars.

Design.   In the case of every product that is made the manufacturing process must be proceeded by design, and the relationships that exist between design and processing are of extreme importance. The designer normally starts with some definite functional requirement that must be satisfied. The environmental conditions of use, expected life, and loading conditions will dictate certain minimum shapes and sizes and limit the possible choice of materials. The designer's problems arise mainly from the fact that a single solution is seldom indicated. Of the many possible materials and shapes that may satisfy the functional requirements, some may have better appearance than others and for many consumer goods the appearance may actually govern the final choice. Even in the designing of parts that may be completely hidden in a final assembly, the designer seldom disregards appearance completely.

Even the original design will be influenced by the method of processing that is anticipated and, in order to give proper consideration to all the alternatives, it is essential that the designer have knowledge about the costs and capabilities of various production methods. It is generally true that costs will be different for different material and processing choices and considerable screening of the alternatives can be done purely on a cost basis. However, the quality obtained with more expensive materials or methods may be superior to that of the cheaper choices and decisions must often be made regarding some combination of quality and cost. A rational decision as to the quality to be produced can only be made with adequate information as to how the market will be affected by the quality.

Obviously the decisions made by the designer are far reaching and of extreme importance. The materials and shapes that he specifies usually determine the basic processes that must be used. Tolerances that he specifies may even dictate specific types of machines and will have a large influence on costs. In many cases his choices are limited by the equipment and trained personnel that are available. Economical manufacture of small quantities can frequently be best accomplished by use of equipment and processes that under other circumstances would be inefficient. Certainly a designer for a plant producing castings would not design a part as a weldment if the continued operation of the plant depends on the production of castings.

In many cases the decisions that govern the choice of materials and processes must be made in an arbitrary manner. The gathering of enough information may not be economically feasible or time may not be available. Particularly where large quantities are not being produced, the cost of finding the most economical method of production may be more than any possible gain over some arbitrary method that is reasonably certain of producing an acceptable product. In some cases, custom governs the choice simply because some set of choices was known to give acceptable results for similar production in the past.

Designers cannot be expected to be experts in all the phases of production that influence the final quality and cost of a product. Production personnel must be relied on to furnish details of process capabilities and requirements.

Processing. While the problems of design and processing are interrelated, once the design decisions have been made the problems of processing are more clearly defined. A design may indicate certain processing steps but basically the problem in processing is to make a *product* whose material, properties, shapes, tolerances, size, and finish meet specifications laid down by the designer. Manufacturing is a term usually used to describe that section of processing starting with the raw material, either metal or plastic, in a refined bulk form, and is concerned mainly with *shape changing.* While the single operation of sawing to length might produce a product useful as fireplace wood, for most manufactured products of metals and plastics a complex series of shape or property changing steps is required.

Fig. 7–1 shows the basic processes which are used in shaping metals. The reduction of ores is essential to any further processing and the choices in processing come later. All but a very small percentage of the metal that is refined is first cast as a pig or ingot, which is itself always the raw material for further processing. It can be noted however that from this point on any process may either produce a finished product or furnish the raw material for some further processing. The reverse flow shown in the lower part of the diagram refers particularly to parts that have been heat treated or welded and must then be machined and generally this step would occur only once for any product.

It is the rule rather than the exception however that many reversals may occur within some of the blocks on the diagram. Steel is commonly subjected to several different rolling operations in a steel mill. Press-working operations generally involve several separate steps to produce a product. The greatest amount of repetition occurs in machining. It is not unusual for a complex part such as an auto engine block to be subjected to as many as eighty separate machining operations.

The majority of manufacturing organizations specialize in one type of manufacturing operation and even the extremely large companies which

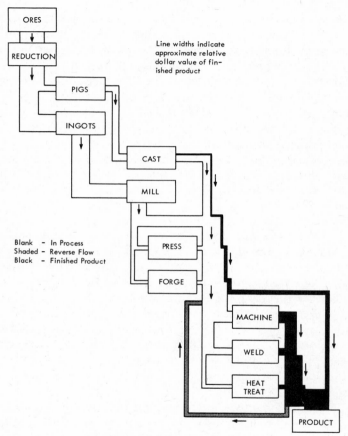

FIG. 7–1. Metals process flow.

may operate in several fields of manufacturing generally have specialized plants for the separate manufacturing areas.

States of Matter.   Material may exist in one of three states of matter, gas, liquid, or solid, but except for some special processes with relatively small use such as vapor deposition, or in the refining of zinc, the gaseous state is of small importance in manufacturing. For manufacturing purposes where shape changing is the objective, the solid state may be thought of as existing in two forms. Below the elastic limit, materials are dealt with as rigid materials and processing involving this form causes no significant relative movement of atoms or molecules of the material with respect to each other. Above the elastic limit solid materials may flow plastically and shape changing may be accomplished by application of external loads to cause permanent relocations within the structure of the material. The end results of dealing with materials in the liquid form are similar to those with materials above the elastic limit. No appreciable density or volume change occurs and the shape may be changed without loss of material.

Shape Changing Processes. Shape changing is possible in any of these states but most manufacturing processes by definition or nature deal with materials in only one of these possible forms. Fig. 7–2 shows the processes for shape changing without material loss and those in which material is added or taken away. In those where no volume change occurs, property changes are usually large and distributed throughout the material. In casting the shape change occurs by melting and subsequent solidification to a prescribed shape. This process can be used with practically all metals and most plastics. The material properties depend on composition and the conditions of the particular casting process, but not on the condition of the material prior to melting. Casting is often the most economical method for producing complex shapes, particularly where reentrant angles exist.

Wrought materials are produced by plastic deformation which can be accomplished by hot working (above the recrystallization temperature) or cold working. Property changes also occur throughout the material with these processes with the greatest changes usually caused by cold work.

Shaping from powders by pressing and heating involves the flow of granular materials which differs considerably from deformation processing although some plastic flow undoubtedly occurs in individual particles. Powder processing is a somewhat specialized process, but, as in casting or the deformation processes, the material is shaped by confinement to some geometric pattern in two or three dimensions. Since the total volume of work material is affected by these processes, large sources of energy, pressure or heat, are required.

Shape changing may also be accomplished by taking material away in chip or bulk form, material destruction, or by combining other shapes. The property changes in these processes are more localized and energy requirements are generally smaller.

Mechanical separation can be performed by removal of chips or by controlled separation along predetermined surfaces. Chip removal by machining can be used with some success for all materials, shapes, and accuracies, and is probably the most versatile of all manufacturing processes. Separation by shearing with localized failure caused by externally applied loads is limited primarily to sheet materials but frequently turns out to be the cheapest method for producing many shapes in large quantities.

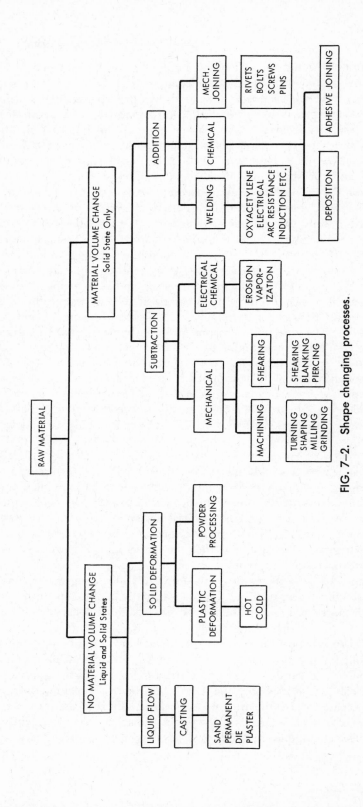

FIG. 7-2. Shape changing processes.

New shapes can be produced by joining preformed shapes either mechanically or by any of various bonding means. In welding, soldering, and brazing, metallurgical bonds are established by heat, pressure, or sometimes by chemical action with plastics. Mechanical fastening by use of bolts, rivets, or pins is primarily an assembly procedure and is often an alternative and competitive joining procedure to welding or adhesive fastening.

Particularly in recent years, with the advent of new materials difficult to fabricate by conventional means, and with many designs requiring shapes and tolerances and material combinations difficult to achieve by conventional processes, a number of electrical and chemical processes have been developed for removing or adding material. Many of these are restricted in use to a few materials and most are specialized to the point that they have only a few applications. Included are metal plating by electrical or chemical means, used primarily as a finishing process, and electrical discharge "machining," chemical milling, ultrasonic grinding, and electron beam machining, all of which are specialized metal removal processes which compete with conventional machining or press working operations where hard materials, special shapes, or low quantities are involved.

Summary. Manufacturing is a complex system. A product always originates as a design concept required to serve some purpose. A multiplicity of choices and decisions nearly always comes between the establishment of the need and the manufacturing of the product. The designer, frequently arbitrarily because of no logical means available, makes decisions which usually, at least broadly, determine the processes which must be used to produce the product. Within this broad framework, however, exist many other choices of specific materials, processes, and machines. Materials, properties, qualities, quantities, and processes are strongly interrelated. The prime effort from original concept to the completion of manufacture is aimed at finding the optimum combination of these variables to provide the best economic situation.

QUESTIONS

1. Why can it be said today that even food production is dependent on modern manufacturing processes?
2. Why does specialization lead to greater output from the manpower used in manufacturing?
3. What factors limit the life of most durable goods?
4. Why, although a designer knows the functional requirements that must be satisfied, is the problem of selecting the material and the shape for a part so complex?
5. What effect do the designer's decisions have on processing?
6. When is an arbitrary choice of materials and processes feasible even though some more economical combination may exist?

7. What is the principal objective of most manufacturing processes?
8. What is the basic objective of manufacturing processes?
9. In what material states are manufacturing processes used to change shape without material loss?
10. Which is the most versatile of all the basic manufacturing processes?

CHAPTER 8

The Casting Process

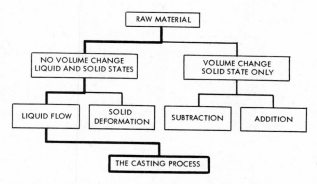

CASTING is a process of causing liquid metal to fill a cavity and solidify into a useful shape. It is a basic method of producing shapes. With the exception of a very small volume of a few metals produced by electrolytic or pure chemical methods, all material used in metal manufacturing is cast at some stage in its processing. Castings of all kinds of metals and in sizes from a fraction of an ounce up to many tons are used directly with or without further shape processing for many items of manufacture. But even those materials considered to be wrought start out as a cast ingot before deformation work in the solid state puts them in their final condition.

The casting or founding process consists of a series of sequential steps performed in a definite order as shown in Fig. 8–1. First, a pattern to represent the finished product must be chosen or constructed. Patterns can be of a number of different styles, but are always the shape of the finished part and roughly the same size as the finished part with slightly oversized dimensions to allow for shrinkage and additional allowances on surfaces that are to be machined. In some casting processes, mainly those performed with metal molds, the actual pattern may be only a design consideration with the mold fulfilling the function of a negative of the pattern as all molds do. Examples would be molds for ingots, die casting, and permanent mold castings. Most plastic parts are made in molds of this type, but with plastics the process is called molding rather than casting.

127

In some casting processes, the second step is to build a mold of material that can be made to flow into close contact with the pattern and that has sufficient strength to maintain that position. The mold is designed in such a way that it can be opened for removal of the pattern. The pattern may have attachments that make grooves in the mold to serve as channels for flow of material into the cavity. If not, these channels or *runners* must be cut in the mold material. In either case an opening to the outside of the mold, called a *sprue* must be cut.

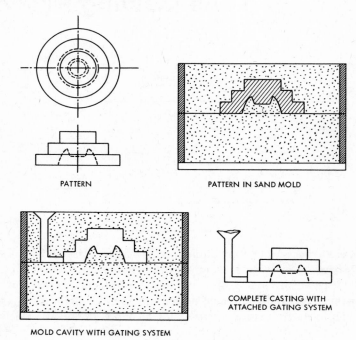

PATTERN   PATTERN IN SAND MOLD

MOLD CAVITY WITH GATING SYSTEM   COMPLETE CASTING WITH ATTACHED GATING SYSTEM

FIG. 8–1. Casting steps for a pulley blank.

Liquid metal is poured through the channels to fill the cavity completely. After time has been allowed for solidification to occur, the mold is opened by destroying it. The product is then ready for removal of the excess metal that has solidified in the runners, cleaning for removal of any remaining mold material, and inspection to determine if defects have been permitted by the process. The casting thus produced is a finished product of the foundry. This product occasionally may be used in this form, but more often than not needs further processing such as machining to improve surface qualities and dimensions and, therefore, becomes raw material for another processing area.

The tonnage output of foundries throughout the United States is very large, consisting of close to twenty million tons per year, which is about 20 per cent of the national product. Foundries are scattered all over the

United States, but are concentrated primarily in the eastern part of the nation with a secondary concentration on the west coast in the two areas where the main manufacturing work is carried on. Because of differences in the problems and equipment connected with casting different materials, most foundries specialize in producing either ferrous or nonferrous castings. Relatively few cast both kinds of materials in appreciable quantities in the same foundry. A few foundries are large in size, employing several thousand men, but the majority are small with from one to one hundred employees. Most of the large ones are what as known as captive foundries, owned by parent manufacturing companies that use all, or nearly all, of the foundry's output. More of the small foundries are independently owned and contract with a number of different manufacturers for the sale of their castings. Some foundries, more often the larger ones, may produce a product in sufficient demand that their entire facility will be devoted to the making of that product with a continuous production type operation. Most, however, operate as job shops which produce a number of different things at one time and are continually changing from one product to another, although the duplication for some parts may run into the thousands.

SOLIDIFICATION OF METALS

The casting process involves a change of state of material from liquid to solid with control of shape being established during the change of state. The problems associated with the process then are primarily those connected with changes of physical state and changes of properties as they may be influenced by temperature variation. The solution to many of the problems of casting can only be attained with an understanding of the solidification process and the effects of temperature on materials.

Some of the following material about solidification is a repetition of subject matter discussed under Nature of Materials in Chapter 3. Here, however, the interest is in the influence this phenomenon exerts on the casting process; its importance warrants repetition.

Solidification. As stated in Chapter 3, energy in the form of heat added to a metal changes the force system that ties the atoms together. Eventually, as heat is added, the ties that bind the atoms are broken and the atoms are free to move about as a liquid. Solidification is a reverse procedure as shown in Fig. 8–2, and heat given up by the molten material must be dissipated. If consideration is being given only to a pure metal, the freezing point occurs at a single temperature for the entire liquid. As the temperature goes down, the atoms become less and less mobile and finally assume their position with other atoms in the space lattice of the unit cell.

In the case of a casting, the heat is being given up to the mold material in contact with the outside of the molten mass. The first portion of the material to cool to the freezing temperature will be the outside of the liquid and a large number of these unit cells may form simultaneously around the interface surface. Each unit cell becomes a point of nucleation for the growth of a metal crystal and as the other atoms cool they will assume their proper position in the space lattice adding to the unit cell. As the crystals form, the heat of fusion is released, thereby increasing the amount of heat that must be dissipated before further freezing can occur. Temperature gradients are reduced and the freezing process retarded. The size of crystal growth will be limited by interference with other crystals because of the large number of unit cell nuclei produced at one time with

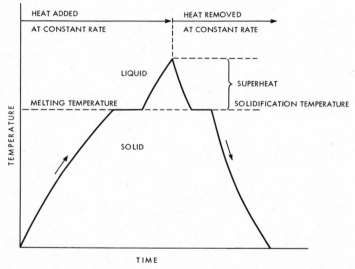

FIG. 8–2.   Heating and cooling curves for temperature increase above the melting point for a metal.

random orientation. The first grains to form in the skin of a solidifying casting are likely to be of a fine equi-axed type with random orientation and shapes.

After formation of the solid skin, grain growth is likely to be more orderly, providing the section thickness and mass are large enough to cause a significant difference in freezing time between the outside shell and the interior metal. Points of nucleation will continue to form around the outside of the liquid as the temperature is decreased. The rate of decrease, however, continues to get lower because of the heat of fusion being added, because the heat must flow through the already formed solid metal, because the mold mass has been heated and has less temperature differential with the metal, and because the mold may have become dried out to the point where it acts as an insulating blanket around the casting. Crystal growth will have the least interference from other growing crystals in a direction

toward the hot zone. The crystals, therefore, grow in a columnar shape
toward the center of the heavy sections of the casting. With the temperature gradient being small, growth may occur on the sides of these columns,
producing structures known as dendrites, Fig. 8–3. This pine tree shaped
first solidification seals off small islands of liquid to freeze later. Evidence
of this kind of crystal growth is often difficult to find when dealing with
pure metals, but as will be discussed later, can readily be detected with
most alloy metals.

As the wall thickness of frozen metal increases, the cooling rate of the
remaining liquid decreases even further and the temperature of the remain-

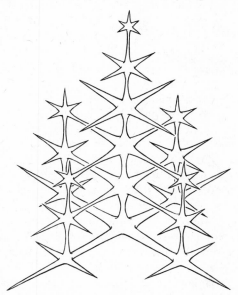

FIG. 8–3. Schematic sketch of dendritic growth.

ing material tends to equalize. Relatively uniform temperature distribution
and slow cooling will permit random nucleation at fewer points than with
rapid cooling and the grains grow to large sizes.

As shown in Figs. 8–4 and 8–5, it would be expected in castings of heavy
section that the first grains to form around the outside would be fine
equi-axed. Columnar and dendritic structure would be present in directions toward the last portions to cool for distances depending upon the
material and the cooling rate under which it is solidified. Finally, the
center of the heavy sections would be the weakest structure made up of
large equi-axed grains. Changes in this grain growth pattern can be caused
by a number of factors affecting the cooling rate. Thin sections that cool
very quickly will develop neither the columnar nor coarse structure.
Variable section sizes and changes of size and shape may cause interference
and variations of the grain structure pattern. Different casting procedures

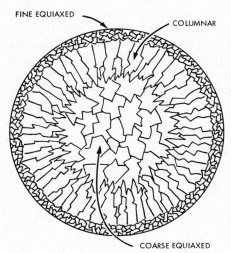

FINE EQUIAXED

COLUMNAR

COARSE EQUIAXED

FIG. 8–4. Typical grain structure from solidification of a heavy section.

and the use of different mold materials can affect grain size and shape through their influence on the cooling rate.

Eutectic alloys freeze much the same as a pure metal. Solidification takes place at a single temperature which is lower than that for the individual components of the alloy. The grain size produced with an eutectic alloy is smaller than that for a pure metal under the same conditions. It is believed that this is due to a smaller temperature gradient and the formation of a greater number of points of nucleation for the start of grains.

The majority of products are made from noneutectic alloys. Instead of freezing at a single temperature as does the pure metal and the eutectic composition, the noneutectic alloys freeze over a temperature range. As the temperature of the molten material is decreased, solidification starts at the surface and progresses toward the interior where the metal is cooling more slowly. Partial solidification may progress for some distance before the temperature at the surface is reduced low enough for full solidification to take place. The material at temperatures between those at which solidification begins and ends is partially frozen with islands of liquid remaining to produce a mixture that is of mushy consistency and relatively low strength. Fig. 8–6 is a graphic representation of this kind of freezing. The duration in time of this condition and the dimensions of the space between the start and finish of freezing are functions of the solidification temperature range of the alloy material and the thermal gradient. The greater the solidification temperature range, in most cases meaning the greater the variation away from the eutectic composition, and the smaller the temperature gradient, the greater in size and duration will be this mushy stage.

Dendritic grain growth is much more evident in the noneutectic alloy metals than with pure metal. When more than one element is present, segregation of two types

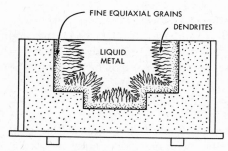

FINE EQUIAXIAL GRAINS

DENDRITES

LIQUID METAL

FIG. 8–5. Grain formation in a heavy sand casting.

occurs during solidification. The first solids
to freeze will be richer in one component
than the average composition. The change
caused by this *ingot type segregation*, is
small, but as the first solids rob the remaining material, a gradual change of composition is caused as freezing progresses to the
center. The other type of segregation is
more localized and makes the dendritic
structure easy to detect in alloy materials.
The small liquid islands, enclosed by the first
dendritic solids, have supplied more than
their share of one component to the already
frozen material. This difference in composition shows up readily by difference in chemical reaction if the material is polished and
etched for grain examination.

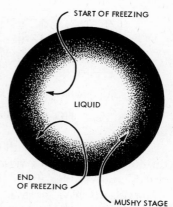

FIG. 8–6. **Progress of freezing in a noneutectic alloy.**

Shrinkage.   Some of the most important problems connected with the
casting process are those of shrinkage. The amount of shrinkage that
occurs will of course vary with the material being cast, but it is also
influenced by the casting procedure and techniques. The three stages of
contraction that occur as the temperature decreases from the temperature
of the molten metal to room temperature are illustrated in Fig. 8–7.

In the melting procedure, preparatory to pouring castings, the metal is
always heated well above the melting temperature. The additional heat
above that necessary for melting is called super heat and is necessary to
provide fluidity of the liquid, to permit cold additives to be mixed with the
metal before pouring, to permit the transfer of the metal and contact with
cold equipment without starting to freeze, and to insure that sufficient
time will elapse before freezing occurs to allow disposal of the material.
Some of the super heat is lost during transfer of the liquid metal from the
melting equipment to the mold, however, as the metal is poured into the
mold, some super heat must remain to insure that the mold will fill. Loss of
super heat results in contraction and increased density, but is not likely to
cause serious problems in casting since the volume change can be compensated for by the pouring of additional material into the mold cavity as
the super heat is lost. An exception exists when the cavity is of such design
that part of it may freeze off, preventing the flow of the liquid metal for
shrinkage replacement.

The second stage of shrinkage occurs during the transformation from
liquid to solid. Water is an exception to the rule, but most materials are
more dense in the solid form than as liquids. Metals contract as they
change from liquid to solid. The approximate volumetric solidification
shrinkage for some of the common metals is shown in Table 8–1. Contraction at this stage can be partially replaced since the entire metal is not

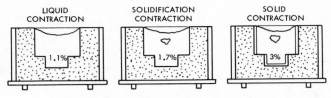

LIQUID CONTRACTION   SOLIDIFICATION CONTRACTION   SOLID CONTRACTION

1.1%   1.7%   3%

SHRINK PERCENTAGES APPROXIMATE ONLY FOR CAST IRON

FIG. 8–7. Three stages of metal contraction.

yet frozen. If a suitable path can be kept open, liquid metal can flow from the hot zones to replace most of the apparent shrinkage. It will be remembered, however, that in the formation of a dendritic grain structure, small liquid islands have been left completely enclosed with solid material. Depending upon the characteristics of the material and the size of the liquid islands, localized shrinking will develop random voids referred to as microporosity, Fig. 8–8. Microporosity causes a reduction in density and tends to reduce the apparent shrinkage that can be seen on the surface of a casting.

TABLE 8–1

Approximate Solidification Shrinkage of Some Common Metals

Metal	Volumetric Shrinkage (Per Cent)
Gray iron	0–2
Steel	2.5–4
Aluminum	6.6
Copper	4.9

Shrinkage that occurs during solidification and microporosity that often accompanies it are minimized in materials that are near eutectic composition. This seems to be due to more uniform freezing with lower temperature gradients and more random nucleation producing finer grain structure.

The porosity of a casting may be amplified by the evolution of gas before and during solidification. Gas may form pockets or bubbles of its own or may enter the voids of microporosity to enlarge them. The evolved gas is usually hydrogen which may combine with dissolved oxygen to form water vapor. These randomly dispersed openings of larger size in the solid metal are referred to as macroporosity.

The third stage of shrinkage is that occurring after solidification takes place and is the primary cause of dimensional change to a size different from that of the pattern used to make the cavity in the mold. Although contraction of solidification may contribute in some cases, the solid metal contraction is the main element of *pattern makers shrinkage* which must be allowed for by making the pattern oversize. This shrinkage varies considerably with different metals as shown in Table 8–2. An actual

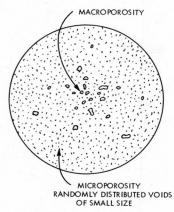

FIG. 8–8.   Porosity.   FIG. 8–9.   Pattern shrinkage allowance.

dimensional change would be equal to the coefficient of expansion (and contraction) for the material multiplied by the dimensions in inches and by the temperature change in degrees Fahrenheit. In practice, rough average values are added to each dimension often by use of shrink rules whose actual length is greater than indicated by the calibration marks. The result of making this allowance is pictured in Fig. 8–9.

TABLE 8–2

Common Patternmakers Shrinkage Allowances

Metal	*Allowance in./ft.*
Gray iron	$\frac{1}{8}$
Steel	$\frac{1}{8}-\frac{1}{4}$
Aluminum base	$\frac{1}{8}-\frac{3}{16}$
Magnesium base	$\frac{1}{8}-\frac{5}{8}$
Copper base	$\frac{1}{8}-\frac{1}{4}$

POURING AND FEEDING CASTINGS

Casting Design. The first consideration that must be given to obtain good castings is to casting design. It should be remembered that volumetric shrinkage of liquid metal may occur in isolated islands caused by variation of heat distribution after the start of freezing. Although volumetric shrinkage of the liquid is thought of as being replaced by extra metal poured in the mold and by hydraulic pressure from elevated parts of the casting system, this can be true only if no parts of the casting freeze off before replacement takes place. Except for the small pockets completely enclosed by solid metal in the development of dendritic structures, the shrinkage of solidification can be compensated for if liquid metal can progressively be supplied to the freezing face as it advances.

The term *progressive solidification,* the freezing of a liquid from the outside toward the center, is different from "directional" solidification. Rather than from the surface to the center of the mass, *directional solidifi-*

cation is used to describe the freezing from one part of a casting to another, such as from one end to the other end as in Fig. 8–10. The direction of freezing is extremely important to the quality of a casting because of the need for liquid metal to compensate for the contraction of the liquid and of the solidification. Casting design and procedure should cause the metal farthest from the point of entry to freeze first with

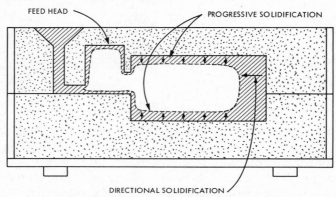

FEED HEAD   PROGRESSIVE SOLIDIFICATION

DIRECTIONAL SOLIDIFICATION

FIG. 8–10. Progressive and directional solidification.

solidification moving toward a *feed head* which may be at the point where metal is poured into the mold or can be located at other points where liquid can be stored to feed into the casting proper.

The highest temperature areas immediately after pouring are called "hot spots" and should be located as near as possible to sources of feed metal. If isolated by sections that freeze early they may disturb good directional solidification with the result that shrinks, porosity, cracks, ruptures, or warping will harm the casting quality.

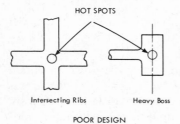

HOT SPOTS

Intersecting Ribs   Heavy Boss

POOR DESIGN

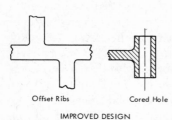

Offset Ribs   Cored Hole

IMPROVED DESIGN

FIG. 8–11. Hot spot elimination.

Hot spots are usually located at points of greatest sectional dimensions. Designs for bosses, raised letters, nonuniform section thickness, intersecting members, and the like are often trouble makers in the production of high quality castings. Solution to the problem involves change of design as shown in Fig. 8–11, or pouring the casting in such a way that these spots cease to be sources of trouble. Change of design might include: coring a boss to make it a thin walled cylinder, relieving raised letters or pads on the backside, proportioning section thicknesses to uniform changes of dimensions, using thin ribbed design instead of heavy sections, spreading and alternating intersecting members and other changes that will not affect the function of the part but will decrease the degree of section change. They then become the desired focus of directional solidification.

As a general rule, section changes should be minimized as much as possible in order to approach uniform cooling rates. When pouring iron, heavy sections tend to solidify as gray iron with precipitated graphite. Thin sections of the same material cooling at higher rates tend to hold the carbon in the combined state as iron carbide with the result that these sections turn out to be hard, brittle white iron. Since it is clearly impossible to design practical shapes without section changes, the usual procedure calls for gradual section size change and the use of liberal fillets and rounds. Some section changes are compared in Fig. 8–12.

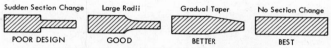

FIG. 8–12.   Section changes in casting design.

The permissible thinness of sections is dependent on a number of factors. The fluidity of the metal, the type of mold and its effect on cooling rates, the other dimensions of the section, and the willingness to accept the properties of fast cooled metal all influence this design choice. It is seldom that thickness of less than one-eighth inch can be tolerated for sand castings and permanent mold castings. In die casting where the cavity fills quickly under pressure and in plaster mold casting where the heat is conducted away slowly it is often possible to design with some section thicknesses of less than one-sixteenth inch, particularly if the thin projections are small in area and are located where they will be filled with the hottest metal entering the mold cavity.

When thought is given to the use of a casting as a manufactured item or part, consideration must be given to the necessary subsequent operations and final use. Surfaces that require high quality finish or dimensional accuracies necessitating machining must be designed with extra metal, *machine allowances*, to be removed later. Consideration must also be given to the need and effect of draft for removal of the pattern from the mold. Draft angles from zero to one or two degrees as in Fig. 8–13 can be used sometimes when the length of draw is short. Larger draft angles usually simplify and decrease the cost of pattern removal, but may increase the over-all part cost if they add to the difficulty or amount of machining required.

The amount of draft desirable is often influenced by the location of the parting line in the mold as shown in Fig. 8–14. Draft angles and parting line locations are often special problems for the pattern maker but unless they are given consideration in the original design, the casting cost may turn out to be higher than necessary because of need for cores, special pattern types, or extra skill in mold making.

Pouring. Pouring is usually performed by using ladles to transport the hot metal from the melting equipment to the molds. Most molds are heavy and could be easily damaged by jolts and jars received in moving them from one place to another. Exceptions exist with small molds usually less

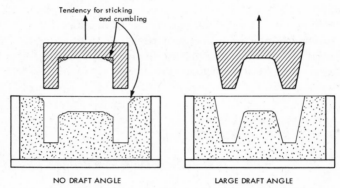

NO DRAFT ANGLE   LARGE DRAFT ANGLE

FIG. 8–13. Draft angles for ease of pattern removal.

than one hundred pounds total weight, or with heavier molds where special equipment is used, that can be conveyorized and moved to a central pouring station. Even these are usually poured from a ladle, though some high production set-ups make use of an automatic pouring station where spouts position themselves over the mold and release the correct amount of metal to fill the cavity.

Casting quality can be significantly influenced by pouring procedure. Turbulent flow which is caused by pouring from too high or excessive rates of flow into the mold should be avoided. Turbulence will cause gas to be picked up which may appear as voids or pockets in the finished casting and may also oxidize the hot metal to form metallic oxide inclusions. The mold may be eroded by rough, fast flow of liquid metal with loss of shape or detail in the cavity and inclusion of sand particles in the metal. *Cold shots* are also a result of turbulent flow. Drops of splashing metal lose heat, freeze, and are then entrapped as globules that do not join completely with the metal that freezes later and are held partly by mechanical bond.

The pouring rate used in filling a mold is critical. If metal enters the cavity too slowly, it may freeze before the mold is filled. Thin sections that cool too rapidly in contact with the mold walls may freeze off before the metal travels its complete path or metal flowing in one direction may solidify and then be met by metal flowing through another path to form a defect known as a *cold shut*. Even though the mold is completely filled, the cold shut shows the seam on the surface of the casting and the metal is not solidly joined and is therefore subject to easy breakage.

If the pouring rate is too high, it will cause erosion of the mold walls with the resulting sand inclusions and loss of detail in the casting. High thermal shock to the mold may result in cracks and buckling. The rate of pouring is controlled by the mold design and the pouring basin, sprue, runner, and gate dimensions. The gating system should be designed so that when the pouring basin is kept full, the rest of the system will be completely filled with a uniform flow of metal.

As mentioned earlier, metals are super heated from one hundred to five hundred degrees above their melting temperature to increase their fluidity and to allow for heat losses before they are in their final position in the mold. For good castings, the metal must be at the correct super heat at the time it is poured into the mold. If the temperature is too low, misruns and

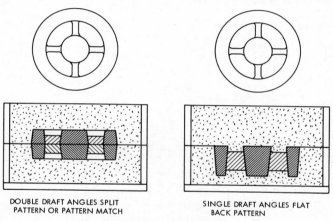

DOUBLE DRAFT ANGLES SPLIT
PATTERN OR PATTERN MATCH

SINGLE DRAFT ANGLES FLAT
BACK PATTERN

FIG. 8–14. Parting line location.

cold shuts will show up as defects in the casting or the metal may even freeze in the ladle. If the temperature at pouring is too high, the metal may penetrate the sand, causing very rough finishes on the casting. Excessive porosity can often be blamed on too high pouring temperatures, or excessive temperature may cause increased gas development leading to voids and increased shrinkage from thermal gradients that disrupt proper directional solidification, but it does increase the mold temperature, decrease the temperature differential, and reduce the rate at which the casting cools. More time at high temperature allows greater grain growth so the casting will cool with a weaker, coarse grain structure.

The Gating System. Metal is fed into the cavity that shapes the casting through a gating system consisting of a *pouring basin*, a *down sprue*, *runners*, and *ingates*. Some typical systems are shown in Fig. 8–15. There are many special designs and terminology connected with these channels and openings whose purpose is that of improving casting quality. Special features of a gating system are often necessary to reduce turbulence and air entrapment, reduce velocity and erosion of sand, and to remove foreign matter or dross. Unfortunately, no universal design is satisfactory for all castings or materials. There are even no rules that can be universally depended upon and experimentation is commonly a requirement for good casting production.

The down sprue, a vertical channel from the top down into the mold, is often used to restrict metal flow. It is usually topped by a pouring basin that accumulates metal as it is poured from the ladle to insure that the sprue remains full once pouring is started. By keeping the pouring basin full, oxides and other light impurities that float can be excluded from the mold. For the casting of iron, the union between the sprue and the runner is not particularly critical; but this connection—when aluminum alloys,

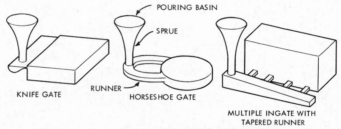

POURING BASIN

SPRUE

KNIFE GATE   RUNNER   HORSESHOE GATE

MULTIPLE INGATE WITH
TAPERED RUNNER

FIG. 8–15. Typical gating systems.

magnesium alloys, and other metals that oxidize readily are being poured —needs to be built with a smooth, gradual, cross-sectional change to minimize turbulence and air entrapment which will cause dross formation.

Sprue design for the casting of steel differs from that for the other metals. Steel has a high melting temperature so it gives up its heat fast on initial contact with the cold mold walls. Since steel solidifies rapidly, fast filling of the mold is a primary consideration and the sprue cannot be used to restrict flow as greatly as with the lower freezing temperature materials.

The channels that convey and distribute metal throughout the mold are called runners. These are placed in the plane of the parting line since location at any other place would require the use of special techniques or the addition of cores. For small production quantities they are usually cut in place in sand molds while the mold is open for removal of the pattern, but for larger production this part of the gating system is often integral with the pattern for the part to be manufactured. Runners need to be proportioned with the sprue and ingates to remain full with a minimim of turbulent flow. If metal flows into the cavity at several points, the cross-sectional dimensions of the runners need to be varied gradually to promote smooth flow.

Ingates or gates are short channels or openings that connect the runner to the mold cavity. These need to be proportioned to each other, if multiple, and to the runner to introduce low velocity metal into the cavity. The number and location of gates is important to casting quality. The points of introduction of liquid metal to the cavity have large influence on directional solidification and normally should connect to the heavier sections so they will solidify last. The metal that finally fills the cavity will be the hottest since it will have been subjected to cooling influences for the shortest period of time and the paths through which it travels will have been heated by previous metal flow.

In designing or cutting gating systems, it is necessary to remember that this excess metal must be removed from the finished casting. The method of removal may influence the practical and economical location of the gates. Runners and ingates are often broken off when working with brittle materials, such as cast iron. The gate itself is sometimes designed to produce a small notch to facilitate fracture. Care must be exercised in breaking off gating systems to prevent breaking out part of the casting. With ductile materials that do not fracture easily, the most common method of removal is by sawing. Hacksawing is sometimes satisfactory, but a relatively large band saw is usually most suitable and more universal. Cast steel is separated with an oxyacetylene torch. Small parts with light gates may be sheared apart with a punch like cutter on a simple, special machine called a gate cutter designed for this purpose.

About the only true machining associated with foundry work is that of rough grinding. The process is used to remove bumps and imperfections and to smooth the spots where gates have been removed. The dangers connected with grinding operations are often overlooked. Equipment with abrasive wheels as cutting tools should never be operated without eye protection. A second major precaution should be the use of adequate ventilation or respirators to reduce inhalation of silicon materials. This last precaution should be taken throughout the entire foundry area where sand and silicon dust prevail.

Risers. Risers, feeders, or feed heads are wells of material attached outside the casting proper to supply liquid metal as needed to compensate for shrinkage before solidification is complete. Although most liquid contraction is taken care of during pouring, a riser may supply replacement for some of this contraction after parts of the casting have frozen solid as in Fig. 8–16. However, the principal purposes of risers are to replace the contraction of solidfication and to promote good directional solidification. The need for risers varies with the casting shape and the metal being poured. Gray iron requires little feeding after the mold is filled, the precipitation of carbon in the form of graphite reduces the density of the solid material and counteracts contraction. In fact, under some conditions, a casting made of gray iron may swell slightly rather than shrink. On the other hand, white iron, which retains its carbon in combined form, may shrink as much as 5 per cent. Aluminum alloy and copper alloy castings that have heavy sections nearly always need the help of a riser to feed replacement metal and prevent damage from excessive shrinkage.

To function successfully, a riser and its connection to the casting must solidify after the casting. This is usually accomplished by designing the riser to have a mass larger than that of the section it is to feed with a low surface to volume ratio. The low ratio will reduce the dissipation of heat so the riser will remain liquid longer than an equal mass with a larger surface. For this purpose, a sphere is the ideal shape, but is difficult to produce in the proper position relationship to the casting. It is more

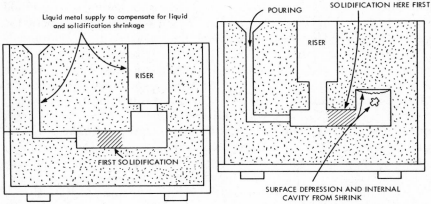

FIG. 8–16. Risers for shrinkage control.   FIG. 8–17. Improper positioning of riser.

common to use a circular cylinder shape with a diameter larger than that of the part to be fed and a height equal to about one and one half times the diameter. Solidification will always proceed toward a suitably sized riser and it is important therefore, that the location of the riser provide proper directional solidification for the casting as a whole. Improperly located risers, such as pictured in Fig. 8–17 serve no useful purpose. The number required will depend upon the casting design. If a number of heavy sections are separated by thinner sections that will freeze quickly, it is likely that a separate riser will need to be attached to each heavy portion to reduce shrinkage effects. Flow from the riser to the casting is by gravity so it must be located above the casting. In some cases, such as feeding a heavy hub of a wheel or pulley, the best location would be directly above with a connection equal in diameter to that of the hub. In other cases, particularly since removal from the casting must be considered, it is more practical to locate the risers above, but to the side of the cavity with heavy connecting channels insuring that a liquid connection will exist until after the casting has solidified.

Blind risers, those that are completely contained in the mold, stay liquid longer than open risers that are exposed to the air at the top of the mold. The insulating properties of the dry sand that exist about the riser after initial heat has driven out the moisture helps the blind riser to retain its heat and stay liquid. When difficulty is experienced in keeping a riser liquid for a long enough period of time, heat may be added or insulation provided. Heat may be added by the use of exothermic materials, such as thermite (aluminum and iron oxide) which burns with the release of large amounts of heat energy. Additional heat may also be supplied from a gas torch or an electric arc source. Insulation merely helps to retain heat already present and involves the use of insulating pads or covers to reduce the escape of heat from the riser.

Help in directional solidification can also be obtained in a reverse manner by the use of *chills* which are heat absorbing devices inserted in the mold. See Fig. 8–18. In order to absorb heat rapidly, chills are usually

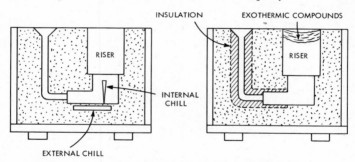

FIG. 8–18. Aids to proper directional solidification.

made of steel, cast iron, or copper and designed to conform to the casting size and shape. Since they must be dry to avoid blow hole formation from gases, it is sometimes necessary to pour a mold soon after it has been made, before the chills have time to collect moisture from condensation. In addition to helping with directional solidification, chills may also improve physical properties. Fast cooling during and after solidification retards grain growth, producing a harder, stronger structure.

Internal chills that become an integral part of the casting are occasionally used to speed solidification in areas where external chills cannot be applied. The design and use of internal chills is critical. Usually the same material of which the casting is to be made is used for this type chill. The chill must be of such size that it functions as a cooling device, but at the same time is heated enough that it fuses with the poured material to become an integral and equally strong part of the casting.

QUESTIONS

1. Briefly describe a nonmetal mold casting process.
2. What is the approximate tonnage output of foundries in the United States?
3. What is a captive foundry?

4. Describe the position and type grains that form first in the solidification of a casting.
5. What is a dentrite?
6. Do all castings have similar grain structures? Why?
7. Why are the majority of castings made from noneutectic alloys?
8. Describe the two types of segregation that may occur during solidification of a casting.
9. What three stages of shrinkage create problems with most castings and how are the problems usually solved?
10. What fault, in addition to segregation, is commonly associated with dendritic grain structure?
11. Define progressive and directional solidification.
12. What faults may result from improper directional solidification?
13. What problems result from section thickness variation in castings and what are the corrections?
14. Should draft angles be large or small?
15. What problems are caused by turbulent flow during pouring?
16. What is a cold shut?
17. What is the purpose of super heat?
18. Sketch a simple gating system including pouring basin, sprue, runners, and ingates.
19. What is the purpose of risers?
20. What is an essential quality for a riser?
21. In what way are chills and risers alike?

CHAPTER 9

Foundry Technology

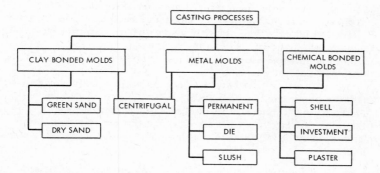

ALTHOUGH the casting process can be used to shape almost any metal, it has been necessary to develop a number of different methods to accomodate different materials and satisfy different requirements. Each of the methods has certain advantages over the others, but all have limitations, some of which restrict use to a few special applications. There are, of course, economic differences based on time, care, and skill necessary for producing a good product and on the cost of equipment needed for doing the work. In addition to these direct cost factors, two more indirect ones have a large influence on the satisfactoriness of a method to produce a casting. One of these is the ability of a mold material to withstand the temperatures at which the liquid metals must be poured. The low melting temperature alloys can be cast by almost any method, providing the over-all economic analysis shows it satisfactory for the quantity, type, and size considered. High temperature alloys, on the other hand, are restricted to being cast by methods making use of mold materials with high *refractoriness*, or heat resisting ability. Another major difference between the processes is in their ability to transfer accurately dimensions and detail from the original pattern to the finished casting. In general, the processes that do the best job will be more costly to operate, although this does not always hold true in large quantity manufacture where some of the costs such as equipment are prorated over large enough numbers that their effect on unit cost is minor.

SAND MOLDING

Sand is the most commonly used material for construction of molds. A variety of sand grain sizes, combined and mixed with a number of other materials and processed in different ways, cause sand to exhibit characteristics which make it suitable for several applications in mold making. A greater tonnage of castings is produced by sand molding than all other methods combined.

The following requirements are basic to sand molding, and most of them also apply for the construction of other types of molds.

1. Sand—to serve as the main structural material for the mold.
2. A pattern—to form a properly shaped and sized cavity in the sand.
3. A flask—to contain the sand around the pattern and provide a means of removing the pattern after the mold is made.
4. A ramming method—to compact the sand around the pattern for accurate transfer of size and shape.
5. A core—to form internal surfaces on the part (usually not required for casting without cavities or holes).
6. A mold gating system—to (as discussed in Chapter 8) provide a means of filling the mold cavity with metal at the proper rate and supply liquid metal to the mold cavity as the casting contracts during cooling and solidification.

The usual procedure for making a simple green sand casting starts with the placing of the pattern to be copied on a *pattern* or *follower* board inside one half of the flask as shown in Fig. 9–1. Sand is then packed around the pattern and between the walls of the flask. After striking off excess sand a *bottom board* is held against the flask and sand and the assembly turned over. Removal of the pattern board exposes the other side of the pattern. A thin layer of *parting* compound (dry nonabsorbent particles) is dusted on the pattern and sand to prevent adhesion. Addition of the upper half of the flask allows sand to be packed against the pattern.

After the sprue is cut to the parting line depth, the upper half of the mold can be removed, the pattern withdrawn, and the gating system completed. Reassembly of the mold halves completes the task and the mold is ready for pouring.

Green Sand.   The majority of castings are poured in molds of *green sand* which is a mixture of sand, clay, and *moisture*. The materials are available in large quantities, are relatively inexpensive, and except for some losses that must be replaced, are reusable. The proportions of the mixture and the types of sand and clay may be varied to change the properties of molds to suit the material being poured. In order to produce good work consistently, it is important that advantage be taken of the properties that can be controlled by varying the constituents of the sand mixture.

The purpose of varying the constituents of molding sand is to accentu-
ate the properties most critical for the application. In most cases, a choice
made to improve one property is likely to decrease another desirable
property, so molding sands are usually compromises to best fit all of a

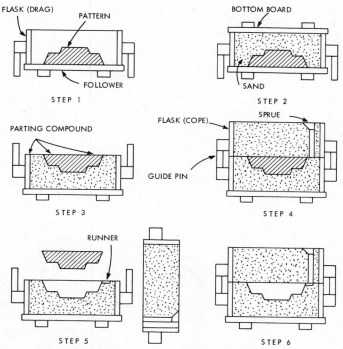

FIG. 9–1. Principal steps for making a sand mold.

particular set of requirements. Properties that are always required to some
degree in molding sands are:

1. High *fusion temperature*—to resist melting and deterioration at the temperatures attained in contact with molten metal.
2. *Thermal stability*—to resist change of size with change of temperature.
   In addition to possible effects on casting size, such expansion, if it occurs
   at different rates at different parts of a mold may lead to cracking, spalling, and buckling of the mold before the casting has solidified.
3. *Permeability*—to allow air in the cavity as well as steam and other gases
   formed during pouring and solidification to escape without interference
   to, or inclusion in, the inflowing metal. Permeability is a function of sand
   grain size, shape, and distribution, clay and moisture content, and the
   closeness of particles established in the making of the mold.
4. *Strength*—to withstand static and dynamic pressures of liquid metals.
   Since the moisture will be driven from part of the molding sand before
   solidification of the metal takes place, the sand must have *dry strength*
   as well as *green strength*.

5. *Collapsability*—to allow casting shapes which are restricted by the mold-ing sand to contract with minimum resistance as the temperature decreases while the metal is still hot and weak. Hot strength is essential while the metal is liquid but after solidification is well started loss of strength is nec-essary if the casting shape provides walls or projections held by the sand, as in Fig. 9–2.

6. *Flowability*—to permit the sand to be compacted to depth and to flow uniformly around the pattern. It is affected by grain size and shape, clay content, and water content.

Sand is disintegrated quartz rock (SIO_2) that is classified in four grain shapes; angular, subangular, round, and compound. *Angular* grains have sharp corners and edges that tend to catch on each other and resist compaction. Since the particles are difficult to move into closely packed relationship, more clay and moisture is usually needed in the mixture to establish a higher strength bond than is necessary with other grain shapes.

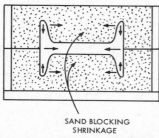

SAND BLOCKING
SHRINKAGE

FIG. 9–2. Need for collaps-ability.

Subangular grains are modified, angular shape grains with slightly rounded edges that allow better compaction. Full strength of a mold made of this shape sand particles can be developed with a reduction of bond-ing material and moisture as well as com-paction work. The subangular grain is the best single grain shape when it is desired to make molds with maximum strength prop-erties.

Because of their shape, *round* grains will have the least contact with each other when packed together. Although strength will be low, flowability of this sand shape is good and the permeability, as based on particle shape only, will be higher than for any of the other sand shapes.

The fourth grain shape classification is really not a shape at all, but a compound structure made up of one or all of the other shapes semi-permanently cemented together. *Compound grains* are not stable at the high temperatures to which they are subjected in a mold and tend to break down.

The sands used for molding seldom consist entirely of any one grain shape, instead are mixtures of the different shapes. The best proportions of the mixture vary with the material being cast. Sands from one location, therefore, may prove to be better for making molds for a particular application than sands from another locality.

The properties of sand are affected not only by the average grain size, but by the size distribution. Sand is a mixture of sizes varying with the source from which it is obtained and the treatment that it has had. It is usually not separated into controlled sizes except that after it has been reused enough to develop a large percentage of *fines*, it may be processed to remove these and increase the average coarseness. Sands with different size values may be combined together to change the average size value or vary the size distribution in order to improve molding properties. The sand grain size is determined by screening a sample through eleven standard screens, No. 6 (.131 inch square openings) to No. 270 (.0021 inch square openings). An average grain fineness number is determined from the percentage of the sample left on the different screens. Curves showing the size distribution can also be drawn from the data thus collected.

In a mold, the sand particles are bound together by clay that is combined with a suitable quantity of water. The most commonly accepted theory of bonding is that as pressure is applied to the molding sand, clay, coating each sand particle, deforms and flows to wedge and lock the particles in place. The clay content can be varied from as little as 2 or 3 per cent to as high as 50 per cent, but the best results seem to be obtained when the amount of clay is just sufficient to coat completely each of the sand grains.

Clays are minerals (one of the hydrated aluminum silicates) of very small grain size. The clay particles are aggregates of plate shaped crystals of maximum diameter of approximately two microns ($\frac{2}{25,000}$ inch). Most of the clay used as an additive for molding sands is of a type known as montmorillonite, more commonly referred to as Western or Southern bentonite, depending upon its source. Western bentonite is mined in a relatively pure state in Wyoming and surrounding states. It is used most for sands used in steel casting and heavy iron casting because of its high dry strength and resistance to high temperatures. Southern bentonite is obtained from Mississippi and is used in molding sand for the production of many nonferrous, malleable iron, and gray iron castings. Its refractoriness and dry strength properties are not as high as those of the Western type. Its high green strength, high flowability, good permeability, and good collapsability make it a desirable bond material for the majority of casting work. Fire clay (kaolinite) may also be added to molding sands when high refractoriness and low shrinkage are important in the application.

Two general types of sand and clay mixtures are used for making green sand molds. Natural bonded sand is used as it is found in nature. Clays found mixed with the sand particles are likely to be mixtures of halloysite and illite as well as those mentioned above. Replacement of the clay bond is necessary as material is burned out in use. The second type sand is synthetic, which can be mixed to control the properties most important for the work to be done by starting with relatively clean sand and adding clay in controlled amounts. Special additives, such as corn flour for better collapsability, sea coal for improved surface finish, wood flour to help control the expansion of the molding sand, and others to improve specific properties are often added.

Water is the third requisite for green sand molding. The optimum quantity will vary from about 2 to 8 per cent by weight depending largely upon the type and quantity of clay present. Thin films of water of several molecules thickness are absorbed around the clay crystals. This water is held in fixed relationship to the clay by atomic attraction and is described as rigid water or tempering water. The clays that have the greatest ability to hold this water film provide the greatest bonding strength. Water in excess of that needed to temper the molding sand does not contribute to strength, but will improve the flowability that permits the sand to be compacted around the pattern.

Patterns.   A pattern is an essential part in the manufacture of castings by most procedures. The mold medium is packed around the pattern in a fashion that will allow the pattern to be withdrawn from the mold and leave a surface image without damage to the mold. Pattern making is an art in itself, so most patterns are made in specialized shops. Large foundries often operate their own pattern shops for pattern manufacture, maintenance, and repair. Small foundries are likely to depend upon independent pattern shops for the supply of this item. Although general rules may be followed in oversizing the pattern to allow for shrinkage (after solidification), it may be necessary with some shapes to use trial and error methods for determination of the best pattern size to produce accurately dimensioned castings. Since the coefficient of thermal expansion is not the same for different metals, a pattern designed for casting of one material cannot be used for another material with the same dimensional results. The pattern maker must know what surfaces of the casting are to be machined and add an allowance for metal to be removed. He must also provide *draft* angles (taper) in the range of from zero to seven degrees to facilitate removal of the pattern from the mold. These allowances are illustrated in Fig. 9–3. The design and manufacture of patterns is time-consuming and expensive so that for single or small quantity manufacture, some form of fabrication other than casting may be more economical and practical.

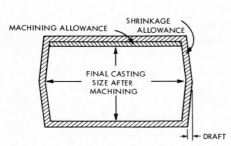

FIG. 9–3. Pattern design allowances.

Patterns may be made of wood, plaster, metal, or any other material strong enough to retain its shape and resist wear. Low use patterns are commonly made of a material that can be easily worked. High use patterns are likely to be constructed of metal for longer life and less susceptibility to damage. Metal patterns are frequently made as castings from patterns of the easier shaped materials. It must be remembered that if the casting process is used in pattern making, shrinkage allowance must be made for the pattern change as well as for the shrinkage of the final product. Under emergency conditions, a finished product may be used as a pattern, but unless the mold cavity is in some way made oversize, the resulting castings will be smaller than the original which was used as a pattern.

Patterns are classified in a number of ways and are given names roughly descriptive of the pattern type or use. *Loose* patterns as shown in Fig. 9–4 are single oversize replicas of the outside shape of a desired surface. If the pattern has a flat surface and draft angles decreasing all the dimensions parallel to that surface in successive planes away from the surface, the pattern is termed *flat back*. The flat surface can be positioned in a flat parting plane of the mold for pattern withdrawal. If the shape of the pattern prevents the mold being separated along a plane, and the mold must be opened along curved or irregular surfaces, the pattern is an *irregular parting* pattern. Loose patterns of this type usually require that the molder dig out material to establish the parting surface at all points of greatest width and length dimensions on the pattern. *Split* patterns are made in two or more pieces with the separation between parts usually a flat plane.

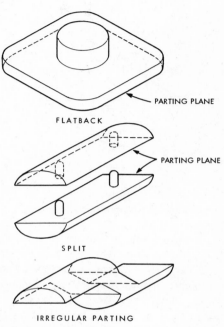

FIG. 9–4. Common loose pattern types.

Draft angle must exist in both directions from the split surface so the pattern parts can be withdrawn from the two halves of the mold constructed with a parting surface to coincide with the split of the pattern. Dowel pins locate the pattern parts together in correct relationship.

The use of any of these loose patterns necessitates the cutting of a gating system to connect the mold cavity with the outside before final closing of the mold after pattern removal. To save production time and to improve consistency of pouring results, loose *gated* patterns may be used. This type pattern has the gating system pattern attached to the casting pattern so the entire mold cavity (usually with the exception of the sprue) may be constructed at one time. Several work patterns may be joined by a common gating system. The draft angle for molding a sprue at the same time would be reversed from that desired for good pouring practice, so the sprue is usually cut instead of molded.

If a pattern that would normally be split is mounted with proper relationship on two sides of a flat plate, the result is a *matchplate* pattern as shown in Fig. 9–5. With a matchplate, pattern parts cannot be lost, register between the cavities formed by the two pattern halves is more certain, and in general, fast, accurate casting production is made easier. In nearly all cases, patterns for the runners and gates are included on the matchplate. The cost of making matchplates is naturally higher than for loose patterns, so they are constructed only for high quantity production parts or for parts that are made intermittently over a long period of time, and in either case, when pattern life should be long for economical operation. With matchplates the parting line is automatically established, molding time is saved, and the accuracy of casting duplication is improved.

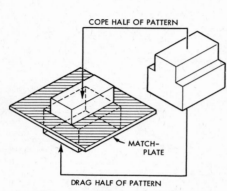

COPE HALF OF PATTERN

MATCH-PLATE

DRAG HALF OF PATTERN

FIG. 9–5. Matchplate pattern.

In the manufacture of large quantities, it is sometimes profitable for two separate molders to specialize in the making of the mold halves. In this case, two matchplates, each carrying a separate half of the pattern, are used on two separate molding machines for construction of the two mold halves at the same time, as in Fig. 9–6.

Most castings are made to be duplicate shapes of patterns as already described. In a few cases, when the quantity is very small and usually when the casting is very large, special methods may be used to make the mold. *Sweeps* or templates, which can be swung about a central axis, may be used to form surfaces of revolution in the mold material for large floor molds. In other cases, a frame may be built on the floor to support and guide the construction of large brick and loam molds. Templates and patterns may be used as aids but a large part of the construction is directly dependent upon the skill of the molder. The process is like sculpturing with a trowel rather than a chisel.

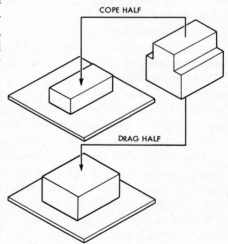

COPE HALF

DRAG HALF

FIG. 9–6.   Cope and drag pattern matchplates.

Flasks. *Flasks* are open-ended boxes in which sand is packed around the pattern. They contain and support the sand during molding and are constructed to allow opening of the mold for removal of the pattern. The

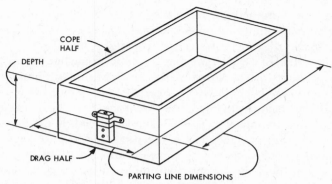

COPE
HALF

DEPTH

DRAG HALF

PARTING LINE DIMENSIONS

FIG. 9–7. Permanent flask.

usual flask, Fig. 9–7, is made in two parts, an upper or *cope* half and lower or *drag* half that are aligned by guide pins to insure accurate relative positioning at the final mold closing. For shapes that require more than one parting surface to allow removal of the pattern, other sections (cheeks) can be inserted between the cope and drag halves of the flask, as in Fig. 9–8.

Flasks are of course needed in different sizes and must always be enough larger than the pattern so that an insulating layer of sand, sufficiently strong to hold in place, will lie between the molten metal and the flask side. Flask sizes are described by the length and width dimensions at the parting surface that is between the cope and drag sections, plus the depth of the cope and the depth of the drag.

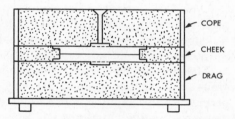

COPE

CHEEK

DRAG

FIG. 9–8. Use of cheek for two parting surfaces.

Permanent flasks are designed to remain on the mold during pouring and are used primarily for large molds and low production work. They are usually made of steel, although for single use on special work a wood frame may be constructed to serve as a flask. Most flasks are constructed with handles to facilitate handling and moving. The larger size molds, where the cope may weigh one hundred pounds or more, are often made where they are to be poured and a hoist is used to help open the mold to remove the pattern by lifting the cope section. *Stack* molding is a set-up in which a number of mold cavities are mounted one above another with a common sprue to supply metal to each. The purpose is to increase production rates, improve economy, and decrease necessary floor space. Stack molds are built up with a drag section flask at the bottom, topped by a number of cope sections of permanent flasks.

The majority of production work and nearly all molding that is done on machines, is performed with removable flasks that can be used over and over. Only one is needed per molder since the flask is removed and the molds are stored without an outside casing. During pouring, however, a jacket consisting of a metal frame of proper size must be slipped down over the unprotected mold to prevent the cope from slipping on the drag when the pressures of the liquid metal act on the mold. Three types of removable flasks are in common use. *Snap* flasks are hinged at the corners, with one corner being constructed so that it can be opened and the flask unwrapped from the mold. A second removable flask is the *pop-off* flask which is made with two diagonal corners solid and the other two filled with a spongy rubber to act as a spring and shield to exclude sand. Cam-like clamps hold the corners tightly closed for molding, but can be released to loosen the flask when it is to be taken off. The third type of commonly used removable flask is the *slip* flask which is made with solid cope and drag sections. Sliding sand strips, operated from diagonal corners, are pushed in to hold the sand during molding and withdrawn when the flask is to be removed from the completed mold. The inside of the removable flasks is generally tapered with from three to seven degree angles to aid removal and to shape the outside of the mold so a tapered jacket can tighten in place.

Sand Compaction. Compaction, packing, or ramming of sand into place in a mold is one of the greater labor and time-consuming phases of making castings. It also has considerable influence on the quality of finished castings produced. Sand that is packed too lightly will be weak and may fall out of the mold, or crack, causing casting defects. Loosely packed grains at the surface of the cavity may wash with the metal flow, or may permit metal penetration with a resulting rough finish on the casting. Sand that is too tightly compacted will lack permeability, restrict gas flow, and be a source of blow holes, or may even prevent the cavity from completely filling. Too tightly packed sand may also lack collapsability so that as solidification occurs, cracks and tears in the casting may be caused by the inability of the sand to get out of the way of the shrinking metal. Each of the several available methods for compacting sand has advantages over the others and limitations that restrict its use.

Peen and butt rammers may be used on a bench or on the floor by manual operation, or in the case of large molds, the work may be done with pneumatic rammers similar to an air hammer. *Peen* ramming involves the use of a rib shaped edge to develop high impact pressures and is used principally to pack sand between narrow vertical walls and around the edges of the flask. *Butt* ramming is done with a broader faced tool for more uniform compaction of the sand throughout the mold. Experience and skill aid greatly in determining when the sand has been packed tightly enough to have sufficient strength but still retain the permeability required for the escape of gases.

Most production work and a large part of work done in small quantities is performed by use of molding machines whose principal duty is that of sand compaction. They are designed to compact sand by either *jolting* or *squeezing*, or both methods may be combined in a single machine. Jolt compaction involves the lifting of the table carrying the mold and dropping it against a solid obstruction. With the sudden stop, inertia forces cause the sand particles to compress together. Jolt compaction tends to pack the sand more tightly near the parting surface, and for this reason is usually not too satisfactory when used alone with patterns that are high and project close to the mold surface. On the other hand, squeeze compaction applied by pushing a squeeze plate against the outside of the sand, tends to pack the sand more tightly at the surface. The combination of jolting and squeezing is frequently used to take advantages of each method, although when both the cope and drag are being made on the same machine, it may be impossible to jolt the cope half (the second half constructed) without damage to the drag. It is often practical to mount a pattern for a pouring basin on the squeeze plate to mark the location of the sprue and to form a pocket into which molten metal can be poured.

Foundries that manufacture quantities of large castings often use sand *slingers* to fill and to compact the sand in large floor molds. The sand is thrown with high velocity in a steady stream by a rotating impeller and is compacted by impact as it fills up in the mold. Fig. 9–9 illustrates the common compaction methods.

Cores. *Cores* are bodies of mold material, usually in the form of inserts that exclude metal flow to form internal surfaces in a casting. The body is

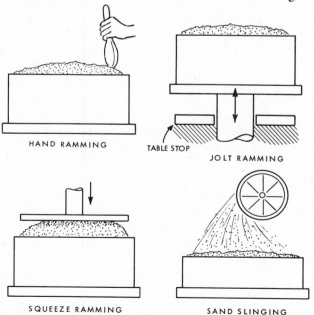

HAND RAMMING   TABLE STOP   JOLT RAMMING

SQUEEZE RAMMING   SAND SLINGING

FIG. 9–9. Common sand compaction methods.

considered to be a core when made of green sand only if it extends through the cavity to form a hole in the casting. Green sand cores are formed in the pattern with the regular molding procedure.

The vast majority of cores are made of dry sand and contain little or no clay. A nearly pure sand is combined with additives that burn out after pouring to promote collapsability and binders to hold the particles together until after solidification takes place.

The properties needed in core sand are similar to those required for molding sand, with some taking on greater importance because of differences in the cores' position and use. Most cores are baked for drying and development of dry strength, but they must also have green strength so they can be handled before baking. The dry strength of a finished core must be sufficient that it can withstand its own weight without sagging in the mold and it must be strong enough that its own buoyancy, as liquid metal rises around it, will not cause it to break or shift. Permeability is important with all molding sands, but is especially so with core sand, since cores are often almost completely surrounded by metal and a relatively free passage is essential for the gases to escape through core prints or other small areas. Collapsability is likewise important because of this metal enclosure. Ideally, a core should collapse immediately after metal solidification takes place. In addition to not interfering with shrinkage of the casting, it is important in many cases that cores collapse completely before final cooling so they can be removed from inside castings where they are almost totally enclosed. For example, cores used to form the channels in a hot water radiator, or the water openings in an internal combustion engine, would be almost impossible to remove unless they lost their strength and became free sand grains. The casting must supply the heat for the final burning out of the additives and binding material.

Cores are usually made with new sand that is lost in the molding sand when the castings are shaken out. An exception is sometimes made when core sand is a large percentage of the mold, when large amounts of core sand added to the molding sand would change the composition requiring considerable testing and bond replacement. A small percentage of water is usually part of a green mixture of core sand, but the principal bond is created by oils or plastics which develop strength when heated and dried. Commercially manufactured core oils are available, or vegetable oils, such as linseed oil or corn oil may be used. Core sand prepared with oils is baked at temperatures between 350° and 450°F. The time of baking is dependent upon a number of factors: the kind of oil, the percentage of oil in the mixture, the size of sand grains, the presence of other additives, the thickness of the core, and the degree of "doneness" required. Experience, know-how, and tests are all ingredients of good core baking, but a rule of thumb satisfactory to establish a starting point is to bake oil bonded cores approximately one hour for each inch of maximum thickness after the oven comes up to temperature.

When cores are to be placed in the mold, the pattern is constructed with projections that form recesses, grooves, or holes adjacent to the cavity that is to form the casting proper to provide locating points and support for the inserted cores. These resting spots are called *core prints*. The core itself has projections to match so it can be accurately located and rigidly supported when the mold is closed. Very large or long slender cores that might give way under pressure of the flowing metal are sometimes given additional support by the use of *chaplets*. Chaplets are small, metal supports with broad surfaced ends, usually made of metal the same as that to be poured, that can be set between the mold cavity and the core. Chaplets become part of the casting after they have served their function of supporting cores while the metal is liquid.

Cores are made in much the same way as are molds. The forms in which they are shaped are a kind of reverse pattern, called a *core box*. Sand may be rammed by hand into a core box which is then removed, leaving the shaped sand on a plate that can be moved into the core oven for baking. They may be made on special core making machines which in addition to jolting the sand for compaction, will provide aid in stripping off the core box, or large cores may even be made on standard molding machines. Cores that are made in large quantities can sometimes be produced faster on *core blowers*. Core blowers are machines that fill a closed core box by moving the sand with high velocity air that escapes from the core box through strategically placed screened vents. Cores of uniform cross section can be produced accurately and at high speeds by *extrusion* of the green sand mixture on to a core plate moving at the same rate as the extrusion.

Cores are often used to produce complicated internal shapes in castings. They are relatively strong after baking and can be sawed, filed, and pasted together. Since they can be assembled in various ways, it is possible by use of cores to produce re-entrant angles and shapes that cannot be made by a pattern that must be withdrawn from green sand.

Green Sand Advantages and Limitations.   For most metals and most sizes and shapes of castings, green sand molding is the most economical of all the molding processes. Green sand can be worked manually or mechanically and because very little special equipment is necessary, can be easily and cheaply used for a great variety of products. The sand is reusable with only slight additions necessary to correct its composition. In terms of cost, the green sand process can be bested only when the quantity of like castings is large enough that reduced operational costs for some other processes will more than cover higher original investment or when the limitations of the green sand process prevent consistent meeting of required qualities.

One of the limitations of green sand is its low strength in thin sections. It cannot be used satisfactorily for casting thin fins or long, thin projections. Green sand also tends to crush and shift under the weight of very heavy sections. This same weakness makes the casting of intricate shapes difficult also. The moisture present in green sand produces steam when contacted by hot metal. Inability of the steam and other gases to escape causes problems with some casting designs and blow hole damage results. The dimensional accuracy of green sand castings is limited. Even with small castings, it is seldom that dimensions can be held closer than plus or minus $\frac{1}{64}$ inch and, with large castings, plus or minus $\frac{1}{8}$ inch, or greater tolerances are necessary.

Dry Sand Molds.   Improvement in casting qualities can sometimes be obtained by use of *dry* sand molds. The molds are made of green sand modified to favor the dry properties and then dried in an oven. The absence of moisture eliminates the formation of water vapor and reduces the type casting defects that are due to gas formation. The cost of heat, the time required for drying the mold, and the difficulty of handling heavy molds without damage makes the process expensive compared to green sand molding and it is used mostly when steam formation from moisture present would be a serious problem.

Most of the benefit of dry sand molds can be obtained by *skin drying* molds to depths from a fraction of an inch to an inch. With the mold open, the inside surfaces are subjected to heat from torches, radiant lamps, hot dry air, or electric heating elements to form a dry, insulating skin around the mold cavity. Skin dried molds can be stored only for short periods of time before pouring, since the water in the main body of the mold will redistribute itself and remoisturize the inside skin.

Floor and Pit Molds.   Although the number of extremely large castings is relatively small, molds must be constructed for one, five, ten, and occasionally, even as much as several hundred ton castings. Such molds cannot be moved about and the high hydrostatic pressures established by high columns of liquid metal require special mold construction stronger than that used for small castings. *Floor* molds made in the pouring position are built in large flasks. The mold can be opened by lifting the cope with an overhead crane, but the cope flask usually must be constructed with special support bars to prevent the mold material from dropping free when it is lifted.

Pit molds use the four walls of a pit as a flask for the drag section. The cope may be an assembly of core sand or may be made in a large flask similar to that used for a floor mold. The mold material for these large sizes is usually loam, 50 per cent sand and 50 per cent clay plus water. The mold structure is often strengthened by inserting bricks or other ceramic material as a large part of its substance.

Shell Molds.   *Shell* molding is a fairly recent development that, as far as casting is concerned, can be considered a precision process. Dimensions can be held within a few thousandths of an inch in many cases to eliminate or reduce machining that might be necessary otherwise and decrease the over-all cost of manufacturing. The cost of the process itself, however, is relatively high and large quantities of duplication are necessary for economical operation.

The mold is made by covering a heated metal pattern with sand that is mixed with small particles of a thermo-setting plastic. The heat of the pattern causes the mixture to adhere and semi-cures the plastic for a short depth. The thin shell thus made is stripped from the pattern, further cured by baking at five or six hundred degrees, then cemented to its mating half to complete the mold proper. Since the shell is thin, approximately ⅛ inch, its resistance to springing apart is low, so it may be necessary to back it up with loose sand or shot to take the pressures set up by filling with liquid metal. The sand particles are tightly held in the plastic bond. Erosion and metal penetration are minor problems so, in addition to good dimensional control, high quality surface finishes are obtained from shell molding.

Core Sand Assemblies. Because of the additional handling and the baking process required, core sand is naturally more expensive than ordinary green molding sand. It is, however, of greater strength, will resist erosion better, and can be formed into thin projections not possible with green sand. It may, therefore, be economical to use where its strength and ability to transfer intricate design are valuable. It has been pointed out that core sand assemblies may be used to cap pit molds. They may also be used for intricate detail on small castings as either part or all of the mold. Cast anchor chain is constructed with core sand molds which, when assembled together, can be poured to manufacture a series of interconnecting chain links.

METAL MOLD AND SPECIAL PROCESSES

Metal patterns and metal core boxes are used in connection with molding whenever the quantities manufactured justify the additional expense of the longer wearing patterns. The metal mold processes refers not to the pattern equipment but to a reusable metal mold that is in itself a reverse pattern in which the casting is made directly. In addition to the metal mold processes, there are others involving either single use or reusable molds, but their use is limited to a comparatively small number of applications where the processes, even though more costly, show distinct advantages over the more commonly used methods.

Permanent Mold Casting. *Permanent* molds may be reused many times. The life will depend, to a large extent, upon the intricacy of the casting design and the temperature of the metal that is poured into the mold. Cast iron and steel are the most common materials of which the mold is made. Permanent mold casting is used most for the shaping of aluminum, copper, magnesium, and zinc alloys. Cast iron is occasionally poured in permanent molds with much lower mold life because of the higher operating temperature. Satisfactory results require operation of the process with a uniform cycle time to maintain the operating temperature within a small range. Initial use of new molds often demands experimentation to determine the most suitable pouring and operating temperatures as well as correction of the position and size of the small vent grooves cut at the mold parting line to allow the escape of air.

The cost of the mold, sometimes referred to as dies, and the operating mechanism by which they are opened and closed, is high but permanent mold casting has several advantages over sand casting for high quantity production. Dimensional tolerances are more consistent and can be held to approximately plus or minus ten thousandths of an inch. The higher conductance of heat through the metal mold causes a chilling action, producing finer grain structure and harder, stronger castings. The minimum practical section thickness for permanent molding is about ⅛ inch. The majority of castings are less than 12 inches diameter and twenty pounds weight. The process is used in the manufacture of automobile cylinder heads, automobile pistons, low horsepower engine connecting rods, and many other nonferrous alloy castings needed in large quantity.

Die Casting. *Die* casting differs from permanent mold casting in that pressure is applied to the liquid metal to cause it to flow rapidly and uniformly into the cavity of the mold or die. The die is made about the same as that used for permanent molding. It is made of metal, again usually cast iron or steel, has parting lines along which it can be opened for extraction of the casting, and is constructed with small draft angles on the walls to reduce the work of extraction and extend the life of the die. Vents, in the form of grooves or small holes, also are present to permit the escape of air as metal fills the die. The machines in which the dies are used however, are quite different since in addition to closing and opening the die parts, they must supply liquid metal under pressure to fill the cavity. The *hot chamber* die casting machine, as shown in Fig. 9–10, keeps metal

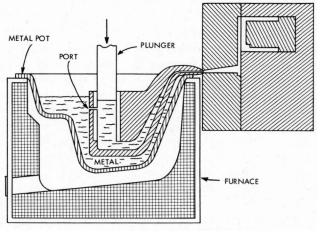

FIG. 9–10.   Hot chamber die casting.

melted in a chamber through which a piston moves into a cylinder to build a pressure forcing the metal into the die. Since the piston and the portions subjected to pressure are heated to the melting temperature of the casting metal, hot chamber machines are restricted to lower pressures than those with lower operating temperatures. Although it is a high speed, low cost process, the low pressures do not produce the high density, high quality castings often desired. In addition, iron absorbed by aluminum in a hot chamber machine would be detrimental to its properties. Pressures as high as two thousand psi are used in the hot chamber process to force fill the mold.

With *cold chamber* equipment, as in Fig. 9–11, molten metal is poured into the shot chamber and the piston advances to force the metal into the

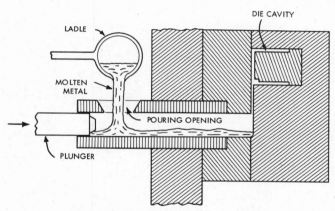

FIG. 9–11.   Cold chamber die casting.

die. Aluminum, copper, and magnesium alloys are die cast by this method with liquid pressures as high as twenty-five or thirty thousand psi.

Dies which must be accurately machined and matched are expensive to manufacture. Die casting machines are more expensive and require more maintenance than the equipment used with most of the other casting processes. It can be expected then that die casting will be economical only when large quantities are needed, but the process is capable of very high production rates with fifty or sixty castings per minute of small parts not being unusual. Of course, as the casting mass increases, more time is required for solidification and the cycle time must be increased. Sections as thin as fifteen or twenty thousandths of an inch with tolerances as small as two or three thousandths of an inch can be cast with very good surface finish by this pressure process. The material properties are likely to be high because the pressure improves the metal density (fewer voids) and fast cooling by the metal molds produces good strength properties. Other than high initial cost, the principal limiting feature of die casting is that it cannot be used for the very high strength materials. However, low temperature alloys are continually being developed and with their improvement, die casting is being used more and more.

Slush Casting. Slush casting is another process that makes use of metal molds. Compared to the major casting processes, the use is very small. The metal mold is filled with liquid metal which solidifies rapidly around the outside because of the high thermal conductivity of the mold. The liquid metal in the center of the mold is poured out before it has an opportunity to solidify, leaving a thin shell fitting the contours of the mold cavity. Brass lamp bases, statuary, and like items that need to be neither solid nor accurately dimensioned on the inside can be produced by slush casting with a savings of time and material.

Investment. Investment casting, Fig. 9–12, is also known as precision casting and as the *lost wax* process. The process has been used in dentistry

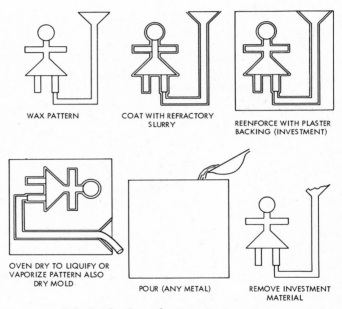

WAX PATTERN   COAT WITH REFRACTORY   REENFORCE WITH PLASTER
                        SLURRY   BACKING (INVESTMENT)

OVEN DRY TO LIQUIFY OR
VAPORIZE PATTERN ALSO
DRY MOLD
                   POUR (ANY METAL)   REMOVE INVESTMENT
                                                MATERIAL

FIG. 9–12. Steps for investment casting.

for many years. A new wax pattern is needed for every piece cast. For single piece casting, the wax pattern may be made directly by impressions, as in dentistry, by molding or sculpturing as for the making of statuary, or by any method that will shape the wax to the form desired in the casting. Shrinkage allowances must be made for the wax, if it is done hot, and for the contraction of the metal that will be poured in the cavity formed by the wax. Re-entrant angles in the casting are possible since the wax will not be removed from the cavity in solid form. Variations of this process involve the use of frozen mercury or low melting point thermoplastics for the pattern.

Multiple production requires starting with a master pattern about which a metal die is made. The metal die can be used for making any number of wax patterns. A gating system must be part of the wax pattern and may be produced in the metal die or attached after removal from the die. When complete, the wax pattern is dipped in a slurry of fine, refractory material and then encased in the investment material—plaster of paris, or mixtures of ceramic materials with high refractory properties. The wax is then removed from the mold by heating in an oven to liquify the wax and cause it to run out to be reclaimed. The mold is also dried during this heating cycle. Investment molds are preheated to suitable temperatures for pouring, usually between 1000° and 2000°F., depending upon the metal that is to fill the mold. After pouring and solidification, the investment is broken away to free the casting for removal of the gating system and final cleaning.

Investment casting is limited to small castings, usually not over approximately five pounds in weight. The principal advantage of the process is in its ability to produce intricate castings with dimensional tolerances of only a few thousandths of an inch. High melting temperature materials that are difficult to cast by other methods can be cast this way because the investment material of the mold can be chosen for refractory properties that can withstand these higher temperatures. In many cases, pressure is applied to the molten metal to improve flow and densities so very thin sections can be poured by this method. It can easily be realized by examination of the procedures that must be followed for investment molding and casting that the costs of this process are high. Accuracy of the finished product, which may eliminate or reduce machining problems, can more than compensate for the high casting cost with some materials and for some applications.

Plaster Mold Casting. Molds made of plaster of paris with additives such as talc, asbestos, silica flour, sand, and other materials to vary the mold properties, are used only for casting nonferrous metals. Plaster molds will produce good quality finish and good dimensional accuracy. The procedure is similar to that used in dry sand molding. The plaster material must be given time to cure after being coated over the pattern and is completely oven dried before it is poured. The dry mold is a good insulator which serves both as an advantage and a disadvantage. The insulating property permits lower pouring rates with less super heat in the liquid metal. These contribute to less shrinkage, less gas entrapment from turbulence, and greater opportunity for evolved gases to escape from the metal before solidification. On the other hand, because of slow cooling, plaster molds should not be used for applications where large grain growth is a serious problem.

Shaw Process. This patented process was developed in England starting in 1938. It resembles both plaster molding and shell molding in some respects but has advantages over each.

Proprietary mixtures of finely ground refractory powders and liquid binders are formulated as slurries which are mixed in metered amounts and poured around the pattern. Chemical action causes the binder to form a gel which solidifies to form the mold which can then be stripped from the pattern.

After stripping, the mold is ignited to cause the volatile liquids to burn. As with almost any similar material, shrinkage occurs as the liquids are removed from the mold. One of the principal features of the Shaw Process is the manner in which the shrinkage takes place. Rather than gross shrinkage which would produce distortion and dimensional change, or shrinkage as it normally occurs in a clay-water mixture which would produce a rough surface, the accelerated removal of the liquid from the surface results in *microcrazing*. A microscopic network of cracks develops which are small enough to prevent molten metal from entering, but large enough to provide permeability.

The process is capable of producing castings with closely controlled dimensions, fine surface finishes, and good internal soundness. Both ferrous and nonferrous metals may be cast. Molds may be made either as thin shells, or as monolithic blocks which have higher strength and require no backing. Aside from its proprietary nature, which has a tendency to restrict use, the principal disadvantages are the need for specialized equipment and special training and knowledge for satisfactory results.

Centrifugal Casting.   Several procedures, Fig. 9–13, are classed as centrifugal casting. All of the methods make use of a rotating mold to develop centrifugal force acting on the metal to improve its density toward the outside of the mold. The true centrifugal process shapes the outside of the casting with a mold, but depends on centrifugal force to form the inside surface making a symmetric shell about the axis of rotation. The principal product of true centrifugal casting is cast iron sewer pipe.

A similar process, which may be termed semi-centrifugal casting, consists of the revolving of a symmetric mold about the axis of the mold's cavity and pouring that cavity full. The density of a casting made in this way will vary, with dense, strong metal around the outside and more porous, weaker metal at the center. Wheels, pulleys, gear blanks, and other shapes of this kind may be made in this way to obtain maximum metal properties near the outside periphery.

A third type of casting using centrifugal force can be termed centrifuge casting. In this process, a number of equally spaced mold cavities are arranged in a circle about a central pouring sprue. The mold may be single or stacked with a number of layers arranged vertically about a common sprue. The mold is revolved with the sprue as an axis and when poured, will be filled with centrifugal force helping the normal hydrostatic pressure force metal into the spinning mold cavities. Gases tend to be forced out of the metal with improved metal quality.

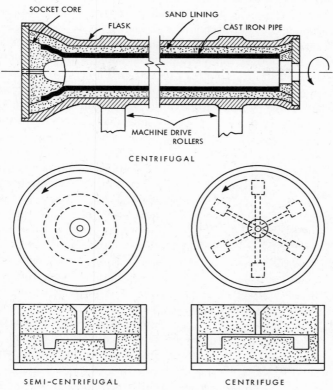

FIG. 9–13. Centrifugal type casting.

MELTING EQUIPMENT

The volume of metal needed at any one time varies from a few pounds to several tons in batch type operations, with a continuous supply of melted metal, usually iron, being required by many large production foundries. The quantity of available metal can be varied by the size and type of melting equipment and the number of units in operation. The temperatures needed for melting to occur range from 400° to 600°F. for lead, bismuth, and tin alloys; from 1000° to 1500°F. for aluminum and magnesium alloys; from 2,060° to 2,600°F. for cast irons; and to as high as from 2,600° to 2,800°F. for steels. The actual pouring temperatures will be from 100° to 500°F. above these, depending on the degree of super-heat desired. The volume and rate of melting and the temperatures required will influence the choice of melting equipment.

Cupola. Nearly all of the cast iron poured is melted in a special type furnace called a *cupola*. In construction and operation the cupola, Fig. 9–14, is similar to the blast furnace described in Chapter 5. A cupola consists of a cylindrical stack, twenty to thirty feet high with an inside diameter of eighteen to eighty-four inches, mounted on legs to provide an open space under the bottom of the cylinder. The steel shell is lined with refractory material to enable it to withstand the high temperatures needed to melt iron. The bottom of the cylinder is closed with hinged doors that are covered with foundry sand for protection. The cupola is charged with layers of coke, pig iron, scrap, and fluxing material in multiple layers to make up the volume of metal to be poured in a heat. The original charges cannot be built up above the height of the charging door, but as the metal is burned down and the coke used up, new charges may be added to the top. After the coke has been kindled, an air blast is introduced near the base of the cylinder through openings called *tuyeres* to cause faster and more complete combustion to provide the heat needed for melting the metal and flux. The melted metal drips down through the coke bed to a well at the bottom where it is accumulated until the furnace is tapped. Tapping involves piercing a hole with a tapping bar through a special brick in the base of the cupola known as the *breast* to allow the melted metal to run out through a refractory lined spout into a ladle for distribution.

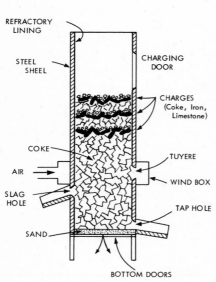

FIG. 9–14.   Cupola.

When all of the molten metal is drawn from the well, or when the ladle is filled, the hole in the breast is plugged with a clay *bott*, pushed into place on the end of a stopping bar and held until the heat bakes the clay. At the rear of the cupola, at the top of the well but below the tuyeres is the slag spout through which the *slag* can be drawn off by allowing the metal to build up in the well. The slag is a mixture of the fluxing agent, usually limestone, and impurities such as oxides, scale, sand, and ashes. The slag is light enough to float on top of the metal and serves as an insulating blanket, but cannot be allowed to develop into too thick a layer and must be drawn off periodically during long operations. Cupolas may be operated as little as an hour or less each day to melt a few charges in small foundries, or may be operated continuously for a week or more where the need exists. As with nearly all refractory lined heating equipment, damage occurs with heating and cooling and each shutdown generally calls for maintenance or repair work.

The composition of metal tapped from a cupola is controlled primarily by the make-up of the material charged into the furnace, although the method of cupola operation has some influence on the composition of the final product. Exposure to a highly carbonaceous environment (coke) at high temperatures will cause the iron to take up carbon with a percentage increase dependent upon original carbon content, temperatures, and length of exposure. Carbon content is kept low by starting with low carbon irons, both pig and scrap, and preventing the melted metal from remaining in the cupola well any longer than necessary. At the same time carbon is being added, from 10 to 30 per cent of the silicon and manganese originally present is lost. These losses, which can be anticipated, are usually compensated for by the addition of special, high silicon and/or high manganese pig iron to the charges, or manganese enrichment can be accomplished with ladle additions of ferro-manganese. Chromium, molybdenum, and nickel additions are also commonly made in the ladle. Large ladle additions though may cool the metal too much, so alloying requiring large changes is more likely to be done in a separate furnace.

Air Furnace. A small amount of cast iron is produced with air furnaces, but the principal work of this equipment is the melting and refining of iron to be malleableized. Malleable iron is made from white iron which requires stricter control of composition than the gray variety. The *air furnace* is a large reverbatory type brick structure, similar to the open hearth furnace used in the melting of steel. The furnace can be charged cold by lifting off the top brick work in its supporting frames (bungs) by use of a crane. After resealing, heat is produced by burning gas, oil, or pulverized coal forced over the surface of the charge through nozzles. The furnace may also be charged with molten metal directly from a cupola. The iron may be held for temporary storage, alloys may be added, or in the process called *duplexing*, further refining may take place to produce malleable iron.

Metal composition changes that take place in an air furnace are different from those in the cupola. Silicon and manganese are lost during melting in the same way, but as the metal is held at its higher temperatures, from 2,600° to 2,900°F., silicon is regained from the slag and the refractories of the furnace to replace gradually that lost earlier. At these same higher temperatures, carbon will be lost from the material by oxidation at a rapid rate unless precautions are used to prevent it. The carbon losses can be cut down by use of a reducing flame (high fuel to air ratio) or can be compensated for by the addition of carbonaceous material such as coke or powdered coal.

Crucible Furnaces. A large amount of nonferrous melting for small volume work is accomplished with lift-out, *crucible furnaces* as shown in Fig. 9–15. The size of the crucible is limited because of the necessity for handling. After being set in a gas or oil fired furnace, the crucible is loaded with pig and scrap metal. The furnace is lighted and left operating with an air blast to intensify the heat and circulate it around the crucible until the metal has melted and reached a satisfactory pouring temperature. At this time, the furnace is turned off and, if required, ladle additions made. The crucible is lifted from the furnace with special tongs and set in a ring shank which serves as a pouring handle. The crucible furnace operates under conditions similar to those of open-flame melting with a resulting absorption of gases from the air and products of combustion. This poor condition can be largely corrected by placing a close fitting lid on the crucible to exclude the gases of the environment.

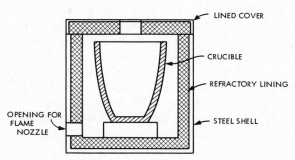

FIG. 9–15. Crucible furnace.

Pot Furnaces. *Pot furnaces* are used for melting larger quantities of nonferrous metals, in sizes that will handle up to several hundred pounds in a melt. The general construction of the furnace is similar to that of the crucible type. The pot, however, is larger than the crucible and is a permanent part of the furnace. The pots are constructed of steel or cast iron and must be coated with a thin layer of refractory material to prevent contamination of the melted metal. Smaller sizes are stationary and the metal must be ladled out. Larger sized furnaces that will handle up to a ton or more of material are designed so they can be tilted to pour the molten metal into ladles for distribution to the molds.

Reverberatory Furnaces.   Some   of   the   largest   foundries   melt nonferrous materials in *reverberatory furnaces* which play the heating flame directly on the surface of the charged material as in an open hearth or air furnace. As stationary furnaces, these can be built to handle an almost unlimited capacity. Gas absorption from the products of combustion in contact with the exposed metal surface is high but advantages exist in the large capacity and the high melting rate that can be accomplished in this manner. Small, tilting type reverberatory furnaces are used for fast melting of small quantities of metal.

Electric Arc Furnaces.   The electric arc is a high intensity heat source that can be used for melting any metal to be cast. Two kinds of electrically heated furnaces use arcs. The *direct arc electric furnace*, in which the arc plays from the carbon electrode to the metal being melted, is used most for the melting of tool steels and alloy materials in which the composition and developed properties must be closely controlled. Since oxygen is not necessary for combustion, the furnace can be rather tightly enclosed to exclude air and other gases. The electrodes automatically space themselves from the surface of the molten pool after the arc has been struck and temperature control is established by the power supplied to these electrodes which may be as large as over one foot in diameter in the larger furnaces. The furnace is mounted so that it can be tilted for pouring after the melting procedure is complete.

The *indirect electric arc furnace* is used principally for melting the copper based alloys. It can be used for other metals as well. The furnace consists of a cylindrical steel shell lined with refractory material. Heat is produced by an arc that is struck and maintained between opposing electrodes. Heat is radiated to raise the temperature of the entire furnace lining as well as the charge. Oscillation of the furnace causes molten metal to flow over heated refractory material and pick up heat by conduction as well as that radiated to it.

Induction Furnaces.   In appearance, an *induction melting furnace* resembles a pot or crucible type furnace. Power is supplied to the furnace in the form of a high frequency, alternating current which is passed through conductors in the body of the furnace to set up a high frequency, varying magnetic field, which cuts through the metal that is being heated. The metal, being a conductor in itself, has voltages induced in it that cause eddy currents to flow and since the flow of electric current through resistance (the metal itself) causes heat, the temperature of the metal is raised.

Induction furnaces are specialized equipment and rather expensive in first costs. Operational cost is dependent largely on the cost of electric power in the locality in which they are used. They do, however, produce rapid melting with no combustion products, thereby minimizing oxidation and gas absorption in the melt.

FOUNDRY MECHANIZATION

As much as several hundred tons of material, varying with the casting size and type, may have to be handled and rehandled for each ton of finished castings produced. The actual making of castings, therefore, often turns out to consist mainly of heavy labor of moving materials through the foundry. Much of this labor can be reduced or even eliminated at some points by application of various mechanical aids.

The degree of foundry mechanization that is economically feasible depends upon the casting size, casting type, volume of production, quantity of reproduction or duplication, and the desired production rates. In practice, the use of mechanization runs the gamut from all manual operation in some of the small, low production foundries to almost completely automatic operation in some highly specialized foundries which concentrate on repetitive production.

Molding.   The mechanization of the molding operation is principally by use of molding machines designed to support the work at a convenient height for the operator and to perform one or more functions of sand compaction and handling of the mold or pattern. Economical practice for many repetitive jobs of mold making calls for specialization in use of equipment, with one machine making part of the mold while the mating part is constructed on another machine. However, when the duplication of molds is low in number, a single machine is generally used for the construction of the entire mold which is closed complete with cores and ready for pouring when it leaves the equipment. Molding machines are classified and named according to the principal function they are designed to perform. Some of the more commonly used molding machines are as follows.

Squeeze machines, Fig. 9–16, compact the sand by application of pressure from a squeeze plate pressed down on top of the mold. The pressure may be applied manually on small machines, but is more commonly produced by high pressure air, acting on a piston in a pneumatic cylinder.

Jolt machines, Fig. 9–17, employ pneumatic cylinders to raise the table

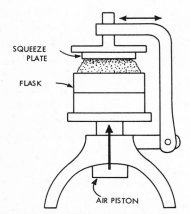

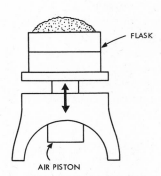

FIG. 9–16. Squeeze molding   FIG. 9–17. Jolt molding
machine.   machine.

supporting the mold and allow it to drop against a solid stop to subject the sand grains to impact loading for compaction. The machine may be constructed with additional features to provide support for the mold after compaction and allow the pattern to be drawn or stripped from the sand. With this change, the machine would be termed a jolt stripper. Some hand ramming is usually associated with the use of a jolt molding machine and the equipment is normally used only for making mold halves.

Jolt and squeeze methods produce different characteristics of compaction. Jolting tends to compact better close to the pattern and squeezing tends to compact better at the outside surface of the mold where the squeeze plate contacts. Since the two methods are complimentary, a majority of molds are made on jolt-squeeze machines which combine the values of the two types. Pins to lift the pattern plate or frames to hold the mold and allow the pattern to be drawn straight down with the table may also be additions to this type machine. The addition of the stripping feature changes the name to jolt-squeeze-stripper and permits the machine to be used in a more specialized way to speed up production by making mold halves only.

The majority of molds made by machines are small enough in size that the operator can lift and handle them. Molds that are too heavy to be lifted easily require that a crane or hoist be available for this purpose or that the machine be especially designed for handling the mold. The jolt rockover pattern draw machine is used for drags only. The mold is jolted and rammed and after compaction, rocked over to the opposite side of the machine with the pattern on top. Drawing of the pattern in this position reduces the danger of damage or fallout of long, thin projections in the sand mold. The jolt squeeze rollover pattern draw machine is similar, but has the additional squeezing feature for compaction and turns the mold by rotation of its table about a horizontal axis through the table center.

Sand *slingers* may be stationary and swing about a fixed point as the molds are conveyed past them for filling. Tractor type slingers can move about the foundry to pick up sand and convey it to the molds as well as fill them. A third type of sand slinger is designed to ride on rails with its fixed path along a line of floor or pit molds.

In most foundries, the work and material handling that goes into core making is small compared to that of producing the molds themselves. In these cases, it is usually more economical to produce cores primarily by manual method. If however, the duplication of cores is very high or the volume of material used in cores is large, costs can often be reduced by using mechanical equipment. Some cores can be made on regular molding machines, but special core making machines designed to jolt, extrude (squeeze) or blow (sling) the sand into place are available.

Material Transport. In very small foundries where space is at a premium, distances are short, and loads are usually light enough that they can be handled by one man, most material movement is by manual operation. Wheelbarrows are used to move sand, castings, and other bulky material. Molds are opened, closed, and shifted by lifting and carrying. Molten metal is delivered from the melting equipment to the molds in ladles supported in ringed shanks which serve as handles for carrying and pouring. However, the huge volume and weight of the materials that must be moved in foundry operation require that for economical operation mechanical aids be used for transporting material in all but the smallest foundries. These aids take on many different forms. Electric or gasoline powered lift trucks, tow trucks, and tractors are commonly used for long distance moving of bulky materials. Hoists and cranes play an important part in most foundries. Fitted with cradle slings, these lifting devices allow molds too heavy to be handled by manual operation, to be opened, rotated, or shifted to various parts of the foundry. Cranes may be necessary to move and position heavy ladles of molten metal in large foundries, but since the majority of foundries are relatively small in size and do not need to handle large volumes of metal at one time, a large part of this work is done with hoists attached by a trolley to a monorail system. Conveyors of various types are also used for moving materials. Sand can be conveniently moved and distributed with belt conveyors and gravity powered roller conveyors may be used to move small molds to a central pouring station and through a cooling cycle after pouring.

Sand Preparation.   When it is considered that an average of four to five tons of sand must be prepared for each ton of castings produced, it can be seen that considerable work energy must be expended to handle and move the sand through its steps of preparation. In the making of small castings, the ratio between sand and metal can be many times higher. The systems used for sand preparation and distribution vary widely. The work can be accomplished entirely by manual effort or entirely by mechanical devices, or some phases may be manual with the rest mechanical. Regardless of how the work is done, the sand must be taken through a series of steps to prepare it suitable for molding purposes. The quality of sand castings is very dependent upon the sand used and the properties that it has. The properties in turn are largely dependent upon the quality and completeness of preparation. Properties such as permeability, strength, and collapsability have large influence on casting quality and can be varied through wide ranges by changes in the sand, clay, water composition proportions and by the treatment during combining or using the mixture.

Sand is normally used over and over again. With each use, water is of course lost and clay or sand particles will be damaged to some extent, with the degree of damage influenced largely by the temperature of the poured metal. Tests are necessary to determine molding sand composition and quality. Water must always be added in preparation and frequent additions of clay and/or sand are necessary for maintenance of essential properties. The mixing of these components can be accomplished manually with a shovel but is more frequently done, even in relatively small foundries, with a powered mixing device know as a *muller*. The muller consists of a tub in which a heavy wheel roller travels about a common central axis to press material tightly against the bottom. Immediately behind the roller are one or more plow blades which lift and displace the material. Repeated squeezing and loosening of the material with the accompanying displacement results, after a period of time, in thorough mixing.

After mixing, aeration and grain separation is necessary to provide a uniform mixture that will compact well but still leave voids to provide the permeability essential for gas escape from the mold. This aeration can be accomplished by tossing the sand with a shovel, but is more satisfactorily performed with an aerator which separates the sand grains with a combing action as projecting fingers on a rotating drum are moved through the sand.

After aeration, sand is ready for use. Sand can be distributed to the molding stations by belt conveyor. The molding and core setting may be done manually on the floor or at a bench, or may be performed with the aid of a molding machine as mentioned previously. After the molds are poured and solidified, castings must be shaken free from the sand.

In small operation, the shakeout may be accomplished manually by picking the castings with attached gates and risers out of the sand with tongs. Loose sand can be freed from the casting by rapping it with a hammer. In mechanized systems, the mold is dumped on a vibrating screen which shakes the sand free, separating the casting. The casting can be picked off the screen and the sand falls through, ready for reclaiming and reuse.

Reclamation of sand involves first the removal of core sand lumps, fine particles of sand, and metallic particles that may have escaped removal during shakeout. If the ratio of core sand to molding sand is small, it may be left combined with the molding sand except for large lumps. Large amounts of core sand, however, need to be removed since they will contaminate the molding sand mixture and change its characteristics appreciably. Exposure to high temperature may cause some of the sand particles to break up and the fines thus produced need to be removed by screening the sand. Screening also removes most of the metal particles that may be included. When working with ferrous materials, it is common practice to pass the sand over a magnetic separator to remove ferrous particles. A magnetic separator consists of a conveyor belt which travels around a magnetized drum allowing the sand to drop free at the end of the

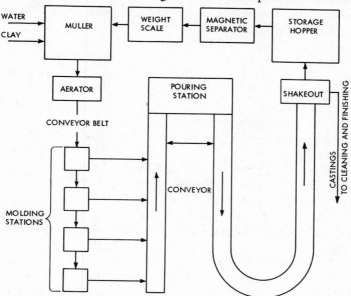

FIG. 9–18. Typical mechanized sand conditioning and distribution system.

belt travel, but carrying magnetic particles back on the returning belt to be released at another point. The sand is then ready for new additions and a new cycle of use. Fig. 9–18 is a schematic diagram showing a typical, mechanized, sand conditioning and distribution system.

QUESTIONS

1. What is the composition of green sand?
2. Why are molding sand compositions usually compromises?
3. List five properties of sand that are important to some degree in any green sand molding application.
4. Permeability is a function of what sand qualities?
5. When is collapsability especially important in sand?
6. List four sand grain types with their principal faults or values.
7. What are Western bentonite and Southern bentonite and what are the major differences between them?
8. Under what conditions, assuming a casting would be satisfactory for function, would some fabricating method other than casting be more economical?
9. What is a matchplate pattern?
10. How do permanent and removable flasks differ in design?
11. By what methods may sand molds be compacted?
12. What are the three most important properties of core sand?
13. How does core sand differ in composition from molding sand?
14. How are cores supported in molds?
15. When is the use of cores essential?
16. Why are castings sometimes made in dry sand molds instead of green sand?
17. Describe shell molding.
18. When is the use of a core sand assembly instead of green sand feasible?
19. What are the principal limitations on the use of metal molds?
20. What are the similarities and differences of permanent mold casting and die casting.
21. Briefly describe the two methods of making die castings.
22. What is the main use for slush casting?
23. To what does the term "investment" refer in investment casting?
24. What is a cupola?
25. Name the three variations of centrifugal casting.
26. Describe the purpose of the components of a cupola charge.
27. What is a crucible furnace?
28. What advantages do electric furnaces exhibit over combustible fuel types?
29. Why are mechanized handling systems especially valuable in foundry operations?
30. Trace molding sand through a cycle of use.

CHAPTER 10

Theory of Plastic Flow

EXTENSIVE USE is made of the property of most metals to undergo considerable amounts of plastic flow. The importance of the manufacturing processes based on plastic flow may be realized by considering some of the products. Of the total annual United States production of one hundred million tons of steel, about 10 per cent is used as castings and the other 90 per cent undergoes deformation of some sort starting in nearly every case with a hot rolling operation. For most products, additional hot rolling or forging operations will involve plastic flow. Over 25 million tons is produced as cold rolled plate or sheet which itself becomes the raw material for press working operations where additional plastic flow produces most of the high production consumer goods such as autos and home appliances. This twenty-five million tons by itself is far more than the total of all nonferrous metals and plastics produced annually.

Numerous factors account for the use of deformation processes. When the quantity is sufficiently high to justify the extensive tooling, many shapes can be more economically produced by deformation processes. One outstanding reason for this is the difficulty of casting very thin sections. Perhaps even more important is the high duplication accuracy of most deformation methods, particularly those in the cold working category on steel.

The properties of wrought materials are in general much improved over their cast counterparts. Rolling, forging, and drawing generally tend to improve both strength and ductility.

The greatest limitation of deformation processes is the need for a ductile stage in the material. Nearly all metals have ductility at some elevated temperature (the major exception being cast iron) and may be at least hot worked. Working at lower temperature is limited to those materials classed as being ductile.

EFFECTS OF DEFORMATION

Work Hardening and Recrystallization. It has been pointed out in Chapter 4 that when loads are applied to a metal that exceed the elastic

175

limit, a permanent change of position is effected and the properties of the material change because of redistribution of dislocations, change of grain size, and other metallurgical effects. In general the most pronounced of these changes is increase of strength and reduction of ductility. When the deformation is accomplished below the recrystallization temperature, these changes of property are permanent and material is said to be *strain hardened, cold worked,* or *work hardened.*

The changes in properties associated with work hardening are due to the strained and unstable position of atoms in the crystalline structure. The changes may be reversed by supplying energy in the form of heat. The atoms, by the process called recrystallization, rearrange themselves into an unstrained condition similar to that which existed before strain hardening. The temperature at which the rearrangement takes place is called the recrystallization temperature and varies with different metals as shown in Table 4–1.

When deformation work is performed above the recrystallization temperature it is termed *hot working* because recrystallization proceeds along with strain hardening. The net result, however, is not different from that which occurs when metal is cold worked, then heated above the recrystallization temperature. Hot working, therefore, permits continuous deformation instead of the cycle of cold working, recrystallization to regain ductility, and more cold working which would be required for large amounts of deformation below the recrystallization temperature.

Effects of Flow Rate.   The changes associated with recrystallization depend on finite movements of atoms within the material, and the formation of new grain boundaries, which take finite amounts of time. The actual time required will depend on the relation between the actual temperature and the recrystallization temperature as well as the rate of straining. However, some critical rate of straining will exist, above which recrystallization cannot proceed fast enough to prevent rupture. If deformation proceeds too rapidly it is possible even above the recrystallization temperature to develop cracks and the closer the working temperature approaches the recrystallization temperature the more likely it is for faults of this type to occur.

A different type of strain rate effect becomes evident at very high (ballistic) speeds where failure can occur with little plastic flow regardless of temperature or the ductility a metal may show in a standard tensile test. However, this type of failure is of little concern to processing except in some new special purpose processes involving high energy rate forming.

Direction Effects.   Any deformation process causes different amounts of plastic flow in different directions. Metals used in manufacture are ordinarily polycrystalline materials with more or less random orientation of the crystals. In single crystals, a considerable difference in properties along different planes usually exists, but in a polycrystalline metal with random orientation of the crystals the differences tend to average out. With plastic deformation, crystal fractures, rotations, and reorientation lead to loss of randomness. As a result the properties become different in different directions.

In products such as drawn wire this directionality is seldom harmful. The best properties, particularly strength, are developed parallel to the direction of drawing where they are most needed in use. In rolled sheet metal, however, the loss of ductility perpendicular to the direction of rolling, but in the plane of the sheet, may cause secondary drawing or bending operations to be difficult or impossible. For some products, the difficulty may be overcome by proper layout of the shape with respect to the direction of rolling as in Fig. 10–1-A. For others, such as Fig. 10–1-B, the part may be orientated 45 degrees with the direction of rolling. Otherwise, the only solution may be recrystallization of the sheet to restore ductility lost not only because of directional effects but because of cold working. The directionality developed by working is never completely eliminated since even recrystallization grains are likely to have preferred orientations.

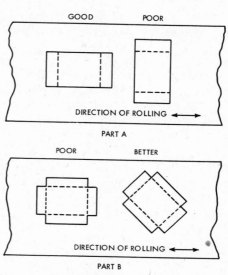

FIG. 10–1. Directional effect of rolling on secondary operations.

A second type of direction effect is illustrated in Fig. 10–2. Metal as normally cast will contain small quantities of foreign inclusions such as scale, oxides, and insoluble compounds and voids or pockets caused by shrinkage and gas evolution during solidification. During working, these defects are elongated in the direction of flow with mechanical property improvement in that direction, generally at the expense of properties perpendicular to the direction of flow. Proper design of the product and the tooling, particular in forging, can take advantage of this directionality which persists even after heat treatment.

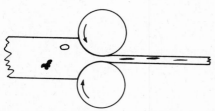

FIG. 10–2. Directional effects from elongation of inclusions and voids.

Temperature and Loading System Effects. A better understanding of the relation between temperature, stress, and plastic flow under different loading systems may be gained by examination of Fig. 10–3 which is based on the following principles and assumptions.

Plastic flow occurs only when some critical shear stress is exceeded in the material. This critical shear stress becomes lower as temperature increases except perhaps at temperatures where recrystallization or crystal transformation take place. Its value also depends on the degree of strain present in the structure, and in the hot working range it depends on the rate of deformation. Strain hardening may be interpreted as an increase in the critical stress required for plastic flow.

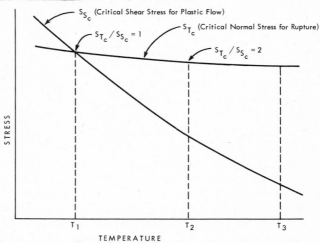

FIG. 10–3. Relation of critical shear and tensile stresses at different temperatures.

Fracture will occur only when some critical tension stress value is exceeded in the material. This critical tension stress appears to be essentially a constant for a given material and temperature. It drops slightly as the temperature is increased but is not affected by strain hardening.

For any given loading system the stresses will increase as the load is increased but within the elastic limit the ratio of maximum tensile stress to maximum shear stress developed will be constant depending on the loading system. The ratios developed in some common loading systems are shown in Table 10–1.

TABLE 10–1

Stress Ratio for Various Loading Systems

Loading System	S_t max./S_s max.
Notched bend	>2
Tension	2
Torsion	1
Most deformation processes	<1

Some prediction of the behavior of a material under different loading systems at different temperatures may now be made from Fig. 10–3. For the material represented by these curves at temperature T_1 under notched bending or simple tension, fracture failure would occur before plastic flow would take place; but in torsion, plastic flow would occur. However, if the temperature were raised to T_2 or higher, plastic flow would take place with either torsion or tension loading. It would be necessary to raise the temperature to T_3 before plastic flow would occur in notched bending.

While the loading system encountered in most deformation processes is quite complicated, the primary loads are usually compressive, and tensile stresses are induced or secondary stresses and are often small compared to the compressive and shear stresses. Consequently much greater percentages of plastic flow may be achieved in an extrusion operation, for example, than can be achieved in a tension test, even below the recrystallization temperature.

Grain Size. For any given metal or alloy the grain size established on solidification will be determined primarily by the cooling rate. The rate will be determined by the mold material, the superheat present in the liquid metal, the specific heat of the metal, the section thickness of the casting, and the ratio of the metal mass to the mold mass. For most products that are to be used as castings, this ratio is small and the castings have relatively thin sections. Consequently, a desirably small grain size is established in most castings. However, when it is intended that metal be subjected to some deformation process it is still necessary to first cast the metal into an ingot and the most desirable forms for ingots are usually quite large with a heavy cross section and a large mass. Therefore, the cooling rate for ingots is quite slow compared to most other castings and the grain size developed in ingots is very large. For best strength and hardness properties for most uses it is desirable that the grain size be small.

Any working operation, either hot or cold, results in crystal fractures, rotations, and realignments that produce a smaller grain size as the material is strain hardened. The actual effect that these grain size changes have on properties is hard to evaluate, however, since the major property changes are due to the strain hardening. However, if following the strain hardening, recrystallization takes place, either because of subsequent heat treatment if the material was cold worked or proceeding almost simultaneously with the strain hardening in hot working, the grain size immediately after recrystallization will always be small. Unfortunately the small grain size established by recrystallization is not completely fixed and a metal that is held at too high a temperature or for too long a time following recrystallization will undergo the phenomenon of *grain growth* during which the grains will combine and grow to larger size again. Given sufficient freedom (time at elevated temperature) crystals tend to grow to a critical stable size which is dependent mainly on their constituents. Fig. 10–4 shows the relations that may exist between grain size, working conditions, and temperature during deformation processes. The slopes of the various lines are only qualitative and may vary depending upon particular alloys, rates of working, and temperatures, and the grain size of the final product will depend on the place where processes stop.

The phenomena illustrated by this figure are of extreme importance because for the majority of nonferrous metals these are the only methods for grain size control. For example, if improper heat treatment during recrystallization following cold work has permitted excessive grain growth, further cold work would be necessary before grain refinement could be accomplished and this would not be possible if the final shape had been established. To sum up, grain refinement for metals that exist in only one crystalline form can be accomplished only by hot working, cold

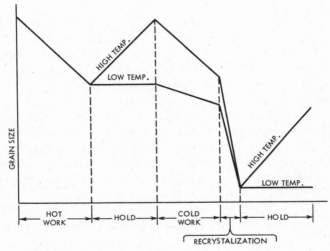

FIG. 10–4. Grain size during deformation processing.

working, and recrystallization following strain hardening, and grain growth will occur any time metals are held at excessive temperatures for sufficient time.

For most ferrous alloys, the grain size changes, not only during working and recrystallization as shown in Fig. 10–4, but, also, as was mentioned in Chapter 4, at any time ferrous metals are heated through the transformation range. Fig. 10–5 shows the nature of these additional changes. For any initial grain size of body centered cubic iron (below the transformation temperature) the face centered crystals that form after transformation will always be smaller. However, the size of the face centered crystals will increase if the metal is held above the transformation temperature, the amount of growth depending on the temperature and time. Whatever grain size is established in the face centered crystals will be preserved when the transformation is made back to body centered cubic iron. This means that the grain size of a steel casting may be refined by heat treatment alone or that the grain size of a hot worked product that is held at excessively high temperature following working may be refined by heat treatment. Note, however, that this refinement requires that the metal be initially below the transformation temperature, and also that strain hardening is not a requirement. In general, for ferrous metals refinement by transformation is much more effective than working or recrystallization.

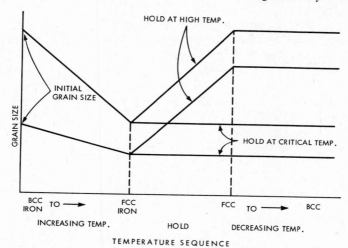

FIG. 10–5. Grain size change with crystal transformation in ferrous metals.

RELATIVE EFFECTS OF HOT AND COLD WORKING

Mechanical Properties. Material that has been hot worked will generally exhibit maximum ductility and minimum hardness and strength for a particular composition, with the possible exceptions of directional effects caused by grain orientation and fibering and effects that cooling from the high temperature may have on the structure of the material. Any effects of strain hardening will have been continuously relieved by recrystallization at the hot working temperature.

Steel is ordinarily hot worked above the transformation temperature where the structure is austenitic and the carbon is in solution. Cooling is generally in air and the effect this cooling rate will have on the structure will depend on the hardenability of the particular steel. For plain carbon or low alloy steels having low hardenability, a normalized structure will be coarse or medium pearlite with properties similar to those obtained from annealing. For higher alloy steels, particularly tool steels, air cooling will result in finer pearlite or even harder structures.

Materials that are hot worked start as ingots having relatively large cross sections. As a casting, this shape and size results in pronounced casting defects such as ingot type segregation (composition differences within crystals), voids (dendritic microporosity and macroporosity from gas evolution), shrinkage cavities, and inclusion of metallic oxides, slag and other foreign matter. Some of these faults are removed by *cropping* the ingot. Cropping involves the removal and discarding of up to one third of the top of the ingot where the largest shrinkage occurs. However, many of the faults still exist in the main body of the ingot but during hot working have their effects minimized by the closing and welding of voids and the elongation of inclusions.

Cold working is used primarily as a finishing process and usually follows hot working which has been used to accomplish the major portion of deformation. The ductility and strength properties of the finished

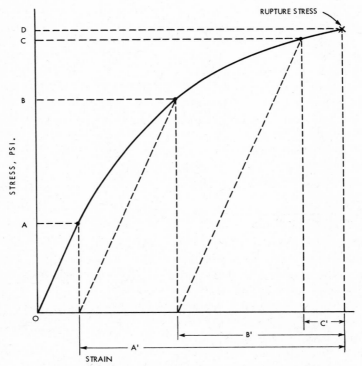

FIG. 10–6.   Effect of cold work on elastic limit and ductility.

product can be controlled to a rather wide degree by the amount of cold working that is performed in the final stage. Fig. 10–6 is a true stress–true strain diagram showing that different combinations of properties are possible in cold worked material. In the annealed or recrystallized state (following hot working) the material has an elastic limit of A psi, ductility of A′, and the breaking strength of D psi. Actually the tension test from which the diagram is made involves cold working and if the test were stopped at point B the material now has a new set of properties with elastic limit of B but with ductility reduced to B′. The breaking strength would remain at D. Further cold working as at C could produce a higher elastic limit up to the breaking strength, but in each case with a reduction of ductility.

With any degree of cold working the material could be restored to the original conditions of elastic limit and ductility by recrystallization and could then be subjected again to cold deformation. The final strength and ductility will therefore depend on the amount of cold working done after hot working or after the last recrystallization treatment.

The application of these principles in practice may be understood by considering the manufacture of cold finished steel sheet. Nearly all such steel is first hot rolled to a thickness of about ⅛ inch. If cold finished to ¹⁄₁₆ thickness by repeated rolling passes with no intermediate heat treatment, the resulting sheet would have high hardness and strength with minimum ductility and be suitable only for products that could be finished with little or no further deformation operations. If an intermediate anneal were followed by only a few cold rolling passes the resulting product would have intermediate hardness, strength, and ductility and be suitable for a limited amount of further cold working operations such as shallow drawing or bending with large radii. If, following the reduction to final thickness, the sheet were annealed, it would have minimum hardness and strength but maximum ductility and would be suitable for deep drawing or other further operations involving large amounts of deformation. Any of these further deformation operations would add to the strength and hardness and reduce the ductility.

Where the products of deformation operations are to be further processed by machining, cold finishing is generally desirable even though the hardness and strength are not needed functionally in the product. The over-all machinability of most metals is improved with reduced ductility because of improved finishability. For this reason, much of the bar material to be finished by machining is cold rolled or cold drawn. The compressive stresses left on and near the surface of most cold worked material are of some benefit where the material is subjected to fatigue conditions in service. Fatigue failures generally start at areas of high tensile stresses on the surface of parts and the residual surface compressive stress reduces the actual value of surface tensile stress due to applied loads.

Finish and Accuracy. Limitations exist as to the surface finish and accuracy that may be obtained by hot working. Most metals are subject to rapid oxidation at their hot working temperatures which are often well above room temperature. In addition to chemical damage, oxide formation is frequently nonuniform and scale may spall off, exposing new metal to oxygen contact. The surface finish and dimensional accuracy obtainable are largely determined by the rate of oxidation and the tendency for spalling. For aluminum and many other nonferrous alloys, the hot working temperatures are low enough that oxidation is not serious and good finishes and close accuracies may be held. For steels, hot working temperatures are generally 1800° to 2400°F. where oxidation is rapid. With the scale that forms at these temperatures, it is not possible to obtain good finishes or close dimensions. Tolerances are generally $\frac{1}{64}$ or greater on hot worked steel products. However, cold working of steel can produce finishes limited only by the rollers or dies used in the process and tolerances of .001 inch are possible.

Steel in particular, because of its high working temperature, is subjected to selective oxidation. The carbon burns at a higher rate than the iron to leave a decarburized shell. Subsequent heat treatment which depends on carbon content does not produce the desired results on the surface and hot worked steel that is to be hardened by heat treatment needs to have sufficient material removed from the surface to get below the decarburized layer. High carbon hot rolled steels are usually at least $\frac{1}{16}$ inch oversize in the raw stock stage.

Process Requirements.   In addition to the maintenance of ductility by continuous recrystallization, one of the principal benefits of hot working is that metals are weaker at high temperatures and can be deformed with lower loads and less work. The lower loads result in lighter and more versatile equipment than would be required for equivalent deformation performed cold. However, a number of disadvantages are connected with hot working in addition to those already mentioned.

Most cold working is performed at room temperature where normal variations are unimportant and no specific temperature control is necessary. The increased conduction and radiation rates at elevated temperatures cause control to be much more difficult. In some continuous working processes involving large amounts of deformation, the energy added by the process affects the temperature and the maintenance of correct temperatures depends on the proper rate of working.

The dies, tools, and other equipment that come into contact with heated materials must be able to maintain adequate hardness and strength. Hot working tools, therefore, must frequently be made of heat resisting alloys or be water cooled for satisfactory life.

Another disadvantage of hot working processes is that operating personnel are often subjected to high temperatures which may be hazardous or, at least, uncomfortable.

QUESTIONS

1. What factors account for the use of deformation processing?
2. Distinguish between hot working and cold working.
3. What influence has the rate of working on the temperature necessary for practical hot working?
4. For the solution shown in Fig. 10–1–B what conclusion can be made about the success of the bending operation to be performed?
5. How is it possible to obtain great amounts of plastic flow without rupture as temperature is increased, even below the recrystallization temperature?

6. Why are greater amounts of plastic flow possible in most deformation processes than in tension tests made at the same temperature?

7. Why is the grain size in an ingot larger than that in most other castings?

8. Why is the control of grain size during deformation processes of greater importance for aluminum than for steel?

9. How will alloy content affect the structure of steel after hot working and normal cooling?

10. What is the purpose of cropping an ingot?

11. How is the final hardness of a cold worked product controlled?

12. How does cold working improve the machinability of most metals?

13. Why may better finishes and greater accuracy be obtained when hot working aluminum than when hot working steel?

CHAPTER 11

Millwork and Forging

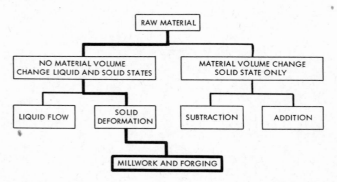

ALTHOUGH some of the softer metals that can be found in a relatively ductile condition in nature, such as copper, lead, gold, and silver have been wrought by hammering methods since the early days of history, most of the shaping of metal articles in the early days of manufacturing was performed by casting processes. As indicated in earlier chapters, casting is still an important shaping process and is frequently the cheapest and most satisfactory method for producing a useful shape from some materials. Some limitations exist, however, that discourage universal use of cast metal products. Picture, for instance, the problems associated with casting thin sheets of large area in any kind of material. Even with thicknesses of an inch or more, the problems of obtaining uniform thickness and properties over large areas are enormous. Unfortunately, many of the materials that have the best castability have other properties that are unsatisfactory for many applications. Porosity and associated problems reduce the strength. Increased brittleness, leakiness, and poor appearance are faults commonly associated with cast materials. With many metals, the internal structure to provide the best properties can be developed only by deforming the material in the solid state, usually by a process involving cold working. The deformation processes, cold or hot, can often be used to provide the double benefits of property improvement and shape changing at the same time.

Even with higher costs, the value of improved properties is so great that approximately 80 per cent of the iron-base metals are finish processed as wrought material. Although nearly all metals are and can be cast in the making of some products, a situation similar to that for iron base metals exists for aluminum-base, copper-base, and other metallic materials and large percentages of each are deformation worked for improvement of their shapes, dimensions, and properties.

The nature of manufacturing enterprises in this country has led to the development of two general types of deformation processing. Hot rolling, extrusion, and pipe and tube making operations all require large, heavy equipment requiring very large investments. Consequently, few individual users of the products of these operations can justify equipment of this type which would be used only a small percentage of the time. These operations are usually done by the same companies that process the ores and frequently at the same site, called a *mill*, and the operations themselves are considered *millwork*.

The actual production of the mill falls into several categories. Some shapes, particularly rails, structural steel, and pipe are essentially finished at the mill, even though the specific design that will incorporate these products is not known.

Most of the output of the mill is in shapes that become raw material for further processing in smaller quantities at some specific user's plant. Typical products of this class include foil for packaging operations, cold rolled sheet for pressworking operations, bar stock for machined parts, and rough rolled billets for forging operations.

The second group of deformation operations are those that are product oriented and are usually performed on a smaller scale in plants fabricating finished products. For practically all of these operations the raw material is bar or sheet stock that is produced in large quantities as a mill operation. For example, the most convenient raw material for a drop forging operation might be a six inch length of two inch square hot rolled steel. This would be cut from a long length of two inch square hot rolled bar. The same two inch square hot rolled bar might be the most convenient size for other fabricators of forgings, for parts that are to be machined by some fabricator, or for welded assemblies produced by another fabricator.

These smaller fabricators are much greater in number than producers of mill products. The equipment for the secondary operations is lighter, the first cost of the equipment is generally less, and the total tonnage of metals used by any individual fabricator is small compared to the output of a mill.

MILLWORK

Rolling. Most steel millwork is performed as part of large integrated operations which involve ore reduction in blast furnaces, coke making for blast furnace operation, open hearth furnace and bessemer converter operation for carbon reduction, blooming and slabbing mills where preliminary rolling operations are performed, and finish rolling operations, at least so far as the mill is concerned, where the final product shape is made. There is some degree of specialization in mills with some concentrating on sheet stock, some on bar and rod stock, and others on tube and pipe, but they are all large plants of several acres in size and with many millions of dollars invested in equipment. The location of the plants is generally a compromise since iron ore, coal for coke, labor, and markets do not exist together at any single location.

Because of the greater quantities of ore that must be handled and the greater power requirements for some reduction processes, such a large

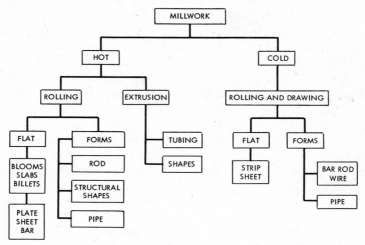

FIG. 11–1. Processes and product types of primary mills.

degree of integration does not always exist in the production of basic nonferrous shapes. The ore reduction will frequently be done at the site of the ore and the metal cast into pigs or ingots which are shipped to the mill where the deformation operations are performed.

The chart of Fig. 11–1 is typical of steel mills and also applies to most nonferrous mills, although emphasis on the operations will vary for different metals. One of the most common mill operations is the rolling of metal into flat and two dimensionally formed shapes. This is accomplished by passing the material between flat or shaped rollers to set up forces that squeeze the material causing it to flow to an elongated form while the cross sectional dimensions are being reduced. For those materials that have little ductility and for large changes of section in any material, the work is usually done hot to reduce the energy requirements and to permit ductility recovery by recrystallization as deformation occurs.

Most materials start as cast ingots following reduction of the ore or in

the case of steel, following carbon reduction, which are rolled initially into
blooms, slabs, or billets. Blooms and billets are approximately square cross
sections of large and small size respectively and slabs are rectangular
shapes. All are destined for further deformation work by rolling, forging,
or extrusion, usually at the same mill but sometimes at an individual
fabricator's plant.

Mill rolling is done by passing the material through rolling stands where
rollers arranged as shown in Fig. 11–2 apply pressure to reduce the section
thickness and elongate the metal. The major portion of stress is compressive and is in such direction that the effect on width dimensions is minor
compared to the others.

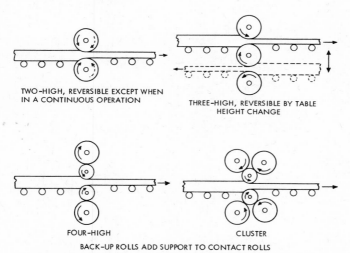

FIG. 11–2. Various arrangements of rolls in rolling stands.

At the blooming mill where the first deformation work is done on the
material, the cast ingot is rolled back and forth between rolls or continuously through sets of stands as the rolls are brought closer together to
control the rate of reduction and establish new dimensions. Mechanical
manipulators are used to turn the block or additional vertical rolls are used
for making an approximately square cross section bloom or rectangular
slab which may be as much as sixty or seventy feet long. Up to one third
of the bloom may be *cropped* (cut away) to eliminate a major portion of
the impurities, shrink, and poor quality metal originating in the ingot.
Near surface defects caused by ingot or rolling faults are removed during
or following primary rolling by chipping, grinding, or *scarfing* (oxygen
torch burning). These long blooms are then sheared to lengths convenient
to handle and suitable for the anticipated final material form.

Blooms are frequently reduced to billet size, maximum cross section of
thirty-six square inches, in a similar stand with reversing features, although
some installations have been set up with a number of rolling stands in

sequence so that billets can be formed by continuous passage through the series.

Some demand exists for small quantities of wrought materials in large shapes not adaptable to rolling. These may be of variable section size, for example a large steam turbine shaft, unusual shapes, or sizes not ordinarily produced by the rolling mill. In these cases the ingot may be worked to the desired shape by a forging operation, usually between flat faced hammers.

Following the primary reduction operations in the blooming or slabbing mill the sections are usually further rolled in some secondary operation, still at the mill. Plate, sheet, and rod shapes are in sufficient demand that many mills produce them in continuous mills where the material

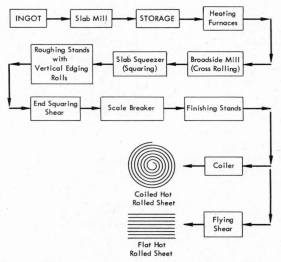

FIG. 11–3. Schematic diagram of a hot strip rolling mill.

proceeds directly from one rolling stand to the next, with progressive reduction and shaping of the cross section and simultaneous elongation along the direction of rolling. Continuous sheet rolling alone accounts for approximately one third of the annual production of steel in the United States. Fig. 11–3 is a schematic diagram of a typical hot strip rolling mill. The illustration has been simplified by omitting many components. Scale breaking rolls are followed by high pressure water or steam sprays for removal of scale. Both the roughing and finishing operations are done in continuous mills consisting of a number of stands in sequence. Some hot rolled strip is used directly as it comes from the hot rolling mill for the making of finished goods such as railway cars, pressure vessels, and boats. Most of the flat hot rolled steel is further processed by cold rolling.

Of the hot rolled products, structural shapes, bars, and rails make up the greatest tonnages that are used as rolled at the mill. Even so, because of the great variety of sizes and shapes, rolling is primarily a job shop operation with insufficient demand for any particular size and shape to permit continuous rolling of the type used for sheet and plate. For the more commonly used shapes such as rectangular bars, angles, and channels, particularly in small sizes, a *merchant* mill is frequently used. This mill consists of many small stands that are left more or less permanently set up with means for guiding the stock to the proper stands for the particular shape to be rolled. Merchant mills have many designs, most of them incorporating at least some continuous rolling stands, but characteristic of all of them is great flexibility which permits quick changeover from one shape and size to another.

For larger shapes, where the demand for any one is even smaller, the investment in the large rolling stands required is too great to permit them to sit idle much of the time as they may in a merchant mill, and the rolls are changed between one product and the next. To reduce the number of stands used and the number of rolls that must be changed, multiple groove rolls, usually in a three high arrangement are most frequently used. Fig. 11–4 shows the shape changes in each of the ten passes required to convert a square billet to a rail.

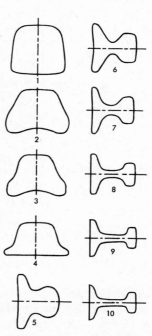

As pointed out in the last chapter, the mechanical properties of hot worked material are affected by the heat to which it is subjected. Working at high temperature permits maximum deformation, but for those materials for which the working temperature is above the oxidation temperature for some of the constituents, burning and scale result, and adverse effects on finish occur. Before use as a product in the hot rolled state, or before cold finishing operations are performed, surface cleaning is required. Cleaning is often done by immersing

FIG. 11–4. Successive shapes in rolling a rail from a billet.

the material in acid baths (pickling) which attack the scale at higher rates than the base metal.

Because of differences in working temperatures affecting shrinkage, difference in oxidation depths, and more rapid wear on the rolls, dimensions are more difficult to hold in hot rolling processes than when finishing is done cold. Tolerance, depend to some extent on the shape and the material. For hot rolled round bars of low carbon steel, they range from plus or minus .005 inch for material up to $\frac{5}{16}$ inch diameter to plus or minus $\frac{1}{16}$ inch for bars six inches in diameter.

Cold Finishing. While most steel is shipped from the mill in the hot rolled condition, much of the material is cold finished by additional rolling in the cold state, or by drawing through dies. The forces set up by either procedure are similar and result in reduction of cross sectional area. Materials that are treated this way must have sufficient ductility to start with but that ductility is reduced as the hardness, yield strength, and tensile strength are increased as the deformation progresses. These relationships are shown in Fig. 11–5. It can be noted that the major effects occur during the first 10 per cent reduction of area. In practice, areas are reduced as much as a total of 90 per cent but this must be done in several steps. Even greater reductions can be achieved but only in relatively small steps. In the manufacture of some wire this may be an economical procedure but for most products, where large reductions are required, interme-

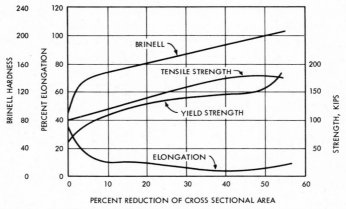

FIG. 11–5. Effect of cold work on properties of 0.12 carbon steel.

diate recrystallization for recovery of ductility permits the reduction in a small total number of passes. The amount of cold reduction following hot working or following the last recrystallization provides a means for controlling the mechanical properties of the finished material.

In all cases, hot rolled material must be well cleaned before being cold worked. Cold working processes themselves do not contribute oxidation or scaling but any foreign material present on the surface will remain during cold working. Along with improved surface finish, dimensional accuracy of cold worked material is better than that of hot worked material of equivalent sizes and shapes, and in many cases approaches that of machined surfaces.

The flat products of a steel mill are called *strip, sheet, plate,* or *bar* depending on the relative widths and thicknesses, and most are cold finished by rolling. For this work the rolling stands are of the four high type illustrated in Fig. 11–6 or the cluster type which performs the same function of permitting small diameter work rolls to be in contact with the material. Fig. 11–7 shows typical arrangements of stands for cold rolling strip or sheet. The tandem mill, with a higher initial investment, is a higher production method but has less flexibility than the single stand reversing mill. Power for reduction may be supplied by the reels alone, by the rolls alone, or by driving both the reels and the rolls. Sheet is normally kept in tension as it passes through the stands.

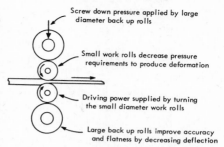

FIG. 11–6. Arrangement of conventional four-high rolling stand.

Bar material can be in the form of square, rectangular, round, hexagonal, and other shapes. In the rolling of strip and sheet, the edges are not confined and the final width of the sheet may vary. Subsequent to shipping from the mill the material is normally trimmed to correct width by rotary

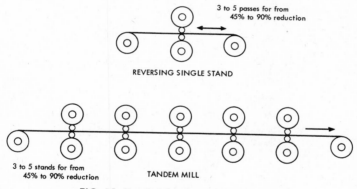

FIG. 11–7. Cold reduction methods.

shears. Most bar shapes are not adaptable to close dimensional control in cold rolling and are therefore finished by drawing through hardened dies as shown in Fig. 11–8. The operation is performed in a machine called a drawbench, shown in Fig. 11–9. The end of the oversized hot rolled bar is first pointed by swaging or forging, then inserted through the die and gripped in the draw head. Connection of the draw head hook to a moving chain provides the power to draw the material through the die. Reductions generally range from $\frac{1}{64}$ inch to $\frac{1}{8}$ inch. Round stock may also be cold finished by rolling between skewed rollers in a process called *turning* or centerless ground for highest accuracy.

While no clear distinction exists between products that are called wire and those that are called bar, in practice, wire is made in long lengths and coiled, whereas rod is drawn straight on a drawbench in relatively short lengths and kept straight. The two types of products overlap some in size.

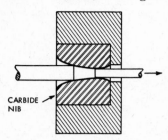

FIG. 11–8. Cross section of a drawing die for bar or wire.

CARBIDE NIB

The principal differences in the production of the two classes of products occur in the means for handling the material and in supplying the force for drawing through the die.

For the production of wire, either steel or copper, billets are first hot rolled down to a minimum size of $\frac{7}{32}$ inch diameter. After cleaning and surface coating for protection and lubrication if necessary, the rod is cold drawn to final size. Coarser sizes of wire are generally drawn on a *frame* type machine where the end of the rod is pointed, started through the die, then reeled on a block. If more than one draw or *draft* is required, the wire is drawn through one or more additional dies with reeling after each draw.

Smaller sizes are usually drawn on continuous machines in which the wire is drawn through multiple dies simultaneously, with draw blocks between dies releasing the wire from one end at the same time it is being coiled on the other. Drawing speeds range up to 1500 fpm.

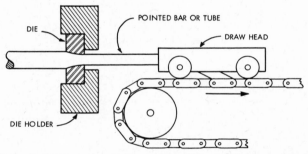

DIE

POINTED BAR OR TUBE

DRAW HEAD

DIE HOLDER

FIG. 11–9. Drawbench for cold reduction of bar or tubing.

As the cross section of the wire is reduced, strain hardening takes place and, depending on the total reduction necessary and the final hardness desired in the finished product, intermediate recrystallization or annealing may be required. For 34 gage wire (.010 inch), one or two anneals are necessary and for finer diameters three are usually needed. As with any cold finished product, the final hardness will depend on the amount of cold work done after the last recrystallization treatment. Copper wire for electrical conductors is nearly always annealed as a last operation to provide the maximum conductivity. At the other end of the scale, fine high carbon steel wire in a hard drawn condition may have a tensile strength as high as 500,000 psi, which is as great as may be achieved in any steel product by heat treat hardening.

Round wire sizes are generally designated by a gage number, but unfortunately no universal gaging system is used and similar wires used for different purposes have sizes designated by different systems. The size of music wire is designated in numbers of the Music Wire Gage (MWG), iron and steel telephone wire in Birmingham Wire Gage (BWG), copper and aluminum wire for electrical use in the Brown and Sharpe or American Wire Gage systems (BSG or AWG), and most other wire in the Steel Wire Gage (STLWG).

Although most wire is round, other shapes such as half round, oval, triangular, keystone, square, and rectangular may be produced, either by drawing through dies or, in the case of most square and rectangular wire, by a special rolling method. The sizes of these shapes are usually specified by actual measurements of the principal or characteristic dimensions.

Tube and Pipe Making.   The terms *pipe* and *tube* have no strict distinctions, but in most common use, the term pipe refers to a hollow product used to conduct fluids. Except for some relatively thin wall welded products, tubing is generally seamless. Whether pipe or tubing, most such products are produced in mills, frequently along with sheet,

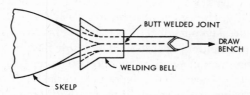

FIG. 11–10. Shaping and welding of pipe in a welding bell.

strip, and bar products. The manufacture of tubular products involves both hot and cold working, in the same order as for other mill products, with hot working being used in the rough forming stages and cold working for finishing and sizing operations. Most pipe made by welding processes is steel. Some steel and nearly all nonferrous tubular products are made by seamless processes.

One of the oldest but still much used processes for making steel pipe consists of drawing heated, bevel edged *skelp* in lengths of twenty to forty feet through a welding bell such as pictured in Fig. 11–10. The skelp is gripped by tongs and drawn through the bell where it is formed to tubular shape and the edges pressed together to form a butt welded joint. Power is supplied by a draw bench as in drawing bar stock.

Fig. 11–11 illustrates the method used for butt welding pipe in continuous manner. Skelp from a reel passes through a furnace and is drawn through forming rolls where it is shaped. Welding rolls then apply pressure to establish the butt welded joint. Following the welding station, rollers squeeze the pipe to smaller size after which it is cut to length by a flying saw. Both types of butt welded pipe may require some cold finishing operations such as sizing between rollers and straightening by stretching or cross rolling before being cut to exact length and finished by facing

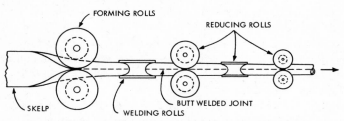

FIG. 11–11. Continuous process of butt welding pipe.

or threading operations. Pipe is produced by pressure butt welding, either short lengths or continuously, in sizes up to four inches nominal diameter.

Light gage steel tubing in sizes up to 16 inches in diameter may be produced by resistance welding of stock that has been formed cold by rolls that progressively shape the material from flat strip to tubular form. The general arrangement is shown in Fig. 11–12. After forming, the tube passes between electrodes through which welding current is supplied and pressure rolls that maintain pressure in the weld area. Since the material is heated only locally, the pressure produces flash on both the inside and outside of the tube. The outside flash is removed by a form cutter immediately following the welding operation. The inside flash may be reduced by a rolling or forging action against a mandrel, depending on size. Since this process uses rolls of strip stock as raw material and is best operated continuously, a flying saw is required to cut the tubing to correct length. Resistance butt welding may be done in a mill, but because of the relatively light equipment needed, frequently is performed as a secondary operation in a fabricator's plant.

For large sizes which are impractical for some methods (about six inches to unlimited upper limit) and which are needed in relatively small quantities, pipe may be manufactured by forming of plate or sheet and welding by any of the fusion processes. In practice, the *submerged arc* method which will be discussed in a later chapter is often the most economical welding procedure. After the edges of the plate have been properly prepared by shearing or machining, the steps shown in Fig. 11–13 are followed in forming the pipe.

A relatively small quantity of larger pipe from about one and one-

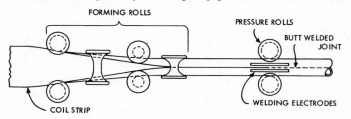

FIG. 11–12. Resistance welding of tubing.

half to thirty inches diameter is lap welded. For this process the skelp is beveled on the edges as it emerges from the furnace. It is then formed to cylindrical shape with overlapping edges. While at elevated temperature for welding, the tube is passed between a pressure roller and mandrel for the establishment of welding pressure.

The making of light gage pipe or tubing as pictured in Fig. 11–14 can be accomplished by resistance welding of a continuous spiral butt or lap joint. A principal advantage of the process is the light equipment required and the flexibility in changing from one size or one material to another. Any material which can be welded can be fabricated into pipe by this method.

It is possible to produce welded tabular products that effectively are "seamless." The weld area can have the same properties as the rest of the pipe or tube and may in fact be undetectable after welding. However, this degree of perfection might require heat treatment after welding and additional deformation or machining to produce uniform thickness. In addition, it would be very difficult to produce perfect welds in higher alloy steels, especially in heavy sections. In practice, the term *seamless tubing* refers to a tubular product that is made without welding. The most common method

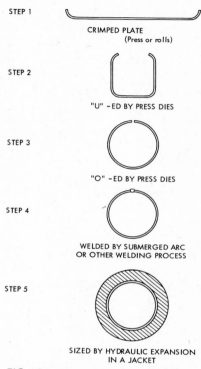

STEP 1

CRIMPED PLATE
(Press or rolls)

STEP 2

"U"–ED BY PRESS DIES

STEP 3

"O"–ED BY PRESS DIES

STEP 4

WELDED BY SUBMERGED ARC
OR OTHER WELDING PROCESS

STEP 5

SIZED BY HYDRAULIC EXPANSION
IN A JACKET

FIG. 11–13.   Electric welding of large pipe.

used for steel involves *piercing* of round billets of relatively large cross section and short length, with subsequent deformation operations to control the final diameter, wall thickness, and length.

Fig. 11–15 shows the most common type of piercing mill used. The skew rollers both flatten and advance the billet with a helical motion. High shear stresses are developed at the center of the billet, at which point the material is forced over a bullet shaped mandrel.

Subsequent operations include *reeling* and *rotary rolling* which are similar to piercing and permit the inside diameter to be further enlarged with a reduction of wall thickness. Rolling between grooved rollers reduces both the outside and inside diameter with elongation along the axis of the tube. Much seamless tubing is finished cold by rolling or drawing through dies with the advantages of improved tolerances, surface finish, and mechanical properties. Squares, ovals, and other noncircular shapes may be produced by drawing through special dies and over special mandrels.

Seamless steel tubing is manufactured from nearly all the common grades of steel including plain carbon up to 1.5 per cent, AISI alloy steels, and stainless steels of most types. In addition to use strictly for fluid conduction, seamless tubing is also much used as a raw material for many machine parts such as antifriction bearing races where considerable material and machine time savings may be made.

In *cupping* operations seamless tubing is produced by a press type operation similar to shell drawing which will be discussed later. A heated circular disc is forced through a die by a punch to form a closed bottom cylinder. The cylinder may be further processed into a pressure container or the bottom may be cut off and the tube processed into standard tube types.

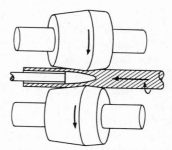

FIG. 11–14. Spiral weld pipe.

FIG. 11–15 Roll piercing of round bar material.

Extrusion. Fig. 11–16 shows various extrusion methods. Indirect extrusion requires lower loads but complicates handling of the extruded shape. Tubing may be extruded by direct or indirect methods with mandrels as shown. Lead sheathed electrical cable is produced by extruding the lead around the cable as it passes through the die.

The high degree of deformation required for extrusion leads to a number of limitations. Most metals are ductile enough for extensive extrusion only at high temperatures and even then the loads are very high requiring large heavy equipment and large amounts of power. Die materials must be able to withstand the high loads and temperatures without excessive wear. This presents a particularly serious problem with steel which must be heated to about 2300°F. to have sufficient ductility for extrusion.

Steel may be extruded with glass as a lubricant, but die life is short; the process is used for steel primarily for sections produced in low quantity where the cost of special rolls could not be justified, and for some high alloy steels that are difficult to forge or roll.

The extrusion process is used primarily for forming shapes of aluminum, copper, lead alloys, and plastics. In fact, except for flat stock which may be more economically rolled, extrusion is the principal process used for producing parts having uniform cross sections from these materials. Many metals may be extruded at room temperature. For lead, tin, and zinc this actually means hot working since the recrystallization temperatures are at or below room temperature and some heating of the metal occurs because of deformation work energy being converted to

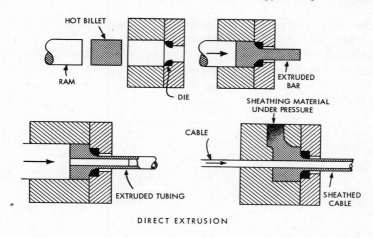

DIRECT EXTRUSION

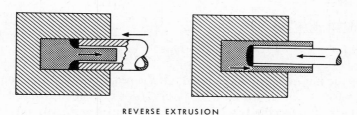

REVERSE EXTRUSION

FIG. 11–16. Common methods of extrusion.

heat. For aluminum, copper, and steel, cold extrusion is possible for some shapes, especially in smaller sizes and where the ratio of length to cross sectional area of the finished extrusion does not exceed about 10 to 1 for aluminum and 3 to 1 for steel. Typical cold extruded products include toothpaste tubes, dry-cell battery cases, and shell cases.

Theoretically extruded parts have no size restrictions. In practice the size of the equipment limits the size of the extrusion that can be produced. Dimensional tolerances depend on the material involved, the temperature, and the size of the extrusion. In hot extrusion, the die tends to expand as the material passes through, resulting in a taper to the extruded part. The principal error is in straightness and most extrusions require straightening.

This is accomplished automatically when the extrusion is cold finished by die drawing.

The principal shape limitations are concerned with maintaining uniform cross sectional thicknesses. Otherwise the extrusion process is quite flexible with odd and hollow shapes possible that would be impossible or not economical to roll.

FORGING AND ALLIED OPERATIONS

With the exception of some tube making operations and some cold finish rolling and extrusion, especially on ferrous metals, the operations so far described are all performed almost exclusively in large mills where the products usually represent only an intermediate stage of manufacture with

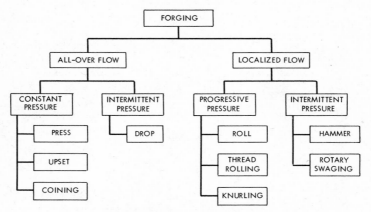

FIG. 11–17. Types of forging.

no specific finished product in mind. Of the remaining deformation operations, most of which are fabrication operations designed to produce specific shapes for specific products, those performed primarily on flat sheet metal will be discussed in a separate chapter.

As opposed to mill operations where the primary shape control is over the uniform cross sectional shape of a product, and press operations on sheet metal where the thickness of the metal is not directly controlled by the operation, *forging* operations exhibit three dimensional control of the shape. For most of these operations, the final shape of the product is forged and further finishing operations are necessary only because of accuracy limitations of the process. Fig. 11–17 shows the types of forging that are used.

The purpose of forging is to confine the metal under sufficient pressure to cause plastic flow. In *open die forging* the metal is alternately confined in different directions with the final result that three dimensional control is gained. With *closed impression dies* the work material is fully confined at least at the completion of the operation in a manner similar to casting except for the state of the material. As in metal mold casting, draft angles are required and there are similar shape restrictions based on removing the part from the die.

The load requirements for forging have led to several means for applying the pressure. In those forging methods where the metal is worked throughout at the same time, the flow can be produced by constant squeezing pressure or by impact. Because of the large amounts of work energy required and the need to exceed the yield strength throughout the material at the same time, these operations are frequently done hot and even then the equipment is massive compared to the size of the workpiece, particularly when constant pressure is supplied. For localized flow the yield strength must generally be exceeded only on small areas at a time, either because of the progressive nature of some rolling type operations or by reorientating the workpiece periodically to present new areas to be loaded, as in hammer forging or rotary swaging.

Open Die Forging.   When the quantity of parts to be manufactured is small and the cost of tooling must be kept low, *blacksmith* or *hammer* forging may be used to alter the shape of the material. One of the simplest examples is the manufacture of a horseshoe from bar stock by using a hammer and anvil with manual power and manipulation. While the village

blacksmith is no longer so prevalent, this method still finds wide use industrially for the manufacture of special tools and low quantity products, often of an experimental nature. Accuracy and shape of the product are greatly dependent on the operator's skill. Because of the close association with the human element, duplication accuracy is limited and large quantities can seldom be economically produced.

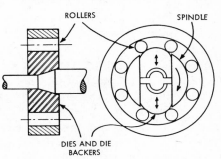

FIG. 11–18.   Rotary swaging.

The manual operation of blacksmith forging can therefore be used only for relatively light work and is almost always performed hot.

Hammer forging is an extension of blacksmith forging for larger workpieces in which power is supplied by pneumatic, hydraulic, or mechanical hammers. The operator is still responsible for positioning the work under the hammer but may lay special tools over the hammer faces for producing some shapes. For very heavy workpieces, mechanical supports and handling devices are frequently used as aids.

A rotary swaging machine as shown in Fig. 11–18 is constructed like a straight roller bearing with the inner race replaced by a powered spindle carrying shaped dies in slots. As the spindle rotates, the backs of the dies are forced inward as they pass each roller. Machines of this type are used most frequently for reducing the ends of bar, tube, or wire stock so it may be started through a die for a drawing operation. Rotary forging may be done either hot or cold, in many cases the choice being determined by the requirements of the drawing operation that follows it. In addition to pointing of stock for drawing purposes, the process is used for closing or necking of cylinders and for the over-all reduction of tubular products.

Closed Die Forging. Most forging was done with flat faced hammers until just prior to the Civil War when matched metal dies were developed. The process was first used in the production of firearms. With flat faced hammers and simple grooving tools no particular connection exists between the tooling and a specific product and it is feasible to forge even a single part. Matched metal dies, like patterns for castings, must be made for each shape to be forged and become feasible only when the tooling investment can be divided among a sufficiently large number of parts.

To some extent forging and casting are competitive, even where different materials are involved with each process. As a general rule, the tooling investment is higher for forging than for casting. Thus, the use of forging tends to be restricted to applications where the higher material properties of steel compared to cast iron, or the higher properties of wrought steel compared to cast steel can be made use of in the design. Since forgings compete best in high strength applications, most producers take particular care in raw material selection and inspection. In many cases either forgings or castings may have adequate properties, and one process has no clear economic advantage over the other.

Proper design for forgings must capitalize on the improvement in properties in certain directions that occurs with metal flow. Voids tend to close and be welded shut under the high heat and pressure and inclusions are elongated to the degree that they have little effect on the strength in some directions.

While forging and casting have similarities, they have one major difference. Since the static strength of liquid metal is practically zero except for surface tension, the metal may be introduced into the mold under relatively low pressure. It is true that higher pressures are sometimes used in die casting in order to insure complete filling before solidification takes place; but theoretically, a casting could be made with only sufficient pressure to provide a hydrostatic head above the highest part of the mold cavity. In forging however, the metal, even for hot forging, still has considerable strength and it is not generally possible in forging to close the die as a permanent mold is closed and then introduce the metal by pressure through a gate as in casting.

In forging, a suitable quantity of metal is placed or held between the halves of the die while they are open, then forced to conform to the shape of the die by pressure from the dies themselves as they are closed. In drop and press forging the dies are not completely closed until the forging is completed, with the consequence that as the dies are closed the metal may be squeezed to the parting line and be forced out of the die in some places before the closing is completed. In order to overcome this difficulty two steps are taken. For most forgings some preshaping operations are used to insure that approximately the right quantity of metal is already at the proper place in the dies before they are closed. These operations are frequently similar to open die or hammer forging and include *upsetting* (enlarging the cross section by pressure from the end), *drawing* (reducing the cross section of stock throughout), *fullering* (reducing the cross section of stock between the ends, *edging* (distribution of the metal to the general contour of the finished stock), and *blocking* (shaping to rough finished form without detail).

Even with the preshaping operations, it is necessary to provide some excess metal to insure that all parts of the final die cavity are filled. The dies are constructed so that in the closed position a crack is left at the parting line through which this excess metal is forced into a *gutter*. The excess metal, called *flash,* is actually part of the forging and must be removed in a secondary operation, generally by trimming in a shearing type die.

Machines used for closed die forging fall into two categories: press forging machines, in which the driving mechanism is capable of exerting sufficient force to close the dies in a single stroke; and drop forging presses, in which the dies are closed by impact, requiring several strokes for each operation. Most press forging machines are hydraulically operated with capacities up to 50,000 tons. For some cold forging and coining operations mechanical knuckle joint presses are used.

Drop forging presses rely on the kinetic energy built up in a moving ram to which one half of the die is fastened. Energy is supplied to the ram either by gravity as with a drop hammer, or by steam or air pressure. The other half of the die is attached to an anvil whose weight is about twenty times that of the ram. Ram weights range up to 45,000 pounds.

Theoretically any metal with enough ductility could be either press forged or drop (impact) forged. In practice, steel is almost exclusively drop forged because of the large capacity presses that would be required for press forging and because the die life would be shortened by the longer time of contact between the die and the heated steel. Most nonferrous metals are press forged. The slow squeezing action appears to permit deeper flow of the metal than in drop forging and the dies may have somewhat less draft.

Many forged products are made by enlarging a portion of wire, rod, or bar stock in the process called upset or machine forging as shown in Fig. 11–19. The material is usually fed to the machine from coiled stock which passes through straightening rollers and is then sheared to proper length. The material is then gripped between the die halves and squeezed in a totally enclosed chamber by movement of a ram or plunger to gather or upset the material with an increase of cross-sectional dimension and decrease of length. Most of the products made by this method are at least close to being symmetrical about the original axis of the stock and include such common items as bolts, rivets, and nails as well as larger parts such as gear blanks. Small sized products are most frequently worked cold, but as size increases, loads and machine sizes increase, making hot work more practical. Cold work of this type is sometimes called *cold heading*. The finished shape produced by the upsetting is fully enclosed, with no flash produced as in drop or press forging.

Machine forging provides high production rates with little or no material loss and is thus close to an ideal process providing that tolerances are acceptable, quantities are large enough to cover tooling costs, and the deformation ratios are permissible under this procedure.

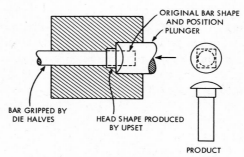

FIG. 11–19. Machine forging.

The operation called *coining* is roughly equivalent to press forging, but performed cold. Because of the much higher strength and reduced ductility of metals below the recrystallization temperatures, coining is limited to relatively small amounts of deformation and is most useful where fine surface detail is to be produced as in the production of coins. The term is also sometimes used for the operation of squeezing metal, either hot or cold, between flat or shaped dies without side restraint to achieve more accurate dimensions or better finish than can be obtained in a normal casting or forging operation.

Forging with Progressive Application of Pressure. In any closed die forging operation it is necessary to provide, either by constantly applied pressure or by impact, a great enough load that the compressive strength of the material is exceeded throughout the material for the forging to be completed. Even for forgings of a few pounds this requires heavy, massive equipment. For a few particular shapes, processes have been developed by which the material is worked only locally with light loads being required, and the area being worked progresses by a rolling action to other parts of the workpiece.

Roll forging, illustrated in Fig. 11–20 is particularly useful when a cylindrical part is to be elongated throughout part of its length. The drawn section may be tapered but the process is not capable of upsetting or enlarging the original diameter. In operation, the heated workpiece is placed between the first groove and the rolls are energized to make one turn, after which the workpiece is moved to the next groove and operation is repeated.

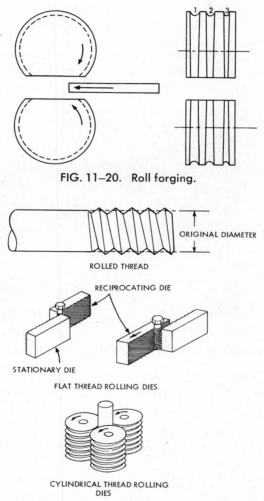

FIG. 11–20. Roll forging.

ROLLED THREAD

ORIGINAL DIAMETER

RECIPROCATING DIE

STATIONARY DIE

FLAT THREAD ROLLING DIES

CYLINDRICAL THREAD ROLLING DIES

FIG. 11–21. Thread rolling.

Figs. 11–21 and 11–22 show two operations more frequently associated with machining than forging, although they involve deformation without metal removal. The majority of bolts and other mass-produced items with external threads, particularly where accuracy requirements are not extreme, are produced by rolling. A blank whose diameter is approximately the pitch diameter of the desired thread is squeezed and moved between flat or cylindrical dies having grooves of the desired thread form. Production rates can be extremely high, sometimes reaching one hundred parts per minute with good accuracy. Thread rolling is normally a cold working operation which results in strengthening of the material, especially at the thread root where the highest stresses occur in service.

Knurling is even more closely associated with machining since the operation is normally performed on engine lathes, turret lathes, or screw machines, frequently as part of a sequence involving normal metal removal operations. Knurling is used for improving appearance, for establishing nonslip gripping surfaces, and for establishing proper fits with mating parts, either by enlarging the part or by providing recesses which provide

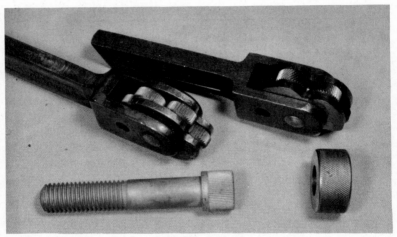

FIG. 11–22.   Knurling tools and knurled surfaces. (Left, straight; right, diamond.)

mechanical connection when metal parts are included as inserts in plastic molded articles. The diamond knurl is the most common for appearance and nonslip uses, while the straight knurl is most used for mating surface union.

QUESTIONS

1. Why are cast materials not universally used as cast?
2. What two material improvements can often be provided at the same time by cold deformation processes?
3. Why are so called mill operations performed by specialist plants?
4. How do secondary deformation operations differ from those of mill work?
5. Why are large shape and section changes by deformation usually done hot?
6. What are blooms, billets, and slabs?
7. Construct schematic sketches showing the arrangement of two-high reversible, three-high reversible, four-high and cluster rolling stands.

8. What is a merchant mill?

9. What property changes are a result of cold finishing?

10. In what way does intermediate recrystallization benefit when large reduction of area is required during cold deformation?

11. Why is copper wire for electrical applications usually annealed after the last deformation?

12. How is the size of most wire designated?

13. Why are pipe and tubing usually mill products?

14. What is skelp?

15. Name the five steps used for manufacturing large pipe by the electric welding method.

16. Briefly describe the piercing process used to make seamless steel tubing.

17. Why is extrusion limited primarily to nonferrous materials?

18. How is three dimensional control established in open die forging?

19. With what other shape producing process is forging most competitive?

20. Describe upsetting and drawing as used in connection with forging.

21. What is the combined purpose of fullering, edging, and blocking?

22. Does the term "flash" have the same meaning for forging that it does for die casting?

23. Describe the two general types of machines used for forging.

24. What are the two possible meanings of the term coining?

25. What is the main deformation process performed in machine forging?

26. Describe knurling.

✍✍✍ CHAPTER 12

Press Working of Sheet Metal

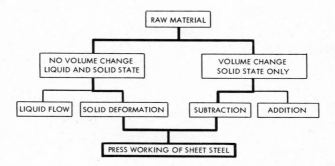

SINCE ITS inception about 1850, the working of sheet metal has grown constantly in importance and today is perhaps the most important method of fabricating metal parts. As pointed out in Chapter 11, about 30 per cent of the output of steel mills is in the form of sheet and plate. Most of this material is further processed by individual fabricators by various press-working operations that involve deformation, usually cold, and shearing operations in which metal is removed. The importance of this form of processing to the economy is especially apparent from an examination of the mass produced metal consumer goods such as automobiles, home appliance housings, and office equipment. In addition to exterior housings, many functional parts are made from sheet metal; for typewriters, business machines, and other equipment made in large quantity, the percentages of parts made by this process may approach one hundred.

Two requisites to this type of processing are: sufficient quantities to justify the high tooling cost which is required and the presence of enough ductility in the material to permit the plastic flow necessary for the particular type of operation being considered. Shearing operations, in which plastic flow is not required, are possible on nearly all sheet materials, even brittle materials such as glass and some of the plastics. All other press-working operations are deformation operations and the degree of processing permissible is dependent on the ductility present in the particular material. Some metals may be cold worked to completion with material as

208

it comes from the mill, some metals require intermediate recrystallization between cold working operations and some require heating for more than shearing or minimum deformation operations.

Pressworking operations, whether shearing or deformation, all involve the failure of the metal by controlled loading. In the case of shearing operations, the metal is loaded in a manner to cause fracture. For bending, drawing, and other deformation operations the metal is loaded past the elastic limit to cause plastic flow only, usually by application of tension or bending loads. Unlike most forging operations where the metal is totally confined, the final thickness of the metal depends on the original thickness and the nature of the operation.

The majority of pressworking operations requires special tooling. In most cases, the cutting or forming tools themselves are attached to a

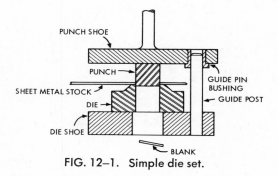

FIG. 12–1. Simple die set.

standardized *die set* which is mounted in the press. Fig. 12–1 shows a simple die set for shearing a round hole or producing a round disc.

When mounted in a press the punch shoe is attached to the ram of the press and the die shoe to the bolster plate which is the fixed member corresponding to the anvil of a forging press. The guide posts insure proper alignment of the punch and die and simplify the setup since the entire die set may be removed from the press and replaced later without any critical adjustments to be made. In some complex dies there may be confusion as to which is the die and which is the punch; in normal use, however, the tool member with a recess, hole, or depression is called the *die*, and the *punch* is the member which enters the hole or depression of the die. In most cases stock feeding and handling problems are simplified by mounting the punch on top and the die on the bottom of the die set.

Shearing.   The term *shearing* as used in pressworking applies specifically to the operation of loading to fracture with opposed edges. *Shear stress* applies to an internal load condition tending to slide one plane on another and various amounts of shear stress occur with practically all loading systems. In a *shearing operation* material is actually loaded by a combination of compressive and bending loads and the internal stress condition is quite complex. Of real importance is the fact that when the external loads become great enough, the internal stresses will exceed critical values for the material and rupture will occur. The rupture may or may not be preceded by plastic flow, depending on the properties of the particular material.

The term *shear strength* refers to an empirical value for a material loaded as in a shearing operation and computed from the formula:

$$\text{shear strength (psi)} = \frac{\text{load for rupture (pounds)}}{\text{area of material sheared,}}.$$
$$\text{(square inches)}$$

The confusion arises from the fact that the applied load in any shearing operation or a shear strength test is more or less parallel to the area of

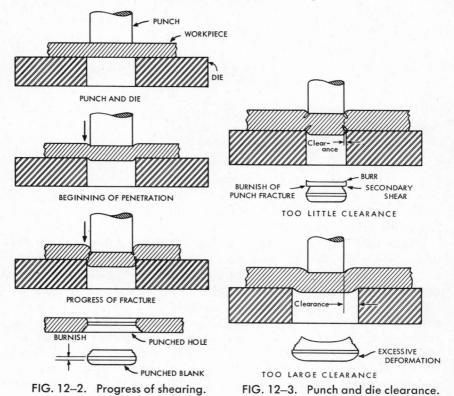

FIG. 12–2. Progress of shearing.   FIG. 12–3. Punch and die clearance.

material failure which implies the idea of shear stress. In reality, shear strength values have no direct connection to the value of shear stress existing at rupture. The failure does not generally proceed parallel to the direction of load but, as indicated in Fig. 12–2, proceeds at an angle from each loaded corner or edge. Fig. 12–3 illustrates the result of varying the *clearance* between the shearing edges. Zero or too little clearance causes excessive loads, rapid tool wear, and rough edges on the workpiece. Too much clearance also leads to excessive loads and considerable bending of the workpiece edges, especially with ductile materials. In practice, the clearance is commonly made from 5 to 20 per cent of the metal thickness, with the smallest values for the hardest materials.

While the maximum load required for a shearing operation may vary considerably depending on the sharpness of the tools, the amount of

TABLE 12–1

Shearing Strength of Some Common Metals

Metal	Shearing Strength (Psi)	Penetration (Per Cent)
Aluminum alloys (annealed)	8,000–22,000	60 max.
Aluminum alloys (strain hardened)	13,000–46,000	30 max.
Brass (annealed)	22,000–36,000	55–25
Steel (0.1 C. annealed)	35,000	60
Steel (1.0 C. annealed)	115,000	10
Steel (1.0 C. strain hardened)	150,000	2

clearance, and other factors, reasonable average values may be calculated. Since values for the shear strength of most common metals, as shown in Table 12–1, have been obtained from tests that duplicate the conditions in a standard shearing operation, these values may be used to predict the maximum load by taking:

$$P_{max} = S_s \times A = S_s \times L \times t$$

where:

$P_{(max)}$ = maximum load
S_s = shear strength
A = area of metal sheared
L = length of sheared edge
t = metal thickness

As the punch progresses through the metal, the load will vary depending on the ductility of the metal, the sharpness of the tools, and the amount of clearance. Fig. 12–4 is typical of such a load curve. Since the dimensions of the curve are load and distance, the area under the curve represents the total amount of work or energy required for the shearing operation. In practice, a good approximation of the total energy may be obtained by using the penetration values given in Table

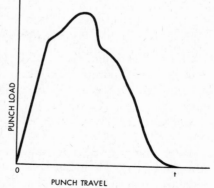

FIG. 12–4. Typical shearing load curve.

12–1 to obtain an average value for the load as a percentage of the maximum load. Then the total energy will be:

$$W = \text{average load} \times t$$

and:

$$\text{average load} = P_{(max)} \times \text{per cent penetration}$$

so that:

$$W = P_{(max)} \times \text{per cent penetration} \times t$$

Fig. 12–5 shows the effect of providing a progressive engagement of the punch and die by providing *angular shear* on the face of the die or the punch. Angular shear leads to distortion of the blank if the angle is on the

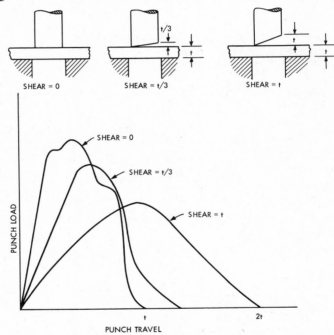

FIG.12–5.   Influence of angular shear on loads.

punch or distortion of the stock if the angle is on the die. The effect is to reduce the maximum load, which may permit shearing of large shapes in small presses, but there is little change in the total energy required for the operation.

A number of different shearing operations exist with some confusion in names. One of the many ways of classifying these operations is the process purpose. The purpose may be to produce an external shape, which may either be a finished shape or be the raw material for some other operation, to remove part of the material or cut it in such a way that an opening or indentation is produced, or to remove material which was necessarily left on the part from some other operation. Shearing operations may be grouped as follows:

Stock preparation and blank producing operations
    shearing
    slitting
    cutoff
    parting
    dinking
    blanking

Hole making operations
    punching
    slotting
    perforating
    semi-notching
    notching
    lancing
    piercing

Finishing operations
    trimming
    shaving

Specifically the term *shearing* refers generally to straight line cutting performed on a squaring shear having permanently mounting opposed straight blades. The upper blade is set at an angle to give progressive engagement and reduce the maximum force required. Squaring shears may be used to reduce large sheet or coil stock to smaller size for handling purposes or to produce parts with finished or semi-finished shapes as indicated in Fig. 12–6.

Fig. 12–7 shows rotary slitting which is used primarily for reducing coil

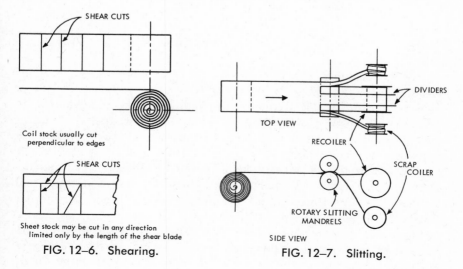

FIG. 12–6. Shearing.

FIG. 12–7. Slitting.

stock to narrower widths. Slitting is usually a mill or warehouse operation, but occasionally is done by an individual fabricator.

The other operations in this group, shown in Fig. 12–8, are all intended to produce a finished shape using punches and dies in presses. Where the shape must be cut on all edges from wide stock, the operation is called *blanking*. If the shape can be produced by single cuts, straight or curved, across the width of strip stock the operation is called *cutoff*, and where the shape is produced by a pair of cuts across the width of the stock, with some scrap, the operation is called *parting*. Leather, paper, cloth, and similar materials are frequently blanked with a *dinking* die which has a single, thin, knife edge contoured to the shape of the part that is brought down against a flat platen of soft metal or wood.

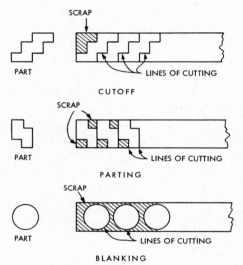

FIG. 12–8. Two-dimensional shapes by shearing.

Some overlapping of terms occurs for the operations in the hole making group shown in Fig. 12–9. *Punching* and *piercing* are terms which may be used to refer to any hole making operation in which the punch cuts on its entire periphery. Where the hole is long and narrow, the term *slotting* may be used and where a number of smaller holes are punched the operation may be called *perforating*. The term piercing may also be used for the hole making operation where a pointed or bullet shaped punch is used with clearance much greater than normal for a shearing operation. Without any actual metal removal a hole is produced and the metal is forced down around the sides of the hole.

Fig. 12–10 illustrates two operations used for shaping the edges of parts without cutting the entire periphery as in blanking. In *semi-notching* a hole is actually produced in the stock but only part of the contour of the hole becomes part of the edge of the finished shape. Semi-notching is most commonly used in progressive setups where the stock is moved from one station to the next for subsequent operations, but the workpiece remains fixed to the strip of stock. The actual separation of the workpiece from the stock is performed later by a parting or cutoff operation. *Notching* is a shape cutting operation on the edge of the part, where the punch cuts on less than its entire edge.

The operation of *lancing* in Fig. 12–11 is generally followed by a bending operation for producing a tab or ear for fastening purposes or to produce louvers. No scrap is produced as a result of lancing.

The nature of many operations, shearing as well as others, often requires that excess material be left that can be removed by a shearing operation. The edge left by blanking or punching operations is rounded over because of the ductility of the metal and is not square because of the nature of the failure in shearing. The edge condition may be improved by re-shearing or *shaving* with a punch and die having little or no clearance that removes only a

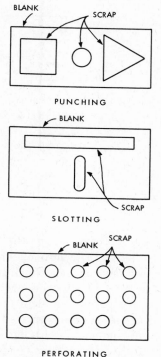

PUNCHING

SLOTTING

PERFORATING

FIG. 12–9. Hole making (piercing).

small amount of material, usually equal to about 10 per cent of the metal thickness. Shaving is actually more closely allied to machining than to shearing but is normally performed as a pressworking operation.

Fig. 12–12 illustrates one of the principal needs for *trimming*. A cup or shell produced from sheet metal has an irregular edge which for many purposes must be corrected. Where the operation can be performed on the flange it is similar to a blanking operation. Where it must be done on the wall of the cup or shell, trimming can be accomplished by rotary shearing on a specialized machine, by horizontal shearing in a patented die which imparts sidewise movements to the die, or by actually machining in a lathe.

Bending. In shearing operations any plastic flow that occurs along the edge is incidental since the purpose of shearing is to cause separation of the metal without

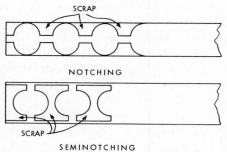

NOTCHING

SEMINOTCHING

FIG. 12–10. Notching and semi-notching.

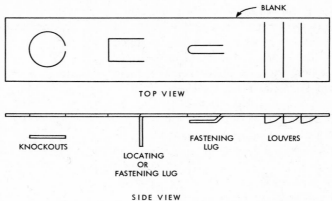

TOP VIEW

SIDE VIEW

FIG. 12–11. Lancing.

any deformation in the sheet itself. *Bending* is intended to cause localized plastic flow about one or more linear axes in the material without causing fracture. Bending is accomplished by loading the material so as to set up stresses which exceed the yield point of the material and cause permanent deformation. Shearing is possible on materials having very low ductility as well as those with high ductility. Bending is possible only on materials having sufficient ductility to permit the required amount of plastic flow. The severity of bends possible will depend on the ductility. While the degree of bending possible cannot be determined directly from a standard tensile test, this test gives useful comparative data. For two materials, the one showing the greatest percentage elongation on the tensile test may be bent more severely than the other.

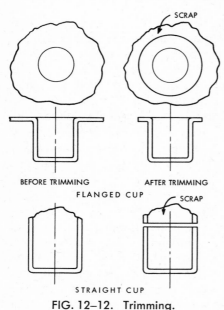

FIG. 12–12. Trimming.

Fig. 12–13 shows the various methods of applying loads. It can be noted by examining the various points at which the loads are applied that little real difference exists between the methods and all are similar to the classical concept of beam loading used in strength of materials. In any case, at the completion of the bend, the forces and stresses are localized and concentrated in the area of the bend. The loads required for a bending operation may be calculated by applying standard beam bending formulas, but in practical bending operations

the length of the moment arms involved
may change as the bend progresses and the
determination of loads may require actual
testing of the operation. Furthermore, for
some bending operations, squeezing of the
metal at completion of the bend sets up
higher loads than those calculated from
beam formulas.

Fig. 12–14 indicates the nature of the
deformation taking place in a bend. The
metal on the inside of the radius is subject
to high compressive stresses which may
cause an increase in width for material
that is nearly square in cross section. With
any cross section, and regardless of how
the operation is performed, the high tensile
stresses on the outside of the bend cause
thinning of the metal. The degree of
thinning will depend on the ratio of bend
radius to metal thickness. In practice, the
distortion must be considered for two
reasons. Unless the metal is actually
squeezed at the completion of the bend
with sufficient force to cause forging, the
outside shape of the bend will not be a true
radius and is uncontrolled. On part drawings the inside radius only should be
specified since this can be controlled by
the tooling. In addition, some consideration of the distortion must be made in
computing the length of flat blank necessary to provide the correct dimensions on
the finished part. Usual practice is to take
the sum of the straight sections plus the
length of the bends at a distance 0.4*t*

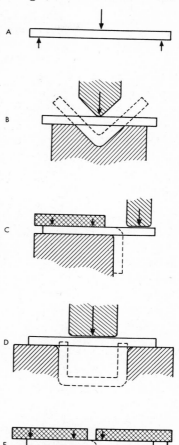

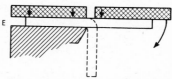

FIG. 12–13. Methods of applying bending forces.

away from the inside radius. The part in Fig. 12–14 would require a flat
blank whose length would be:

$$L = l_1 + l_2 + \frac{90}{180}\pi(r + 0.4t) .$$

One of the principal difficulties in bending operations arises from the
fact that whenever metal is stressed, even in the plastic range, when the
loads are removed elastic recovery will occur—contraction where the
stress is tension, and elongation where the stress is compression. When
bending loads are removed the metal on the inside of the radius tends to

elongate and the metal on the outside tends to shorten which leads to a reduction of the angle of the bend called *springback*. Corrections include *overbending* by an amount necessary to insure the correct angle after springback has occurred, *striking* the metal at the completion of the bend, or keeping the metal under high tensile loading when the bend is made. Striking is a coining operation which sets up compressive stresses throughout the region of the bend and while elastic recovery still takes place it will occur in the same direction on both sides of the bend. High tensile loading has a similar effect in the opposite direction.

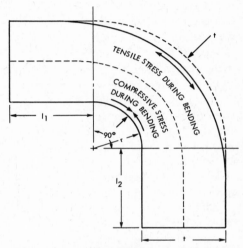

FIG. 12–14. Distortion during bending.

By a strict definition, bending would include only operations where the plastic flow is confined to a narrow straight line region where the bend is made. It is not possible to perform a bend along a curved axis without there being plastic flow in the material away from the line of the bend. This type of operation would more strictly be called drawing. In practice, however, a number of operations are considered bending that do include some drawing. The term *forming* is sometimes used in a broad sense to include simple bending, multiple bends made along more than one axis, operations that are primarily bending but include some drawing, and some operations that are basically drawing in nature but are of shallow depth or confined to a small area of the workpiece only.

Fig. 12–15 illustrates some of the more common terms used for bending and forming operations. Simple straight bends may be made by any of the methods shown in Fig. 12–13. Long punches and dies of the type shown in "B" of this figure are frequently permanently mounted in a specialized machine called a press *brake*. It is used for only straight bends in individual workpieces. A similar machine with permanent tooling but generally lighter construction uses the rotary motion shown in "E." Where special tools are made for individual workpieces and used in die sets in conventional presses, any of the methods "B," "C," or "D" may be used.

A flange is a bend near the edge of a sheet or part used for strengthening or to establish a joining surface. Note that for other than a straight flange, some stretching or shrinking of the metal is necessary which is more characteristic of drawing than bending. Hems may be used for strengthening or smoothing edges, for making seams in cans and other cylindrical parts, and for joining two or more parts together. Wiring and curling are similar to hems but may incorporate a wire for additional strengthening.

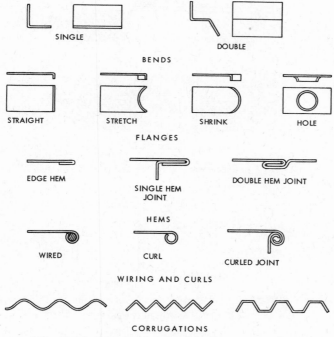

FIG. 12–15. Bending and forming.

Roll forming, illustrated in Fig. 11–12 in connection with tube making, is not a press operation, but the metal is shaped by means of a continuous bending action. While the completed shape could be produced by bending only, some stretching occurs during the actual forming as the strip changes from flat to formed. Roll forming is used for making tubing, architectural trim, and other similar parts where a uniform cross section in relatively long length is necessary. An economic choice between roll forming or shaping by conventional press tooling may frequently occur.

Drawing. The most complex press operation, from the standpoint of the stresses involved, is *drawing*. In simple bending a single axis exists about which all the deformation occurs and the surface area of the material is not significantly altered. Drawing involves not only bending but also stretching and compression of the metal over wide areas. While examples of drawing are many, including such items as automobile fenders and other body parts, aircraft wing and fuselage panels, kitchenware, and square or rectangular box shapes, the simplest illustration is *shell drawing* in which a flat circular blank is pushed through a round die to form a closed end cup or shell as in Fig. 12–16. The metal in the bottom of the

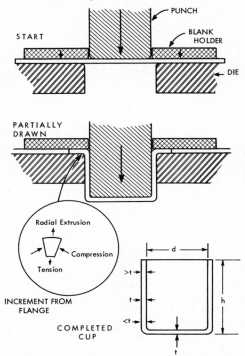

FIG. 12–16. Shell drawing.

shell is undeformed with the same thickness as the original blank. Near the bottom of the shell the material is about 10 to 15 per cent thinner than originally and near the top about the same amount thicker. The net result is that the total surface area of the blank is approximately the same as that of the completed shell. This fact may be used in determining the blank diameter necessary to form a shell with given diameter and height. Neglecting the radius at the bottom of the shell and using the mean diameter since the metal is thin compared to the diameter, the required blank diameter is:

$$D = \sqrt{d^2 + 4dh}.$$

The severity of the deformation involved is clear from the figure. The wedge shaped section in the flange must be deformed so that it is of uniform width in the shell wall. In order for the shell to be formed the material throughout the flange must be loaded above its yield strength. The force for this loading is transmitted from the end of the punch through the wall of the shell; the maximum diameter of flange that can be deformed without rupturing the shell wall is limited. Stated another way, the reduction in diameter that may be made with a given blank diameter is limited. In practice, the shell is never less than about half the diameter of the blank (reduction equal to 50 per cent) with reductions of 30 to 40 per cent being more common. The load requirement imposed on the wall of the shell is increased by the bending as the flange enters the die and frequently by the necessity for a hold down device for the flange during drawing. The circumferential compressive stresses induced in the flange tend to produce column action which leads to buckling and wrinkling of the metal as it is drawn. Where the metal thickness is more than about 3 per cent of the flange diameter, little trouble is experienced but for thinner metal a hold down ring is required to prevent wrinkling. This ring adds to the load requirements since the friction of moving the metal from under the ring must be overcome.

In many cases, the dimensions of the required shell are such that it cannot be completed in a single step. For example, to produce a shell of 3 inches diameter and 4 inches height a blank of 7.55 inches diameter would be needed and if the maximum reduction permissible were 40 per cent the resultant cup would be 4.53 inches diameter. However, it would be possible to *redraw* the cup, as in Fig. 12–17, although the permissible reduction in the second step would be less since the metal would be coldworked and strain hardened from the first drawing and have less ductility than originally. With a redraw of 30 per cent reduction, the diameter could be reduced to 3.18 and a second redraw would be necessary to produce the final diameter of 3 inches. The operation could be accomplished with a single redraw if the part were heated for recrystallization after the first draw to restore the original ductility and permit a greater reduction in the first redrawing operation. The actual choice of a single draw and two redraws as opposed to a single draw, recrystallization and one redraw would depend on the economics of the particular situation involving quantities, equipment, and other factors.

Other than shell drawing and cupping, few drawing operations have specific names. In many cases some flat material is left at the top of the drawn shape. In shell drawing this is accomplished by not pushing the material completely into the die but leaving some of the flange undrawn. For some shapes, particularly square and rectangular boxes with straight sides, it is necessary to leave a considerable flange in order to prevent the formation of wrinkles in the box wall. This flange must be removed in a trimming operation. The general terms *shallow* drawing and *deep* drawing are the most descriptive of the type of operation being done but there is no clear distinction between the two.

Fig. 12–18 shows the operation called *ironing*. Either in combination with the drawing operation for shallow draws, or as a second operation for deeper draws, the cup or shell is pushed through a die where the clearance between the punch and die is less than the metal thickness. Multiple ironing operations may be used to thin the shell wall even more. The resultant shape has a thin wall and a relatively thick closed end which is the

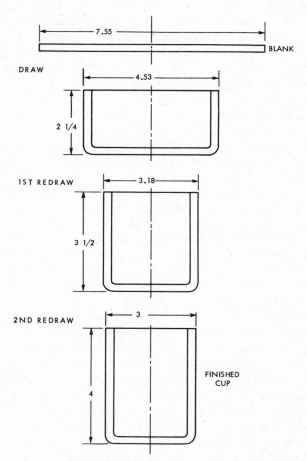

FIG. 12–17. Redrawing of cups.

most desirable distribution of material for flat ended pressure devices such as shell cases. The burnishing action in ironing may be used to improve the finish in the wall of drawn parts.

Equipment. In practically all cases the working of sheet metal imposes special requirements on equipment. For shearing operations in particular, extremely large forces may be required for relatively short periods of time. The tools themselves must withstand these high forces and must be of hard and wear resistant materials which increases the difficulty of making them.

The design of presses is characterized primarily by the high load requirements which results in rather massive frames and driving members

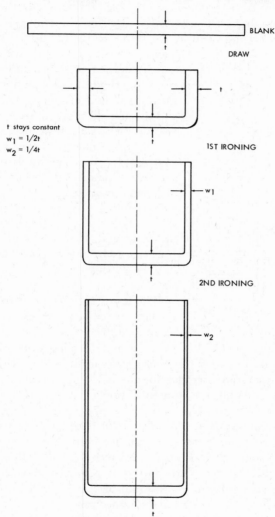

FIG. 12–18.   Ironing for wall thinning.

even for presses of relatively small capacity. Presses differ in one or more of a number of features which are as follows.

The most obvious feature of a press is generally the *frame*. Fig. 12–19 shows the most common type of mechanical press which has a "C" frame. The open front with this construction gives good accessibility but requires a very heavy back member for good rigidity. Presses with "C" frames may be vertical, horizontal, or inclinable as in the figure. The inclinable feature in combination with an opening through the back of the frame frequently aids in the removal of parts or scrap from the press. Other variations include *horning* presses where the bottom of the "C" is a straight cylinder for working on tubular products, and a *knee* frame where the bottom of the "C" is adjustable.

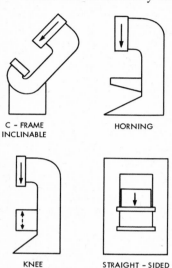

C - FRAME INCLINABLE   HORNING

KNEE   STRAIGHT - SIDED

FIG. 12–19. Common press types.

Where the accessibility of a "C" frame is not required, or where the loads would require an excessively large "C" frame, the *straightsided* frame is used. In this method of construction the bed of the press and the crown containing the ram and driving mechanism are connected on two or more sides instead of being made with the cantilevered construction of a "C" frame press. Variations in names are somewhat descriptive of the method of construction and include solid frame, arch frame, tie rod frame, and pillar frame. These constructions differ largely in detail only. As with the "C" frame type, these presses may be either horizontal or vertical but the vertical type is by far most common.

The term "action" refers to the number of slides or rams a press has. For practically all shearing operations and most simple bending and forming operations a single action is sufficient. For deep drawing presses it often becomes desirable to have a second operating member for the hold down that prevents wrinkling of the flange. While it is sometimes possible to operate the hold down with springs on a single action press, the pressure from the springs increases as the drawing proceeds rather than decreases as would be more desirable. The latter may be accomplished with a double action press having both an inner and an outer ram independently driven. A triple action press has a third ram at the bottom which may be used for imprinting or forming operations on the bottom of drawn parts or for removing the drawn part from the die after the upper rams return.

The press *drive* refers to the mechanism providing the motion of the press. Typical mechanisms are shown in Fig. 12–20. Two general methods, mechanical and hydraulic, are used. The most common mechanical drives are crank and eccentric types which are similar. Knuckle joint presses can exert very high forces for a short portion of travel near the bottom of the stroke and are used primarily for coining or cold forging operations. A screw drive is sometimes used for similar operations but because of its lack of speed is seldom used for sheet metal operations.

Hydraulically driven presses are generally slower than mechanical types but have some distinct advantages. They can exert full tonnage over the entire length of stroke and the length of stroke is readily adjustable. In addition the ram has constant speed throughout its stroke. None of these features is true of crank or eccentric drives. Hydraulic presses are seldom used for shearing operations where the maximum load requirement occurs at the bottom of the stroke and a crank type is faster, but are common for deep drawing operations.

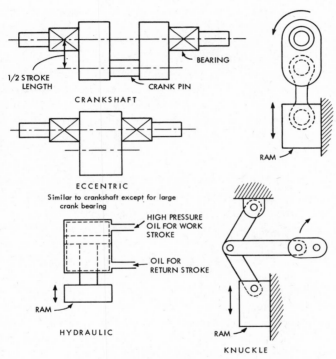

FIG. 12–20. Typical press drives.

Since the maximum load requirement occurs only during a small percentage of the total time involved, especially on crank driven presses, it is common to make use of a relatively large flywheel and a comparatively small motor. During the long lightly loaded portion of the cycle, the motor may build up the speed of the flywheel. During the actual working portion of the stroke the flywheel slows down but provides the major portion of energy for the actual operation. Some high speed presses use the weight of the motor armature itself as a flywheel.

There are many other variations in features. Motors may be directly connected to the flywheel or drive the flywheel through a belt. One or more sets of reduction gears may be between the motor or flywheel and the crankshaft. Practically all mechanical presses have a clutch of some type which permits the crankshaft and ram to remain stationary while the motor and flywheel continue to turn. The term *suspension* refers to the number of driving points on the ram. A single crankshaft may have two throws or eccentrics (2 point suspension) or the press may have two or more crankshafts, each having two or more throws. The space available for the die set, both horizontally and vertically may differ even on presses of the same tonnage and the speed of presses may be either fixed or adjustable. Fixed speed mechanical presses range from about five to over five hundred strokes per minute, with speeds of fifty to one hundred being most common for presses of moderate size used for blanking, punching, and simple forming operations.

Safety of press working operations presents some problems. Many operations are automatic with the parts made from strip stock so that the operation may be enclosed. However, in many other cases, parts must be individually hand fed involving considerable danger to hands and fingers. The problems may be approached in many ways; few of them are completely foolproof, however, since in many cases some interference with the operation by the safety device is a necessity and operators are likely to become careless with increased familiarity. When usable, the best protection is a guard completely excluding all parts of the human body. Other solutions include electric eye interlocks which present engagement of the clutch if the operators hands or arms are too near the operating parts of the press, mechanical sweeps which are operated by the press mechanism and sweep across the press opening as the ram descends, and multiple controls which require that all operators have both hands out of the press before it can operate.

The different types of tooling common for many press operations may be illustrated by considering the manufacture of a simple flat round washer. It could be manufactured by first blanking round discs from strip stock in one simple punch and die, then placing these discs one at a time in a second simple punch and die for piercing the hole, as illustrated in Fig. 12–21. This would probably be the cheapest possible tooling method but productivity would be low and the concentricity of the hole with the outside of the washer would depend on the location method in the second operation. Even though it would be slow, this method would likely be used for small quantities because of the low tooling costs.

For higher quantities or greater accuracies a different method could be used. Fig. 12–22 shows a *compound* die that could be used for producing the same parts. One complete washer is produced for each stroke of the press and the concentricity will depend on the accuracy of the tooling which can be very good. Fig. 12–23 shows a third method making use of a *progressive* die for the same part. On the first stroke of the press the stock is fed only far enough that the piercing punch operates. For the second and subsequent strokes the stock is fed a distance equal to the distance between the center lines of the two punches, and a completed washer is produced with each stroke of the press. Compared to the compound die, the progressive is of generally simpler construction and is easier to maintain, can for many parts operate with a shorter press stroke which may permit a higher press speed, and with many stations in the die permits complex parts to be completed in one setup. The principal advantage of the compound die is in increased accuracy since the relationship of the operations done in different stations in a progressive die depends on the distance the stock is fed each time and it is difficult to control this distance precisely. The figure indicates a pointed end on the blanking punch whose purpose is to enter the previously punched hole and correct any slight error in the feed distance. Where this is not possible, notches may be cut along the edge of the stock in the first station, to be used to regulate the feed as the stock progresses through the die.

In normal blanking or punching operations, the nature of the failure is such that the hole is a tight fit on

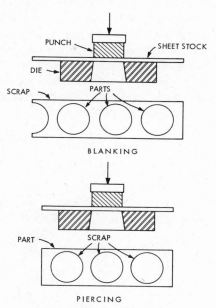

FIG. 12–21. Simple dies.

the punch and without some means of restraint the stock would be lifted with the punch on the return stroke and feeding would not be possible. The removal of the stock from the punch is known as *stripping* and Fig. 12–22 indicates a stripper plate that may be fastened to the die with a slot for passage of the stock or may be fastened to the ram or punch in such a

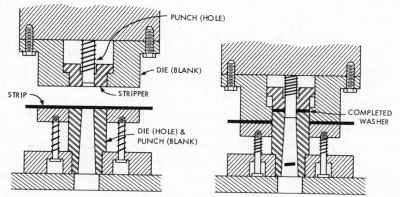

FIG. 12–22. Compound die.

manner that it contacts the stock before the punches but can retract against springs as the punches proceed into the work.

Feed of the stock may be manual but for most high production operations coil stock is used and some automatic feeding mechanism is desirable as is a means of coiling or cutting the scrap stock as it leaves the machine.

The materials used for press tooling depend to a large degree on the requirements of the particular operation. Hardened steel is the conventional material for shearing punches and dies. Much of the high cost of press tooling may be attributed to the requirement for close mating between the punch and die. Even though the tolerances on the workpiece may be much greater, the punch and die must be made with tolerances of a few thousandths of an inch or less in order to establish the proper clear-

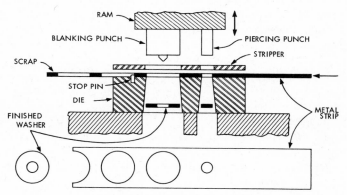

FIG. 12–23. Progressive die.

ance between them. Hardened steel tools must usually be finished by grinding. The cost and time for grinding punches and dies become great for other than simple circular shapes.

Shearing tools are frequently made from hardened flat stock which is fastened to unhardened back up material. The thickness of the hardened portion ranges from several inches for tools that are to be resharpened down to a plate of ¼ inch thickness or less which may be flame hardened only along the cutting edge if the quantity requirements are low or the work material is particularly easy to shear.

For shearing aluminum in low quantities, as frequently occurs in the aircraft industry, a technique has been developed making use of a hard brittle zinc alloy as a die material. A steel punch is first made with tolerances governed by part tolerances rather than by clearance requirements. The die is made of a relatively thin sheet of zinc alloy with an undersized hole. After mounting, the first stroke of the press forces the punch through the zinc alloy and shears the hole in the die to the exact size of the punch. Although such tooling operates with an undesirable zero clearance, the cost is low and the life is sufficient for several hundred parts in most aluminum alloys. Such quantity is sufficient for many aircraft parts.

For extremely large quantities (several million) involving the shearing of steel, increasing use is being made of cemented carbide as a tool material. This material will be discussed in more detail as a cutting tool material for machining. The cemented carbides are extremely hard and abrasion resistant, but are commonly available only in rather small shapes and dies must generally be built up of smaller pieces. Grinding and shaping for finishing or sharpening require diamond grinding and other special processes.

For bending, forming, and drawing operations, hardened steel is the conventional material for steel workpieces. As for shearing operations, the aircraft industry with low quantity requirements has developed methods that make use of easier to form tool materials with lower life. Wood, plastic, lead, concrete, and zinc as well as steel are all used sometimes in combination with each other for the construction of low cost tools.

Alternative Methods for Limited Production. Several methods attempting to simplify the tooling, the machine used for the operation, or both have resulted from industries' requirement of parts that are naturally best made from sheet metal but needed in such low quantities that the cost of conventional tooling would be excessive. Many of these methods also simplify the production of drawn shapes having a cross section at some point greater than the opening in the finished part.

The procedure called *drop stamping* is particularly useful for low quantity production of shallow drawn parts of fairly large size. Matched punches and dies are needed but are usually made from wood, wood faced with zinc, or plastic. Instead of using a machine having the load capacity to form the part in one single stroke, a more lightly constructed machine, similar in concept to a drop forging press is used. The die is fastened to an anvil on the bottom of the press and the punch is attached to the moving ram which is alternately raised with an air cylinder and dropped on the workpiece with repeated blows until the shape is completed. While the time for the operation is longer than it would be with a conventional hydraulic press of large capacity, the over-all cost is reduced.

Several low tooling cost methods have been developed for forming and for shallow drawing operations. One of the features of all these methods is the use of only a punch or die but not both for each shape to be produced. The oldest and most used of these methods is that shown in Fig. 12–24. The rubber block or pad in the head of the press acts as the second die member and conforms under pressure to the shape of one single solid die member. The machine used is normally a large capacity hydraulic press since the pressure must be developed over the entire surface on the enclosed cavity. This method is most useful for shallow drawn parts of fairly large area.

A variation is shown in Fig. 12–25 where a single solid split die and rubber punch are used to perform a *bulging* operation. Bulging may also be performed by filling the cylindrically drawn blank with water, soluble oil, or round steel shot of small diameter, and developing pressure with a piston that fits the inside diameter of the blank. Any of these methods

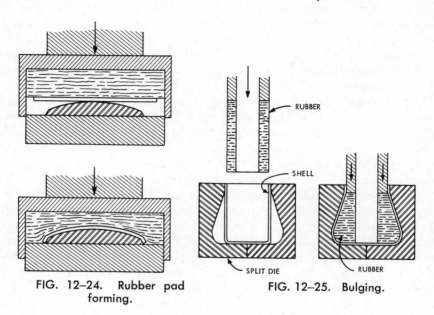

FIG. 12–24.   Rubber pad forming.

FIG. 12–25.   Bulging.

requires a rigid die which must be made in two or more parts for removal of the finished shape.

Fig. 12–26 illustrates the short-run method known as *stretch forming*. The sheet to be formed is held under tension with sufficient force to exceed the yield point and pulled down over, or wrapped around, the

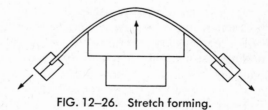

FIG. 12–26.   Stretch forming.

single form block. Considerable trimming allowance must be left along the edges of the part and the process is restricted to shallow shapes with no reentrant angles. However, the method is capable of forming operations on large parts and has been used most in the aircraft industry for large wing and body sections.

One of the oldest production methods for cylindrical drawn shapes is *spinning,* shown in Fig. 12–27. Prior to the manufacture of automobiles and other consumer goods in mass quantities after 1900, spinning was the predominant method for forming deep drawn shapes and is still used to a considerable extent where smaller quantities are produced. Most spinning is done cold, but for heavy materials, or materials with insufficient ductility at room temperature, elevated temperatures are used. Typical parts include pressure tank ends, kitchenware of a special design and in special metals, and many experimental parts that will in production be produced by conventional deep drawing in steel dies.

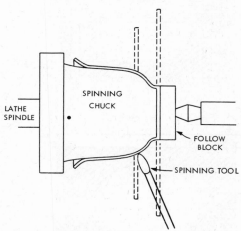

FIG. 12–27. Spinning.

Tooling is generally low cost and, for light gage ductile materials, wood is the most common form material. Shapes produced may be shallow or deep and bulging operations are possible with special setups. Nearly all metals may be spun, most of them cold. Limitations include the operation time involved and the skill required of the operator because the spinning tool is held and manipulated manually except in highly automatic setups where the process loses its low tooling cost advantage. Usually some thinning of the material and the problems of wrinkling and tearing occur as in conventional drawing operations, particularly with thinner materials.

New Developments in Sheet Metal Forming. Most of the new developments in this area have at least two features in common. Like the processes just discussed, most are low tooling cost methods, useful for low production quantities and most make use of a single forming surface instead of matching dies. All of them use nonconventional energy sources, usually some system which releases large amounts of energy in a short time. This feature has led to the use of the term *high energy rate forming* (HERF).

Most highly developed of these methods is explosive forming shown in Fig. 12–28. Two general methods have been used. In the first, sheet metal structures are sized or formed by drawing, using high explosives detonated in air or in water at some predetermined distance from the workpiece. Pressures as high as four million psi are developed by the explosion, which creates a shock wave in the fluid medium that transmits the energy to the workpiece. In the second method a closed die is used and lower pressures

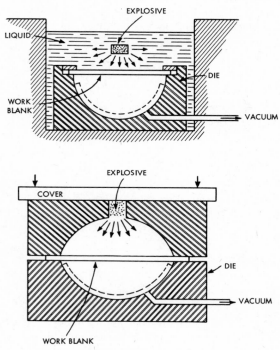

FIG. 12–28. Explosive forming.

of about forty thousand psi are developed by slower burning propellants or gas mixtures. This system is particularly useful for bulging operations. In either case a number of advantages exist when compared to conventional press forming. The capital investment is low compared to conventional press equipment, tooling is simple and inexpensive, and sizes can be shaped which would be impractical with conventional equipment; the principal restriction is that production time is large so the processes can not be economically used for quantity production. There has been some indication that greater amounts of deformation may be achieved by explosive forming than by conventional press forming.

Similar methods are based on the sudden release of electrical energy stored in banks of condensers. In one method a spark is created between two electrodes while they are submerged in water or air near the workpiece. In a second method a high current discharged through a relatively small diameter wire results in vaporization of the wire. In either case, a shock wave is created which transfers energy to the workpiece.

One of the newest methods involves the release of stored electrical energy through a coil near the workpiece as in Fig. 12–29. The rapidly created magnetic field induces eddy currents within a conductive (though not necessarily ferro-magnetic) workpiece, setting up fields that interact with the coil fields to create high forces. With properly designed coils tubular shapes may be expanded into a die or compressed onto a mandrel or various inserts. Flat workpieces may be forced into a shallow drawing die. One of the

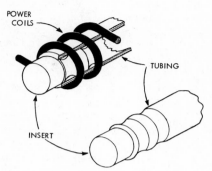

FIG. 12–29.   Electro-magnetic forming.

principal uses has been in assembly of tubular components with end fittings. The system has been called either electromagnetic forming or inductive-repulsive forming. It does not appear to be limited to low production as are most of the other high energy rate techniques.

QUESTIONS

1. How do sheet metal forming operations differ from forging?
2. What is the purpose of the guide post and bushings in a die set?
3. What is the normal arrangement for the parts of a punch, die, and die set when in position in a press?
4. What is shear strength?
5. What are the effects of incorrect clearance for a shearing die?
6. What would be the maximum load to shear a 3″ × 4″ rectangle from 0.1 carbon annealed steel, 0.062 inch thick?
7. What effect does the use of angular shear have on the maximum load and the total work required for a shearing operation?
8. Distinguish between cutoff and parting operations.
9. What is the purpose of a shaving operation?
10. What different material requirements exist for shearing and bending operations?
11. Why is it desirable that the inside rather than the outside radius of a bent part be specified?
12. What are the common ways of correcting or compensating for springback?
13. What is the difference between drawing and bending?
14. On what basis may the required blank size be determined for a drawn part?
15. What is the function of a hold down ring in a drawing operation?
16. How is breakage prevented by breaking a drawing operation down into a number of steps?

17. What desirable features does an inclinable "C" frame press provide?
18. What is the usual function of the second slide on a double action drawing press?
19. What advantages have hydraulic presses over crank driven types?
20. Where multiple operations are to be performed on a part what is the usual order of tooling costs, accuracy, and productivity for individual punches and dies, a compound die, and a progressive die?
21. What are the principal factors accounting for the high cost of most conventional press tooling?
22. What principle is involved in drop stamping?
23. What is the common tooling cost reduction involved in most of the low quantity methods used for shallow drawing and forming operations?
24. What is the major restriction on the shapes that may be produced by spinning?
25. How is it possible to form magnetically materials that are not ferromagnetic?

⬛⬛⬛ CHAPTER 13

Powder Metallurgy

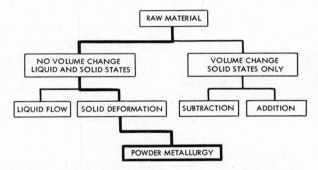

THE DEFINITION for the term *powder metallurgy* as provided by the Committee for Powder Metallurgy of the American Society for Metals is: "The art of producing metal powders and objects shaped from individual, mixed, or alloyed metal powders, with or without the inclusion of nonmetallic constituents, by pressing or molding objects which may be simultaneously or subsequently heated to produce a coherent mass, either without fusion, or with the fusion of a low melting constituent only."

References to the granulation of gold and silver and subsequent shaping into solid shapes go back as far as 1574. It is also noteworthy that in the nineteenth century more metallic elements were produced in powder form than in any other form. For the most part however, these were all precious or rare metals for which powder metallurgy was the only practical method of manufacture and it has only been within the last fifty years that this process has become competitive with more conventional processes in the manufacture of articles from iron, copper, aluminum, and the other more common metals.

Early developments in powder metallurgy were based on two factors. During the production of platinum, tantalum, osmium, tungsten, and similar refractory metals, reduction was a pure chemical process from which the reduced metal was obtained as a precipitate in flake or powder form.

235

Since furnaces and techniques were not available for complete melting of these materials, the only procedure for producing them in solid form was to press them into coherent masses and *sinter* at temperatures below the melting point. This procedure still applies in the production of some metals, especially tungsten. A second major advantage of the process that led to early use and still applies today is in the production of porous shapes obtained with lighter pressing pressures or lower sintering temperatures. Materials in this form are useful as chemical catalysts, filtering elements, and bearings.

Fig. 13–1 shows the steps ordinarily required in the production of a part

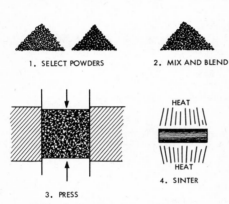

1. SELECT POWDERS

2. MIX AND BLEND

HEAT

HEAT

4. SINTER

3. PRESS

FIG. 13–1.   Elements of powder metallurgy.

by the powder metallurgy process. Suitable powder must first be produced. While theoretically any crystalline material may be fabricated by powder metallurgy, the production of suitable powder has presented restrictions in many cases either because of difficulty in obtaining adequate purity or, for economic reasons. After selection and blending of the powder, and manufacture of a die for the shape to be produced, the powder is pressed to size and shape. The application of heat results in crystalline growth and the production of a homogenous body. Various combinations of heat and pressure may be used. Some sintering takes place under high pressure at room temperature. However, cold pressing is usually followed by sintering at a temperature somewhat below the lowest melting point of any of the constituents. An intermediate elevated temperature may be used during pressing, then the shape removed from the press and subjected to higher temperature. In hot pressing, the final sintering temperature is applied simultaneously with the pressure.

Powders.   The characteristics of any final product of powder metallurgy will depend to a great extent on the properties of the powders used as raw materials. In addition to the actual metal of which the powder consists, the properties of greatest importance are particle size, particle size distribution, shape, crystalline structure, density, flowability, compactibility, and purity.

For spherical particles, the diameter is a complete description of the size. However, many particles have flake, needle, or jagged shapes and no simple method exists for specifying sizes completely. The normal size range for powders is from about one tenth micron to one thousand microns (1 micron = 0.000039 inch), or from colloidal size up to about $\frac{1}{32}$

inch. Sizes down to about forty microns may be graded by passing through screens or sieves in much the same manner as molding sand is tested. For smaller sizes microscopic or sedimentation methods are used. As a rule somewhat larger sizes may be used in the manufacture of parts where only a single metal powder is used but smaller sizes are necessary where a mixture of two or more powders is used.

Of perhaps even greater importance than the actual size of the particles is the size distribution, or the relative amount of different sizes that are present in the powder. The importance of this factor may be seen by considering the percentage of space which would be left under an optimum packing arrangement of spheres. For spheres of uniform size, a minimum of 26 per cent of the total volume will be space and with random arrangements the figure would likely be higher, usually exceeding 40 per cent and sometimes approaching 90 per cent.

In general, smaller sizes are preferred over coarse sizes since the greater surface to volume ratio produces greater contact area and cohesion between particles resulting in better physical characteristics. An exception to this rule exists for copper or iron which are to be either hot or cold worked after sintering and for large shapes where fine powders require excessive pressures to obtain uniform densities.

In addition to its effect on contact area, particle shape has a large influence on the *flowability* of loose particles. Spherical shapes are most ideal for both sintering and for pressing powder into close contact. Irregular shapes tend to *bridge* (form arches) more easily, limit the depth of pressure effects during pressing, and cause irregularities in compaction. The shape is largely determined by the method of manufacture, ranging from nearly true spheres for some chemically produced powders to irregular flakes from some mechanical attrition processes.

Metallic powders are produced by many methods, including mechanical, chemical, physical, and electrical. Only a few, however, are of commercial interest for the powder metallurgy process. Many of the others are of importance for the production of powders for paints and metallic coatings, and as chemical catalysts. Elimination of the majority of powder making methods is due to their inability to produce the required sizes, shapes, and purities required for powder metallurgy.

Low temperature melting metals such as tin, lead, zinc, and aluminum are frequently powdered by *atomization* or *shotting*. In shotting, liquid metal is forced through screens or orifices into water or other quenching media. In atomization, high pressure gas contacts the molten metal causing it to break up into very fine particles which solidify almost immediately. For those metals which oxidize easily, inert gases must be used to maintain purity of the powder.

The most flexible and economical method, and therefore one of the most important commercially for making powder metallurgy powders, is chemical reduction. Pulverized metallic oxides are treated in a reducing atmosphere at elevated temperatures which are usually well below the melting point of the metal and oxide. Hydrogen, carbon monoxide, and natural gas are among the materials used as reducing agents. The process is subject to many variations for developing powders with different characteristics. The majority of parts made of iron, copper, nickel, and tungsten are produced from powders made by this method.

The third powder making process of importance is that of electrolysis. Its value is in its ability to produce an extremely high degree of purity with a variety of metals, so that even though costly, the method becomes necessary when high purity is essential.

Mixing and Blending.   Most powders as initially produced require some further processing before pressing and sintering. Generally, to be satisfactory, powders must be free from stresses to press properly and must contain little or no surface oxides which would inhibit proper bonding during sintering.

A typical procedure for preparing powders starts with washing to remove any foreign chemicals such as electrolytic acids. Drying would then be done at a high enough temperature to produce an annealing action in a reducing atmosphere to further eliminate any oxides present. The high temperature involved in these treatments promotes some sintering resulting in spongy, flaky or other aggregate forms, which may require re-crushing in jaw, ball, or hammer mills. The material would then be graded for particle size through sieves and finally selected in the quantities needed to produce a specific analysis.

Mixing is required for even a single metal powder to promote homogeneity with a random dispersion of particle sizes and shapes. Single materials are often mixed from a variety of sources to develop improved properties. The mixing and blending is even more important for combinations of materials which depend on uniform alloying to develop final properties. Small amounts of organic materials may be added to reduce segregation and others both organic and inorganic may be added to act as lubricants during pressing or sometimes in the final product.

All kinds of mixing devices are used for mixing and blending metallic powders. Ball and rod mills roll and crush the particles together. Blenders make use of tumbling motion to provide the mixing action and mullers, similar to those used in sand conditioning for foundry work, alternately pack and loosen the particles by rolling and plowing. The time required for mixing may vary from a few minutes to several days.

Pressing.   The bond that is established between particles in powder metallurgy varies all the way from mechanical interlocking to the growing of new, common crystals across the borders of the initial particles. Every atom is surrounded by a force field which is effective at up to a few atom diameters. Proper bonding then depends primarily on bringing adjacent particles close enough together that these atomic forces can be effective. The effective closeness is dependent on both particle size and shape. Mixed sizes and shapes, at least with random packing, provide the maximum closeness and the greatest number of contact points. Most metals can be plastically deformed, and with these, pressure can be applied to cause the contact points to grow into relatively large areas. The face centered cubic metals such as nickel, copper, and lead do not work harden readily and can be deformed with comparatively low pressures. The metals that work harden easily and which are also usually harder and stronger to begin with, such as the body centered cubic structures of iron, tungsten, and vanadium, require much higher pressures to establish suitable contact areas.

Surface atoms will be rearranged both by plastic flow and by mutual attraction with atoms of the adjacent surface. Increasing temperature aids both of these mechanisms by decreasing resistance to plastic flow and increasing the energy of the atom. Particles that have been severely work hardened as a result of the plastic flow may recrystallize at elevated temperatures and the new crystals may actually cross the original particle boundary to establish complete atomic bonds.

The pressures required in powder metallurgy depend on the material composition and purpose of the pressing operation. Briquetting to establish material volume and to preform complicated shapes may be accomplished with tin at about one thousand psi, but requires fifty thousand psi for tungsten. Cold pressures for the establishment of maximum contact areas require about ten thousand psi for tin, one hundred thousand psi for iron and nearly two hundred thousand psi for tungsten. Required pressures are affected by grain shapes and sizes. Large grains flow more easily than small ones but may require higher final pressure to complete the necessary deformation. Round grains flow more easily in the initial stages of compression but require higher pressures than irregular shaped grains for establishing large contact areas.

Compacting of metallic powders ideally would be done by applying pressure in all directions at one time. This is usually impractical for commercial use and most compaction is done along a single axis. Pressure is sometimes applied for one direction only but in other cases opposing motions are used to reduce the effect of sidewall friction. Fig. 13–2 shows the effect of sidewall friction on the density of a compact. The effectiveness of pressing is most often evaluated by measuring the density of the

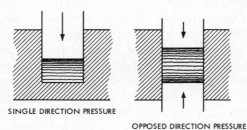

SINGLE DIRECTION PRESSURE

OPPOSED DIRECTION PRESSURE

FIG. 13–2. Density variation from sidewall friction.

material and expressing it as a percentage of the theoretical density for solid metal of the type being treated. Densities depend on the particle size and shape, the material, the pressure, time, and temperature. The figure illustrates the variation in density as the distance from the source of pressure increases. This variation depends primarily on the length to width or diameter ratio of the compact and ranges from as little as 3 per cent for a ratio of one fourth to as much as 25 per cent for a ratio of two. The density variation problem is further complicated by shapes that are other than simple cylinders. Partial solution to this density variation problem may be accomplished by pre-pressing or the use of multiple punches as shown in Fig. 13–3. Development of pressure by centrifuging may produce more uniform density since each particle of material supplies a force of its own. Rods of various cross-sectional shapes may be extruded with relatively uniform density throughout their length. Thin coatings of powdered materials may be applied to rigid backings by rolling. This procedure is especially useful for various bearing materials.

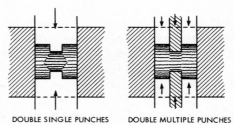

DOUBLE SINGLE PUNCHES   DOUBLE MULTIPLE PUNCHES

FIG. 13–3. Multiple punch for density control.

Sintering.   The term sintering is used to identify the mechanism by which solid particles are bonded by application of pressure and/or heat. In its broadest sense the process includes such things as welding, brazing, soldering and the firing of ceramics and the union of plastic flakes or granules. Each of the areas other than those involving metal in powder form are important enough and of such wide usage as to have developed their own language and technology.

Sintering can be accomplished at room temperature with pressure alone but is most often performed at elevated temperature either at the same time, or after pressure has been applied. With some multiple constituent compositions some of the low temperature melting materials may be melted, but in most cases sintering is a fully solid state process. The two most common sintering procedures are first, application of heat and pressure together called *hot pressing* and second, the application of heat after the particles have been closely packed by a *cold pressing* operation.

In hot pressing, the plasticity of the particles is greater and they recrystallize more readily, permitting high densities to be achieved with lower pressures than would be necessary at lower temperatures. For some materials, densities high enough to provide acceptable properties in the finished product are possible only by hot pressing. However, a number of problems are involved. The high temperatures involved (above 2500°F. for some materials) require expensive die materials whose life may be very short. For some materials, a graphite die is used for each part pressed. Gas that is evolved may be trapped within the material, leading to porosity defects as in castings.

Cold pressed parts that are subsequently sintered may be heated in conventional manner by being placed in ordinary furnaces or salt baths. In those cases where heat is supplied by convection or radiation it is usually necessary to provide a protective atmosphere of inert or reducing gas to protect the part from corrosion or chemical change.

Sizing and Post-Sintering Treatments. Because of variations of density and other factors, shrinkage of powder metallurgy products during sintering is difficult to control. Parts that require close tolerances must nearly always be finished by some dimensional treatment. Cold working may be used for minor changes of dimensions but this procedure is limited by the lack of ductility normal to powder metallurgy products. Repressing in the hot state, sometimes referred to as coining, improves the density, strength, and ductility of the material although even with this process it is seldom that these properties are equal to those of a similar material produced by fusion. Most commercial deformation working is done hot or by cold working at elevated temperatures with frequent interruptions for recrystallization.

Powder metallurgy products may be heat treated in the same ways as other materials of similar chemical composition but the treatments are usually not as effective as for the fusion produced metals, mainly because of the porous structure restricting the heat conductivity. Many of the voids within powder metallurgy products are stress concentration points which not only limit service loads but increase the stresses arising from thermal gradients during heat treatment. The treatments include re-sintering for stabilization and homogeneity, annealing for softness, grain refinement for improved ductility, and hardening for improved wear resistance. The hardening processes may be quench hardening of carbon steels, precipitation hardening of nonferrous materials, or surface hardening by carburizing, cyaniding, and nitriding.

The machinability of sintered materials is usually poor, but machining is sometimes necessary for final control of dimensions or to establish shapes that are not practical for the powder metallurgy process. With some types of products, such as the cemented carbides, grinding is the common finishing process both for control of size and shape and, in many cases, to eliminate the surface produced in the sintering process. The original surfaces may contain faults or inclusions damaging to use of the product.

One important finishing step is that of impregnation. Inorganic materials such as oils or waxes may be impregnated into porous metal products for purposes of lubrication. An entirely different kind of product can be produced by impregnating high melting temperature metals with low melting temperature metals. The principal use of this technique is in the production of *cemented steels*. A porous, skeleton iron compact, which may be produced from low cost iron powder, is impregnated with molten copper. The resulting product has better strength, ductility, and machinability than conventional powder metallurgy parts and may be more readily plated or joined by brazing. Sintered iron has also been impregnated with lead alloys to improve antifriction properties for use as bearings.

Equipment.   As in the cases of deformation forming and die casting, the dies for shaping and compacting powdered metals must be designed for specific cases. Their design is performed empirically and in many cases, when new shapes or conditions occur, modification will be required after testing in order to get uniform densities and suitable sizes. All compacted metals shrink in varying degrees during sintering and allowances must be made to compensate for this in the die design. Pressing of some metals requires extremely high pressures and the die must be strong enough to withstand these. Since dies are expensive to manufacture they must last for a considerable time for economical production, and for this reason are often made of cemented carbide materials.

The presses used for compacting powdered metals are usually of special design. They are frequently made with multiple action to permit manufacture of complex shapes. Those used for lower loads (up to about 150 tons) are usually mechanical with eccentric and crank, toggle and knuckle, or cam action to produce the closing motion. Mechanical presses have the advantage of higher speed operation over the hydraulic presses which are used for higher loads. In addition to higher capacity, hydraulic machines are more flexible and safer against overloads which might damage dies or other equipment.

Application for Powdered Metal Products.   Powder metallurgy occupies two rather distinct areas. It is a basic shape producing method for practically all metals, in direct competition with other methods. In addition, for many refractory (high melting point) materials, both metals and nonmetals, powder metallurgy is the only practical means of shape production. It must be remembered that for the metals used in large tonnages, the initial step in any conventional manufacturing sequence is always a casting process. This may or may not be followed by hot or cold working but the melting and casting of the metal is necessary to produce the first solid shape. Tungsten is typical of the refractory metals with a melting point of 6150°F. and no satisfactory mold or crucible materials exist for conventional casting techniques. Tantalum and molybdenum are similar. For some other metals, possible to melt, impurities picked up by the liquid from the containers would be undesirable and powder metallurgy offers the most economical means of obtaining solid shapes.

Cemented carbides form one of the most important groups of materials that can be fabricated into solid shapes only by powder metallurgy. These materials will be discussed as cutting tools in a later chapter but their method of manufacture may be noted. The principal material used is tungsten carbide although titanium carbide and tantalum carbide are also sometimes used in combinations with tungsten carbide. While it is possible to press and sinter these metal carbides in pure form, the resulting solid material is too brittle for most practical use. However, the addition of from 3 to 20 per cent cobalt or nickel powder yields a product of somewhat reduced hardness but with sufficient shock resistance to be useful in many applications where high hardness and wear resistance at high temperatures are of importance. The final combination of hardness and ductility may be controlled by the percentage of nickel or cobalt added with the smaller amounts yielding the hardest but most brittle products.

A further area where powder metallurgy produces products not practical by other means is in the manufacture of materials with controlled low density. One of the first mass produced powder metallurgy products was sintered porous bronze bearings. After cold pressing, sintering, and sizing, the bearings are impregnated with oil which in service is made available for lubrication. Although not true fluid film bearings they provide long service with low maintenance. Porous materials are also useful as filters.

Composite electrical materials form a group similar to the cemented carbides. Tungsten and other refractory metals in combination with silver, nickel, graphite, or copper find wide application as electrical contacts and commutator brushes and powder metallurgy not only provides a means for producing the combination but also provides the finished shape for the parts. Many of the currently used permanent magnet materials are produced by powder metallurgy.

In the applications noted so far, powder metallurgy is in a somewhat noncompetitive position so far as the specific products are concerned. Competition exists between cemented carbides and other cutting tools but cemented carbides can be fabricated only by powder metallurgy. For many of the other products made of most metals more direct competition exists between powder metallurgy and other methods strictly as processes where the final products may be identical. In this area powder metallurgy has a number of advantages and disadvantages. In many cases the powder metal product is completely finished as a result of the process with no material loss. Production rates are high, finishes and tolerances are good. Powder metallurgy is particularly useful for shapes with two parallel faces but a complex cylindrical contour in the other dimensions.

One of the biggest disadvantages of powder metallurgy is the high raw material cost. In addition, the high die cost means that the process is competitive with conventional processes only when large quantities are to be produced. Without impregnation treatments, which add to the cost, the mechanical properties of sintered metal are nearly always lower than those of cast or wrought material of a similar composition.

Some general comparisons may be made with more conventional processes. Powder metallurgy competes successfully with sand casting and forging only where high tolerances or complex shapes require extensive machining on the castings or forgings. Sand casting has greater capacity for producing complicated, cored, and undercut shapes. Although powder metallurgy and die casting compete to some extent, the lower material costs of casting usually put it in a favorable position. Tool costs for die casting are often lower for extended runs than for powder metallurgy. Powder metallurgy competes somewhat more successfully with investment molding because of the high labor costs involved in this process.

Powder metallurgy parts are most frequently in direct competition with parts machined from bar stock. The economics of the final choice are sometimes remote but must be based on these differences. Powder metallurgy has higher tool and material costs and considerably less design flexibility than machining, and the mechanical properties of the machined stock are better. On the other hand, powder metallurgy involves little or no material loss, production rates are greater, and labor costs are lower than for machining.

The furnaces used for sintering are of standard types similar to those used for other heating procedures. Either batch or continuous designs may be used depending on production rates. Nearly all are of controlled atmosphere type because of the need for corrosion protection for the metallic particles before sintering is complete.

Gas fired and electrically heated nichrome element furnaces are used for temperatures up to about 2000°F. Temperatures in this range are satisfactory for most nonferrous sintering. Higher temperatures are possible with other electrical heating elements. Silicon carbide elements permit temperatures to about 2400°F., molybdenum elements to about 2900°F., and specially designed furnaces with carbon used as the heating element to 3600°F. The sintering of some materials, in particular refractory metals, requires even higher temperatures which can be obtained to about 5400°F. by induction heating and to about 5800°F. by direct resistance heating where the current passes through the parts being heated.

QUESTIONS

1. For what metal or metals is powder metallurgy the only practical primary production process today? Why?
2. What are the four steps normally used in powder metallurgy?
3. When are small powder particle sizes necessary?
4. What is the importance of the size distribution of a metal powder?
5. Name the three important processes used for making powders for powder metallurgy.
6. Why are organic materials often mixed in with metal powders?

7. What is the influence of grain shape on the pressures required for compacting?

8. How may the effectiveness of pressing be expressed?

9. What does the term sintering mean?

10. Distinguish between cold pressing and hot pressing.

11. How do the properties of powder metallurgy products compare to those of products produced by other methods?

12. What would be the purpose of impregnating a powdered iron part with copper? With lead?

13. What shapes are most easily produced by powder metallurgy?

14. Why may it be said that powder metallurgy has a double advantage in the manufacture of cemented carbide parts?

15. With what casting process does powder metallurgy compete most successfully?

ﯼﯼﯼ CHAPTER 14

Plastics

FOR SOME TIME the fastest growing field of materials has been the group called plastics. Any thorough treatment of plastics, especially concerning the chemistry of the materials, would require a number of volumes. On the other hand, plastics cannot properly be ignored in any treatment of manufacturing processes since they are in direct competition with most metals. Since 1958, a greater tonnage of plastics has been produced annually than all nonferrous metals combined.

A study of plastics is complicated by the tremendous number of material variations possible. There are roughly as many important families of plastics as there are commercially important metals. While it is true that many of the metals are alloyed to different combinations, the number is relatively small when compared with the number of distinct plastics possible in each family. Furthermore, while for metals the hardness and strength seldom exceeds a ratio of perhaps 10 to 1 for any particular alloy group, many plastics which are under a single name are produced with properties ranging from liquids that are used as adhesives or finishes to rigid solids whose hardness and strength compare favorably with metals.

The word plastic is derived from the Greek word "plastikos" which meant "fit for molding." Many of the materials called plastics today, such as finishes and adhesives, are not molded at all and on the other hand many materials are molded that are not called plastics. Many metals and most ceramics are molded at times. Plastics might best be defined as a group of large molecule organic compounds, primarily produced as a chemical product, and susceptible to shaping under combinations of pressure and heat. To include all the plastics, the term organic must be expanded to include silicon based materials as well as carbon based.

Historically, the development of plastics has occurred in two general periods. Chemists in France, Germany, and England during the period from 1830 to 1900 isolated and named many materials that are called plastics today. The actual commercial production of most of these materials was delayed until production methods and facilities became available that permitted them to compete with the more traditional materials.

246

The second period of even more rapid developments has been in the United States, particularly since 1940 when many new methods of manufacture and treatment as well as new plastic materials have been developed.

Chemically, plastics are all *polymers*. The smallest unit structure or molecule which identifies the chemical involved is called a *monomer*. By various means, including heat, light, pressure, and agitation, these monomers may be made to join and grow into much larger molecules by the process of *polymerization*. In general, the first polymerization involves the connecting of the monomers into long chains, usually with a progressive degree of solidification or increase in viscosity as the polymerization proceeds. For most plastics the properties depend on the degree of polymerization, which explains to a large degree the wide range of properties available. For the group of plastics known as *thermosetting* a second type of polymerization takes place in which cross-linking occurs between adjacent chains. This thermosetting reaction frequently results in greatly increased rigidity.

Types of Plastics. There are two broad groups of plastics, based originally on their reaction to heat, but more properly on the type of polymerization involved. Plastics that are called *thermoplastic* have the degree of polymerization controlled in the initial manufacture of the plastic raw material or *resin*. These materials soften with increasing temperature and regain rigidity as the temperature is decreased. The process is essentially reversible but in some cases chemical changes are produced by heating which may cause some deterioration of properties.

As noted before, the *thermosetting* plastics undergo a further cross-linking type of polymerization, which for the early plastics was initiated by the application of heat, but which in many modern "Thermosetting" plastics may be initiated by other means. In the fabrication by molding of thermosetting plastics, an initial thermoplastic stage is followed by the thermosetting reaction at higher temperatures or with prolonged heating. Thermoplastics may be resoftened by reheating but the thermosetting reaction is chemical in nature and irreversible so that once it has taken place further heating results only in gradual charring and deterioration.

The origin of the resin distinguishes a number of different types of plastics. Some true plastics are found in nature and used essentially as found. These include shellac, used most frequently as a finish for wood, and as an adhesive constituent, and asphalt, used as a binder in road materials, as a constituent in some finishes, and with fibrous filling materials as a molding compound.

A number of plastics are natural materials that have undergone some chemical modification but retain the general chemical characteristics of the natural material. Cellulose may be produced as paper with slight modification, as vulcanized fibre with slightly greater modification, and as cellulose acetate with even more modification. Wood in its natural state has thermoplastic properties that are made use of in some manufacturing processes. Rubber latex, as found in nature, is a thermoplastic material but is generally modified by chemical additions to act as a thermosetting material.

The greatest number of plastics presently used are most properly called *synthetic* plastics. While many of them make use of some particular natural material such as petroleum as the principal constituent, the chemistry of the raw material and the chemistry of the finished plastic has no direct connection. The raw material may be thought of simply as the source of elements and compounds for the manufacture of the plastic.

Plastic Constituents.   The largest single use for plastic materials is as molding compounds. The characteristics of the final plastic part are controlled by the ingredients of the molding compound and influenced to some extent by the processing.

The most important constituent of the molding compound is the plastic resin itself. The final chemical resistance, heat resistance, transparency, strength, moisture resistance, surface hardness, weatherability, electrical characteristics, and cost are largely determined by the resin, which may make up from 10 to 100 per cent of the molding compound. It is the resin which determines whether a molding compound is thermoplastic or thermosetting.

Of almost equal importance in many compounds is the *filler* used. As much as 90 per cent of various materials, generally chemically inert so far as the chemistry of the plastic is concerned, may be mixed with the plastic resin. The principal purpose of the filler may be to add bulk and reduce the cost of the molding compound. In nearly all cases the properties of the plastic will be changed by the addition of filler. When the principal purpose is to add bulk at low cost, wood flour or other forms of cellulose are most commonly used. These materials lower moisture resistance of many resins to some extent but take color well and permit the making of good surface finishes.

Numerous fillers are used for the improvement of specific properties. Fibrous materials such as cotton linters or glass fibers add particularly to impact strength which is low in most pure molded resins. Tensile strength is improved most with woven or felted fillers of similar materials. Heat resistance may be improved with asbestos fillers, friction properties controlled with graphite or molybdenum sulphide, and the electrical characteristics altered by the addition of iron powder or mica.

With the exception of phenol formaldehyde, most of the common plastic resins are either transparent or translucent. The color of the final product may be controlled by the addition of *dyes* or *pigments* to the molding compound. Dyes are materials having mutual solubility with the resin. Pigments are insoluble compounds which are denser and more opaque than dyes. Over eight hundred different dyes and pigments are in use in the plastics industry. In some cases, the dye or pigment may have some effect on the other properties of the plastic.

Over three hundred different chemicals are used as *plasticizers* which exhibit control over both the viscosity of the material while it is being molded and the rigidity of the final product. They act by providing a liquid phase which disrupts some of the polymer bonds.

Lubricants with low volatilizing temperatures may be added during the manufacture of the resin or the mixing of the powder and serve primarily to simplify proper blending of the components. With higher volatilizing points they remain in the mixture at the higher temperatures of molding and serve to ease the flow of material into and through the dies. Mold *release agents* are silicones or waxes that are sprayed or brushed onto the surface of the mold to prevent or reduce adherence of the plastic to the surface of the mold.

With thermosetting plastics, a chemical catalyst may be used to control the rate of the thermosetting reaction. Such materials are not useful with thermoplastics since there are no chemical reactions to speed up or slow down. The purpose of catalysts depends to some extent on the manner in which the plastic is processed. An *accelerator* may simply reduce the time necessary for the reaction to take place and the purpose would be to speed the processing cycle. For some plastics, accelerators are available which reduce the temperature necessary to initiate the thermosetting reaction, sometimes to as low as room temperature. Several adhesives and resins used with fiberglass fillers are in this category. An *inhibitor* raises the temperature or prolongs the time necessary for setting to occur. This may permit the successful molding of parts with variable section thicknesses more readily or may prolong the shelf life of unset resins.

A principal use for chemical solvents is in the manufacture of finishes and coatings, particularly thermoplastics. Many of these materials may be dissolved in a solvent, applied as a finish and, when the solvent evaporates, remain as a uniform film. Most lacquers are thermoplastics with appropriate solvents. Many air drying cements or adhesives are similar mixtures and in some cases a solvent alone may be used as a cement for joining two plastic parts. The plastics industry uses over five million tons of solvents annually.

A number of molding compound additives have been developed for specific use. Numerous proprietary compounds are available to act as *destaticisers*. The problem of charge build-up on plastics arises because of their electrical nonconductivity. Additives called *stabilizers* which prevent or reduce degradation caused by age, heat, or light, are especially useful with vinyls. While all of these components may be used in a single molding mixture, it must be remembered that in some cases simple mixtures or even a pure resin may be molded. Many of the components may serve multiple purposes. The filler may provide the necessary color, the plasticiser may serve as a lubricant, or a catalyst may serve as a filler.

Characteristics of Plastics. Tables 14–1 and 14–2 give the principal characteristics and typical uses for most of the plastics in common use. No such list can be completely thorough because new plastics are constantly

TABLE 14-1

A Summary of Principal Characteristics and Uses of Thermoplastic Plastics

Resin Type	Principal Characteristics	Forms Produced	Typical Uses	Relative Cost
ABS	High strength, toughness, colorability	Injection moldings, extrusions, formable sheet	Pipe, appliance cabinets, football helmets, handles	50–60
Acetal	High strength, colorability, high fatigue life, low friction, solvent resistance	Injection moldings, extrusions	Gears, impellers, plumbing hardware	80
Acrylic	High strength, colorability, optical clarity, low service temperature	Injection moldings, extrusions, castings, formable sheet, fiber	Transparent canopies, windows, lenses, edge lighted signs, mirrors, high quality molded parts	46–55
Cellulose Acetate	Moderate strength, toughness, colorability, optical clarity, wide hardness range, low service temperature	Injection moldings, extrusions, formable sheet, film, fiber	Toys, shoe heels, buttons, packaging, tape	36–58
Cellulose Acetate Butyrate	Moderate strength, high toughness, good weatherability, colorability, optical clarity, low service temperature	Injection moldings, extrusions, formable sheet, film	Telephone handsets, steering wheels, appliance housings, outdoor signs, pipe	40–62
Cellulose Propionate	Moderate strength, high toughness, good weatherability, colorability, optical clarity, low service temperature	Injection moldings, extrusions, formable sheet, film	Radio cabinets, pen and pencil barrels, auto parts	40–62
Ethyl Cellulose	Moderate strength, high toughness, flexibility, colorability, moisture resistance, better electric properties than other cellulostics, low service temperature	Injection moldings, extrusions, films	Refrigerator parts, aircraft parts, flashlight housings, door rollers	65–75
Cellulose Nitrate	Toughest of all thermoplastics, good formability, poor aging, high flammability, low service temperature	Extrusions, formable sheet	Ping pong balls, hollow articles	70–200
Chlorinated Polyether	High chemical resistance, moderate strength	Injection moldings, extrusions, sheet	Valves, pump parts in corrosive environments	250

Resin Type	Principal Characteristics	Forms Produced	Typical Uses	Relative Cost
TFE (Tetrafluoroethylene)	Chemical inertness, high service temperature, low friction, low creep strength, high weatherability	Sintered shapes, extrusions, formable sheet, film, fiber	Pipe, pump parts, electronic parts, nonlubricated bearings, gaskets, antiadhesive coatings	350–550
CFE (Chlorotrifluoroethylene)	Higher strength than TFE, lower chemical resistance than TFE, high service temperature, high weatherability	Injection moldings, extrusions, formable sheet and film	Coil forms, pipe, tank lining, valve diaphragms	700–800
Nylon (Polyamide)	High strength, toughness, work hardenability, low friction, good dielectric properties	Injection moldings, extrusions, formable sheet, film, fiber	Gears, cams, bearings, pump parts, coil forms, slide fasteners, gaskets, high pressure tubing	100–200
Polycarbonate	High strength, toughness, chemical resistance, weatherability, high service temperature	Injection moldings, extrusions	Gears, hydraulic fittings, coil forms, appliance parts, electronic components	150
Polyethylene	Moderate strength, high toughness, good dielectric, low friction, chemical resistance, flexibility	Injection moldings, extrusions, formable sheet, film, fiber, rigid foam	Housewares, pipe, pipe fittings, squeeze bottles, sports goods, electrical insulation	32–38
Polypropylene	Similar to polyethylene, more rigid, higher creep resistance, higher temperature resistance	Injection moldings, extrusions, formable sheet, film, fiber	Housewares, electronic equipment, automotive parts, pipe, pipe fittings	42–58
Polystyrene	High strength, low impact resistance, high dielectric strength, colorability, optical clarity, low service temperature	Injection moldings, extrusions, formable sheet, film, foam	Toys, electrical parts battery cases, light fixtures, rigid conduit	22–43
Vinyl	Wide range of properties, strength, toughness, abrasion resistance, colorability, low service temperature	Compression moldings, extrusions, castings, formable sheet, film, fiber, foam	Electrical insulation, floor tile, water hose, raincoats	24–43

TABLE 14–2

A Summary of Principal Characteristics and Uses of Thermosetting Plastics

Resin Type	Principal Characteristics	Forms Produced	Typical Uses	Relative Price
Epoxy	Moderate strength, high dielectric strength, chemical resistance, weatherability, colorability, high service temperature, strong adhesive qualities	Casting, reinforced moldings, laminated, rigid foam, filament wound structures	Chemical tanks, pipe, printed circuit bases, short run dies, radomes, pressure vessels	45–80
Melamine	Hardest plastic, high dielectric strength, moderate service temperature, colorability, dimensional stability	Compression and transfer moldings, reinforced moldings, laminates	Dinnerware, electrical components, table and counter tops	42–45
Phenolics	Moderately high strength, high service temperature, dimensional stability, color restrictions	Compression and transfer moldings, castings, reinforced moldings, laminates, cold moldings, rigid foam	Electrical hardware, poker chips, toys, buttons, appliance cabinets, thermal insulation, table and counter tops, ablative structural shapes	20–35
Polyester (including Alkyds)	Moderately high strength, colorability, dimensional stability, fast cure, easy handling, good electrical properties, high service temperatures, chemical resistance	Castings, reinforced moldings, laminates, film, fiber, compression and transfer moldings	Electrical parts, auto ignition parts, heater ducts, trays, tote boxes, laundry tubs, boats, auto bodies, buttons	31–60
Silicone	Highest service temperatures, low friction, high dielectric strength, flexible, moderate strength, high moisture resistance	Compression and transfer moldings, reinforced moldings, laminates, rigid foam	High temperature electrical insulation, high temperature laminates, gaskets, bushings, seals, spacers	275–540
Urea	Moderately high strength, colorability, high dielectric strength, water resistance, low service temperature	Compression and transfer moldings	Colored electrical parts, buttons, dinnerware	19–34

being introduced and the time span from discovery of a useful plastic to commercial use is decreasing. The cellulose plastics among thermoplastics and phenol formaldehyde (a phenolic) among the thermosetting plastics were the first plastics to be developed and are still in wide use today, but many of the plastics in use were unknown ten years ago.

Some comments may be made about the chart, keeping in mind that most general rules have exceptions. As a group, thermoplastics are of somewhat lower strength and hardness but higher in toughness than thermosetting materials. The thermosetting plastics generally have better moisture and chemical resistance than the thermoplastics. The terms high and low when used for strengths, service temperatures, and other characteristics are only relative and apply to plastics as a total group. None of the plastics have useful service temperatures that are as high as those of most metals, and the modulus of elasticity of all plastics is low compared to most metals. While the ultimate strengths of many metals is greater than that available with plastics, some specific plastics offer favorable comparisons. Nylon, for example, is one of a few plastics that, being truly crystalline, may be hardened by working. Drawn nylon filaments may have a tensile strength of fifty thousand psi which is actually greater than some low strength steels. Plastics excel in some applications as insulators or where chemical resistance is important. The greatest tonnage, however, is used in direct competition with other materials where plastics may be favored because of their low fabrication costs in large quantities, light weight, and easy colorability.

PLASTICS PROCESSING

Fig. 14–1 indicates the principal methods used for processing plastics. Plastics processing has many similarities to the processing of metals. In a general way, the forming of sheets of plastic may be compared to the pressworking of metals: many of the techniques are similar. Most of the casting methods used with plastics are similar to permanent mold casting of metals. The most important area of plastics processing is matched die molding. In this area, *compression molding*, and *cold molding* are like forging and powder metallurgy in that the material is introduced into an open die and the forming pressure is applied by the closing of the dies. *Transfer molding* is essentially cold chamber die casting, and *injection molding* is quite like hot chamber die casting. In fact, the equipment used for these processes is usually similar in appearance. Extrusion of plastics is directly comparable to the extrusion of metals.

Many of the procedures have been developed because of the nature of the plastics groups, particularly because of the difference between thermosetting and thermoplastic materials. While the initial treatment of these two types is similar and both soften during initial heating, this ductile stage of thermosetting plastics is of limited duration and the setting reaction proceeds with time particularly at elevated temperature. Thermoplastic materials, however, may be held in the softened condition for prolonged periods of time with little or no chemical change.

The entire plastics industry is like the metals industry in many other respects. The numbers of processors of raw materials into resins and molding compounds and large companies which refine ores and produce

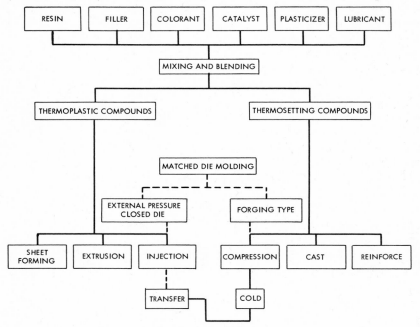

FIG. 14–1. Plastics processing.

primary shapes in metals are both relatively few. Both industries have many individual fabricators of finished goods, some specializing in certain types of processing or types of products. Also, as in the metals industry, some processes with low tooling costs are designed for limited production, and some processes are feasible only when large quantities are to be produced. It is this latter type of processing which is most important to plastics since in many cases only a single step is necessary to make a finished product whose cost is low when sufficient quantities are marketable.

Compression Molding.   The oldest and simplest of plastic molding processes is compression molding, shown in Fig. 14–2. Material in powder, granule, pill, or preformed shape is first introduced into the mold, followed by the application of pressure and heat. With thermosetting plastics, for which the process is normally used, the first effect of the heat is to soften the material in a thermoplastic stage where the particles coalesce and flow under pressure to fill the mold cavity. With prolonged application of heat, the thermosetting reaction takes place and the material becomes permanently rigid. The mold may be opened while still hot and the finished part removed although partial cooling is sometimes beneficial to the dimensional stability of the product. The setting time varies from a few seconds to several minutes depending on material, temperature, method of heating, and section thicknesses. It is possible to compression mold thermoplastics; but after the pressure and heating portion of the cycle, the mold must be cooled before removal of the part.

Variations in compression mold design are aimed primarily at solving the problems of obtaining dimensional and density control. In a straight plunger type mold, the density is controlled by the closing pressure but any variation in the amount of plastic introduced into the mold will cause a variation in dimensions parallel to the direction of closing. In the landed plunger mold, dimensions are controlled by the seating of the land, but the density will vary with any variation in the amount of material. In a flash type mold, the problem is solved in a manner similar to that used in forging metals. An excess of material is always charged and the excess is squeezed out through a relatively narrow opening. This action provides for constant pressure to control the density, and the positive seating of the plunger provides accurate dimensional control.

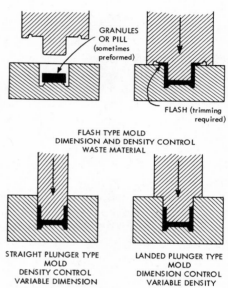

FIG. 14–2. Compression mold types.

The pressures required to compact and form run to several thousand psi and dies must be rigidly constructed of strong wear resistant material. Steel is the normal material for die construction with the type and hardness being determined by the particular plastic and the quantity to be molded.

Many degrees of automation are involved in the practice of plastics molding. Hand molds are built as self-guided units similar to the die sets used in pressworking. This type unit is ordinarily loaded, placed in a press having heated platens which transfer heat and force to the die, then removed from the press for removal of the finished part. Semi-automatic molds remain in the press and contain ejection pins or plungers operated by the machine for removal of the part. With the mold fixed to the press, the heating means can be more efficient and controllable. Fully automatic molds may have loading, pressure and heat application, and unloading all performed automatically according to a timed cycle. Once set up, such a machine can run unattended except for occasional filling of the material hopper and minor adjustments.

Both mechanical and hydraulic presses have been used for compression molding with hydraulic being most common, especially for articles with high vertical walls. In multiple installations, it is common to have one large capacity hydraulic system operating several presses. Any individual press can take advantage of the large capacity to close a mold quickly during the relatively short period of time in which most thermosetting materials are in the flowable thermoplastic state. Electric heating is the most flexible and controllable, but steam heating is quite common because of its economy. High frequency induction heating has been used to some extent, particularly for the preheating portion of the molding cycle.

Compared with other molding techniques, a number of advantages and limitations are associated with compression molding. Size restrictions are relatively few, and the largest molded articles are generally made by this method. There is no waste material and little erosion of the dies since the material does not flow under high pressure from outside the mold. Because of the short, multidirectional flow of material within the mold, distortions and internal stresses within the mold may be minimized. On the other hand, undercuts and small holes are not practical, and the nature of the process requires that the shape of the article be such that the two halves of the mold can fit telescopically together to insure filling. The high pressures required, together with the low viscosity of most thermosetting materials in the plastic state, result in filling clearances between mold parts even when they are on the order of $1/1000$ inch. Thus, not only will removal of flash from the part be required, but also cleaning of the mold parts between successive cycles will be frequently necessary.

Cold Molding. A variation of compression molding is known as *cold molding*. The process is most frequently used with phenolic resins with which sufficient solvent has been mixed to ensure coalescence of the particles under pressure without heat. The operation is carried out in conventional compression molding dies and presses except that no heating equipment is used during molding. Following molding, the parts are removed from the die and baked at relatively low temperatures for rather long periods of time to promote the thermosetting reaction. Such a procedure provides articles that have high heat resistance in service; and the production rate per mold can be high since no curing time is directly involved in the press cycle. However, high molding pressures are required since the only softening of the plastic is provided by the solvent, there is considerable shrinkage during baking as the solvent is driven off, and the resulting surface finish is often dull and unattractive. Many parts used for their electrical insulation and arc resisting qualities are molded by this process.

Closed Die Molding. By far the most important molding processes used are those that introduce the plastic into closed dies by some external pressure system. The principal difference between these methods and die casting used in the foundry is the softened plastic condition of the material rather than the liquid state of metals. Because of the similarities, the terminology is mostly the same as that used in the foundry.

The variations are due principally to the differences between thermoplastics and thermosetting materials. Transfer molding, used with the latter and shown in Fig. 14–3, is like cold chamber die casting in all important respects. A predetermined quantity of molding compound, always including some excess, is introduced into the transfer chamber. This material is usually preformed and may be preheated. Sufficient heat is supplied to the material in the transfer chamber to bring the plastic to the softened state. Pressure is applied to force or "transfer" the charge to the die cavity. Additional heat is supplied to the die for the thermosetting reaction. The excess material in the transfer chamber and the sprue and runner system also set, resulting in a *cull* which must be removed at the completion of the cycle. This cull is scrap since the thermosetting reaction may not be reversed.

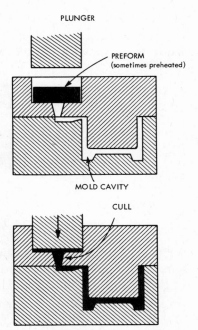

FIG. 14–3. Transfer molding.

Two general methods are used for providing the pressure. In a *pot type* mold, the cross-sectional area of the plunger is made larger than the projected area of the part and runner system and the application of force to the plunger automatically maintains sufficient pressure to hold the halves of the die closed. Such a mold may be used in a conventional compression molding press with a single ram. Two rams are provided in the *plunger mold*, one to hold the die closed and the other to transfer the softened plastic.

Compared to compression molding, transfer molding can provide thinner sections and closer tolerances. The cycle time is generally reduced and the die life is usually longer since the material is in a softened condition when it flows into the mold. There is more freedom in shape since a telescoping action is not required and less flash is produced. Conversely, the mold costs are higher for transfer molding. More material is lost as scrap with the percentage becoming quite high for small parts. Multiple cavities are more frequently used with transfer molding.

For thermoplastic materials, the transfer process is simplified because of the nature of the material. The term *injection molding* is used to describe the process. Prolonged heating is not necessary or desirable, and the material may be forced into a cool die where the material becomes rigid as a result of cooling rather than chemical change. As indicated in Fig. 14–4, a measured charge of raw material is introduced when the plunger is withdrawn and, on the working stroke of the machine, the material is forced around the spreader where heat is supplied. Material for from four to eight working strokes or *shots* is normally kept in the heating chamber. Temperatures are controlled so that the sprue separates at the nozzle when the parts are removed, with the material in the nozzle remaining heated sufficiently to be injected on the next cycle without the cull losses normally expected with transfer molding of thermosetting plastics.

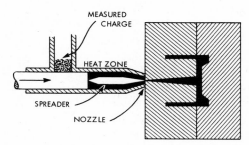

FIG. 14–4.   Injection molding.

Some injection molding of thermosetting materials is done, but precise temperature and time controls are necessary to prevent premature setting of the material in the injection chamber. When used for these materials, the process is known as *jet, flow,* or *offset* molding.

The molding machines are similar in appearances and function to hot chamber die casting machines. Injection pressures of eight thousand to twelve thousand psi are common with hydraulically actuated plungers. Dies may be closed and held hydraulically or with toggle actions. Sizes are specified by the size of die blocks the machine can use and the quantity of material that can be injected in each shot. Capacity ranges from a few ounces up to three hundred ounces per shot.

Injection molding is not directly comparable to compression or transfer molding since in most cases a different type of plastic is used. In general, however, cycle times are much lower for injection molding primarily because thermoplastics need not be held at elevated temperatures for polymerization. The excess material in sprues and runners is often ground and reused, although with repeated heating and cooling some degradation of properties, particularly that of transparency, may occur.

Casting.   With the exception of acrylic rod and sheet materials which are cast against glass, and some protective coatings applied by dipping, casting of plastics is primarily a low tooling cost procedure restricted to thermosetting resins and used for low production of jewelry, novelty items, laboratory specimens, and similar parts. Polyesters, epoxies, and phenolics are most frequently used in syrupy or liquid form with hardening promoted by chemical catalysts or by prolonged heating at low temperatures.

The materials used are generally expensive and the process relies on low tooling costs for economical production in small quantities. Molds of almost any material may be used. In one common procedure, a steel master with the finished part shape is made, then dipped repeatedly in molten lead until a coating of sufficient strength to serve as a mold has been built up. Subject to the parting and draft restrictions that apply to withdrawing any pattern, the lead is removed and used as a mold into which the plastic is poured. Plaster molds are useful for larger parts and flexible rubber or plastic materials may be used for making molds with recesses and undercuts, but they exhibit poorer dimensional control than those made of more rigid and permanent materials.

Extrusion. Most plastics that are furnished as sheets, tubes, rods, filaments, films, and other shapes of uniform cross section are produced by extrusion. With some plastics which have a high degree of crystallinity, higher strengths may be developed by stretch deforming the material after extrusion.

Two methods are used for producing film. In one, the film is extruded through a slit of appropriate size. In the other, the material is extruded as a tube which is then expanded by air pressure and either slit or passed between heated rollers where it is welded into a single sheet. Films of less than $\frac{1}{1000}$ inch are produced in large quantities for food wrapping and other packaging by the expanded tube method.

Thermoplastics, for which the process is most used, are cooled after extrusion by air blasts, liquid sprays, or liquid baths. In the manufacture of some types of rayon filaments (cellulose plastics), the material is extruded in a partially polymerized form into a chemical bath where final polymerization takes place. For thermosetting materials, additional heat for the setting reaction is required after extrusion. Few thermosetting plastics are extruded, both because of the temperature controls needed and because the nature of most applications calling for extruded shapes is better satisfied by thermoplastic materials with their generally lower rigidities.

The process differs in one respect from the extrusion of metals where the material is charged as a solid billet into a piston and cylinder arrangement and the amount of material extruded is determined by the size of the billet. For plastics the pressure is supplied by a continuous feed screw resembling a food grinder, as shown in Fig. 14–5. Material in granule form is continuously fed from a hopper with heat supplied as the material proceeds through the screw chamber so that the length of extrusion which may be produced has practically no limits.

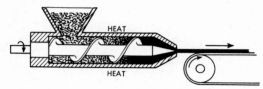

FIG. 14–5. Plastics extrusion.

Reinforced Plastic Molding. One of the fastest growing fields in recent years has been the production of relatively large plastic articles with filler in the form of reenforcing fibers in loose, woven, or sheet form. The principle is old; plywood is an example although the early adhesives used for plywood were not considered to be plastics and the wood fibers were not fully saturated with resin as is common with most molding of this type now.

Glass fibers and paper are the most common filler materials used. Wood and fabric in various forms also have some applications. At present, the process is limited to thermosetting materials both because of the nature of the processing used and the higher strengths available. Phenolics, polyesters, melamines, and epoxies predominate.

In nearly all variations of the process, the filler and resin are brought together in the process itself and the thickness of the molded parts is established more by the placement of the filler material than by mold pressures.

The simplest procedure is *contact layup* where successive layers of manually placed filler material are brushed or sprayed with resin as they are applied to the mold which may have either a concave or a convex shape. The mold may be of almost any material that can be properly shaped including wood, plaster, concrete, metal, or plastic, and there are almost no size limitations. The resins used may incorporate catalysts which promote setting at room temperatures or heating may be required. In either case, since no pressure is applied, the ratio of resin to filler must be high to ensure complete saturation of the fibers. One of the more interesting applications involves the use of glass filaments, coated with resin, that are wound on mandrels into the shape of spheres or cylinders. With proper winding techniques, the filaments may be oriented to make most efficient use of the longitudinal strength of the fibers; tensile strengths up to 150,000 psi have been reported for structures produced by this method.

The commonest variations of the contact layup method, *vacuum bag* molding, *expanded bag* molding, and *autoclave* molding, are all methods for developing some pressure on the surface of the molding to permit a lower resin to filler ratio. Vacuum bag molding is identical with the contact layup method except that a sheet of vinyl plastic film is placed over the mold after the layers are built up and the mold evacuated to cause atmospheric pressure to be applied. In the expanded bag process, pressures up to fifty psi may be provided by blowing up a bag that conforms to and is held in contact with the molding. The autoclave method is similar to the expanded bag, except that heat and pressure are supplied by steam in a closed chamber.

In a direct variation of compression molding, matched metal dies are used to form reenforced products. This process is used most for flat sheet manufactured for table and counter tops but is also used for curved shapes such as chairs, trays, and sinks. Filler materials are generally preformed before molding for the curved shapes. The use of matched metal dies is the only way to produce good finishes on both sides of the finished part and the high pressures used permit up to 90 percent filler, resulting in higher strengths than would otherwise be possible.

The success of "fiberglass" boats, auto bodies, and similar large shapes attests to the value of reenforced plastics. The simplicity of tooling and equipment required (even for amateur home building projects) makes the contact method ideal for low quantity production and permits rapid design changes when desired. Strength and shock resistance are generally quite high but depend primarily on the type and proportion of filler material.

Post Forming. Two general classes of operations are performed on plastics after the initial shape has been produced by one of the methods already discussed. Conventional material removal processes, including sawing, shearing, dinking, and blanking, are possible with any plastic but are most frequently used for the preparation of sheet stock prior to a further hot forming operation. Machining is possible but is generally practical for small quantities only, and other processes are usually cheaper for large quantities. Cutting speeds for thermoplastics must be kept low to prevent heating and softening of the material.

The widest use of post forming operations is made on thermoplastics in sheet form that are heated and made to conform to a single surface mold or pattern by pressure or vacuum. Variations are based primarily on the method of applying pressure and include *draping* where gravity only is used, *drawing* and *stretch forming* which are identical to the same operations when performed on metal, *blow-dieing* which is a combined drawing and air bulging operation, and *vacuum forming* which is similar to vacuum molding of reenforced plastics except that no external film is used. Some small, relatively flat items such as brush handles and buttons are shaped by forging heated sheet stock in closed dies.

Design Considerations. The choice of plastic materials involves the same considerations that apply in choosing metals to fulfill a need. In fact, the two classes of materials are frequently in direct competition with each other. A number of different materials will usually satisfy the functional requirements of a part or product, and the choice depends primarily on the economics of manufacturing for which the material, fabrication, and finishing costs must all be considered. Many plastics require no finishing at all; often a single plastic molding can replace an assembly of parts made of metal with resulting cost decrease, although the material cost alone may be higher.

The stability of properties and the durability of the appearance of plastics are usually poorer than for metals. They are generally better for thermosetting materials than for thermoplastics, but the thermosetting plastics are usually slower to process and more expensive. The dimensional stability for plastics ranges from poor to excellent. The low rigidity and thermal conductivity when compared to metals may be either advantages or disadvantages, depending on the application.

Strengths are generally lower than for metals. Most plastics have tensile strengths below ten thousand psi, but some of the reenforced materials have extremely high strength to weight ratios, at higher cost. Many plastic articles compete successfully with metals only through the use of metal inserts for bearings, threads, and fastenings.

Most plastics excel in corrosion resistance to ordinary environments. This is true to the extent that many metals are coated with plastic films for protection.

Molding Problems.   In the more important plastic production methods, where dies are used, the same types of problems are encountered as with metals and are even exaggerated because of the high shrinkage rates of many plastics. Fillets, draft angles, and bosses must receive the same consideration as in metal casting. Section thickness changes are even more critical than with metals, especially for thermosetting materials which may overheat in thin sections and be subject to deterioration before thicker sections have been properly polymerized. Because of the thermal, chemical, and pressure changes occurring, considerable dimensional change frequently occurs after the molding is completed and close tolerances are usually difficult to hold.

Minimum section thicknesses are dependent on the components of the molding compound and on the process being used but may be thinner than possible with cast metals. The usual minimum range is from .015 to .035 inch for thermoplastics and from .035 to .125 for thermosetting materials.

QUESTIONS

1. Why is the term "plastics" not definitive for the materials so called?
2. Why were few plastics produced in the nineteenth century although they were known chemically?
3. What is polymerization?
4. Give three examples of natural thermoplastic materials.
5. What are the two general reasons for which a filler may be used in a molding compound?
6. Why are accelerators or inhibitors not used with thermoplastic molding compounds?
7. What are the usual advantages and disadvantages of plastics when compared with metals?

8. What similarities exist between plastic and metal shaping processes?

9. Why are thermoplastics not often compression molded?

10. Of the variables density and dimension, which are controlled in straight plunger, landed plunger, and flash type compression molds?

11. How does cold molding compare with compression molding?

12. What is the principal problem to be overcome in injection molding thermosetting plastics?

13. Why does more waste normally result from transfer molding than from injection molding?

14. What types of plastics are most often cast?

15. How is plastic film produced?

16. What is the principal difference between reinforced plastic molding in matched metal molds and conventional compression molding?

17. What is the principal disadvantage of the contact layup method of molding compared to vacuum bag, expanded bag, or matched metal die molding?

CHAPTER 15

The Welding Process

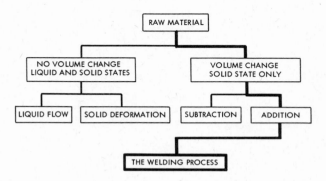

CASTING and deformation processes are all similar in that shapes are produced by *changing* the shape of some given quantity of material. Welding is a *joining* procedure in which shape changes are only minor in character and local in effect. In a sense, the discussion of sintering in connection with powder metallurgy was a discussion of welding since welding may be defined as "the permanent union of metallic surfaces by establishing atom to atom bonds between the surfaces." In practice, some distinction is usually made between true welding, in which the joint is made of the material or materials to be joined and any filler material has a composition similar to the base metal or metals; brazing and soldering, in which the filler is a metal with a lower melting point than the base metal or metals; and adhesive joining, in which the filler is an organic compound, usually one that is classed as a thermosetting plastic.

Welding is both an ancient and a new art. Evidence indicates that prehistoric man, finding native metals in small pieces and being unable to melt them, built up larger pieces by heating and welding by hammering or forging. On the other hand, arc welding was first used in 1880 and oxyacetylene in 1895. Even after these developments, welding remained a minor process used primarily as a last resort in maintenance and repair until about 1930. After this date, the increased knowledge in metallurgy and testing and the development of improved techniques led to increased confidence and use, so that today welding may be considered a basic shape producing method in direct competition with forging, casting, machining, and the other important processes.

While it is true that welding itself does not change the shape of the individual components, the finished *weldment,* or assembly of parts, constitutes a unified structure that functionally has the properties of a solid part. In some cases, particularly with spot welding, welding is purely an assembly procedure and competes with mechanical fastening such as riveting or bolting. In other cases, the goal in welding is to provide a joint that has the same structure, strength, and other properties of the base metal so that the weld area itself would be undetectable. This goal is approached in producing some pipe and high pressure vessels but usually requires elaborate precautions to prevent contamination, heat treatment of the entire weldment after welding, and thorough testing, usually by radiography. In most cases, these procedures would not be practical or economical and some reenforcement of the welded area is provided by building up filler material or designing with reenforcing plates or gussets.

With the exception of some of the special purpose techniques in other areas, welding is in a greater period of growth than any of the other manufacturing procedures. Welding has largely replaced riveting in shipbuilding and is in many cases replacing riveting and bolting in structural steel work for bridges and buildings. In the manufacture of automobiles and home appliances of sheet metal, most of the joining of large shapes is by welding and in many cases these welds are not even apparent in the finished product. A typical automobile for example has over 4500 spot welds in addition to other welding.

BONDS

Nature of Bonding. Most welding definitions include some reference to heat and pressure and in practice most welding processes do make use of heat or pressure, or both. However, neither of these is theoretically necessary. As noted in the discussion of powder metallurgy, if two perfectly matched clean surfaces are brought together atomic bonds will automatically be established between the surfaces and the surfaces would in fact be welded. The essential features are not so easy to realize, however. Atomic cleanliness requires that atoms exposed on the surfaces actually be the atoms of the materials to be joined. Even if this condition is set up on a surface, exposure to the atmosphere results in almost immediate formation of oxide or sulphide films on most metals. Atomic closeness requires that when brought into contact the distances be that at which atoms are normally spaced in the crystalline structure of a metal. Normally when two surfaces are brought into contact this condition will occur only at a number of points since surfaces of even the best quality have a finite roughness of a much larger order than atomic distances.

Various means may be used to establish these two essential conditions of atomic cleanliness and closeness. Cleanliness may be established by chemical cleaning (fluxing) providing the products of the cleaning operation may be removed from the surface, by melting the surface area in which case the surface films float to the surface of the molten material, or by fragmentation as a result of plastic deformation of the base metal. Atomic closeness may be established by filling with a liquid metal as in brazing and soldering without actually melting the joined metals, by elastically or plastically deforming the surfaces until contact is established, or by actually destroying the surfaces by melting and allowing molten base metal or melted filler material to resolidify in contact with the unmelted base metal.

Welding may be accomplished as a result of any combination of conditions that establishes the two essential elements of atomic cleanliness and atomic closeness.

Fusion Bonding.   Most of the important welding processes, particularly those where high strengths are a principal goal, make use of *fusion* bonds in which the surfaces of the pieces to be joined (*parent* or *base* metal) are completely melted, as shown in Fig. 15–1. Liquid metal then flows together

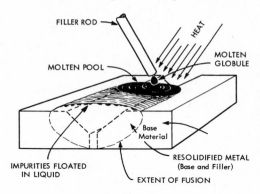

CONCENTRATED HEAT PROVIDED TO MELT BOTH BASE
AND FILLER MATERIAL

FIG. 15–1. Fusion bond.

to form the union and cleanliness is established as the impurities float to the surface. No pressure is necessary and it is essential only that the parts to be joined be located and held in proper relationship to each other.

The resolidification of the metal results in a localized casting for which the unmelted base metal serves as a mold. It can then be expected that the same metallurgical changes and effects such as grain size variation and shrinkage that occur in casting will occur in fusion welding. It is also implied that simply heating an entire structure that is to be fusion bonded would not be satisfactory since the entire structure would reach the melting temperature at the same time. The heat must be supplied locally to the area to be melted and the rate of heat input must be great enough to prevent overheating of the adjacent areas. This requirement leads to some difficulties in welding aluminum, copper, and other metals having very high thermal conductivities.

In fusion welding, at least the surface of the parts being welded is always melted and this amount of molten metal may be sufficient to form the weld. In the more used fusion welding processes, however, additional molten metal (*filler*) is supplied, usually by continuously melting a rod or wire. The use of filler is nearly always necessary in welding sheet and structural shapes over ⅛ inch in thickness and, in many cases, permits more freedom in joint design by making possible the filling and build up of gaps and cavities.

The strength of fusion welded joints will depend on the composition and metallurgical structure of the filler material and base metal, on any structural changes that take place in heated areas of the base metal adjacent to the weld, on the perfection with which the desired geometry of the weld is established, on residual stresses built up as a result of the differential heating and cooling, and on the presence or absence of impurities in the weld. It is at least theoretically possible to produce 100 per cent efficiency in a fusion weld as compared to unwelded base metal.

Pressure Bonding.   The term pressure bonding is somewhat misleading in that some heating is involved in the processes called *pressure* bonding or pressure welding. As will be discussed later, pressure alone may be sufficient to form a bond, but heat is used for two principal reasons. The close union required is established by plastic flow as indicated in Fig. 15–2 and, in general, metals become more plastic and strengths are lower as the temperature is raised. Pressure and flow cause some fragmentation of the oxides on the surface since most are quite brittle and cannot maintain a continuous film as the metal flows plastically.

Of even greater importance are the two effects heat has on this oxide layer which must be removed or dispersed before bonding can be effective. First, the fragments tend to assume spherical shapes as their total energy is raised. With spherical shapes they disrupt a lower percentage of the surface areas to be joined, allowing greater contact between exposed base materials. This same

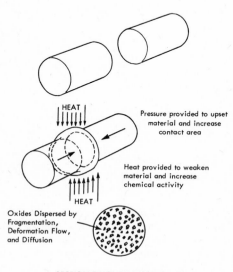

HEAT

Pressure provided to upset material and increase contact area

Heat provided to weaken material and increase chemical activity

HEAT

Oxides Dispersed by Fragmentation, Deformation Flow, and Diffusion

SECTION THROUGH UPSET JOINT

FIG. 15–2. Pressure bond.

type of spheroidization accounts for the malleabilizing of cast iron and for the effect on the cementite particles in the prolonged heating of high carbon steels. The second heat effect is that the solubility of oxygen in the base metals is raised with increased temperature and some dissociation of the oxides occurs with the oxygen being diffused into the base metal.

While a small amount of fusion of the base metal may occur in some cases, it is incidental, no pronounced solidification shrinkage occurs as it does with fusion welds. Consequently, distortion after welding is usually very slight. The efficiency of pressure bonds, based on the original area, may be as high as 95 per cent. Even though there are some inclusions in the weld area that lower unit strength, pressure welded joints may actually be stronger than the original cross section as a result of the enlargement that occurs with plastic flow. This is especially true in butt welding procedures as used in the manufacture of some chain links and fittings.

Flow Bonding.   When a filler material of different composition and lower melting temperature than the base metal is used, the mechanism is described as *flow* bonding, Fig. 15–3. While some fusion of the base metal

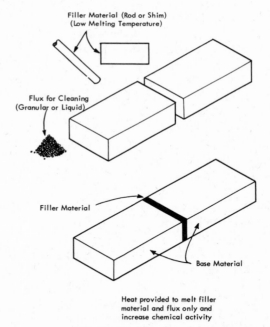

FIG. 15–3. Flow bond.

may occur, it is not essential to the process and is usually undesirable. The closeness necessary for bonding is established by the molten metal conforming to the surface of the base metal. The required cleanliness is produced by use of fluxes, ordinarily metal halides or borax, which dissolve the surface oxides and float them out of the joint.

Three different operations using flow bonds have been named: braze welding, brazing, and soldering. In *braze welding*, the filler material is a metal or alloy having a melting point above 800°F. and a composition significantly different from the base metal. In practice, the commonest alloys used as filler are copper or silver based. Occasionally, pure copper is used for braze welding steel. The filler is usually in rod form and the procedures are similar to those employed in some fusion welding except that only the filler material is melted. Fluxes are heated on the joint surfaces for cleaning. Braze welding is used mainly for joining and repairing cast iron and is being replaced by fusion welding in many areas. The joint strength is limited to that of the filler material in cast form.

The word *brazing* when used alone designates the use of filler materials similar to those used in braze welding but applied to a close fitting joint by preplacement or by capillary action. Filler material may be rod, wire, foil, slug, or powder form, and fluxes similar to those used in braze welding are necessary. Heat may be furnished by torch, furnace, or induction, and, in production quantities, by dipping in molten salts which may also provide the fluxing action.

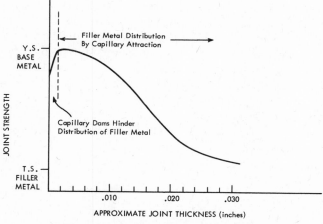

FIG. 15–4. Strength of brazed joints.

Fig. 15–4 shows the importance of thickness on the strength of a brazed joint. The low strength of very thin joints is due to the formation of "capillary dams" caused by uneven surfaces which prevent complete filling. This fault can be overcome to some extent by use of special techniques such as application of ultrasonic vibration while brazing. The fact that the strength of the joint can be higher than that of cast filler is due to the differences in modulus of elasticity between the filler and base material. The filler metal is prevented from yielding by the more rigid base metal, resulting in high shear stresses normal to the direction of the load in the filler material. These shear stresses generate tensile stresses in such direction, that when they are combined vectorially with the direct tensile stresses caused by the load, a lower stress value is produced on the plane normal to the load than would occur in a homogenous material. When the joint becomes thicker there is less restraint in the center of the filler layer, the shear stresses are lower and their effect in compensating for direct load stresses is reduced.

The third type of flow bonding, *soldering*, actually includes applications similar to both braze welding and brazing. The essential difference is in the melting temperature of the filler metal which for soldering is below 800°F. The most important materials in this class are lead tin alloys with melting points from 361°F. to slightly above 600°F. The mechanical strengths of soldered joints, particularly built up joints of the braze weld type, are low, and the greatest use for soldering is in providing fluid tightness, for electrical connections, and for sheet metal joint filling in automotive assembly work.

Cold Bonding. In fusion, pressure, and flow bonding, heat is used to help establish the closeness and cleanliness necessary, but heat, as such, is not essential for proper bonding between metallic surfaces. With greater loads than used in pressure bonding, plastic flow of the required order for fragmentation of surface impurities can be established in ductile materials at room temperature. If two fresh surfaces of lead are twisted together, a weld is made with a strength approaching that of the base metal, and any metal may be made to weld to some degree by wiping two surfaces together at sufficiently high normal pressure. However, the results would be inconsistent and the practical application of cold bonding depends on inducing deformation parallel to the interface while it is subjected to high normal pressure.

In practice, welds are made by squeezing the metal between two punch faces that cause metal flow normal to the direction of load, Fig. 15–5. As the area of contact is increased, the brittle surface oxides fragment and cover a

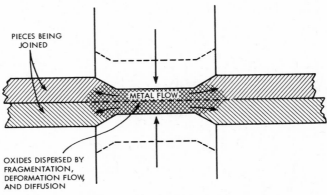

FIG. 15–5. Cold bond.

smaller percentage of the area, exposing clean metal to metal contacts. The greatest success so far has been with copper and aluminum base metals.

Adhesive Bonding. The elements of an *adhesive bond* are shown in Fig. 15–6. An adhesive is most commonly considered to be a material with some "tackiness" or "stickiness" and the animal glues used almost exclusively up to the present century met this requirement. Modern adhesives however have wide range in this respect. Contact cements have sufficient tackiness that bonding with considerable strength occurs immediately under only moderate pressure. Some thermosetting plastic compounds have little or no tackiness as applied and develop strength only after the setting reaction has been promoted by heat, pressure, or chemical reaction with the parts held in place.

No clear distinction can be made between the terms *glue, cement,* and *adhesive.* Common to all of them however is the property of *adherence* to a surface, and this property is not essentially different from the metallic bond established between metallic surfaces brought into close contact. At least four mechanisms may be responsible for adherence. *Electrostatic* and *covalent* bonds result from the sharing of electrons by different atoms and account for the formation of most common chemical compounds. Even after bonds of these types are established the positive and negative charges of most atoms are not completely neutralized and *Van der Waal' forces* provide additional bonding between the atoms. While not strictly an adherence phenomenon, *mechanical interlocking* may take part in the action of some adhesives although this action appears to be secondary to true adhesion.

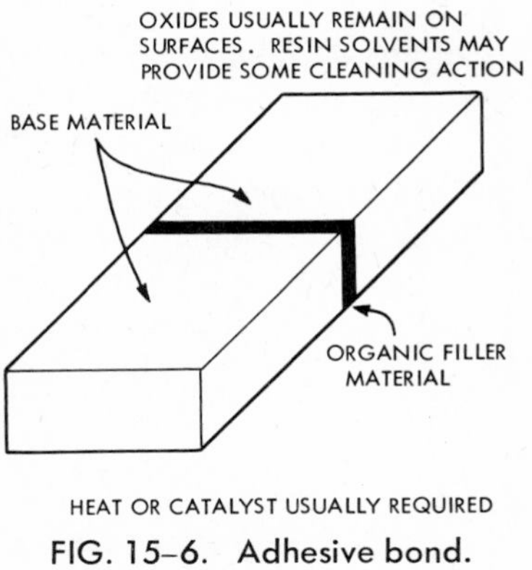

As in welding of metals, the proper performance of an adhesive requires that intimate contact be established between the adhesive and the surfaces to be joined. Different means are used to provide closeness. An adhesive can be applied as a solution in a volatile liquid. Evaporation of the solvent is necessary for the adhesive to develop the desired properties and as evaporation proceeds, the adhesive proper is drawn to the bare material surfaces. Adhesives of this type are useful for porous materials such as wood, paper, and fabrics into which the vapors can penetrate, but for nonporous materials, extremely long drying times may be required since the edge of the joint is the only area exposed for evaporation.

OXIDES USUALLY REMAIN ON SURFACES. RESIN SOLVENTS MAY PROVIDE SOME CLEANING ACTION

BASE MATERIAL

ORGANIC FILLER MATERIAL

HEAT OR CATALYST USUALLY REQUIRED

FIG. 15–6. Adhesive bond.

Some relatively new materials are normally solid but become liquid with the application of pressure, then resolidify when the pressure is released. Other adhesives are purely thermoplastic in nature, softening or liquifying from heat and hardening on cooling.

The most important adhesives for the bonding of metals are thermosetting compounds applied as liquids, pastes, or powders, then polymerized in place through the action of catalysts, heat, or pressure.

In addition to the increasing importance of the traditional uses of adhesives in the manufacture of plywood and for the assembly of wood parts, there is considerable growth in the use of adhesives for bonding of metal structures. These uses are becoming more important as higher strength materials are developed. Adhesives with tensile strengths above ten thousand psi and shear strengths above four thousand psi are available for bonding metals. Many new applications of joining of dissimilar materials such as rubber to metal are appearing.

Other advantages may apply to specific cases. Elevated temperatures are not necessary for most adhesives, so that distortion associated with welding may be avoided. Thin structures that would be difficult to join by other methods may be used. In most cases, automatic sealing of joints which may not be true of mechanically fastened ones is achieved. Adhesives may be chosen to provide corrosion resistance or insulation and damping qualities. In many instances, adhesive bonding is used because it does not require expensive equipment and highly trained personnel.

WELDING METALLURGY

The final properties of a welded or brazed joint are influenced by many factors. Some of the metal is actually melted in most cases and welded parts are subject to deformation and high shrinkage on cooling. The metallurgical changes in a weldment may include all that take place under any kind of processing including melting, alloying, solidification, casting, hot and cold working, recrystallization, and heat treating. In the case of welding, most changes are intensified because of the high thermal gradients developed and the fast rates of heating and cooling encountered. These side effects are often overlooked or neglected since the principal objective of the welding procedure is the joining of material.

The conditions under which most welding is performed are far from ideal. Tremendous energy inputs, especially in fusion welding, may lead to localized overheating to the point of vaporization. Exposure of high temperature and chemically active materials to atmospheres difficult to control leads to the formation of undesirable compounds. Most gases are highly soluble in molten metals but have decreasing ability to stay in solution as temperatures lower, leading to problems of gas entrapment.

Composition Effects. The conditions existing in the weld area are frequently conducive to significant changes in the composition of either the base or the filler metal. The rapid solidification rates may lead to segregation of some elements, particularly coring type segregation as may occur in casting some brasses. Gas may enter the molten metal not only by solution but as a result of agitation which occurs with many fusion welding processes. These entrapped gases can form voids or brittle compounds within the structure of the metal. One of the most serious conditions is the embrittlement resulting from hydrogen trapped in steel. With the rapid solidification, slag and oxides may not have time to float and may be trapped beneath the surface to appear as solid inclusions in the completed weld.

Ideally, it is possible to produce a fully homogenous material without defects in which it would be difficult if not impossible to detect the welded metal. In practical applications, this situation can be approached but often requires posttreatment to produce completely uniform structure and properties.

Fillers of composition different from that of the base metal are often used to compensate for welding faults that might otherwise be expected. The attempt is not usually to use a filler that will exactly compensate for the losses of the welding process but rather overcompensate for improvement of certain properties. Thus, high nickel filler may be used in welding cast iron to control grain growth and give ductility to the weld area, and stainless steel filler used with higher alloy content than the base material to ensure adequate corrosion resistance. Brazing and soldering alloys are used principally to avoid high temperature effects in the base metal.

The amount of alloying that occurs between base metals and filler metals of different composition depends on several factors, but chiefly the actual metals involved. Alloying is not essential to true bonding but at the high temperatures reached, diffusion proceeds at a high rate and for some metals alloying will occur for some distance in both directions away from the original interface. Soft solders in particular produce brittle intermetallic compounds that reduce ductility and lower strength.

Effects on Grain Size. Grain formation in fusion welds can best be understood by remembering that a fusion weld is a casting and all the effects present in casting will be duplicated. However, the mold wall is not fixed and the solidification and cooling rates are faster than normally occur in casting, Fig. 15–7. Fusion welds are subject to solidification and cooling

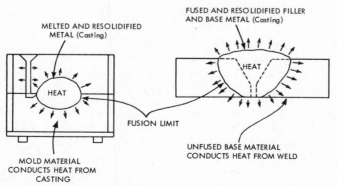

FIG. 15–7. Comparison of fusion weld with casting.

shrinkage as shown in Fig. 15–8. The grain size effects are not confined to the molten metal since temperature high enough to result in annealing, allotropic transformation, and recrystallization extends for some distance into the base metal, as shown in Fig. 15–9. The fused material is cooled rapidly by the high thermal conductivity of the surrounding metal result-

| WELD METAL LIQUID | SOLIDIFICATION BY THE FORMATION OF COLUMNAR GRAINS | SLIGHT SHRINKAGE AT THE WELD SURFACE |

FIG. 15–8. Solidification of a bead weld.

ing in small grain size. The zones indicated in the drawing do not have sharp dividing lines and represent only typical results. The results can vary from those shown depending on the shape and size of the parts, the initial temperature of the base material, the rate of heat input, and the alloy content. In any case, for steels an area immediately surrounding the molten metal will be heated above the transformation temperature and some

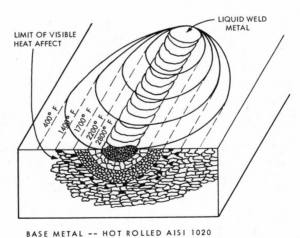

BASE METAL -- HOT ROLLED AISI 1020

FIG. 15–9. Grain structure in a fusion weld.

degree of austenitization can occur as might be predicted by use of the partial iron-carbon diagram, Fig. 15–10. Final results will depend on the time at temperature and the cooling rates which cannot always be accurately predicted. Grain growth can proceed and for the metal heated near its melting temperature the final grain size can be large. The metal heated only slightly above the transformation temperature is effectively normalized and will have a small final grain size which can be smaller than that of the unheated base metal. Any heat treat or cold work hardening that existed in the area heated below the transformation temperature will be subject to tempering or recrystallization, depending on the actual temperature reached and the preweld condition.

Again, depending on cooling rates induced and compositions involved, for the metal heated above the transformation temperature, the cooling may be equivalent to that required for annealing, normalizing, or actually

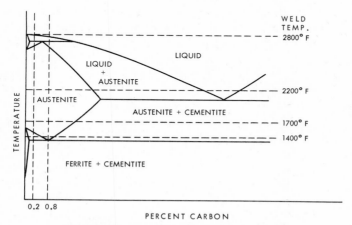

FIG. 15–10. Partial iron-carbon diagram.

quenching to martensite, provided enough carbon is present. Some of the latter nearly always occurs in unpreheated carbon steel weldments and, when combined with the uneven shrinkage that may be present, can result in brittle structures subject to cracking. Alloy rods or rods of different carbon content may be used for controlling some of the possible defects. Low carbon filler material is often used in welding higher carbon steels to avoid the formation of excessive amounts of martensite. Fig. 15–11 shows the probable results of this combination on the structures formed. In the fusion zone where cooling rates are high, the composition would be near the composition of the filler material. Even with rapid cooling, the structure would consist mainly of ferrite with sufficient ductility to shrink without cracking. In the base material adjacent to the liquid metal, the cooling rate would be somewhat less but still sufficiently rapid to form fine pearlite and some martensite. It must be remembered that grain size and structure are two different considerations; in this region, grain size will be large because of the long time at high temperature but structure fine because of the rapid cooling. At a greater distance from the molten zone but still within the area raised above the transformation temperature, the cooling rate would be nearer that usual with normalizing and the resulting structure would be medium to coarse pearlite.

Fig. 15–11 also shows the effect on cooling rates obtained from preheating the base metal surrounding the area to be welded. At any given point in the weld area, the cooling rate will be reduced because of the reduced thermal gradient established. Average grain size will be larger because of the longer times at high temperature but structures will be softer because of the reduced cooling rates.

Effects similar to those of fusion welding will be observed in pressure welding but with lower temperatures, and frequently higher thermal gradients, the heat affected zone will be smaller. Shrinkage problems are reduced because of little or no fusion and more uniformly welded cross sections.

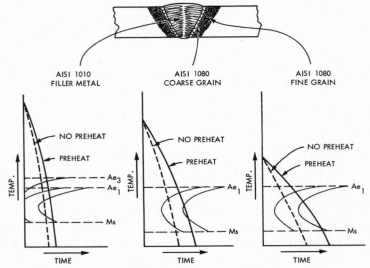

FIG. 15–11. Effect of preheat on cooling curves.

Effects of Welding on Properties. In an ideal weld, the composition of the weld zone could be made like that of the base metal and, with proper heat treatment the strength of the final weldment would be unaffected in any way by the presence of the weld. In most practical situations, compositions cannot be kept exactly the same and heat treatment sufficient to establish completely uniform structures would be uneconomical if not impossible. The result is that the strength of most welds is different from that of the base metal. With no heat treatment of welded steel, the strength and hardness will vary from that of annealed to that of quenched material. Ductility will vary inversely with the strength. Many weldments are at least normalized to obtain more uniform properties and to relieve stresses.

The possible presence of discontinuities and inclusions in a weld may lead to reduced strengths for which consideration must be given in weld design. The designer must either gamble on weld quality, require special inspection procedures to determine weld quality with possible rewelding of some structures, or overdesign welded joints on the basis of lowest expected strengths.

Corrosion resistance of many welded metals is likely to be affected adversely. As already pointed out, composition and structural changes accompany the usual conditions required to produce a weld. High temperatures in particular lead to diffusion and precipitation effects that change the chemical characteristics of the metal. Some stainless steels are subject to the formation of chromium carbide during welding and may lose much of their corrosion resistant qualities without proper subsequent heat treatment. Even with protective procedures such as inert gas shielding or slag coverings, discoloration and surface oxidation occur in the heat affected zone. Materials under high stress are subject to increased corrosion, and welds are prone to highly stressed areas unless special treatment is used for their removal.

The variable qualities, in particular hardness and toughness, frequently cause machining difficulties. The harder structures may be detrimental to tool life, and the variations in structure are often apparent in the finish of a surface that includes a weld. Relief of localized residual stresses by machining is likely to cause distortion of the weldment.

DISTORTIONS AND STRESSES

A homogenous unrestricted body may be heated to any temperature below its melting point without shape change. A volumetric expansion will occur with heating, but if this expansion occurs uniformly no stresses will be introduced. As the body is cooled, the process reverses and the final result will be the original unstrained state.

With restraint either on heating or cooling or with heating or cooling of localized areas at a more rapid rate than others (self-restraint), the picture will be changed. Many welds have a vee cross section, and the molten and heated areas will have a related shape. Furthermore, the heat input and higher temperatures occur on the open side of the vee. The result of cooling on this cross section is illustrated in Fig. 15–12 for various weldments joined with vee welds. The greater shrinkage occurring on the wide side of the vee leads to angular distortion as shown. The effect is amplified by multipass welds where a number of weld deposits are made along the length of a single vee. Each pass contributes to the distortion with the deposits from previous passes serving as a fulcrum for increased angular movement.

While a vee weld will always tend to distort angularly in the manner shown, the lateral distortion between members of a weldment may vary in direction and amount, depending on the size of the members compared to the weld, the numbers of passes made, the rate of heat input, and the speed

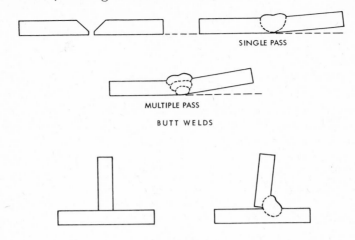

SINGLE PASS

MULTIPLE PASS

BUTT WELDS

FILLET WELD

FIG. 15–12. Angular distortion.

of welding, Fig. 15–13. As the weld proceeds along the groove, the heating of base metal along the edge of the groove but ahead of the actual weld leads to a spreading of the plates. On the other hand, the shrinkage accompanying the solidification and cooling of the completed weld tends to pull the plates together.

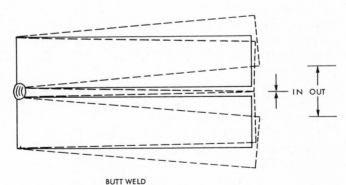

IN OUT

BUTT WELD

FIG. 15–13. Lateral distortion.

In the discussion so far, it has been assumed that little or no restriction is placed on the members of the weldment. If sufficient restraint is placed on a member while it is heated, distortion may be reduced, but only by the introduction of high stresses. Consider the member shown in Fig. 15–14 which is prevented from expanding longitudinally as it is heated. With no restraint, the expansion of a steel member being heated 1000°F. would be:

$$L_2 - L_1 = L_1 \times 1000 \times .0000064$$

where:

L_1 = original length
L_2 = expanded length
.0000064 = coefficient of thermal expansion for steel, in/in/ degree F.

If the original length is to be maintained by the restraint, it must be by the introduction of a compressive stress sufficient to neutralize this expansion. Such a stress would have to be

$$S_c = \frac{(L_2 - L_1) \times 30,000,000}{L_1}$$

where:

S_c = compressive stress, psi
30,000,000 = modulus of elasticity for steel, psi

Combining the two expressions the compressive stress would be:

$$S_c = 1000 \times .0000064 \times 30,000,000$$
$$= 1,820,000 \text{ psi}$$

Obviously, such a condition cannot be met. The stress would build up linearly as the temperature is increased and with a rise of less than 100°F. would reach the yield strength of the material for that temperature. Fig. 15–15 indicates the manner in which the yield strength of steel varies with temperature. As the temperature is increased above this point, yielding would continue but at no time could the stress exceed that required for yielding.

Cooling could result in different conditions. If the member were not fixed to the walls, it would maintain contact as the cooling started but stress would decrease. Zero

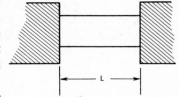

FIG. 15–14. Structural member under longitudinal restraint.

stress would be reached with a relatively small temperature drop. Below the temperature at which zero stress occurred the member would shrink and contact would be lost with the walls. Stress would remain at zero.

If the member were to be fixed to the restraining walls, conditions would be altered on cooling at the point where zero stress was reached. With continued cooling the member could maintain its length only by being stretched, which would introduce tensile stresses. As on heating, these stresses would reach yield values with less than 100°F. temperature change, and the material would then yield in tension with the actual stress being determined by the changing yield strength of the material at successive temperatures. The condition at room temperature would then be a residual tensile stress with a value equal to the yield strength at room temperature.

Practical weldments never have absolute restraint or absolute freedom, and the actual degree of restraint and temperature difference cannot always be predicted or measured. However, some degree of restraint

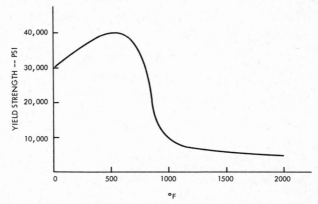

FIG. 15–15. Yield stress of mild steel at various temperatures.

always exists, at least in the parent metal adjacent to the weld zone, even for members that as a whole are free. It can be safely stated that any fusion weld will contain some residual stresses when completed and cooled to room temperature. These stresses will be both tensile and compressive since a balance must exist for the member to be in equilibrium.

Some practical results are indicated in Fig. 15–16. For a weld along the edge of a plate, the longitudinal shrinkage will cause curvature as indi-

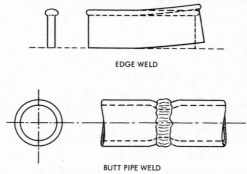

EDGE WELD

BUTT PIPE WELD

FIG. 15–16. Longitudinal distortion.

cated. Although the plate has no external restraint, it will be subject to stresses similar to those resulting from external loading that would cause equivalent curvature. In the case of the weldment, however, there will be two neutral axes with both edges in tension and the center under compression.

For a circular weld around a pipe, similar self-restraint exists. The shrinkage along the length of the weld results in a reduction in diameter that is resisted by the solid pipe adjacent to the weld. The result would be high tensile stresses in the weld and high compressive stresses in the pipe on both sides of the weld.

Even where the welded members have no external restraint or apparent gross distortion, high residual stresses can exist. Fig. 15–17 indicates the

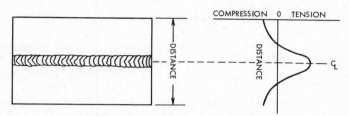

FIG. 15–17. Longitudinal stress in a butt weld.

kind of stress distribution to be expected from a longitudinal butt weld between two plates.

The most widely accepted method of reducing residual stresses in the weldments is based on the two facts that no stresses higher than the yield stress can exist in a material at any given temperature and that, if an entire unrestrained body is cooled uniformly from any given temperature, no increase in stress will occur. If a weldment is heated to an elevated temperature, yielding will occur and the stresses reduced to correspond to those shown in Fig. 15–15. As the temperature is reduced, the entire weldment will shrink but no new stresses will be introduced. Residual stresses cannot be completely eliminated by this method but, as the figure shows, the yield strength at elevated temperature is quite low.

Normalizing provides stress relief and in addition increases the uniformity of the grain structure. Stress relieving of weldments is frequently performed by heating to about 1200°F. While grain refinement is not obtained, the chances for distortion are less than those that might be introduced by the allotropic transformation, which occurs at higher temperatures.

QUESTIONS

1. What is a weldment?
2. At what time did the development of welding, as it is known today, start?
3. What two conditions must be met to accomplish a weld?
4. By what methods are the conditions of question 3 most frequently met?
5. Describe fusion bonding.
6. Sketch a fusion bonded joint requiring filler material and name the elements.

7. Why are aluminum and copper alloys usually more difficult to weld than steel?
8. What purpose does heat serve in pressure bonding?
9. Name the main advantages pressure bonds have over fusion bonds.
10. How is cleanliness established for flow bonds?
11. What are the characteristic differences between braze welding, brazing, and soldering?
12. How can the strength of a brazed joint be greater than that of the filler material with which it is made?
13. How are the conditions necessary for welding accomplished in cold bonding?
14. Is there any similarity between adhesive bonds and those more commonly thought of as true welding?
15. Why are the commonly used welding processes so complex that they require great study and knowledge for successful results?
16. For what reason is filler rod composition often different from the base material on which it is used?
17. Why is high carbon steel more difficult to weld than low carbon steel?
18. By what method does preheating of a weldment affect the properties that result from welding?
19. Why does fusion welding create stresses in nearly all cases of use?
20. Will the final stress in a weldment that is fully restrained on both ends be tension or compression? Explain.
21. Do both compressive and tensile stresses exist in the same body?
22. Explain how stress relief of weldments by heat treatment works.

CHAPTER 16

Welding Processes and Design

IN THE preceding chapter, the essential welding requirements of atomic closeness and atomic cleanliness were pointed out. It was noted, in the discussion of bond types, that while not always essential for welding, heat is an important part of most practical processes. Heat is necessary for fusion, metals become more plastic when heated, and heat assists in obtaining cleanliness in many processes. The more important welding processes differ primarily, and in fact are usually named, on the basis of the heat source.

An integral part of practical welding processes is the method of obtaining, and of equal importance, maintaining, cleanliness in the weld area. Not only is it necessary to obtain atomic cleanliness for proper fusion but the heated metal, particularly when fusion welding, must be protected from excessive contamination from the atmosphere.

HEAT FOR WELDING

Energy sources used for welding, Fig. 16–1, are characterized by two important features, the degree of localization permissible and the rate of heat input possible. Heating in a furnace by radiation and conduction may permit a large total heat input but results in thorough heating of the entire part or assembly. This method would be unacceptable for fusion welding since melting of the entire weldment would occur but may be the preferred method for brazing and soldering. The base metal temperature being uniform, stresses caused by temperature changes are minimized. The ease of control makes furnace brazing adaptable to production quantities. Furnace heating is the usual method of preheating weldments to permit stress equalization and lessen the possibility of cracking.

The process called *forge* welding is named from the initial method of heating using a special type of furnace in which the parts to be heated were placed directly in the fire of a forge. The parts, heated either locally or throughout, are then subjected to pressure (manually hammering in the case of blacksmithing) to produce the weld. The blacksmithing art is still important today but forge welding has been largely replaced by other methods for joining materials together.

The most important welding processes make use of localized heating. For fusion welding this is a necessity to prevent excessive melting and to restrict the heat affected zone in the base metal. The temperature differential in the weld area will depend not only on the rate of heat input and the degree of localization but on the thermal properties of the base metal and the geometry of the weldment. Heat sources differ in the maximum temperature possibilities, the degree of concentration, and in the maximum practical amount of energy that may be transferred.

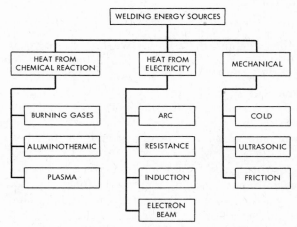

FIG. 16–1. Sources of energy for welding.

The choice of a heat source may be governed by the contaminating influence on the base metal. With some heat sources, particularly those of chemical nature, the atmosphere to which the weld is subjected is determined by the heat source. With most types of electric heating, the atmosphere may be controlled exclusive of the heat source.

Economic considerations always play a large part in the final determination of a heat source. The actual energy costs, based on fuel or electricity, differ to some extent, but the choice is more frequently made on the basis of initial equipment cost, availability, portability, and on the suitability of the process and equipment for the amount of welding and kind of material to be welded.

Chemical Reactions. The oldest and still most used source of heat based on a chemical reaction is the burning of acetylene (C_2H_2) and pure oxygen. The chemical reaction takes place in two stages. For each cubic foot of acetylene (at 68°F. and 14.7 psi), an inner cone reaction occurs first:

$$C_2H_2 + O_2 \rightarrow 2\ CO + H_2 + 501\ BTU$$

surrounding this inner cone is an outer envelope reaction:

$$CO + H_2 + O_2 \rightarrow CO_2 + H_2O + 956\ BTU$$

Fig. 16–2 shows the appearance of oxyacetylene flames with various ratios of oxygen and acetylene. With an excess of acetylene the flame has chemical reducing characteristics and shows a *feather* extending past the inner cone. An approximate measure of the composition is made by comparing the length of feather with the length of the inner cone and indicating this ratio. A 2X flame then would have a feather twice as long as the inner cone. A reducing or carburizing flame prevents or reduces decarburization and causes less oxidation of steel. An excess of oxygen

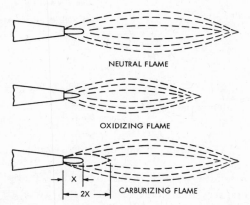

NEUTRAL FLAME

OXIDIZING FLAME

X
2X   CARBURIZING FLAME

FIG. 16–2.   Oxyacetylene flame characteristics.

produces a strongly oxidizing flame that has only limited use but the maximum temperatures available are with a flame of this type. With three parts oxygen to one part acetylene, the temperature is 6300°F. Other temperatures range from 1500°F. for acetylene burning in the atmosphere to 5700°F. at the tip of the inner cone of a neutral flame (one to one proportions of oxygen and acetylene.)

Oxyacetylene has advantages of portability, low first cost, and flexibility. With relatively simple equipment, operations ranging from brazing and soldering to flame cutting may be performed. For fixed installations and high production processes, the electric arc is used more than oxyacetylene because of the greater heat input that may be obtained and the lower cost of electrical energy.

Other gases burning with oxygen are also used but to a much more limited degree. Oxyhydrogen can provide a strongly reducing flame without the soot associated with oxyacetylene and is used for welding aluminum and lead. Natural gas, propane, or butane, burned with oxygen, are used for preheating and for brazing and soldering but have limited temperatures, making them less useful than oxyacetylene for fusion welding.

Another chemical reaction method which has somewhat limited application is the aluminothermic process, available under various proprietary names. Fig. 16–3 shows roughly the details of the process. Because of their relative positions in the electrochemical series, aluminum is strongly reducing to iron oxide. As a result, when powdered iron oxide and aluminum are mixed and ignited, the reaction is exothermic and self-sustaining with the products being molten iron and aluminum oxide. The process is older

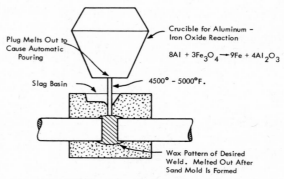

Crucible for Aluminum – Iron Oxide Reaction

$$8Al + 3Fe_3O_4 \rightarrow 9Fe + 4Al_2O_3$$

Plug Melts Out to Cause Automatic Pouring

Slag Basin

4500° – 5000°F.

Wax Pattern of Desired Weld. Melted Out After Sand Mold Is Formed

FIG. 16–3. Aluminothermic welding.

than most other welding processes, having had wide application for welding rail ends when street cars and interurbans were in greater use. Present use is primarily for repair and joining of heavy castings. As the figure indicates, the process actually makes a casting with the chemical reaction being used only to provide a source of superheated molten iron.

Electricity.   Practically all production welding today makes use of electricity as an energy source. The first application was the electric arc, developed about 1880 (Fig. 16–4) but restricted in use until the develop-

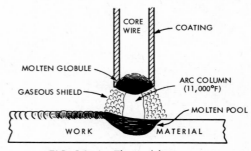

CORE WIRE

COATING

MOLTEN GLOBULE

GASEOUS SHIELD

ARC COLUMN (11,000°F)

MOLTEN POOL

WORK

MATERIAL

FIG. 16–4. The welding arc.

ment of coated electrodes. The electric arc is one of the hottest sources of energy available except for nuclear reactions. Arc column temperatures are near 11,000°F., which is well above the melting points of common metals and alloys. With typical arc welding conditions of 25 volts as 300 amperes, the total energy supplied would be 26,000 BTU/hour at an energy cost of only 3 to 15 cents, depending on the location.

Most gases, in particular the atmosphere, are very poor conductors at room temperature and the voltage necessary to maintain an arc over any practical distance would be very high. However, gas molecules at arc temperatures have such high velocities that they ionize (lose some electrons by collision) in numbers sufficient to make the gas highly conducting for electric current. When the arc is extinguished, it cools and loses its ionization in the order of one thousandth of a second and reionization must occur before the arc can be reestablished. The temperature of the arc is essentially constant throughout the length and diameter of the arc column. The electrical characteristics, including the voltage drop in the arc and at the surfaces at which the arc terminates are determined by the composition and length of the arc. With long arcs and highly conductive gases such as hydrogen, higher inputs are required to maintain the arc.

The electrodes between which the arc burns are the anode (positive) and the cathode (negative). The arc may exist either between the work and a metal rod, which progressively melts and serves as filler material, or between two nonconsumable electrodes, in which case the arc serves simply as a heat source.

Figs. 16–5 and 16–6 show the relationships that exist between arc

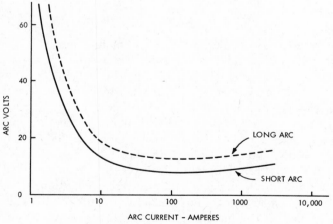

FIG. 16–5. Arc volt-ampere curve.

voltage, arc current, and arc length. The total drop of voltage along the length of the arc is the sum of the voltage drops in the electrode regions (nearly constant at about 15 volts), and the drop along the column of the arc which is proportional to the length of the arc column. Low current arcs take more voltage than high current arcs because of their smaller diameter which gives a higher surface to volume ratio and higher radiation losses.

Welding arcs with consumable electrodes transfer this metal in molten form to the weld pool on the work. Transfer may be by fine metal spray or relatively large globules and rivulets which may even short circuit the arc temporarily. The rate of burn-off of electrode is almost directly proportional to the welding current for any given rod diameter. However, the range of currents that may be used with any electrode in order to obtain a balance between burn-off and heating of the base metal is limited. From 10 to 30 per cent of the melted rod is normally lost through vaporization and spattering outside the molten pool.

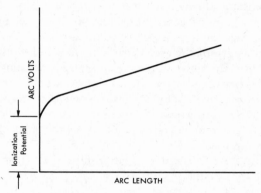

FIG. 16–6. Arc volt-length curve.

During transfer across the arc gap, the molten metal is shielded by protective gases from oxidation and other reactions with the arc atmosphere. These gases may be provided by the burning of coatings on the welding rod itself, by flux powders beneath which the arc burns, or by a flow of shielding gas from an external source.

With certain welding rods, the polarity of the rod with respect to the work exerts a measurable influence on burn-off rate and the amount of spattering. Most welding is done with the rod negative. This is called *straight* polarity. When the rod is positive the setup is called *reverse* polarity. Manufacturers designate the preferred polarities for most rods.

Arc welding has developed into the most versatile of all welding processes. Power supplies of almost unlimited capacity are available and deposition rates in excess of one hundred pounds per hour are used with the faster procedures. Many production processes have been developed, most with automatic regulation of current, rod feed, and speed of travel along the proper path. With proper shielding, most metals and alloys may be arc welded. Products that are regularly arc welded include tanks and other pressure vessels, structural steel, large diameter steel pipes, ship hulls and fittings, large machinery frames, and aircraft structures.

One other use of the electric arc is made in *percussive* welding, a process more closely associated with pressure than fusion methods, and used only for making butt joints between the flat ends of workpieces without filler material. The workpieces are connected to a large capacitor charged to about 3000 volts, then driven toward each other by high spring or air pressure. Before contact can take place, arcs with current on the order of 50,000 to 100,000 amperes are established. These high currents quickly heat the surfaces of the work to vaporization temperatures. The vapor holds the workpieces apart until the capacitor is nearly discharged, at which time the pressure completes the contact against a thin film of clean molten metal. Equipment costs are high and applications are limited, but percussive welding may be used for joining widely dissimilar materials. Heat effects in the base material are limited in extent.

A further variation in the use of an arc for welding is in the process called *stud* welding, developed in the shipbuilding industry for attaching steel studs to the steel deck of a ship. These studs are then used for holding the wood overdeck. The stud is supported in a special gun and forms the electrode in much the same manner as the filler material in conventional arc welding. It is then moved to the work until an arc is established, drawn back, then forced into the work—after a short period of arc heating—with sufficient pressure to cause some upsetting of the end of the stud. The process is used primarily for attaching threaded fastening devices in applications similar to that described above.

Heat for an important group of hot pressure welding processes is supplied by the passage of electric current through the work. The rate of power expenditure in any electrical circuit is given by:

$$P = I^2 R$$

where P is the power in watts, I the current in amperes, and R the resistance in ohms. Fig. 16–7 gives the elements of a typical *resistance welding* circuit. Power supplies generally use transformers with a single or very few secondary turns, capable of high amperage, low voltage output.

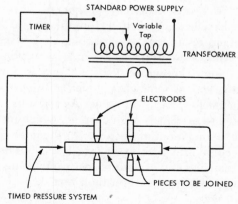

FIG. 16–7. Typical resistance welding system.

Heat is generated throughout the circuit, and resistance welding processes are based on the fact that the highest resistance occurs at the interfaces between metal surfaces where the contact is limited to a number of points of relatively small area. This condition occurs not only at the interface between the workpieces, where maximum heat is desired, but also at the contacts with the electrodes, for which the heating effect is minimized by using high conductivity copper alloys with water cooling and high pressure contact of formed surfaces.

As the contact points heat between the work surfaces, they become plastic and the clean metal union is expanded by deformation and by the fragmentation, spheroidization, and diffusion of the oxides into the base metal. Some local melting may take place but is not necessary for the process to be successful. Even with the increased area of contact, the interface area remains the point of greatest heat generation since the resistance of the base metal rises as its temperature is increased. The duration of the current is controlled by a timer which in most cases regulates the periods of current flow by controlling the number of cycles of alternating current permitted to flow through the primary of the step-down transformer. The pressure is also timed, with an increase to cause plastic flow after heating has occurred.

Nearly all metals, as well as most combinations of different metals, may be resistance welded. Difficulties are sometimes encountered with high conductivity metals such as aluminum and copper or when joining parts of different thicknesses. Experimentation for extablishment of the best weld conditions will produce satisfactory welds for most applications.

Resistance heating is used in a number of specific processes. Resistance *butt* welding is used for joining the ends of rods, bars, wire, and similar shapes. Sufficient pressure is applied to *upset* the ends of the workpieces with an increased area at the joint. Buttwelded sections are generally stronger at the weld than in the parent stock as a result of this enlargement. Even with the enlarged section machined down to the original size, joint efficiencies of 90 to 95 per cent may be obtained because most of the surface impurities have been eliminated from the central area. Typical uses include the manufacture of chain, the attaching of soft shanks to hardened steel working sections of cutting tools, and the making of pipe.

The type of joining known as *flash* welding is a variation of butt welding. Applied voltage is somewhat higher and the initial contact pressure is held momentarily at a lower value. As a result, the initial contact points are subjected to extremely high currents which melt the metal with sufficient speed to "flash" it out of the joint. As the joint continues to close, additional points come into contact and are burned. The surface may be almost entirely cleaned of oxides with proper timing, and the final application of increased pressure produces a high quality weld with a reduced amount of upsetting.

The most important applications of resistance heating are for *spot welding* and its variations. Used primarily for lap joints between flat sheets, spot welds are obtained by concentrating the pressure and current flow with shaped electrodes as in Fig. 16–8. Accurate control is necessary to prevent burning of the electrodes and excessive heating of the base material which would cause too much plastic flow under the pressure of the electrodes. Spot welding is sometimes facilitated by interrupting the current flow and using a series of short heating periods to provide a different heat distribution.

The two most common variations are *seam* and *projection* welding shown in Fig. 16–9. In seam welding, a series of overlapping spot welds

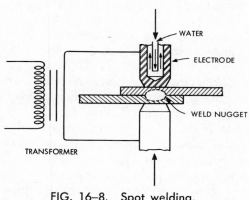

FIG. 16–8.   Spot welding.

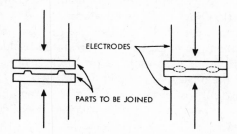

PROJECTION WELDING

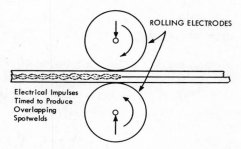

SEAM WELDING

FIG. 16–9.   Variations of spot welding.

produce a continuous joint used primarily where pressure or liquid tightness is a requirement as in automotive gasoline tanks. In many cases, multiple spot welds or single spot welds of highly localized character may be made by confining the area of contact to projections on the surface of one or both workpieces. Large electrodes shaped to the contour of the work may be used, and the exterior of the part has little or no marking from the electrodes. Uses of *projection* welding include the joining of electrical contacts to relay and switch parts and the manufacture of fencing in which the projections are inherent in the product where the wires cross.

Spot welding and its variations are among the most used joining processes in the manufacture of high quantity goods, such as automobiles, home appliances, office equipment, and kitchenware. Dissimilar metals and parts of different thicknesses may be joined. Little cleaning of the parts is necessary either before or after welding. The greatest limitations are the initial cost of equipment, the experimentation sometimes necessary with new applications, and the restrictions to joining relatively thin material except in the case of projection welding.

Furnaces and Dip Tanks.   The use of furnaces and dip tanks differs from the previously discussed heating means in application rather than in the basic heat sources used. Furnaces may themselves be heated by burning gases or by electrical means, either resistance or induction. The workpieces are heated by conduction from the furnace atmosphere, radiation from the walls, and, in the case of induction furnaces, the eddy currents induced in the work. Other than for preheating of weldments to prevent distortion and post heating for stress relief, the greatest use of furnaces in connection with joining processes is for brazing and soldering. Processes may be set up on either a continuous or batch process depending on furnace types and the quantities to be heated.

The temperature control possible together with the uniform thorough heating of the work causes less residual stress than occurs in differential heating. Contamination of the joint and deterioration of the surface of the workpiece may be minimized by controlling the atmosphere within the furnace.

SPECIAL WELDING PROCESSES

As in the case of sheet metal forming, a number of limited use joining processes have been developed for special applications. These may be concerned with the welding of refractory or easily oxidized metals, metals that require extremely high rates of heat input, heavy sections, or may simply involve special procedures that assist some otherwise conventional process. Most are of rather limited use because of special equipment required, the restriction of sizes, the high cost involved, or being new, lack of widespread knowledge.

Electron Beam Welding. Energy for heating may be made available in many forms. In the *electron beam,* Fig. 16–10, a stream of high energy electrons is focused electrically toward a spot on the surface to be heated. Rapid localized heating takes place with the possibility of melting for welding or complete vaporization if metal removal is desired. The process is carried out in a vacuum so that no products of combustion and no

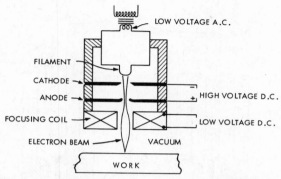

FIG. 16–10. Schematic diagram of a simple electron beam gun.

contamination or oxidation of the heated work occur. The boiling of the molten metal at the high temperatures obtained actually removes impurities that may be present and the resulting weld may be of higher quality than the base metal. The high rate of heating restricts the heat affected zone and there is minimum distortion and alteration of physical properties. A ratio of fusion depth to width of as much as twenty is possible.

The process uses high cost equipment and the total amount of heat available is small. At present, practical welding is restricted to beryllium, molybdenum, zirconium, hafnium, and other refractory metals difficult to weld by other methods.

Plasma Arc. For most gases the stable molecular form at room temperature contains two atoms but when ionized the gas becomes *monatomic* in form. A *plasma* is a gas that has been heated to such a temperature that the gas is ionized. A reduction in temperature results in the recombination of atoms to the molecular form with the release of energy as heat. The gas column in arc welding is ionized, but in this case it is a relatively small, stationary quantity of gas that is involved.

In the *arc plasma* process, a stream of gas is ionized by heat as it is passed through an electric arc by one of the two methods shown in Fig. 16–11. Thermal expansion of the gas stream causes it to flow at supersonic speeds as its diameter is restricted by the magnetic properties of the arc. The drop in temperatures caused by contact with the relatively cool work surface results in loss of ionization and the release of large amounts of heat directly at the surface to be heated. The process has high intensity and a high rate of heat transfer making it useful for welding high conductivity metals such as aluminum, for which a similar process called *atomic hydrogen* welding has been used for many years.

Ultrasonic Welding.   One of the principal limitations on cold bonds is the excessive deformation required to provide enough fragmentation of the oxide layers on the contacting surfaces. Cold bonding may be per-

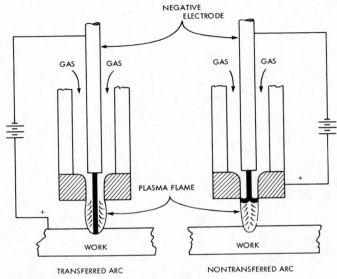

FIG. 16–11.   Plasma arcs.

formed with less deformation by applying high frequency mechanical energy in the process called *ultrasonic* welding. The vibrations introduce shearing forces which assist in the fragmentation with the result that over 50 per cent clean metal contact may be established.

Both spot and seam welds may be made and the widest use has been for metals difficult to join by conventional processes. These include stainless steel, molybdenum, zirconium, various bimetal combinations, and thin foil or sheet aluminum. The upper limit is about .100 inch, although thin sheets may be welded to thicker sections.

Friction Welding.   In ultrasonic welding, mechanical energy is supplied to facilitate fragmentation. In *friction* welding, Fig. 16–12, mechanical energy is supplied not only for this purpose but also to develop heat. Used

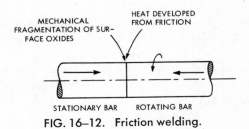

FIG. 16–12.   Friction welding.

almost exclusively for making butt welds in heavy round sections, the bars are brought together with high force while one is rotated. The friction develops sufficient heat to make the metal plastic and permit cleaning and closeness to be achieved in much the same manner as in resistance butt welding.

Electroslag Welding.   The principal of *electroslag* welding is illustrated in Fig. 16–13. The edges to be joined are placed in a vertical position

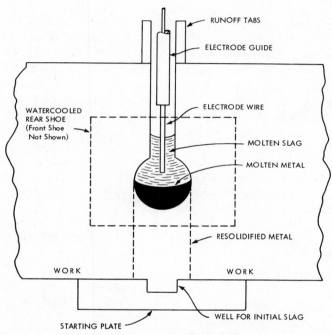

FIG. 16–13.   Electroslag welding.

with a gap between them. Water cooled copper shoes or slides cover the gap where the welding is in process. Slag is first deposited in the gap and a wire electrode introduced to form an arc. Once the arc has melted the slag, the arc is automatically extinguished and heat is produced by the passage of current through the molten slag. The electrode is fed into the slag as it melts and, as the gap fills, the copper shoes and electrode guide are gradually raised. The process might well be defined as continuous casting with the base metal and the copper slides forming a moving mold. The slag forms a protective layer for the weld pool, and in addition, forms a coating over the copper slides that protect them from the molten metal. By changing the rate of wire feed and the electrical input, the rate of deposition and the penetration into the base metal may be controlled.

A single electrode is used for sections up to about two inches thick. For thicker sections, multiple electrodes may be used and melting rates of up to forty pounds per hour for each electrode are possible. While the principal applications have been for forming butt welds between plates and for producing heavy walled cylinders rolled from flat plate, shaped rather than flat slides may be used for producing tee joints or special built up shapes on the surface of a part. In a newer variation of the process, an arc is used continuously, without slag, but with a protective gas atmosphere fed through ports at the tops of the copper slides.

WELDING DESIGN

Welding may fulfill either one of two basically different design concepts. As a basic shape producing means, welding competes with other basic processes, particularly forging and casting. The individual parts making up a weldment are most frequently cut from rolled sections that are produced in high quantities at low cost. Ideally the finished weldment may be thought of as an homogeneous structure equivalent to a single part. Even with less than 100 per cent joint efficiency, the single piece concept may still be used in design with appropriate consideration of the maximum permissible stresses, and increase of joint areas where necessary.

The single piece concept is used in many applications. In much welded pipe the weld is undetectable without critical examination, a drill or reamer shank is continuous with the body of the tool, even though they are of different materials. In modern welded structural steel assemblies, the joints may be stressed as continuations of the beams involved, although strengthening plates are sometimes necessary. In many instances, welding permits the one piece concept to be applied to designs that would not otherwise be possible. A one piece drill and shank could not be produced of different materials except by welding, some sheet rolling mills operate "continuously" by butt welding the end of one coil onto the next, and a complex structural steel assembly as a single forging or casting would be highly impractical if not impossible.

The second concept of welding is as an assembly means in competition with mechanical fastenings. The welded assembly is generally permanent but the individual parts retain their identity and the strength of the structure is frequently governed by the strength of the joints. The use of spot, seam, and projection welding is normally in this class. In many cases, not only are the mechanical fasteners eliminated but preparation by drilling or punching holes is also unnecessary and gaskets are no longer needed for sealing. Fitting of parts together may be simplified because alignment of holes is not required and they may be merely positioned with proper relationship to each other.

In the final analysis, welding must compete economically with other methods. Welding often requires longer setup time and higher equipment costs; thus, for many assemblies, mechanical fasteners would be cheaper for limited production and welding cheaper for large quantities. Non-permanent type fastening is essential, of course, for those applications needing separation for maintenance or use. When the single piece concept applies, a single weldment may be cheaper than a single forging or casting because of pattern or die costs, but in large quantities forgings or castings could have the economic advantage.

Joints. The terminology applied to the shapes of welded joints is somewhat loose. The type of joint and the type of weld are two different considerations. Two flat plates, for example, may have their edges butted together, one may be lapped over the other, or they may be placed at right angles to each other. The configuration adopted would be referred to as the type of *joint*. Although some joints are more conveniently welded by some processes than others and some processes are restricted to certain types of joints, the specification of a joint type does not automatically specify the welding method or the manner in which filler material is to be placed. The actual shape of the bonded area or the cross-sectional shape of the filler material, frequently governed by the preparation given the edges of the part to be welded, is known as the type of *weld*. In the lapped position, the plates might be joined by building up fillets along the edges, filling in holes or slots in one plate with weld metal, spot welding, or seam welding. Frequently, a close connection exists between the type of weld and the process that may be used. Either term, joint or weld, is sometimes used to refer to both the relative positions of the parts to be welded and to the type of weld.

Fig. 16–14 shows the weld types that may be produced by fusion

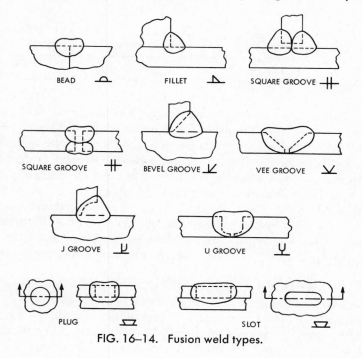

FIG. 16–14. Fusion weld types.

welding. Following the name is the drawing symbol for each type. Bead welds are often used for building up metal on a surface where joining is not needed. The type of groove weld used will have considerable influence on the penetration into the base metal necessary for good bonding and on the amount of distortion encountered. A vee or bevel weld requires simpler preparation than an "U" or "J" weld but results in greater distortion because much more heat is present at the opening of the vee than at the bottom. The heat difference is not so great in an "U." Where access is available to both sides of the members, many of the groove welds are made in double form, especially for heavy members. Adequate penetration with square grooves is generally possible only by welding from both sides. The weld types shown also apply to braze welding, except that in this application no melting of the base metal would occur and the dotted lines in the figure would be the extent of fusion.

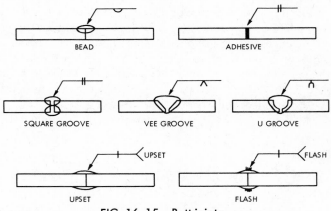

FIG. 16–15. Butt joints.

Little confusion occurs in the terms used for pressure welds since the names are in most cases completely descriptive of the weld type and the processes are limited in the joint types to which they may be applied. For brazing and adhesive bonding, the requirement for strength is thinness of joint. Most such bonds would be best defined as types of square grooves.

Five basic types of joints are used for welding. These are shown in Figs. 16–15 through 16–19. The types of welds that may be used with each and the standard weld symbols that apply are shown. Fig. 16–20 illustrates the elements of a welding symbol used on drawings to designate the details of a weld. Any part of the symbol which is not needed for clarity may be omitted.

Fig. 16–21 shows the manner in which the symbol would be used to describe a welded corner joint together with the result of following these specifications. The joint is to have a ¼ inch unfinished fillet weld on the inside of the corner (opposite side) and a ¼ inch bead weld on the outside (near or arrow side) that is to be ground flat. The shielded metal arc welding process is to be used. It is to be a continuous weld along the corner since no pitch or spacing is designated.

Design Considerations. It has been fully realized in recent years that welding is a unique process and that all of the design rules applied to other processes do not necessarily apply to welding. Welding started as a repair method and developed from this, primarily as a substitute for other

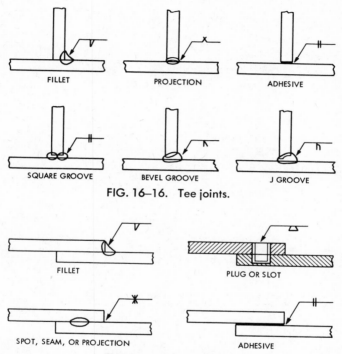

FILLET   PROJECTION   ADHESIVE

SQUARE GROOVE   BEVEL GROOVE   J GROOVE

FIG. 16–16.   Tee joints.

FILLET   PLUG OR SLOT

SPOT, SEAM, OR PROJECTION   ADHESIVE

FIG. 16–17.   Lap joints.

methods of *joining*. Where it is used strictly as a joining method, particularly by spot welding, little trouble is experienced. However, when parts are fully joined to form rigid, *one piece* structures, designers have not always realized that such structures do not respond to loading in the same way as a bolted or riveted structure. Many structures must allow for yielding or shifting in service which might be permitted by a bolted structure but not by a weldment unless the design were changed.

A number of failures of welded ships and storage tanks have been traced to cracks that can grow to a large size in a welded structure but would be interrupted by a mechanically fastened joint. Monolithic welded structures have been found to be somewhat more notch sensitive with a corresponding drop in impact strength, particularly at low temperatures.

On the other hand, designers have not always taken full advantage of the potential joint strengths offered by welding. Welding can produce rigid joints which improve beam strengths. The material would be used inefficiently if a welded structural steel assembly were designed according to rules that permit freedom in the joints as is generally assumed for bolting or riveting. Large improvements in joint strength and ductility have resulted from improved methods for preventing contamination of the

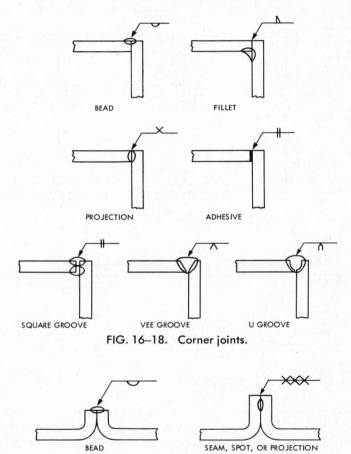

BEAD   FILLET

PROJECTION   ADHESIVE

SQUARE GROOVE   VEE GROOVE   U GROOVE

FIG. 16–18.   Corner joints.

BEAD   SEAM, SPOT, OR PROJECTION

FIG. 16–19.   Edge joints.

weld metal and as the metallurgical changes that take place in a weld have become fully understood.

The relative ease with which a sound union may be produced between two parts by welding is known as the *weldability* of a metal. A number of factors must be considered. Some metals may be more easily contaminated than others. The contamination may consist of gross oxide inclusions or voids that would be very apparent in a cross section of the weld, or microcontamination that results in structural changes detectable only by examining the metallurgical structure. Gross defects not only reduce the actual cross section of the weld but introduce stress concentrations that are particularly harmful in a metal with low ductility. The principal effect of structural changes is reduced ductility. Contamination can be controlled by providing the correct environment for the molten metal.

Especially important for steels is consideration of the hardenability of the metal. It will be remembered that this term is related to the cooling rate necessary to form a structure of given hardness in a steel. Again remembering that as hardness is increased, ductility decreases, the effect of hardenability on weldability can be predicted. In all the important welding processes, the metal is heated near or above the melting temperature and cracking or high residual stresses as the metal cools differentially can

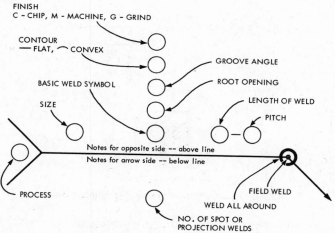

FIG. 16-20. Elements of the welding symbol.

be prevented only by yielding of the metal in the weld area. With few exceptions, any element that is added to pure iron increases its hardenability and therefore decreases its weldability by reducing ductility and increasing the possibility of cracks or high residual stresses. Therefore, increased welding difficulty can be expected as carbon or alloy content is increased in any steel. The major exception to this rule is the addition of vanadium which reduces hardenability.

Another factor affecting weldability is the thermal conductivity of the metal. If a metal has infinitely high thermal conductivity, it could not be fusion welded at all since it could not be locally melted. Aluminum, for example, has such high conductivity that high rates of heat input are required to prevent excessive melting of the base metal. On the other hand, stainless steels have low conductivity which results in hot spots and very high temperature gradients in the weld zone leading to increase of the stresses developed on cooling.

Composition can have other effects than those on hardenability. Stainless steels may not be hardenable to martensite at all but develop higher stress on cooling than carbon steels with equivalent strength at room temperature because they have higher yield strengths at elevated temperatures. The chromium in stainless steel is especially subject to oxidation and chromium oxide does not separate out easily from the molten weld pool. Many nonferrous alloy constituents are subject to segregation when cooled rapidly.

Heat produces other effects on structure than those of quench hardening of steels. Material that has been cold worked is automatically recrystallized during welding, usually for a considerable distance away from the actual weld. Most aluminum alloys begin to recrystallize at about 300°F. so a weldment made from work hardened aluminum may actually be more

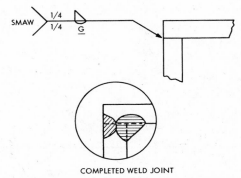

COMPLETED WELD JOINT

FIG. 16–21. Example of welding symbol use.

ductile in the heat affected zone than in the unheated base metal but only with an accompanying reduction of strength. Grain growth will follow recrystallization and even subsequent heat treatment cannot restore a desirably small grain size in most nonferrous metals.

The corrosion resistance of stainless steels may be especially affected by welding. At low cooling rates, small amounts of carbon can combine with chromium and reduce the corrosion resistance. Nearly all cooling rates will exist somewhere in the weld area so it is likely corrosion resistance will be lowered in some spots. Postheat treating of stainless steel weldments is nearly always required to restore maximum corrosion resistance.

In addition to the structure effects, heat causes other changes. The surface of practically all metals is oxidized at welding temperatures. While surface oxidation may not directly affect strength, it does affect appearance and may produce surface imperfections that lead to fatigue failures or serve as focal points for intergranular corrosion.

Even when the residual stresses do not lead to actual failures, they cause other difficulties. The dimensions of a weldment are usually different before and after welding, and machining is nearly always necessary for close dimensional control. The machining itself may release residual stresses to cause further dimensional change. When close tolerances must be held, stress relief prior to machining is usually required.

A number of precautions and corrections exist to alleviate the problems caused by stresses and distortions. If the amount of distortion can be predicted, the parts to be welded may be purposely off-positioned before welding to compensate. This procedure is somewhat like overbending sheet metal to compensate for springback. Some automatic compensation will occur in a double groove weld made from both sides of a joint but the first side welded usually will have the greatest effect. When a number of welds are to be made at a number of locations in a weldment, distortion may be controlled by choosing the proper sequence for making the welds.

The most universal solutions to the problems of stresses and distortion are preheating and postheat treatment of weldments. Preheating does not eliminate shrinkage and yielding that lead to stresses but, by lowering the yield strength of the base metal, it provides a greater volume through which the shrinkage may be distributed and by lowering the thermal gradients in the weld zone it reduces the size of the stresses by distributing them over greater areas. Postheat treatment relieves stresses by permitting yielding to occur at reduced stress levels and can also help to restore a uniform structure with an improved grain size, particularly in steel.

When materials have sufficient ductility, correct dimensions can be established by straightening. This may involve pressing operations in fixtures or localized heating with torches.

The factors that lead to residual stresses and distortion generally have an adverse effect on the strength of welded metals. Inclusions or voids not only reduce area but are stress concentration points. Composition changes in the weld area may either increase or decrease strength with a corresponding change in ductility. In some nonferrous alloys, brittle intermetallic compounds may form that have a serious effect on ductility.

The efficiency of a fusion welded joint may depend on the amount of *penetration* achieved. Although melting of the base metal is not absolutely necessary for bonding and, in any case, proper bonding requires only that the surface of the base metal be melted, practical joint shapes cannot generally be heated to melting only on the surface. In order to obtain proper bonding at the bottom of a square groove weld with most heat sources, it is necessary to melt a considerable amount of base metal. Heat sources differ in their ability to penetrate, that is in the depth to width ratio of the molten zone that may be produced dependent largely on the degree of heat concentration.

QUESTIONS

1. Why, even though heat is not essential to produce a weld, is it an important part of most important welding processes?

2. Describe forge welding.
3. On what are the thermal gradients dependent for fusion welding?
4. Show the complete chemical reaction and heat output from burning one cubic foot of acetylene in oxygen.
5. What is a 2X oxyacetylene flame?
6. What is the temperature at the tip of the inner cone of a neutral oxyacetylene flame and what maximum temperature is possible?
7. List the advantages and the principal disadvantage of oxyacetylene as compared to the electric arc heat source.
8. How is heat produced and used in the aluminothermic welding process?
9. What is the maximum temperature reached in an electric arc column?
10. Why is the range of current that can be satisfactorily used with any particular electrode for shielded arc welding limited?
11. By what methods in electric arc welding may the molten metal, during transfer and in the pool, be protected from oxidation and other chemical reaction?
12. In resistance welding, what causes the heat to be generated at the desired location instead of some other portion of the circuit?
13. How does flash welding differ from the usual butt resistance welding?
14. Describe projection welding.
15. Why is electron beam welding limited mainly to work on the most difficult to weld materials?
16. What significantly important part does plasma play in arc-plasma welding?
17. Which bonding process is associated with ultrasonic welding?
18. How does friction welding differ from ultrasonic welding?
19. For what kind of application is electroslag welding used?
20. Name the two design concepts for which welding is used.
21. Sketch illustrations and show the symbols for bead, fillet, square groove, level groove, vee groove, J groove, U groove, plug, and slot welds.
22. Sketch the five basic types of weld joints.
23. What is the welding symbol?
24. Why are the rules for bolted and riveted assemblies not suitable for welded design?
25. With what property of steel is weldability most closely associated?
26. What grain size problem exists with the welding of many nonferrous products?
27. Name four methods that might be used to correct or prevent distortion problems associated with welding.
28. What limits fusion-welded butt joints to relatively thin materials?

CHAPTER 17

Welding Equipment
and Procedures

MOST OF the basic shape producing methods make use of a relatively small number of equipment types for each of the individual processes. For both practical and economic reasons, the majority of welding processes make use of heat to establish the conditions necessary for welding. Most heating means are used at one time or another so the equipment design varies over a wide range. Welding is still in an earlier stage of development than casting, forging, pressworking, or machining and new techniques with associated equipment are constantly being developed. At some future date, a higher degree of equipment standardization is likely but at present, each new development adds another piece of specialized equipment.

Three principal areas differ in welding equipment. First is the heat source. Included here are variations in the energy input rate available and the maximum temperature attainable. Second are differences of portability. Relatively little machining or casting is ever done outside of manufacturing plants having fixed equipment for specializing in these processes. Some welding equipment is also of a fixed type but portability is required for many large welded structures such as pipelines, structural steel assemblies, and ships that are fabricated in place. Even for welding that is done in fixed plants, the general procedure is to bring the equipment to the work rather than the work to the equipment as is common with most other processes.

Third, as with any process, the productivity of the equipment varies considerably. In general, welding is more limited to job shop procedure than most other processes since many weldments are large assemblies that are not built in large quantities. Production equipment does exist, however, for large quantity welding where needed. This is particularly true of pressure welding equipment used for assembly of sheet metal components.

The cost of most welding equipment is low compared to other manufacturing process equipment. This is true because of the relatively simple

305

requirement of providing heat, because of the lack of high tolerance requirements for most welding, and because of the job shop nature of much welding equipment. The simplicity of the equipment means, though, that higher skill, knowledge, and judgment are required of the operator of welding equipment than may be true of other processes.

GAS WELDING

Oxyacetylene. Welding equipment varies in heat source, portability, and productivity as noted above, but it is the heat source which controls most of the characteristics of the equipment. By far the most important heat source using gas is that used in the oxyacetylene process. Acetylene is produced by the reaction of calcium carbide and water as follows:

$$CaC_2 + 2H_2O \rightarrow C_2H_2 + Ca(OH)_2$$

Acetylene is a colorless gas having a characteristic garlic-like odor. It is not highly poisonous but has an anesthetic effect causing nausea and headache when breathed in sufficient quantities. Acetylene is combustible at tem-

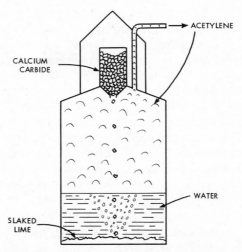

FIG. 17–1. Acetylene generator.

peratures above 1435°F. with as little as 2.5 per cent in atmosphere. The gas can form violently explosive acetylides with copper, mercury, or silver. At pressures above thirty psi, acetylene may be self-explosive if impurities are present. Safe practice, therefore, sets maximum pressures of approximately fifteen psi for the pure gas.

Acetylene is produced in generators of the type shown in Fig. 17–1. In large fixed installations with sufficient demand, the gas may be piped directly to the point of use. In most cases, the gas is produced at large producer plants and transported in cylinders to the users. Because of the possible danger from acetylene at high pressures, a special technique is used to permit a large quantity of gas to be held in the cylinders. The tank is first filled with a paste of balsam wood, charcoal, fullers earth, cement, and asbestos. After baking to drive out the moisture, the inside is left filled with a porous coke composed of millions of tiny cells.

The tank is next partially filled with acetone which can absorb about twenty-five volumes of acetylene for each fifteen psi pressure increase. The average cylinder contains 250 cubic feet (at atmospheric pressure) of acetylene in solution in the acetone at a tank pressure of 250 psi. The small cells in the porous filler of the cylinder prevent large volumes of gas from collecting and permit absorption of the heat of reaction. A fusible plug prevents pressure buildup if the tank is overheated.

Oxygen is normally produced by fractional distillation of liquid air and, because of the expensive equipment required, the only inplant installations are at some steel mills where large quantities are used.

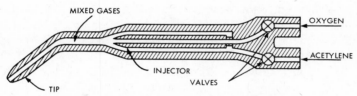

FIG. 17–2.   Injector type torch or blowpipe.

Practically all of the oxygen used for welding is distributed in tanks pressurized to 2200 psi and holding either 122 or 244 cubic feet of oxygen. The tanks are owned by the distributors and are subject to rigid inspection under Interstate Commerce Commission control.

Oxygen is colorless, odorless, and tasteless and by itself is neither poisonous nor explosive. However, pure oxygen can cause an explosion when combined with oil or grease, and many materials that do not burn in the atmosphere will burn in pure oxygen. Iron and steel are in this category so transmission lines for oxygen are made of either nonferrous alloys or heavy walled steel.

The actual burning of the acetylene and oxygen requires a system of regulating and mixing. The gas tanks are equipped with regulators that permit the oxygen and acetylene to be metered to the lines at controlled pressures. Acetylene is used at pressures ranging from less than one psi up to fifteen psi. Oxygen pressures at the torch range from five to fifty psi.

The gases are mixed and burned in a *torch* or *blowpipe* as shown in Fig. 17–2. The torch shown in the figure is known as an injector or venturi proportioning type in which the oxygen issues through a central orifice at high velocity and draws the proper amount of acetylene into the mixing chamber. Small variations in oxygen pressure do not affect the quality of the flame since more or less acetylene will be drawn out and the proportions remain substantially the same.

In an equal pressure torch, the proper proportions are controlled by the sizes of the orifices through which the gases are metered and either gas may come through the central orifice. The unequal pressure type has no venturi, and the proportions are controlled by varying the pressure of the gases. One type of torch has no decided advantages over the others, except that only the venturi type may be used with low pressure acetylene generators which supply acetylene at less than one psi. Most torches are manufactured to use interchangeable tips with different orifice sizes to control flame size and heat output.

Gas fusion welding is normally done with uncoated filler rods for addition of material. The molten metal, base and filler, permit floating and movement of impurities for the necessary cleanliness and the surface of the hot metal is separated from the atmosphere by the flame and excess gases. Extra acetylene will protect against oxidation. Increased oxygen composition will decrease oxidation protection as it increases flame temperature. The composition of the rod may be the same as that of the base metal or it may be of different alloy content to provide a finer grain structure or compensate for some composition change or other heat effect. Low carbon rod is frequently used even when welding high carbon steel to prevent excessive hardness and cracking in the weld.

Oxyacetylene welding has dropped in importance as electric arc welding has been improved, but it remains a highly versatile process. Initial equipment cost is low, maintenance costs are low, the equipment is easily portable with no requirement for other power sources, and almost any material may be welded. However it is somewhat slower for most applications than arc welding and the degree of skill required for satisfactory welding is higher. Because of the lower and more controllable heat input possible, it is still the preferred method for much welding of thin materials.

The equipment used for burning other types of gases is similar to that used for oxyacetylene welding. Oxy-hydrogen was the first gas fuel system to be developed for welding, but since the temperature is limited to 3600°F. its use is restricted to brazing operations and welding light gage metal where the relatively low temperature gives better control. A reducing atmosphere may be maintained and the quality of oxyhydrogen welds is comparable to that obtained by other processes. Natural gas or propane, burned either with air or oxygen have limited flame temperatures but can produce large quantities of heat at low cost and they are useful for preheating weldments as well as for soldering and brazing.

ELECTRIC ARC WELDING

Power Sources.   It is not practical to arc weld directly from power line sources since voltage and current control are not adequate. The welding power supply must provide electric current at the proper arc voltage and provide some means of restriking or establishing the arc after outages. The common types include direct current generators driven by electric motors, or by gasoline engines for portable service, alternating current transformer supplies which reduce the line voltage and provide for current and voltage control, and transformer-rectifier supplies which not only reduce the line voltage but also convert the alternating current to direct current.

Most *direct current welding generators* of the rotating type are driven by three-phase, 60 cps induction motors, which can be started across the line by a simple electromagnetic contactor, and operate at nearly constant speed. Typical sizes are from 5 to 25 horsepower, and typical speeds of rotation are 1800 to 1200 rpm.

The ordinary rotating direct current welding generator, the electrical circuit of which is shown in Fig. 17–3, is a differentially compounded

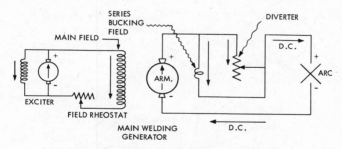

FIG. 17–3. Schematic diagram of a d.c. welding generator.

machine, with the main field windings supplied from a separate exciter generator usually mounted on the same shaft as the main generator. The exciter is a small shunt connected generator supplying the field windings of the main generator with a small current of from 5 to 10 amperes controlled by the field reostat.

The series or "bucking" field winding carries part of the welding current as determined by the diverter, and serves to reduce the output voltage by setting up opposition to the main field as welding current is increased. This produces a "drooping" volt-ampere characteristic, as shown in Fig. 17–4. The generator voltage output, with no current, is controlled by the field reostat and must be relatively high to provide for starting the arc. For any given starting voltage, the shape of the output curve is determined by the diverter setting. The effect of two diverter settings at each of two field reostat settings is shown. The operating point is determined by the arc volt-ampere curve intersection with the generator volt-ampere curve.

With given settings of the field reostat and diverter, the current will change only slightly with small changes in arc voltage which might be caused by changes in arc length. This "feed-back" is a form of automatic control which has been standard in welding power supplies for over half a century. It constantly adjusts welding generator output current and voltage to meet varying needs of the welding arc, without constant attention by the operator.

Rotating welding generators with the characteristics outlined are built with capacities of from 150 to 750 amperes. The upper size limit comes largely from practical considerations. Rod diameters above $\frac{5}{16}$ inch become exceedingly difficult to control and large size rods are restricted to making welds in the flat position. Welders may occasionally be connected in parallel when higher capacity can be used. For some applications, it is

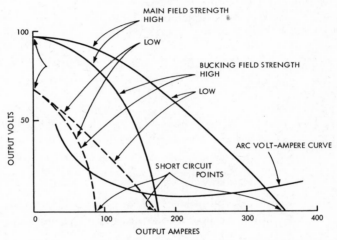

FIG. 17–4. Typical d.c. generator volt-ampere curves.

possible to use generators whose electrical characteristics provide a constant voltage output and vary the current as the demand requires. Generators of this type are built up to 900 ampere capacity.

Rotating generators are being replaced in many applications by *transformer-rectifier* units with no moving parts, other than possibly a cooling fan, which are cheaper to build, easier to maintain, and may offer the choice of alternating or direct current output. Fig. 17–5 shows a schematic diagram for a power supply of the transformer-rectifier type capable of supplying direct current. The main constant-voltage transformer reduces line voltage to the order of 90 volts secondary voltage (corresponding to the no-load voltage of rotating generators). A series reactor or adjustable choke coil serves as a valve for the output current from the transformer. It provides the drooping volt-ampere characteristic needed for arc control in many kinds of welding.

Arc current is adjusted by modifying the setting of the series reactor, either through changing the air gap in the reactor or introducing a small direct current which saturates the core of the reactor. Arc restriking voltage is supplied automatically when needed by a series inductance whose magnetic field reacts instantly to provide restriking voltage to the arc when arc current fails.

The output may either be used as alternating current or it may be rectified by selenium or silicon rectifiers to provide pulsating direct current which is still subject to periods of zero voltage. In many cases, special assistance to maintain or restrike the arc is provided by a special high-frequency, high voltage oscillator which applies voltage across the arc to keep its path ionized and conducting during the periods of zero current.

Many specialized welding power supplies and controls are available for special welding processes. Welding processes using inert or other forms of gas shielding have controls for gas flow. These turn on the flow of gas before the arc is struck, and turn it off after a suitable interval when welding

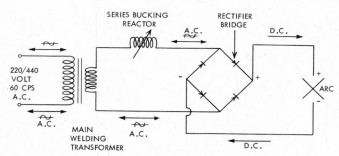

FIG. 17–5. Schematic diagram of an a.c. transformer-rectifier.

is interrupted. Other processes using tungsten or other nonconsumable electrodes require water cooling of the electrode holders. Automatic controls for water flow are usually provided in such units. In stud welding, arc current flows only for a brief, predetermined period, after which the stud is forced into the base metal molten pool. Submerged arc welding burns the arc under a layer of granular flux, and the rate of wire feed is automatically adjusted to correspond to the rate of burn-off. Many other specialized power supplies and control units have been developed for special purposes, including a development in which magnetic flux is applied to core wire as it is fed to the welding arc.

Arc Welding Electrodes. Early welding rods were bare iron wires, with which it was difficult to maintain stable welding arcs, and whose deposited metal was frequently porous or contained oxides and other inclusions. Modern welding rods for manual use are usually heavily coated with constituents which serve to alleviate these problems.

The first function of the coating is to provide a gaseous shield which flushes away the atmospheric gases, to avoid oxidation and other gaseous contamination of molten metal during transfer from the rod and after deposition in the molten pool. The gaseous shield generally also contains ionizing constituents which assist in ionizing the arc atmosphere (by reducing the effective ionization potential so the arc may burn with lower applied voltage). Sodium salts are commonly used for direct current welding rods. Potassium salts are used with rods for alternating current welding for which arcs are more difficult to maintain since the current passes through zero 120 times each second (twice for each cycle of 60 cps current).

In addition, the coating may provide slag-blanket forming materials, which form a protective layer over the deposited weld metal. The insulating coating reduces the rate of cooling by heat loss to the atmosphere and protects the hot metal from atmospheric oxidation and gas absorption at the higher temperatures where gases are readily soluble in the metal. For welding on vertical and overhead surfaces, special coatings with high slag viscosities are needed to prevent the slag from running off the surface of the metal during the period when the slag itself is molten.

In high-deposition rate rods for flat position welding, extremely heavy coatings may be employed to carry powdered iron or iron oxide materials which combine with the deposited metal to add to the deposition rate. *Contact* electrodes are designed with coatings which burn off slowly enough to support the rod at a proper distance above the work for good arc length with less operator skill than demanded by the usual manual procedure. The operator merely drags the electrode over the work, yet maintains a good arc position as the coating burns away in unison with the melting of the metallic material.

Welding electrodes are commonly designated by the American Welding Society code numbers starting with the letter "E" and followed by four or five digits. The first two digits (or in five digit numbers the first three digits) indicate the approximate ultimate tensile strength of properly deposited weld metal, in thousands of pounds per square inch. The next to last digit designates the welding positions in which the rod may be used. A rod with a code showing the digit "1" is suitable for use in all positions, with the digit "2" for flat and horizontal filler positions only, and with the digit "3" for flat position only. The more restricted positions are usually prescribed for higher-deposition rate rods whose slag and metal, while molten, must be held in place by gravity until solidified. The final digit specifies such characteristics as type of current (AC or DC), electrode polarity (whether the work or the electrode is positive), and special uses.

For example, a rod with the designation E6010 is a low carbon rod with ultimate tensile strength of sixty-two to sixty-eight thousand psi, may be used for welding in all positions, and is for use with direct current and reverse polarity (electrode positive with respect to workpiece). The various classes of rods may be quickly identified by special color codes, such as spots and bands of color.

Modification of Arc Welding for Special Purposes. By far the largest number of installations in use today are for manual welding; they have coated electrodes of consumable types, where shielding of the arc is provided by burning of the electrode coating. The core wire provides the deposited metal. These electrodes are manufactured in stick form with core wires of various diameters and coatings for various welding purposes. Manual welding is costly in terms of time and labor as compared to automatic production processes but requires little or no setup time. Speed of manual welding is increased, where feasible, by using work positioners. These permit welding on complex shapes to be carried out in optimum welding positions, flat or horizontal if possible. In this way, high deposition rate electrodes may be employed to speed the work and lower its cost. Certain applications, such as repair and maintenance welding, construction of bridges and structures, and welding of cross-country pipelines, do not

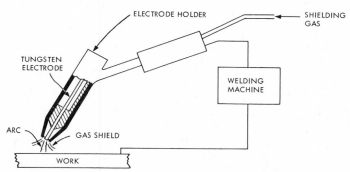

FIG. 17–6. Schematic diagram of gas tungsten-arc welding.

permit positioning of the work. Skilled welders receiving high pay rates are commonly found in such jobs. Even so, welding often proves to be far cheaper, and able to produce more reliable structures than other fabrication methods.

When manual arc welding cannot provide welds of high enough quality or when the nature of the work, especially the amount of welding to be done, permits higher setup and equipment costs with reduced operating labor time, a number of modifications are available.

Welding of many modern metals and alloys, such as magnesium, titanium, stainless steels, and others is done was *gas tunsten-arc welding*, Fig. 17–6. In this process, first developed during World War II for welding magnesium alloys, an arc is maintained between a nonconsumable tungsten electrode and the workpiece, while shielding is provided by an inert gas or gas mixture, most commonly argon or helium. Filler metal may or may not be added as the particular application requires. This method has been well developed and finds many applications today, particularly for welding some of the difficult materials. In the past, this nonconsumable electrode process has been referred to as tungsten inert gas welding.

Several variations of *gas metal-arc welding*, Fig. 17–7, have been developed. Processes of this type have in common the use of a filler material in wire form that is continuously fed into the weld metal pool and a shielding gas, or mixture of gases, to provide the protective atmosphere. Filler wire diameter may range from 0.020 to 0.125 inch and currents from 90 to 800 amperes. Equipment is available both for hand-held and machine-guided operation.

Argon, helium, or mixtures of them are the commonest shielding gases, particularly for high alloy steels and nonferrous metals, because of their complete chemical inertness. However, the gas mixture has considerable effect on the depth of penetration, the contour of the weld surface, and the arc voltage. From $\frac{1}{2}$ to 5 per cent oxygen is sometimes added to

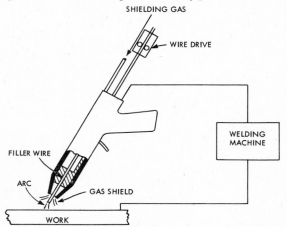

FIG. 17–7. Schematic diagram of gas metal-arc welding.

improve the weld contour. The high cost of these inert gases has led to the use of carbon dioxide as a shielding gas. CO_2 gas is restricted to use when welding mild steel; even then it is difficult to avoid porosity in the weld. Weld quality may be improved by providing a small amount of dry flux either as a magnetic powder that clings to the rod as it emerges from the holder or is contained in the center of hollow filler wire. Similar improvement may be obtained by using two shielding gases, a small amount of inert gas such as argon or helium near the rod and a larger flow of cheaper carbon dioxide surrounding this.

Alternating current has been found unsuitable for gas metal-arc welding and direct current power supplies of either the rotating generator or transformer-rectifier type are used. Power supplies with a drooping output characteristic are useful for hand-held units where the operator can control the arc length. For automatic units, however, this type of power supply can lead to freezing the electrodes in the bottom of the weld pool or to the arc burning back into the electrode gun if the current and wire feed rate are not properly matched. This difficulty has led to wider use of constant voltage and adjustment of the current to maintain an arc of nearly constant length, regardless of rate of wire feed.

The highest production process in wide use today in *submerged arc welding*, Fig. 17–8. The power supply and feeding arrangement are similar to those that would be used with gas metal-arc welding but shielding is provided by a granular flux fed from a hopper to surround the arc completely. Part of the flux is fused by the heat of the arc to provide a glassy slag blanket that protects the molten metal and the solidified weld as it cools. In addition, the normally nonconductive flux becomes conductive when fused and permits very high current densities that give deep penetration. Because of the greater penetration with a saving of filler material

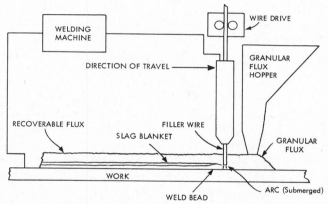

FIG. 17–8. Schematic diagram of submerged arc welding.

and a higher welding speed for a given current, smaller grooves may be used for joint preparation with this process than others.

Large weldments of heavy plate are often welded by this process. Machine-controlled units feed core wire and granular flux at predetermined rates, and high welding currents (500 to 2000 amperes) are used to obtain high deposition rates. By using multipass techniques, high quality welds may be produced in materials up to seven inches or more in thickness.

RESISTANCE WELDING

Power Supplies. At least two factors introduce problems for resistance welding equipment. One is the peak nature of the current demand. The actual time that welding current is required for most resistance welds is only a small percentage of the total time, but without some means of energy storage the equipment and more especially the power line supply must be extremely large to be capable of meeting this peak demand.

The second factor involves the nature of the electrical circuit used in resistance welding which inherently requires either direct current or single phase alternating current. Most industrial power supplies are three phase alternating current, so without special equipment, only one phase of the power supply may be used. This kind of operation leads to unbalanced loads on the power supply during the peak demand of welding.

Even with these difficulties, the simplicity of design and low cost has led to the use of single phase transformer power supplies for about 90 per cent of all resistance welding equipment. In plants having a large number of resistance welding installations, the power line load may be approximately balanced by connecting different machines to different phases of the supply line. With a number of machines in operation, the demand tends to level out with random use of the machines.

An iron core transformer with a tapped primary is ordinarily used as a power supply. Secondary voltages are in the range of 2 to 20 volts. Because of the very high secondary currents (1000 to 10,000 amperes for a 20 KVA machine), heavy secondary windings and circuit connections are required.

Resistance welding power supplies are rated in KVA (thousands of volt amperes) at a 50 per cent duty cycle. The duty cycle is the percentage of actual time that welding current is used. A 50 per cent duty cycle means "on" and "off" times would be equal and a 25 per cent duty cycle means "off" time would be three times as great as the "on" time for each cycle of operation. For most machines, the peak demand may be increased at lower duty cycles and must be lowered for duty cycles above 50 per cent.

A number of attempts have been made to make more efficient use of the power line by storing energy during the period of no demand. In this way it may be possible to average out the peak demand or to make use of all three phases of the power line, or both, in a single power supply. One such system uses a three phase motor to drive a generator. The three phase motor presents a balanced load to the supply line and the inertia of the motor-generator, which may also include a flywheel, averages out the peak demand.

In an *electromagnetic* stored energy system, the magnetic field of the primary of the welding transformer serves as a storage system in much the same way as the primary of the ignition coil of an automobile. In the welding supply, the turns ratio is reversed, however, and the secondary has only a few turns which supply large currents at low voltage to the work when the magnetic field is made to collapse.

Storage batteries connected in parallel to provide high currents have been used for some supplies. Such a system provides an almost ideal means for balancing and leveling the demand on the power line because of its high capacity, but problems arise in switching. Most resistance welding supplies accomplish the switching on the primary side of the welding transformer where the currents are low, but in a storage battery system heavy current at low voltage must be connected to the load and then disconnected. Some success has been achieved with carbon pile resistors as switches.

The stored-energy system which has widest use today makes use of *electrostatic* storage. A large condenser bank is charged through a three phase rectifier system to from 1500 to 3000 volts and discharged through a very high turns ratio transformer. Total energy is controlled by presetting the voltage to which the condenser bank is charged. The duration and wave form of the discharge depend on the turns ratio of the transformer.

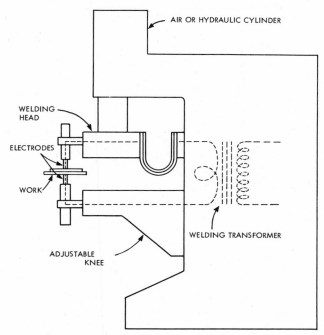

FIG. 17–9. Schematic diagram of a press type spot welder.

Machines. Most of the compexity of resistance welding equipment is in the power supply and controls. The machines are primarily simple presses and may be as shown in Fig. 17–9. The lower electrode holder, mounted on a knee similar to that of a horning press used in sheet metal presswork, is adjustable for work thickness. The pressure is supplied to the upper electrode by a hydraulic or air operated cylinder. The welding transformer and controls are contained in the body of the machine. Many spot welding machines use a rocker principle to actuate the upper electrode. This is especially adaptable to foot pedal operation of smaller units and portable equipment.

Portable spot welding units generally consist of a separate control unit, an overhead transformer with some freedom of movement, and a welding gun, consisting only of electrode holders and an air cylinder to provide closing motion. The gun is supplied with heavy cable from the secondary of the transformer, with water lines for cooling the electrodes, air for operation of the electrodes, and electrical connections to the control unit for proper synchronization of pressure and welding current.

Projection welding machines are similar in appearance and construction to spot welding machines and in fact are really the same except for the type electrodes. Seam welding machines are similar in principle with somewhat more elaborate control systems to provide proper spacing and timing of the welds. They are almost universally of the press type rather than rocker type and have one or both wheels (electrodes) driven, usually by a constant speed electric motor. The wheels are usually fixed so that work passes between them but some machines are built with traveling electrodes that permit large workpieces to remain stationary.

Many special machines have been built for high production work. Representative of these are multiple spot welding machines capable of making a number of welds simultaneously. They may operate from a single transformer and control system or may have individual transformers for each pair of electrodes.

The control systems and power supplies for most other types of resistance welding, including butt welding and flash welding, are similar to those used in spot welding. The machines themselves are much less versatile and are frequently built for some special purpose such as the butt welding of chain.

Electrodes.   In any resistance welding machine, the electrodes must serve the purpose of conducting the welding current to the workpiece. In spot welding, projection, and seam welding the electrodes also supply the welding force. In butt or flash welding, the force may be supplied independently of the electrodes. A major problem arises in spot and seam welding, since the area of contact must necessarily be small to supply correct welding pressure and control weld size. The small contact area carries current densities as high as 70,000 amperes per square inch, making it difficult to avoid overheating and deformation of the electrode tip since this current density occurs at pressures as high as sixty thousand psi.

Commercially pure copper has excellent electrical conductivity and is sometimes used for butt welding electrodes which can be large in area compared to the area of the weld. For spot welding electrodes, however, some electrical conductivity must be sacrificed to gain sufficient deformation resistance. Various copper alloys are used, including some standard bronzes and special copper tungsten alloys which retain hardness at higher temperatures. Water cooling is essential for spot, seam, and projection welding electrodes that are in direct contact with the weld area.

SUPPLEMENTAL PROCEDURES

Work Positioning.   For most other means of assembly, the design of the parts determines the positions the parts must have when assembled. Parts that are bolted together for example must be positioned so that the bolts pass through the holes in the parts and tightening the bolts automatically provides the correct position. In most welding, however, this position is not automatically established and some means must be provided for establishing the correct relationship between parts of the weldment.

Some kind of clamping mechanism is nearly always needed to satisfy this positioning and holding requirement. In production welding, use is frequently made of *jigs* or *fixtures* which are holding devices used to establish the correct relationship between specific workpieces. In addition, they may reduce distortion by providing rigid support for the weldment during cooling. Because of the definite need for positioning of parts, special holding devices, particularly of the simpler designs, are economically sound and useful for relatively small quantity manufacture. The terms *jigs* and *fixtures* are used pretty much interchangeably in the welding field, but as will be pointed out later, have distinctly different meanings when used in connection with machining and other operations.

Horizontal welds are easier to make than vertical welds and flat position welds are the easiest of all. Most weldments require the processing of joints along different axes and some are certain to be more difficult than others. For large pieces, rigid assemblies, and many instances of field welding, no movement of the work is possible and difficult welding positions, even overhead, must be overcome by use of high skills. For suitable size work, mainly in shop operations, various design devices called positioners are available. These consist primarily of universally adjustable tables to which the work can be fastened. The work can then be moved to the most desirable position for welding and visibility. The table may serve as a base for location and clamps or jigs and fixtures may be used to support the work. Positioners are particularly useful for manual fusion welding performed with either gas or arc heat sources.

Joint Preparation. It was pointed out in the discussion of weld and joint types that for adequate penetration in most fusion welds some space between the parts to be welded is necessary. The normal methods of cutting metal stock (plate, bar, rod, structural shapes) are shearing or sawing. These methods (cutoff) produce plane surfaces that in the usual operation are square with the axis or plane of the workpiece. Square grooves are a suitable kind of fitup for many butt, tee, and corner joints. However, they are limited in the material thickness for which they are satisfactory, and even then frequently require welding from both sides. Problems exist in establishing and maintaining correct groove width since the parts can not be brought into actual contact before welding.

Shearing and sawing, sometimes requiring special setups, may be used for producing angular cuts to form vee grooves but some vee and all "J" and "U" grooves require some other kind of preparation. Vee grooves in heavy stock are commonly produced by burning or may be machined, often by grinding. Machining, which is a high cost method, is required for

"J" and "U" grooves but benefit is derived from the better fitting of parts and easier production of high quality welds.

For fusion welding, the quality of the surfaces is of less importance than the shape of the edges. Oxides and surface dirt are not particularly harmful since they will be floated to the surface of the molten metal and combined with the slag during welding.

Upset and flash welding usually require no special preparation. Square ends or edges left by standard cutoff operations are, except in particular cases, adequate and the processes can handle the normal amount of surface oxidation that may be present. Specially shaped edges are sometimes used to promote better directional flow. If the initial contact area is small, the heating is more localized. With the application of pressure after heating, this small area is expanded and the total amount of surface oxide to be fragmented and diffused is smaller than it would be with square surfaces covering the entire cross section of the parts. With the proper shape on the ends before welding, the resulting upset or enlarging of the parts can be controlled to a closer degree.

Spot, seam, and projection welding owe much of their success to the fact that little or no preparation is required in most instances. The processes are most used for lap welding of cold rolled sheet metal, and the surfaces left by the stock processing are adequate for resistance welding. Heavy oxidation must be avoided and oil, grease, or dirt may have to be removed, but this is easily accomplished by standard commercial cleaning operations.

Projection welding is also used more on sheet metal than any other stock form and the projections are easily formed by sheet metal deformation operations. Many small parts such as electrical contacts may have projections formed by machining but these are usually high production items and the cost is not high. Projections in heavy sections may be forged. In many products, such as fencing, the projections occur naturally and require no preparation.

Adhesive joining and brazing require close fitup of surfaces in order to develop high strength. Whenever the natural shape of the parts does not provide this close fit, machining is the usual preparation method.

Post-Welding Operations.   Many welding procedures produce heavy oxidation, form some slag, and may spatter molten metal on adjacent surfaces. At best, welds produce a discontinuity of shape by leaving a bead or projection. Cleaning of the weld area is therefore nearly always necessary except in the case of some resistance welds. In particular, spot, seam, and projection welds with controlled localized heat produce a minimum of oxidation of exposed surfaces.

The most common cleaning procedure for fusion welds is wire brushing to remove slag and heavy oxide followed by chipping to remove spattered particles and irregularities in the weld surface. Rough grinding is frequently used for removal of projections and imperfections although high accuracy of surface shape or dimension may require standard machining procedures. These would include finish grinding, turning and boring, and shaping operations.

QUESTIONS

1. Why is there such a great variety of welding equipment?
2. What three kinds of difference exist in welding equipment?
3. Show the chemical formula for production of acetylene and describe the gas.
4. How is acetylene stored?
5. What are the pressure ranges used for acetylene and oxygen in oxyacetylene blowpipes?
6. What one advantage does the venturi or injector, type torch have over the pressure controlled types?
7. During oxyacetylene welding, what, if any, protection is provided against oxidation?
8. Why is a rotating welding generator constructed with a differentially connected compound circuit?
9. What advantages are offered by transformer-rectifier power units when compared with rotating generators?
10. For what reason is a low power, high frequency current sometimes connected to flow across the arc path of a transformer welding power supply?
11. What purposes may be served by the coating on arc welding rods?
12. Briefly describe gas tungsten-arc welding.
13. How does gas metal-arc welding differ from manual shielded arc welding?
14. Why is carbon dioxide sometimes used as a shielding gas and what problem exists in its use?
15. Why is submerged arc welding a production process?
16. What is the most common type power supply for resistance welding?
17. How is the capacity of resistance welding power supplies rated and what does the rating mean?
18. Describe seam welding.
19. What is a welding fixture?
20. Why are "J" and "U" groove welds limited in use but important when needed?
21. What type joints are most frequently associated with spot, seam, and projection welds?

CHAPTER 18

Machining Fundamentals

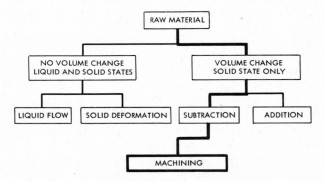

MACHINING as a shape producing method is the most universally used and the most important of all manufacturing processes. Machining is a shape producing process in which a power driven device causes material to be removed in *chip* form. Most machining is done with equipment which supports both the workpiece and the *cutting tool* although in some cases portable equipment is used with unsupported workpieces.

Machining occupies two distinct areas in manufacturing. For casting, forging, and pressworking, each specific shape to be produced, even one part, nearly always has a high tooling cost. The shapes that may be produced by welding depend to a large degree on the shapes of raw material that are available. Making use of generally high cost equipment but without special tooling, it is possible by machining to start with nearly any raw material form, so long as its exterior dimensions are great enough, and produce any desired shape from any material. Machining is usually the preferred method for producing one or a few parts even when the design of the part would logically lead to casting, forging, or pressworking if a high quantity were to be produced.

The second field of application for machining is based on the high accuracies and surface finishes possible. Many of the parts machined in low quantities would be produced with lower but acceptable tolerances if produced in high quantities by some other process. On the other hand, many parts are given their general shapes by some high quantity deformation process and machined only on selected surfaces where high accuracies are needed. Internal threads, for example, are seldom produced by any means other than machining, and small holes in pressworked parts are machined following the pressworking operations.

Machining, as well as forging and pressworking, is based on the fact that one material can be harder and stronger than another. If the harder one is properly shaped, it can be called a tool; when brought into contact with a weaker workpiece with sufficient force, failure results in the workpiece. All deformation operations are based on the proper control of this failure. The loading is controlled in machining so as to produce only localized failure in the workpiece, resulting in the removal of material in the form of chips without significant deformation in other parts of the workpiece.

In order to understand better what is involved in machining, it might be well to consider what is involved in some of the other fabrication methods and then see how machining differs from these.

In casting, energy is added in the form of heat so that the internal structure of the metal is changed and it becomes liquid. In this state, the metal is forced by pressure, which may consist of only the force of gravity, into a shaped cavity where it is allowed to solidify. The shape changing is therefore accomplished with the metal in such condition that the energy form is primarily that of heat and little energy in the form of force is required. Welding involves placing the metal in a molten or near molten condition, again by the addition of heat, and affecting a union by fusion which may involve pressure. Neither of these methods changes the shape of the metal while it is in its solid and strong state.

In forging, bending, drawing, rolling and extruding operations, advantage is taken of the property of metals to deform plastically. In forging, rolling, and extrusion, pressure loading is applied so that the primary stresses produced in the metal are compression. In drawing operations, metal is pulled or drawn through a controlling die with a complex stress distribution involving tension and compression at the point of metal flow. The forces used to produce shapes by bending result in compressive stresses on one side of the material and tensile stresses on the other. All of these operations are basically the same in the sense that a given quantity of metal is placed in a new shape without any appreciable change in volume.

In order to "remove" metal in machining, the material must be made to fail in some manner. The failure may be a plastic deformation of material or an actual fracture or some combination of the two failure types. All metals, however brittle they may seem, undergo some plastic deformation in the machining process.

Chip Formation. Some controversy exists over the theory that best explains the formation of a chip in metal cutting. The following, whether or not it is completely correct, is one of the more generally believed theories which serves a good purpose in helping provide a better understanding for tool design and use.

First, let it be understood that a cutting tool is merely a device for applying external loads to the work material. Contrary to some beliefs, if a tool is strong enough that it will not fail and the work is rigid enough to resist deflection away from the tool, a chip will be produced by a relative motion between the two regardless of the shape of the cutting tool edge in contact with the work. Although any shape edge may cause a chip to be formed, certain shapes will be more efficient in use of work energy than

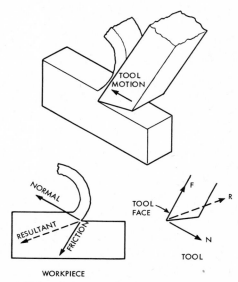

FIG. 18–1.   Forces in chip formation.

others and will exhibit less tendency to set up forces of such magnitude that the tool or work will be damaged. Fig. 18–1 shows a single point tool moving into the work, subjecting it to compressive loading. The load may be broken down into two forces: a force perpendicular to the tool *face* which is called the normal force; and since this is a dynamic situation, a force along the tool face which is the friction force. The two forces may be added vectorially to produce a resultant which, as is shown, projects downward into the work material. The direction and magnitude of the resultant are dependent on its two component forces and are influenced by the angle of the tool face and the coefficient of friction between the chip and tool face. Equal and opposite forces will occur in the tool but these are of little interest providing the tool is strong enough to withstand the applied loads.

As pointed out in the discussion of stresses in Chapter 2, an external force applied in a single direction may set up stresses in other directions within the material. Fig. 18–2 shows that maximum shear stresses are induced at an angle of approximately 45 degrees to the direction of the resultant and that the plane region extending from the tip of the cutting tool to the uncut surface of the work is subjected to these maximum shear stresses. In Chapter 10, it was indicated that plastic failure will occur when the shear stresses reach a critical value for any material. As plastic flow

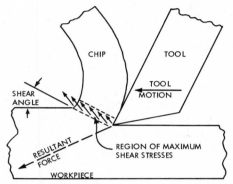

FIG. 18–2. Shear stresses in chip formation.

occurs along this plane, work hardening will increase resistance to further flow, higher stresses will develop and fracture failure near the tip of the tool will cause the separation of a chip which will ride over the face of the tool, thereby creating the friction which causes one of the component forces acting on the work. If the material is of brittle nature, it will be able to stand only a small amount of plastic deformation without fracture failure. If it is of ductile nature, the chip may hold together in a long continuous strip or ribbon, deforming considerably, but not fracturing except near the tool tip where it separates from the parent stock.

Fig. 18–3 indicates the probable nature of the deformation in the chip, assuming a homogeneous work material with uniform round crystals. Since actual materials are not completely homogeneous, a single plane of maximum shear probably does not exist, but rather there is a shifting plane creating a region or zone

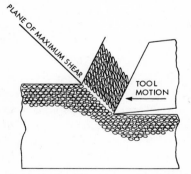

FIG. 18–3. Deformation of chip material.

in which plastic flow of the work material occurs. In this region, the material is deformed in such a way that the chip is always thicker and shorter than the material from which it is made. The amount of change in shape is dependent not only upon the characteristics of the work material, but also on the direction of the applied forces.

Chip Types. The types of chips produced in metal cutting are affected by cutting speeds, tool design, and temperatures in the cutting area, but are established primarily by the properties of the work material. Borderline types of chips exist that are difficult to identify as any particular kind, but in general they fall into either a *discontinuous* or a *continuous* class.

Discontinuous or segmental chips, Fig. 18–4, are produced when working with brittle material. If the work material has little capacity for plastic flow, fracture failures across the chip are produced during chip formation and the chip is broken up into short segments. Chips of this type are easily disposed of and good finish on the work surface is produced when the pitch of the segments is small. Some control of the chip size is obtained from the tool geometry which affects the magnitude and direction of the forces producing the chip.

A tool that produces a discontinuous chip fails progressively by a slight rounding of the sharp edge and wearing back of the tool tip to develop a flat surface parallel to the direction of cutting motion, as shown in Fig. 18–5. This worn surface on the tool is referred to as a *wear land*. When the

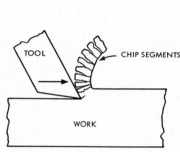

FIG. 18–4. Discontinuous chip.

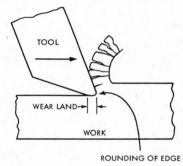

FIG. 18–5. Tool wear with discontinuous chip formation.

land becomes sufficiently large, considerable pressure is required to hold the tool in cutting position, rubbing action between the wear land and the finished surface causes a burnished or sometimes roughened surface on the workpiece, frictional heat is increased, and tool wear is accelerated.

When material with sufficient ductility is machined, the chip does not break into segments but instead comes off in a long continuous ribbon, produced under one of the sets of conditions shown in Fig. 18–6.

Case 1 shows a situation in which all of the material, placed under load by the action of the tool, escapes uniformly in chip form. The velocity of deformation at all points along the shear plane would have to be the same for this condition to exist. Studies have shown that Case 1 is rare, if in fact it ever exists.

Case 3 shows work material that has been work hardened adhering to the tool face where it can serve as a projection of the cutting edge. This condition is referred to as a *built up edge* and may exist to some degree in all types of machining. It was explained in Chapter 15 that metal to metal bonding will automatically occur when surfaces are brought into intimate contact while perfectly clean. In machining, the contact is established by the high loads on the material and the cleanliness is obtained from the scrubbing action of the chip on the tool face. Consequently the tool and work material in the region of chip formation act as a unified system, and failure does not necessarily occur along the face of the tool if stresses are higher at some other point. Under the temperature and pressure conditions of cutting, the build-up continues until it becomes unstable, at which

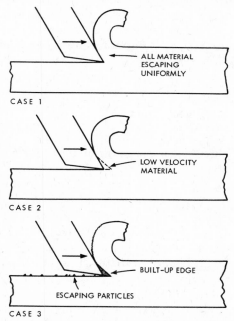

CASE 1

CASE 2

CASE 3

FIG. 18–6. Variety of continuous chip formation.

time it breaks down and escapes with the chip or under the tool tip producing a rough finish on the machined surface. The build-up cycle is of high frequency and can seldom be observed directly during the machining operation, although in many cases some of the built-up material remains on the tool after the cutting action is stopped.

Studies with high speed photography or low speed machining models show the existence of relatively stationary material near the tool tip, indicating that even when the material does not adhere tightly to the tool tip a situation similar to built-up edge may exist in all cutting operations. This condition is illustrated in Case 2.

Elimination of excessive build-up may be difficult with some materials but may be attempted by setting up optimum machining conditions. These would include reduction of the coefficient of friction between the chip and tool by polishing the tool face, lubrication, choice of tool and work materials that have little affinity for each other, and the choice of proper tool geometries. Higher cutting speed almost universally reduces the tendency for build-up to form and improves surface finish, provided the temperature of the tool does not exceed a usable limit.

Tool wear under conditions producing continuous chips causes wear lands similar to those occurring with discontinuous chips, but in addition the tool face is worn by a *cratering* action, as shown in Fig. 18–7. The roughness created on the face of the tool by the crater increases the resistance to chip flow, thereby changing the cutting conditions and increasing the tendency for build-up to form. It is this effect rather than the weakening of the tool that usually results in a need for the tool to be resharpened or replaced. There is indication that at least in some cases the built-up edge, or relatively stationary material near the tool tip,

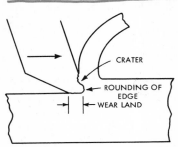

FIG. 18–7.   Tool wear with continuous chip formation.

is beneficial to tool life since it causes the crater to form at a distance back from the actual cutting edge.

Relative Motions.   The machining of a surface involves a relative motion between the tool and the work that causes a chip to be formed and also in most cases must include another relative motion that carries the tool cutting edge into new portions of the surface being manufactured.

The first of these is known as the *cutting motion* and is the relative motion of the tool with respect to the work which results directly in the forces that form the chip. Either the tool or the work may move in a number of patterns to produce this motion. In the illustrations used so far, where a single pass of a tool was assumed to produce a flat surface on the edge of a workpiece, cutting motion was the only relative movement considered. The rate of this motion is known as *cutting speed* and is always expressed in feet per minute.

If a surface is to be machined with a tool of the type shown in Fig. 18–8, more than one pass of the tool would be required and a second motion would be needed. This additional motion, which is necessary to present new material to the cutting edge for each pass of the tool, is called *feed motion;* it may occur coincident with or at a different time from cutting motion.

Feed motion, as a rule, is very slow when compared to cutting motion. The word *feed* is used to describe the distance of feed motion per cycle of operation. A cycle of operation may be a revolution of the workpiece or of the tool, a stroke of the workpiece or of the tool, or in some cases where multipoint tools are being used, the distance each cutting edge moves into the material. In the latter case, the measurement is usually called *feed per tooth*. With some machine equipment, the measurement of feed motion may be in the form of *feed rate* in which case the dimensions would be inches per minute.

CUTTING TOOL DESIGN

Cutting tools are used in an almost infinite number of shapes, forms, and types. Some are *single point* tools (single cutting edge) and even in this simplest type exist in a great number of shapes. Others are multipoint, most with cutting edges related to each other. Although any shape cutting edge will produce a chip, certain shapes are necessary to produce some surfaces. In any case some tool shapes provide more efficient metal removal than others. Therefore, general rules exist for the design of cutting tool edges.

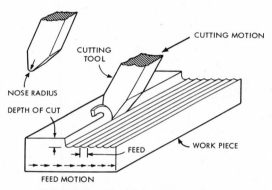

FIG. 18–8. Machining terminology.

Tool Geometry. The surface shown in Fig. 18–8 could be produced by a number of different tools. If the feed were small enough, the final surface would be determined by the direction of feed motion alone. With larger feeds, the tool shape would have a direct effect on the elements making up the surface, and the degree of conformance to the desired surface could be varied by change of either edge shape or feed. The edge contour should be that which will most efficiently produce the desired surface.

The tool pictured has a definite *nose radius* and with some finite feed could be used to produce a relatively flat surface. Although sharp points are sometimes necessary on tools to produce sharp corners, they should be avoided whenever possible because they are easily damaged by pressures of cutting, they tend to wear rapidly, and heat cannot be conducted from the cutting area well because of the small tool mass near the work. On the other hand, too long a contact between the cutting edge and the work may cause vibration or chatter to be set up by excessive forces or deflection of the tool or work.

Tool Nomenclature. Fig. 18–9 shows a tool used to produce a flat surface with a straight line cutting motion and an intermittent straight line feed. It should be emphasized that the nomenclature presented here applies to any cutting tool, since in every case a direction of cutting motion for

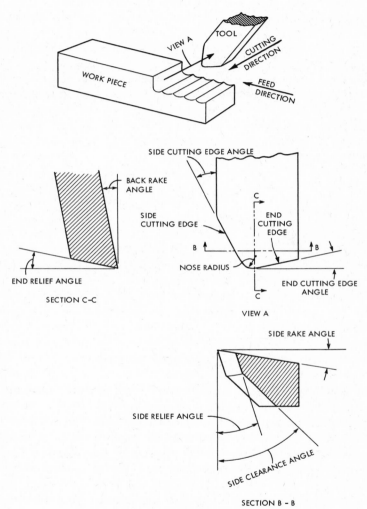

FIG. 18–9. Cutting tool nomenclature.

principal reference will exist. In some cases, the cutting action is obtained by rotation of the tool or work, and the cutting direction must be defined as the direction of the tangent to the diameter of the tool or work at the point of cutting.

The following definitions apply:

Face—the surface of the tool on which the chip impinges.

Flank—the surface of the tool which intersects the face to form the cutting edge of the tool.

Side cutting edge—the principal cutting edge of the tool, usually nearly normal to the direction of feed.

End cutting edge—the secondary cutting edge of the tool.

Nose—the portion of the cutting edge connecting the side cutting and end cutting edges; may be a point, arc, or chamfer.

Side cutting edge angle—the angle between the side cutting edge of the tool and a plane perpendicular to the direction of feed.

End cutting edge angle—the angle between the end cutting edge of the tool and the direction of feed.

Rake angle—the angle between the face of the tool and a plane perpendicular to the cutting direction.

Back rake angle—the rake angle measured in a plane perpendicular to the direction of feed.

Side rake angle—the rake angle measured in a plane parallel to the direction of feed.

Relief angle—the angle between the flank of the tool and the direction of cutting motion.

End relief angle—the relief angle measured in a plane perpendicular to the direction of feed.

Side relief angle—the relief angle measured in a plane parallel to the direction of feed.

Clearance angle—increased relief of the flank of the tool, generally not present but necessary to prevent interference of some rotating cutters or workpieces or to simplify regrinding. May be either side or end clearance.

Relief Angle. In order for a cutting edge to function, a positive relief angle must exist behind all portions of the cutting edge which form the chip. Existence of the angle permits the cutting edge to penetrate the work material by preventing rubbing of the flank on the finished work surface. Any angle greater than zero could prevent contact except that, because the work material is under compression, some elastic recovery occurs as it passes under the cutting edge and some provision must be made for tool wear. The smaller the relief angle the less wear of the tool is necessary to cause a large area of contact between the tool flank and the work. The larger the relief angle the greater the wear that must occur before a large wear land is established but the large relief angle causes reduced support for the tool tip. With less support the tool is more subject to fracture failure, can chatter more easily, and is less able to dissipate heat from the cutting action. A practical relief angle is therefore a compromise between the two extremes and for most applications is in the range of from six to eight degrees. In some cases, angles as small as two or three degrees may prove more satisfactory by producing greater rigidity and support for the cutting edge without a significant reduction in tool life.

Rake Angle. "True" rake angle would be in the direction of chip flow over the tool face. However, this direction is difficult to determine and the angle difficult to measure so it is more common to locate the tool face by measuring back and side rake angles. In the case of some rotary multipoint cutters, such as those used in milling operations, the terms are changed to radial and axial rake angles respectively.

The direction of the normal force applied to the workpiece to form the chip is determined by the face of the tool. Therefore, the rake angle for efficient cutting will vary with different materials. In general, the greater the rake angle the greater the shear angle along which material deformation takes place and the less will be the force required to form the chip. When working with ductile materials, the lower forces result in lower friction on the tool face and less tendency for built-up edge to form, but at the same time, the greater angle results in a weaker tool with lower capacity for heat dissipation. With brittle work material a segmental chip is produced. The best results are obtained when the pitch of the segments is small. Some control over the size of these chips is exhibited by the rake angle. In order to deform the material more severely, causing the chips to break into smaller parts, rake angles of small positive, zero, or even negative values are most satisfactory.

Some machining operations with lead, copper, or their alloys are also done more satisfactorily with small rake angles. With these materials, a low coefficient of friction exists between the chip and the tool face and a large positive rake angle can lead to the resultant force on the tool having a component toward the work surface. The design of most machine tools would permit backlash to be pulled out if force were applied in this direction, allowing the tool to move into the work from its original setting.

Another exception to the use of the theoretically best rake angle for chip formation occurs when certain hard, brittle tool materials are used. Some of the most commonly used tool materials are very strong in compression but relatively weak in tension. With small or negative rake angles, the principal load on the tool is compression and even though total loads may be greater, increased tool life is obtained.

With the many combinations of work material and tool material possible, it is difficult to present universally recommended values for rake angle. They range from 20 to 30 degrees negative when machining hard brittle work material with brittle tool materials to as high as 40 degrees positive when machining soft ductile nonferrous alloys with high speed steel cutting tools. Under any one set of conditions (tool material, work material, cutting tool shape, type of machining operation, cutting speed, feed, and depth of cut), considerable variation of the rake angle may produce no significant effect on the results. Considerable experimental work has failed to establish numerical correlations between rake angle and tool life. It is known, though, that the effect of rake angle on tool life is small even when the angle is varied over wide ranges.

Large positive rake angles are usually desirable for better work finishes, although under some cutting conditions at high speeds, small positive or negative angles produce acceptable results. Care must be exercised in increasing rake angles to large positive values because of the weakening effect on the tool. Large rake angles also increase the tendency for chatter which not only affects the work surface by causing a tool mark pattern but also may reduce tool life.

CUTTING TOOL MATERIALS

Tool materials have always played an important part in the economy of the world. In the earliest days of history, stone was the principal tool material. As late as the nineteenth century, the American Indian used flint for arrow points, spear heads, knives, and other types of cutting edges. Even today some primitive peoples use stone as one of the main tool materials. During the Bronze Age, copper alloys took the place of stone in the more civilized areas. With the discovery of iron and steel, a tool material was found that has been used for hundreds of years and was added to only after the Industrial Revolution and the development of mass production principles called for tool materials that could operate at higher speeds. Since the beginning of the twentieth century, a number of new tool materials have been developed and most of them play some part in present manufacturing.

The requirements for a satisfactory cutting tool material are that it be harder and stronger than the material it is to cut, that it be abrasion resistant to reduce wear, and that it be able to maintain these properties at the temperatures to which it will be exposed when cutting. The latter requirement has become increasingly important during recent years because of the development of work materials with superior properties and the need for operating at higher cutting speeds to increase production. The principal difference between the tool materials in common use is in their ability to maintain hardness and strength at elevated temperatures.

Carbon Tool Steel. Until about 1907, *carbon tool steel* was the only cutting tool material in common use. It is a plain high carbon steel containing from 0.9 to 1.2 per cent carbon. Carbon tool steel can be machined in its softer (annealed or spheroidized) state and has a forging temperature range at about 1800°F., where it can be shaped by pressure or impact. The normal procedure for producing a tool from this material is to machine or forge the steel to a suitable shape, after which it is necessary to harden the material for use as a cutting tool. Suitable hardness is established by heating to the austenitic range (approximately 1400°F.) and quenching to obtain martensitic structure. The material thus treated is extremely brittle and not satisfactory for application of high loads or shock and must be further treated by tempering or drawing. Some of the hardness is sacrificed in order to relieve the high residual stresses resulting from quenching and to provide the toughness required in a cutting tool.

The tempering temperature selected depends to some extent on the type of tool and the conditions of use. The initial hardness after quenching is approximately Rockwell "C" 67. Tempering at 400°F. lowers the hardness to about Rockwell "C" 61 but provides adequate shock resistance for most applications. Where greater toughness is necessary such as in a thread cutting tap, a higher tempering temperature must be used with some additional loss of hardness. The physical properties of the material are "fixed" only if the tempering temperature is not exceeded either in use or in sharpening by grinding. It is evident then that the processing of the tool material has set some of the maximum limits under which it can be used.

Carbon tool steel is presently of only minor importance for metal cutting where its principal application is for low use tools that will be used for only short runs. Many cutting tools for nonmetallics are still made of carbon tool steel, mainly because of its lower cost, although even at higher initial cost some of the other tool materials might be more economical in the long run. Carbon tool steel is used in large quantities for forging and casting dies, sheet metal presswork tooling, and other nonmachining applications where hardness, strength, and wear resistance are important.

High Speed Steel. In the early twentieth century, a group of alloy steels were developed that came to be called *high speed steels* because of the greater cutting speeds at which they could be used when compared with carbon tool steel. One of the most common, 18–4–1, contains 18 per cent tungsten, 4 per cent chromium, and 1 per cent vanadium. Variation in the quantity and type of alloying elements provides different physical properties, making the high speed steels applicable for many uses. High speed steel contains less carbon than plain high carbon tool steel but, even with only about 0.6 per cent carbon, cutting hardness can be maintained at higher temperatures than for carbon tool steel. The alloying elements also impart greater hardenability to the material making possible satisfactory treatment of heavier sections.

High speed steel is hardened by much the same procedure as that used for carbon steel except that higher temperatures are used. The austenitizing temperature is approximately 2200°F. and tempering is performed between 1000° and 1200°F. The higher temperature (tempering) permits the tool to be used at cutting speeds approximately twice those permissible with carbon tool steel.

Both carbon tool steel and high speed steel differ from most other cutting tool materials in present use in that they have a temperature range where they may be forged or otherwise hot worked and both may be annealed to permit machining.

Most drills and reamers and many milling cutters are made of high speed steel. The use of the material for single point tools is limited to special shape tools and to those used in tool room or job shop operations where speed of cutting and length of tool life have relatively small effect on overall cost. Many tools used in other manufacturing processes are made of various grades of high speed steel, especially where high hardness must be maintained at high temperatures.

Cast Nonferrous Alloys. During the first World War, *nonferrous tool alloys* composed of cobalt, tungsten, and chromium were developed. As the "nonferrous" name implies, iron is present in the material only in the form of impurities. These materials do not have a soft condition in which they can be machined easily nor do they have a plastic range in which they can be hot worked. The material is made into a tool by casting roughly to shape and finishing by grinding. The hardness of the nonferrous tools does not drop off abruptly with increased temperature as it does with the heat treated steels and cutting hardness is maintained to approximately 1500°F.

The material can be used at higher cutting speeds than either carbon tool steel or high speed steel. Because of the greater difficulty of working it and its higher initial cost, however, use is limited mainly to the machining of malleable and cast iron, particularly in the making of interrupted cuts. The tool form is usually single point for use on lathes, shapers, and planers. Both high speed steel and the nonferrous alloys have wide application as structural materials, particularly in high temperature environments. The nonferrous also have high resistance to many chemicals and to abrasive action.

Cemented Carbides. One of the most important groups of cutting materials in use today is *cemented carbides,* the manufacture of which was discussed in connection with powder metallurgy. Both carbon tool steel and high speed steel depend on the formation of metal carbides for their hardness. In plain carbon steels, it is iron carbide (cementite) and, in high speed steels, primarily chromium carbide that provides hardness and abrasion resistance. Most metal carbides are by themselves extremely hard materials and have potential as cutting tools. Metal carbides may not be melted and cast as metals are and the only practical means of manufacture is by powder metallurgy. Pure metal carbides may be pressed and sintered, but with the exception of some laboratory success with titanium carbide, the resulting material is too brittle for practical use. All of the presently used cemented carbide cutting tool materials contain from 3 to 25 per cent cobalt or nickel as a binder.

Cemented carbide was first used as a cutting tool material prior to 1930. The earliest tools consisted only of tungsten carbide and cobalt and their use was restricted to machining nonferrous materials and cast iron because of their lack of toughness and their tendency to weld with steel. Variation of composition and treatment has since developed a wide range of hardness and toughness properties that are applicable to most machining operations. Many of the variations have been classified into standard grades suitable for various cutting uses.

Tools intended for use on nonferrous metals and cast iron are still primarily tungsten carbide. Tools for use in cutting steel contain in addition some titanium carbide, tantalum carbide, or both. In either case, tools may be classed as roughing, general purpose, or finishing, depending on the toughness characteristics that are controlled primarily by the amount of binder used with the carbide. Hardness values of the different grades run from approximately Rockwell "C" 65 to 90.

Carbides have a high modulus of elasticity of fifty million psi or above, compared to thirty million psi for steel. The quality of rigidity indicated by this value is important in applications where minimum deflection under load is desired. Cemented carbides have high damping qualities giving them an additional value in many machining operations where vibration might otherwise be a problem. Compressive strength varies from five hundred thousand to nine hundred thousand psi.

Almost any kind of tool may be made of either solid carbide or with carbide as a small tip on a steel shank. Cemented carbides, like cast nonferrous alloy tools, cannot be hot worked or machined except by grinding or electrical discharge machining. Both of these procedures have very slow metal removal rates on carbides and grinding usually requires two steps with silicon carbide abrasive for roughing and diamond for finishing. The initial cost of cemented carbide tools is from two to ten times that of high speed tools of similar design, not only because of the higher cost of the material but also because of the increased difficulty of shaping the material. High initial cost, however, is often recoverable in a short time because of the higher speed of operation and the longer wear life of the material.

Diamonds. Although the diamond is the hardest material known, it has rather limited use for cutting tools because of its high cost, the difficulty of shaping it, and its extreme brittleness. Its use is limited to light, high speed cuts on low tensile strength materials. It is particularly valuable for machining abrasive materials such as carbon, hard rubber, and some plastics. The combination of small depth of cut, high cutting speed, and low coefficient of friction between the tool and the work results in superior finishes on aluminum alloys and sintered bronze bearing materials. One large use for diamonds is in the turning and boring of pistons for internal combustion engines.

Ceramics. The newest addition to the family of cutting tools is the ceramic or cemented oxide material. This is a nonmetallic material processed by powder metallurgy in much the same way as cemented carbide. References may be found of the experimental use of sintered aluminum oxide cutting tools as early as 1907, but current use in metal cutting dates back only to about 1950. Some of the most successful tools to date have been made of almost pure aluminum oxide, sintered without binder. The resulting block of material demonstrates high abrasion resistance, chemical inertness, high compressive strength, and high temperature resistance, but as in the case of cemented carbides, a weakness in tensile strength. The shock resistance is even less than that of cemented carbide.

Although the use of ceramics has been somewhat successful in multipoint milling cutters used on cast iron and nonferrous alloys, most applications have been in single point turning and boring operations. The material is nearly always positioned with negative rake angle to minimize tensile loading. For machining of steel, it has been found almost essential to condition the cutting edge with a chamfer or honed radius in order to obtain satisfactory tool life. So far the material has not proven very satisfactory for interrupted cuts on any material. For simple turning operations, the cutting speeds are more often limited by the machine tool than by the ability of the tool to withstand high temperatures. Steels can frequently be cut at speeds as high as 2000 feet per minute and it has been demonstrated that under special conditions the tool material can cut at speeds as high as 18,000 feet per minute.

Abrasives. All of the above tools are used for single point cutting tools and multipoint tools in which the cutting edges are related to each other. Another group of tool materials known as *abrasives* is used in connection with grinding operations. These are definitely multipoint tools, since each grain of abrasive material on the surface of the tool serves as a cutting edge. The orientation of these grains varies over the surface of the wheel and the rake and relief angles of the individual grains are different. With random orientation, most of the grains present large negative rake angles, and for a given contact area the pressures between the tool and the work in grinding are higher than with other types of tools. The total load may be less because of the small total contact. As cutting proceeds, the grains chip and become dull on the edges. Built-up edge development also increases the unit pressure with the work. In order to continue to cut efficiently, the wheel must "resharpen" itself. This is accomplished by the combined action of grains of abrasive fracturing to present new cutting edges and completely worn grains pulling free from the bond that holds them together.

Regardless of this action, however, cutting action is essentially the same as it is with any other cutting tool. The abrasive grains apply load to the work material causing material failure and the formation of a chip as each comes in contact with the work.

Grinding wheels and other abrasive tools are manufactured by combining crystalline abrasive, carefully screened for size, with one of several bonding materials. The mixture is pressed to suitable shape and baked or dried, depending on the bond material, to produce the final tool strength.

Although many materials can serve as abrasives, three fulfill most of the needs for industrial manufacturing. *Aluminum oxide* is a tough, strong grain that receives the greatest amount of use in the construction of grinding wheels and tools. This is the same material that is used in the manufacture of ceramic cutting tools. For grinding work, the grain size is very large compared to the small particles used in ceramic tools, and the bonding process holding the particles together is very different.

Crystals of *silicon carbide* are harder and sharper cornered than those of aluminum oxide, but with these good features is the poor characteristic of greater brittleness. Silicon carbide wheels are used mainly for grinding low tensile strength materials such as cast iron and aluminum which are not strong enough to promote proper breakdown and resharpening of aluminum oxide grinding wheels, and for tool sharpening work where the rapid breakdown of silicon carbide keeps the wheel sharp and cool cutting.

The third important abrasive is the *diamond*. Crushed particles of diamond, either man-made or natural, are graded for size, combined with a bond material, and applied to some supporting material in the form of a ring or band to produce a grinding wheel. As would be expected, diamond wheels are expensive, costing as much as several hundred times that of a comparable sized wheel of aluminum oxide. Since they have a long life and can do work that cannot be accomplished with the other materials, they are economical purchases for many applications. One of the most important uses of diamond grinding wheels is for finish grinding of cemented carbide and ceramic tools. Finish grinding with a fine diamond abrasive leaves a smoother surface than can be produced with silicon carbide wheels, thereby reducing the chance of tool failure because of stress concentration at scratches and tool marks. Diamond wheels also have wide use in cutting and shaping many hard nonmetallics such as tile, brick, ceramics, and quartz.

MACHINABILITY

Machining at best is an expensive procedure when compared in general terms to most other manufacturing processes. When used for making only one or a few parts, most of the expense comes from setup and adjustment. The actual cutting time may be a small percentage of the total time required. Under these conditions, tool life is of relatively small importance and high speed steel tools are used predominantly because of their lower initial cost and ease of shaping and grinding. Low cutting speeds can be used without increasing the cost of the finished part materially. In production operations, however, the setup of a machine becomes permanent or semi-permanent and the largest portion of the manufacturing time is frequently the actual cutting time. Under these conditions, the final cost of the part is more directly influenced by the cutting speed, which in practically every case, has a direct relationship to the life of the tool.

Prior to about 1900, machining was largely tool room style; but with the development of the mass production of consumer goods having large numbers of machined surfaces, the demand for more economical cutting increased. In most cases, greatest economy depends not only on the choice of the best tool material, but also on the proper choice and control of many other factors. The complexity of the problem and difficulty of

determining optimum conditions becomes evident when it is noted that all
the following variables have been shown to have significant effects on tool
life, work finish, and accuracy.

Work Variables	Tool Variables	Cutting Conditions
Composition	Composition	Cutting speed
Microstructure	Mounting rigidity	Feed
Hardness	Side edge angle	Depth of cut
Size	End edge angle	Coolant material
Shape	Nose shape	Coolant application
Surface condition	Rake angles	Impact conditions
Temperature	Relief angles	Machine rigidity
	Cutting edge sharpness	Cutting motion
	Surface finish	Feed motion
	Chip breaker design	Chip disposal

Some of these variables are determined by the requirements of a particular operation. The work may have some fixed size, shape, and composition over which there is no control, the tool geometry may be limited by
the type of cutter, and the feed and depth of cut are frequently determined by the finish required or the amount of material to be removed.
Many of the factors are important because they affect the amount and
type of vibration which occurs. One of the most important of these, which
always has a large effect and over which there is usually some control, is
cutting speed.

Machinability. Nearly everyone has at some time used a pocket knife
to whittle some shape from wood. While such an operation does not fill all
the needs of a definition of machining, it is nevertheless a chip forming
operation that uses a hard and strong tool to cause localized failure in a
workpiece. The whittler has doubtlessly also noticed that some woods are
easier to shape than others. He is faced with an inherent difference in the
"whittleability" of different kinds of wood. This ease of working is
affected not only by the kind of wood but by the moisture content and the
state of seasoning.

A similar consideration arises in machining metals. Different metals may
be cut at different rates, different amounts of power are required, and
different finishes are obtained. These differences depend not only on the
kind of metal or alloy but also on its prior history of processing, including
deformation and heat treating operations that affect its hardness, strength,
and grain structure.

The term *machinability* is used to describe the relative ease with which
any material may be machined. In one respect, the term is like the word
"strength," for a material can have tensile strength, shear strength, impact
strength, fatigue strength, and compressive strength, all of which are
measured in different ways and any one of which does not necessarily

correlate with the others. That is, materials having equal tensile strengths do not always have the same impact strength or fatigue strength. Three different measurements—finish, power consumption, and tool life—may be considered in machinability. Unlike measurements of strength properties, these do not always give precise numerical information, but are more often relative to some standard.

Finish. To have real meaning, any measurement of finish would have to be made with all the variables which might affect finish under strict control and the values obtained would be reliable only for a particular set of machining conditions. The relative finishability of different materials has somewhat more reliability. For example, brass normally finishes better than steel under any given set of conditions.

The geometry of any surface is affected to different degrees by different factors. The gross conformance of a surface to its intended or theoretical shape is controlled by the accuracy of the machine tool motions, by vibrations or deflections of the machine tool or workpiece, and by deformations that may occur as the result of temperature change or the release of residual stresses. The term *waviness* is used to describe these variations of conformance which are relatively widely spaced or large in size.

The term *roughness* is used to refer to the relatively finely spaced surface irregularities, the height, width, and direction of which establish the predominant surface pattern. These irregularities are superimposed on the waviness. Roughness may be due to higher frequency vibrations, to feed marks occurring as a result of the combination of tool shape and machine tool relative motions, or to the particles of built-up edge that have escaped under the cutting edge and been smeared on the finished surface.

The *lay* of a surface is the direction of the predominant surface pattern. Lay is determined primarily by the direction of cutting motion used to machine the surface and may be a single direction, circular, or random in nature.

The exact classification of many surface irregularities frequently depends on the method of measurement. Most surface finish measuring instruments may be adjusted to respond only to variations of less than some particular width so that feed marks, or low frequency vibration, or chatter, may or may not be recorded in the measurement. Measurements of both waviness and surface roughness will generally be different when measured in different direction because of the effect of the lay.

Any surface may contain, in addition to roughness and waviness, randomly distributed flaws or imperfections. These are most often due to inherent faults, such as inclusions or voids in the material, that are exposed only when the outside surface is machined away. Scratches or marks caused by mishandling also fall in this category.

While surface finish depends on many variables and in many cases on the particular combination of all the variables, especially when vibration is encountered, it is possible to make some general statements about the effect of the more important factors. Table 18–1 shows the most likely effect on surface finish caused by increasing the more important machining variables from some standard set of conditions. The predicted results are intended to be qualitative only and even then apply only if one variable at a time is changed. There are major exceptions when vibration is considered. Changing almost any condition can often stop vibration, even when the change is in the direction that would otherwise produce a poorer finish. Further exceptions occur at feed rates and depths of cut near zero. With either of these variables at very low values, finish is frequently poor, especially as tools become dull. With a very small depth of cut or feed, and a worn tool, the rake angle is decreased with increased forces and greater tendency for built-up edge.

TABLE 18–1
Relation of Machining Variables to Surface Finish

Variable	Finish Effect with Increase of Variable
Cutting speed	Improvement
Feed	Deterioration (degree dependent on nose shape)
Depth of cut	Deterioration
True rake angle	Improvement
Relief angle	Little effect
Nose radius	Improvement
Work hardness	Improvement

Some compromise is frequently involved between finish, tool life, and machining time. Decreasing the depth of cut or feed may improve finish but either change would increase machining time. Increasing cutting speed almost universally decreases tool life. Increasing the rake angle may make the tool subject to edge chipping or fracture failure, or may induce chatter.

Power Requirement. A further consideration in machinability is the amount of power required for chip formation. The specific energy required to form a large chip and that required for a small chip is somewhat different because of the different surface to volume ratios involved. For this reason, in addition to the greatly different tool geometries involved, grinding requires more energy for a given amount of work than other machining operations where larger chips are produced. Provided that extreme values of feed, depth of cut, rake angle, and cutting speed are not considered, the amount of energy required to remove a given volume of work material is a constant for the material in any operation with approximately the same cross-sectional area for the chip. Table 18–2 lists the average power required for machining various materials in drilling, milling, planing, or turning operations.

The values in this table refer to the actual power required for the chip formation process and do not take into account power lost in the machine tool drive components and the power required for feeding. The actual motor size required for any operation would depend on both the power required for cutting and the overall efficiency of the machine.

Tool Life. In the great majority of machining operations, the machine tool has more than adequate power and the required finish may be maintained by the proper choice of the factors involved. In any case, power requirement and finish are either acceptable, or not acceptable, with a distinction between acceptability and nonacceptability fixed by the machine tool and the work specifications. Tool life is a different kind of measure of machinability. Any cutting tool will cut most work materials under practically any cutting conditions, provided the tool shank is not actually fractured from gross overloading. However, the life of the tool under different sets of cutting conditions will be vastly different. It is this

TABLE 18–2
Power Requirements for Machining

Material	Horsepower per CuIn per Min
Magnesium	0.2
Aluminum	0.4
Brass	0.4
Cast iron	0.6
B 1112 steel	0.8
AISI 1020 steel	1.2
Copper	1.3
AISI 10100 steel	1.7

consideration of tool life that is generally the most important aspect of machinability. Tool life has a major influence on machining cost and determines the maximum productivity of any setup.

Any consideration of tool life must start with a definition of the term. The "life" of a tool may be determined by measuring the total time the machine operates, provided the percentage of cutting time can be determined, by measuring the actual cutting time, by determining the volume of metal removed, or by counting the number of workpieces machined.

Of equal importance with the method of measurement is the method of determining the end of tool life. This can be complete failure so that the tool is unable to cut, a change in the finish of the workpiece indicating a change in the geometry of the tool, a change in the amount of force or power required for cutting, a change in the dimension of the workpiece, or a given amount of wear on the tool, measured either as rounding of the cutting edge or as a wear land on the flank of the tool.

Complete failure is seldom used except in roughing operations with tools that are to be discarded without resharpening. For tools that are to be resharpened, the nature of tool wear with time must be considered. Generally, some rapid initial rounding of the cutting edge is followed by a relatively long period of time during which the flank wear proceeds at a constant rate. At some point in time, the flank wear accelerates (probably because of temperature increase above some critical point). For the most efficient regrinding, the tool should be removed at a point immediately proceeding the start of the accelerated wear rate. In practice, measurements are frequently made of the wear land and the tool resharpened when some arbitrary value is reached. Flank wear is also the common method of terminating laboratory tests of machinability.

As indicated previously, many variables can effect tool life. Most of these variables are fixed by the design of the workpiece, which may specify the material; by the shape of the surfaces to be machined, which limits the type of operation that may be used and may control the tool shape; by the machines which are available for the operation; and by the tool materials that may be chosen because of availability or because the tool type is limited to certain types of tool materials.

Cutting fluids will increase tool life in practically all cases, but their use and method of application depends on overall economic considerations. The cost of using the fluid must be balanced against the gain in tool life. The reason for using a cutting fluid is as likely to be for finish improvement as for tool life gain.

Tool life is greatly influenced by the continuity of the cutting as affected by vibration and complete stoppage. The conditions which control vibration are influenced not only by the shape and strength of the workpiece, but also by the rigidity of the machine tool and the tool mounting and the factors which determine the rate of material removal. A single point turning tool may start a cut and continue with a uniform chip until the cut is completed. With a similar setup, the workpiece might contain a longitudinal keyway which would subject the tool to impact and thermal shock each revolution. The teeth on a milling cutter are subject to starting and stopping the cut one or more times for each revolution of the cutter. In each of these cases, expected tool life would differ because of differences in the tool work contact.

Most of the conditions mentioned are subject to some choice, but once they have been fixed, change is more difficult. However, three important machine variables are nearly always subject to some change after all other conditions have been set. Each of these, cutting speed, feed, and depth of cut, has some effect on tool life.

The development of accurate information, regarding the effect of any variable on tool life, is complicated by the large number of variables which may affect the results. Information obtained under one set of conditions may not be useful under other sets of conditions. An additional problem is the large amount of material and time required to make accurate tool life tests. Many attempts have been made to shorten tool life tests, but significant results have been lost in some cases because of improper simplifying assumptions. Some involve testing to a small wear land and extrapolating the information to greater wear lands, assuming some known relationship between time and rate of wear land development. Such tests may be satisfactory providing validation from previous knowledge or testing is available. Some success has been achieved by using radioactive tools and measurement of the radioactivity transferred to the chips as an indication of rate of tool wear. The first comprehensive tool life data were reported by F. W. Taylor (the developer of high speed steel) in 1907 and his work has been the basis of most later work.

Taylor showed that the relation between cutting speed and tool life could be expressed empirically by:

$$VT^n = C_t$$

where:

V = cutting speed, fpm
T = tool life, minutes
C_t = a constant depending on work material, tool material and other machine variables. Numerically it is the cutting speed which would give one minute tool life
n = a constant depending on work material and tool material

This equation predicts that when plotted on log-log scales there is a linear relationship between tool life and cutting speed. An exception to this relationship occurs at low cutting speeds with brittle tool materials where chipping of the tool may occur and the tool life is less than predicted by the equation. The exponent "n" has values ranging from 0.13 for high speed steel tools cutting copper, to 0.41 for any tool material cutting aluminum. The average value when machining cast iron is 0.25.

It has also been found that the effects of feed and depth of cut on tool life may be expressed as:

$$V_t = \frac{C_a}{D^x \times F^y}$$

where:

V_t = any fixed tool life in minutes
C_a = a constant depending on tool material, work material, and other conditions of cutting
D = depth of cut, inches
F = feed, inches
$x, y,$ = constants

The constants "x" and "y" have been found to depend primarily on the work material. For cutting steel, the latest available figures are 0.14 for "x" and 0.42 for "y."

A large part of the difficulty in using these figures arises in making a first choice, since the constants C_t and C_a depend on all the conditions of cut. However, the figures are useful in evaluating the effects of changes in feed, speed, and depth of cut, once the tool life has been determined for

one set of variables. As an example, consider a turning cut made with the
following conditions:

Workpiece—annealed 1040 steel
Cutting tool—cemented carbide
Depth of cut—0.125
Feed—0.011
Cutting speed—540 fpm

If C_a were 61 (a typical value), the tool life would be sixty minutes.
Suppose it were desired to remove the same volume of material in half the
time it would take with these conditions. This could be accomplished by
doubling cutting speed, depth of cut, or feed, provided the machine had
adequate power, the setup had sufficient rigidity, the amount of metal to
be removed permitted doubling the depth of cut, and the finish remained
acceptable. The results would be as follows:

Variable Doubled	New Tool Life
Cutting speed	6 minutes
Depth of cut	53.5 minutes
Feed	44 minutes

Increase of either feed or depth of cut will increase the size of the chip
being produced. More work has to be accomplished and more heat generated but, since the mass of the chip is larger, much of the additional heat
will be carried away without proportionate increase in the heat transferred
to the tool. Changes in feed and depth of cut, therefore, have minor effect
on tool life when compared to changes in cutting speed.

The significance of these effects can be more clearly understood by
considering that with a doubling of any of the variables the metal removal
rate is doubled. If the life of the tool were to be measured in volume of
metal removed before failure, it would be clear that increase of either
depth of cut or feed would result in an increase in the amount of metal
removed. For the example used, doubling the depth of cut would result in
78 per cent increase in the volume of metal removed before failure and
doubling the feed would provide a 47 per cent increase. Increasing cutting
speed, however, reduces tool life at a more than proportionate rate. For
the example, the tool life in metal removed would be decreased by 80 per
cent.

The economic conclusions cannot be based entirely on these calculations. Machine wear would likely be greater with any variable increased
and the final answer would be greatly influenced by costs of labor and
tools. In practically all cases, however, it is true that so far as metal removal
rate is concerned, more economical machining may be obtained with
depth of cut and feed increased to limits set by rigidity, power, and finish
requirements rather than by considerations of tool life.

The effect of cutting speed on costs is always influenced by the relative
costs of labor and tools, and by the nature of the work to be done. It is

desirable, particularly in job shop and tool room work, to have available some average values of cutting speed such as those shown in Table 18–3. The lower values of such tables are generally conservative since it is impossible to anticipate exact cutting conditions. Much of the total time spent in tool room and job shop work is in setup rather than actual cutting. Higher values are generally used in production and in many cases are arrived at by trial and error methods.

It should be remembered that choice of all machine variables, including cutting speed, is not for the purpose of making the tool last as long as possible, but instead, is an attempt to choose a set of cutting conditions from which the greatest economy can be derived. In many cases (especially true of low cost tools), a life of only a few minutes duration at very high cutting speed may be the most economical. A complete study, including consideration of the costs of the machine, direct labor, tools,

TABLE 18–3
Typical Recommended Cutting Speeds

Material	Turning		Milling	
	H. S. Steel	Carbide	H. S. Steel	Carbide
B 1112 steel	175–350	450–750	175–200	400–500
1040 steel	125–275	350–600	70–115	250
18–8 stainless	80–150	250–375	60–120	240–300
Med. C. I.	90–150	200–350	80–130	250–500
Med. brass	225–350	500–700	200–300	600–1000
Aluminum	400–1000	1000–3000	400–700	800–1000

down time, and tool sharpening, is necessary to completely evaluate the cutting speed that should be used. This is true, however, only for long production runs since the time and cost of such a study might be more than any possible saving in tool room or job shop operations.

Hot Machining.   Some of the greatest problems of tool life occur when machining hardened conventional alloy steels or high temperature resistant alloys. Many of the high temperature materials may not be annealed so as to have a soft state at room temperature. Using normal machining practices with these materials, it is necessary to use very low cutting speeds (10 to 15 fpm in some cases) and even then tool life may be very low. The materials can all be ground, but grinding at best is an expensive process and is especially so when large amounts of metal are to be removed.

One promising approach to machining such materials is to heat the work material to high temperature before cutting. This method (*hot machining*) seems paradoxial since it is known that tool life is increased if the temperature of the cutting edge can be kept low. Nevertheless, tests have shown that with the workpiece heated to as much as 1000°F., tool life may be increased by factors up to one hundred. It must be remembered that tool wear is a function not only of temperature, but also of the loads placed on it and the abrasive qualities of the work. The temperature of the tool depends not only on ambient tool and workpiece temperatures, but on the rate at which heat is being added to the tool by the formation of the chip. This latter factor is undoubtedly decreased greatly in hot machining.

Two approaches have been used. The entire workpiece may be heated in a furnace, then transferred to the machine tool for machining. Such a procedure obviously would destroy the heat treat hardness of any conventional steel but does not seriously affect some of the heat resistant alloys. Considerable distortion of the workpiece and oxidation of all the surfaces also occurs, including those not machined, but some success has been achieved in roughing operations, especially in milling.

The second approach is to heat locally only that portion of the work that is to be removed. The success of this approach depends on the ability to transfer a large amount of energy to a small spot on the workpiece surface immediately ahead of the point of chip formation. With proper control, it is possible to limit the extent of heat penetration into the workpiece but still reduce the amount of energy required to form the chip. Torch, electric arc, high frequency resistance, and induction heating have all been used with some success.

There is little doubt that hot machining can extend tool life in many applications. The biggest drawbacks to wider application of the method appear to be the practical difficulties of heating and handling the workpiece, the cost of equipment, the high degree of specialization of the setup, and the distortion that occurs.

Coolants. The performance of physical work requires a transformation of energy that often results in evolution of heat. In machining, almost all of the work that goes into deforming the work material and the chip must appear as heat. Additional work is necessary to overcome friction, heat is produced from the rubbing of the chip on the tool face, and to a smaller degree by the rubbing of the tool tip on the finished work surface. When metal cutting is performed efficiently, the principal source of heat is from the work required to deform material. All of the heat must be dissipated to the work, to the chip, to the surrounding medium, or into the tool doing the work, with proportions depending on many variables. In most cases, the major portion of the heat can be carried away by the chip where it will do no particular damage. An exception exists in those cases where the cutting area is restricted in such a way that the chip is in contact with the tool and the work for long periods of time and the heat can be transferred into these parts. Heat causing temperature increase of the workpiece will cause thermal expansion, making the holding of close dimensions difficult and possibly producing distortion of the work. Excessive temperature rise of the tool may cause it to soften so that it wears faster or may cause thermal shock producing fracture failure. In general, anything that can be done which results in less deformation in the chip or less friction will result in a reduction of the heat generated and decrease the rate of temperature rise of both the work and the tool.

Regardless of the procedure, a certain minimum amount of heat will be produced for any given rate of doing work. Since heat will always be a product of machining work, it becomes important to prevent that heat from raising the temperature of the tool and work sufficiently to cause significant damage. A method of control used in much industrial machining is the application of a fluid as a surrounding medium to carry heat away from the cutting area before it does damage. Coolants may in some cases be gases, but are more frequently liquids that serve several purposes. They absorb heat in the cutting area, carrying it away to be dissipated elsewhere, keeping the temperature of the tool and work lower. A second purpose of a coolant is to reduce friction between the chip and the tool. This friction reduction is probably accomplished in two ways. In the boundary areas, where the pressures are not too high, it is likely that the metal is separated from the tool by a coolant film. For this purpose, the maximum benefit would be derived from oils with high film strengths. The second action of a coolant in reducing friction is a chemical action to produce solid low shear strength films between the chip and tool. Most coolants contain chlorine and sulphur compounds or fatty acids which will form metal chlorides, metal sulfides, or soaps. These compounds have low shear strength and when formed at the interface of the chip and tool, offer less resistance to sliding than would metallic alloys formed between the chip and the tool if they were in direct contact under the cutting pressure and temperature conditions.

Reduction of friction which resists sliding of the chip has multiple benefits. It reduces the wear that will occur on the tool face and it reduces the friction force which is one of the components helping produce the chip. The change in this force system has the effect of increasing the angle of the plane of maximum shear, resulting in a shorter shear plane and less energy being required to deform the chip. Reduction of friction, together with alteration of the chip form, results in less tendency for a built-up edge to form; and, of course, reduction of friction reduces directly the heat generated between the chip and the tool. Although the effect on overall power consumption is minor, friction reduction cuts down the necessary work energy to perform the work.

Although not usually the primary reason for their use, coolants may also be used to carry chips away from the cutting area. An air suction, the cooling effect of which is small, is sometimes used in the grinding of cast iron to pick up the chips and carry them away. Coolant is supplied under pressure through oil hole drills to the cutting area at the tip, primarily to pick up heat, but in flowing out through the flutes of the drill, it aids clearing of the chips from the hole. Coolants are used in grinding to cool the work material so size can be maintained, but an important function they play is in carrying away chips of metal and abrasive material from the wheel to prevent uncontrolled scratch marks being made by loose particles in the area.

Coolant materials must be such that they do not cause corrosion of the machine or work. It is possible, by choice of a suitable coolant, automatically to coat finished workpieces with a corrosion protection film, thus eliminating a bench operation.

Coolant Materials.   Various fluids are used as coolants, depending principally upon the purpose for which the coolant is intended, but depending also to a lesser degree upon the material of the work and the tool. Gases are seldom used as coolants because of their limited ability to carry away heat, although if a coolant is used in the machining of cast iron, it frequently will be air under suction. In this case, the principal use of the coolant is for carrying away the small chips produced in the operation.

Because of its high specific heat and good cooling properties, water is frequently used as a coolant. Water must be conditioned for use by the addition of some kind of rust inhibitor. Alkaline materials, such as sodium carbonate, borax, or trisodium phosphate, are sometimes added to reduce the tendency for rust to occur on iron and steel parts, but other materials are more frequently used as additives for this purpose. So-called "soluble oils" are oils containing a wetting agent causing them to break up into minute droplets to be dispersed throughout the water. These oils are then carried to all places the coolant reaches, coating the surfaces with an oily film, providing protection and at the same time, giving some lubricating value to the coolant. These oils may be used in various concentrations, depending upon the particular application and the need for oily type lubrication. Lubricating qualities may be added to water by the use of chemically active additives produced commercially under a number of trade names. Most additives will contain ingredients to control bacterial growth, retarding rancidity and development of bacteria that cause strong odors or harm to personnel.

In many cases where relatively large chips are being produced and cutting pressures are high, oils are used as coolants. These may be from animal, vegetable, or mineral sources. Lard oil is the most common animal oil used for this purpose and may be compounded with mineral oils. Vegetable oils are not too commonly used for coolant application, because there is a relatively good market for their other uses and their cost is likely to be high. The mineral oils most frequently used are kerosene and paraffin oil, often compounded with the fatty oils for the development of better characteristics. Most of the oil type coolants contain sulphur or chlorine compounds as additives to improve their ability to reduce the coefficient of friction by the formation of metallic sulfides and chlorides upon the work or tool materials.

In order to perform satisfactorily in the dissipation of heat, coolants need to be used in high volume. After passing over the cutting area, the fluid drops into a sump where most of the heat is dissipated to the air, and chips or dirt may be settled out or strained before recirculating the coolant to the cutting tool. The usual and most satisfactory method of applying the coolant for general purpose work is the flooding of the area with a large volume of material under low pressure. Some attempts have been made to design better methods of coolant application but most of these other methods have been satisfactory only for limited types of work. In large operations, it is possible to supply coolant from a central system. After return from the machines, the fluid can be filtered and sterilized to prevent the spread of the disease carrying and odor causing bacteria.

QUESTIONS

1. Define machining.
2. In what two areas does machining usually surpass other shape producing processes?
3. What one single quality above all others must a cutting tool possess?
4. Sketch the active forces in a simple cutting tool setup and indicate the region of material failure.
5. Why is a chip always thicker than the material of which it is made?
6. Discuss the types of chips produced in metal cutting.
7. How may the tendency for built-up edge formation be reduced in machining?
8. Describe tool wear occurring with the different types of chips.
9. Define cutting motion.
10. What are feed motions?
11. If any shape tool can produce a chip, why have fairly definite rules been established for cutting edge shapes?
12. What influence does rake angle have on chip formation?
13. When are negative rake angles likely to be used?
14. For what kind of tools is carbon tool steel used?
15. Name five tool materials used for shaped edges.
16. How do abrasives differ from other tool materials?
17. Name and describe the main characteristics of the three most used abrasive materials.
18. When is tool life of relatively small importance and when is it the opposite?
19. What is meant by "machinability" and what are its most important elements?
20. What three dimensional qualities must be considered in measuring surface finish?
21. What is meant by the lay of a surface?
22. Why is the life end point of a tool that is to be resharpened less than if the tool were to be thrown away?
23. Why are tool life tests difficult to interpret?

24. Assuming that no problems arise concerning available power, support rigidity, finish quality, or dimensions, what cutting variable should be increased to increase rate of material removal by machining? Why?

25. How long should a good tool last?

26. What is meant by "hot machining"?

27. Name four functions a coolant may perform.

28. Why do many coolant materials contain sulphur or chlorine in some form?

CHAPTER 19

Machined Shapes

SURFACES are defined mathematically as the three dimensional loci of points or lines in space. It is not possible to *produce* a surface in solid material purely by movement of a line or a point since a line or point must be infinitely small in at least one dimension, although this concept is approached in some ceramics manufacture where fine wires are used to cut shapes, or in a common cheese slicer which uses the same principal. It has been established that machining consists essentially of producing surfaces by allowing a properly designed cutting tool to remove that part of the work material that interferes with the path of the tool, but the mathematical concept of surfaces consisting of the loci of points or lines still applies. The surface is produced by removing all the material with which the tool interferes from one side of the surface. The final surface consists either of the final locus of a straight or curved cutting edge for which a single cycle of operation is sufficient to define the surfaces, or the envelope (boundary) of a number of successive positions of a cutting edge requiring a number of cycles.

The possibilities for machined surfaces are almost as great in extent as the number of surfaces which might be described mathematically, provided a machine were built that provided the correct relative motions between the cutting edge and the workpiece. In practice, however, only a relatively few sets of motions have been incorporated in standard machines, based largely on the functional product needs that have developed over the years. Many nonstandard motions are used for particular products, but these are usually built only in specialized machines.

Most machine tools may be classified by the relative motions that may occur between the tool and workpiece, into one of four basic groups with a fifth containing some of the features of the first four. Fig. 19–1 illustrates the relative motions involved and *one* of the normal means of producing a surface with each of the basic types of machines. Note that these illustrations are examples only and that each of the machine types may be used to produce other types of surfaces.

352

Turning machines have, as standard motions, the rotation of a work-piece and several possible straight line feed motions. It may be noted that the operation indicated is the production of an external circular cylinder, not only because of the relative motions but also because of the relative *positions* of the work and tool. With the same motions, but a different tool type and position, as internal circular cylinder could be machined, in which case the operation would be called *boring* rather than *turning*.

Drilling machines normally use a rotating multipoint tool that is given a straight line feed parallel to the axis of the tool. *Milling* machines also normally use rotating multipoint tools with straight line feed motions, but the feed motion is applied to the work rather than the tool and is usually at right angles to the axis of rotation of the tool. *Planing* and *shaping* are

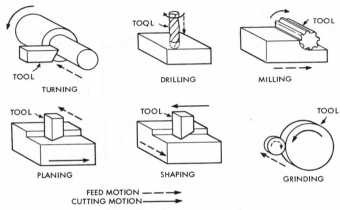

TURNING   DRILLING   MILLING

PLANING   SHAPING   GRINDING

FEED MOTION — — —▶
CUTTING MOTION——————▶

FIG. 19–1. Feed and cutting motions.

representative of machine tools that use straight line cutting motion. They differ only in the elements having the cutting and feed motions, as illustrated, but the relative motion is the same. Other straight line tools use more complex cutting tools, frequently multipoint.

Grinding uses a rotating multipoint cutter, as does milling, and in some types of grinders the feed motion is similar to that used in milling. The figure shows cylindrical grinding in which the feed motion is a combined axial and rotating motion of the work. Note that this is only a feed motion as opposed to the rotation of the work in turning which is the cutting motion. With the exception of a sphere which consists of a single double curved surface, most objects are made up of a number of different surfaces of one or more kinds related to each other. The accuracy of the surfaces themselves and the accuracy of their relationship determines the precision of the product. Machining, the removal of material in chip form, is capable of greater accuracies of both types than most of the other manufacturing processes.

As pointed out above, the sphere is one of the few surfaces that exists entirely by itself. Other shapes are made up of various combinations of flat, cylindrical, partial cylinders, warped, and double curved surfaces. The machining process used to produce any surface type will be determined to a large extent by the shape of that surface, but considerable influence will also be exhibited by the desired quality of the surface and its relationship to other surfaces. Some machine tools have wide versatility and are capable of producing surface shapes of all types. Others are intentionally more specialized in order to obtain higher accuracies or greater productivity and are limited to the production of only a few surface types. Even those machines with wide versatility are generally limited to surfaces that are closely related to shapes that are particularly feasible for that process. For example, a flat surface can be made on a lathe, but the machine is seldom used for this kind of work except when the flat surface is related to a cylindrical surface for which the lathe is particularly suited. It cannot be over emphasized that the choice of process will always be dependent in some way on cost, and if the lowest overall cost is dependent on the using of a slow step in the processing, there is no reason for not doing so. Many products are given their principal shapes from some other basic shape producing method, such as casting or forging, and then machined on only part of their surface for increased accuracy or for the production of surface shapes that would not be practical otherwise.

It is this capability of producing practically any shape from a larger solid mass that accounts for the tremendous importance of machining in tool room and job shop work where parts are produced in small quantities. Although the cost per part is high when parts are produced entirely by machining, the cost for one part, if dies or patterns have to be made, would be even higher. The surfaces on the dies or patterns would themselves probably be most economically produced by machining and the cost of producing a die or pattern is likely to be many times that of a single machined part. Machining occupies a very important role in the manufacture of tools and machines for practically all other processes, including not only other metal manufacturing methods, but also textile, printing, food processing, building, and other industries that do not produce a product which itself could be made by machining.

In addition to the manufacture of small quantities of parts, that if produced in larger quantities might have at least some of the shape produced more economically by another method, machining is the most economical method for many shapes even in high quantities. This is true most often when the shape may be produced from rolled stock that conforms generally to the desired shape and the volume of metal to be removed is small, when certain complex shapes such as gears or internal threads are required, and when higher accuracies or surface finishes are demanded than can be produced by other methods.

Flat Surfaces. A *flat surface* is defined as being a surface made up of straight line elements, all of which contact two intersecting straight lines. Fig. 19–2 shows such a condition. The production of flat surfaces is not limited to straight line cutting action however. Since any cutting process for which the cutting action is bounded by a single plane, can produce a flat surface, this shape may be produced by several motion and tool combinations.

Straight line cutting motion, accompanied by straight line feed motion in a direction perpendicular to the cutting motion, is commonly used with such machines as shapers, planers, hack saws, and band saws for the making of flat surfaces, as shown in Fig. 19–3. The term *generated surface* is used to describe surfaces such as these since the overall shape is controlled by the feed motion. With an infinitely fine feed, the shape of the

A SURFACE COMPOSED OF STRAIGHT LINE ELEMENTS
CONTACTING TWO INTERSECTING STRAIGHT LINES
(STRAIGHT LINE ELEMENTS IN ANY AND ALL DIRECTIONS)

FIG. 19–2. Flat surface.

cutting tool would have no effect on the surface. In practice, some feed must be used and the shape of the tool will affect surface finish when measured across the lay, but would have little effect on the average shape so long as the marks left by the tool did not affect use as a flat surface.

Sawing is a fast, versatile method of producing flat surfaces of somewhat limited accuracy and is used primarily for stock cutoff operations preparatory to further operations. Shaping and planing have better accu-

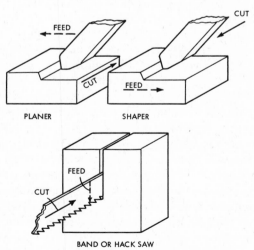

FIG. 19–3. Flat surfaces by straight line cutting motion and straight line feed.

racy but both are relatively slow in action because of the time lost in return of the tool or work after the cutting stroke. Both, however, are versatile and easily set up, so they find wide application in tool room and job shop work.

Fig. 19–4 shows the production of flat surfaces by the use of straight

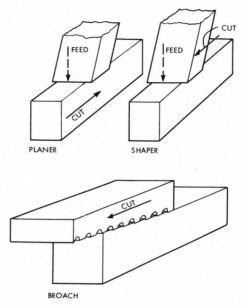

FIG. 19–4.   Flat surfaces by straight line cutting motion and straight cutting edge.

line cutting motion and a straight edged tool. A complete flat surface is produced by each cutting edge in broaching or in shaping and planing but the removal of more than a few thousandths of an inch of material, requires multiple cutting strokes or multiple teeth. The final surface is then determined by the last tooth on the cutter in the case of single pass broaching or by the last cutting stroke of multiple pass, single edge tools. Surfaces of this type, the shape of which is controlled by the shape and position of the cutting edge, are called *formed surfaces.*

Forming of flat surfaces on shapers and planers is practical only for relatively narrow surfaces, not for theoretical reasons, but because the design of the machines and tool will not permit long edge cutting contact without the development of chatter. Broaching machines are designed to use wider cutters with a series of cutting edges following each other at increased depths.

Generated flat surfaces may be made with rotary cutting motion and feed in a plane perpendicular to the axis of rotation, as in Fig. 19–5. This combination of motions is normally referred to as facing and may be accomplished on lathes, milling machines, and grinding machines. On the lathe, a single point tool of suitable shape for proper chip formation is fed in a path perpendicular to the axis of the rotating workpiece. The shape of the tool and the rate of feed must be such that the spiral tool marks do not become large enough that the surface would be considered a scroll rather than a flat surface. In milling, a number of cutting edges, carefully ground

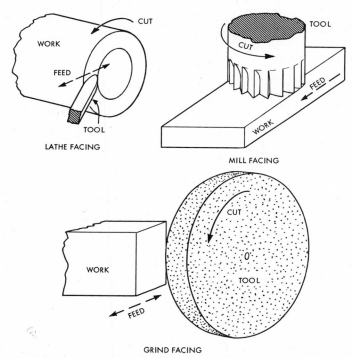

FIG. 19–5. Flat surfaces by rotary cutting and straight line feed (generating).

so that they will rotate through the same plane, remove material as the workpiece is fed in a line perpendicular to their axis of rotation. This is also a generating action since the shape of the cutting edge has little to do with the average shape, although it may to some degree control the finish of the work surface.

Multipoint rotary cutters may also be used to produce flat surfaces by using cutters on which the teeth are cylindrical elements, Fig. 19–6, and by feeding the work in a straight line perpendicular to the axis of rotation. If the teeth on milling cutters used for this operation are parallel with the axis of rotation they are straight teeth and clearly cut with a forming action. On helical cutters, the teeth are curved but effectively are straight edged as they swing around to the cutting position so that the shape produced, although different from the shape of the cutting edge, would still be considered formed because the cutting edge controls one of the shape dimensions.

Similar motions are used to produce flat surfaces by one type of grinding. In some cases, however, it is impractical to use a grinding wheel as wide as the surface to be produced so the normal feed is combined with an intermittent side feed parallel to the axis of the wheel. If the axial feed is small, the surface would be considered generated. If the axial feed is large and the grinding wheel is dressed with a true cylindrical periphery, a series of formed elements side by side would make up the flat surface.

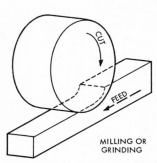

FIG. 19–6.   Flat surfaces by rotary cutting, straight line feed, and straight edged tool.

Fig. 19–7 shows a somewhat more limited method for producing flat surfaces using a straight edged forming tool combined with a circular cutting motion. Multiple edge cutters of this type are commonly used in the operations called counterboring and spot facing, which are done most on drilling machines in which the cutter rotates. The shoulder left at the termination of a generated cylinder produced on a lathe may be a flat surface if the side cutting edge angle is zero.

Other, less frequently used methods also produce flat surfaces. Face milling may be accomplished with the cutter revolving, as in Fig. 19–5, but making use of a rotary feed motion in a single plane imparted to the workpiece. One type of production grinder uses this same combination of motions. Lapping is an important surface finishing process using a random cutting motion between the workpiece and a flat lap charged with abrasive particles on its surface.

Circular Cylinders and Cones.   One of the most important shapes in manufacturing is the *circular cylinder*. Most prime movers supply power with rotational motion. Mechanical power is transmitted from one position to another most frequently through belts and pulleys, gears, and other systems that make use of rotating shafts. In these applications, rotating bearings set up a requirement for high accuracy of dimension, close conformance to the true circular shape and quality of surface finish that are not producible normally except by machining methods. Since bearings involve the use of both internal and external surfaces, both are of interest. A large portion of metal stock used in manufacturing is produced in cylindrical shapes. Because the circular cylinder is an easily worked with shape, it is used for many parts in which the shape has no specific function.

A cylinder has different possible mathematical definitions. One defines a cylinder as the surface formed by a straight line moving in a path while it remains parallel to a fixed straight line. A circular cylinder is one whose

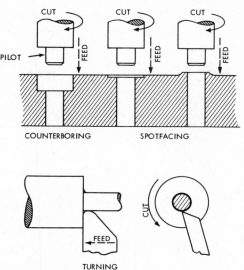

COUNTERBORING   SPOTFACING

TURNING

FIG. 19–7. Flat surfaces by rotary cutting,
axial feed, and straight edged tool.

intersection with a perpendicular plane is a circle. Unless otherwise qualified, when the term cylinder is used in this text, it refers to a circular
cylinder.

A surface closely related to the
cylinder and frequently manufactured by similar methods is the
cone. A circular cone would be
the surface defined by the hypote-
nuse of a right triangle as the triangle is swung around a circle
with one of the perpendicular
sides as an axis. The circular cone
can also be considered as being
made up of straight line elements
which contact a circle on one end
and intersect at a common point
on the perpendicular center line
of the circle. This last definition
would also hold true for a cylinder if the common point of intersection were at infinity, as shown
in Fig. 19–8.

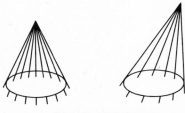

A SURFACE OF STRAIGHT LINE ELEMENTS
INTERSECTING AT A POINT

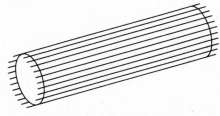

A SPECIAL CASE OF A CONICAL SURFACE IN
WHICH THE INTERSECTING POINT IS AT
INFINITY

FIG. 19–8. Cylindrical and conical
surfaces.

By far the greatest number of
circular cylinders and cones are
produced with lathe and drilling type machines making use of rotary cutting motion and straight line feed, as shown in Fig. 19–9. Drilling machines

are limited to a single feed motion parallel to the axis of rotation and can generate only cylindrical surfaces. However, if the drilled hole does not pass completely through the work, the closed end of the cylinder is a formed surface with a shape depending on the shape of the end of the cutting tool. Drilling machines are not normally used to produce external cylinders although the operation could be done with a special tool.

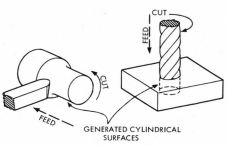

GENERATED CYLINDRICAL SURFACES

FIG. 19–9. Cylindrical surfaces by rotary cutting motion and straight line feed.

Most lathes have some adjustment which permits straight line feeds at angles other than zero with reference to the axis of revolution of the work. Fig 19–10 shows the different surfaces that result from some of the straight line tool paths. The term *facing* is used specifically to refer to the production of flat surfaces by feeding at 90 degrees to the axis of rotation. *Turning* refers to any operation done on the outside surface of a workpiece in a lathe. The surfaces would be called turned cylinders or turned cones when produced with straight line feed. With the proper tool position, the metal may be removed from the internal surface and the operation is called *boring*. Boring, likewise, is not limited to the production of cylinders.

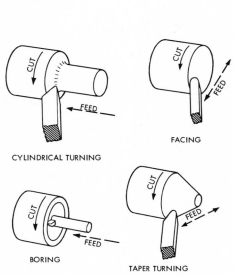

CYLINDRICAL TURNING

FACING

BORING

TAPER TURNING

FIG. 19–10. Lathe operation terminology.

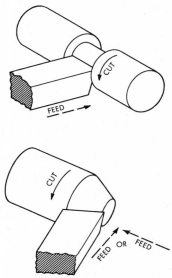

FIG. 19–11. Cylindrical and conical surfaces by rotary cutting and straight edged tool.

If a straight edged single point tool is plunged into a rotating work-piece, as in Fig. 19–11, the resulting surface will be formed since the tool controls one of the cross-sectional dimensions and the surface will be cylindrical or conical depending on the position of the straight cutting edge. Dimensional limits will be set in forming operations of this kind by the strength of the work and tool, because heavy loads are imposed with the long contact distance between tool and work and vibration or chatter tends to develop as deflections increase. It is usually possible to use a forming tool with a width up to two and one half times the diameter of the supported end of the workpiece when the surface being machined is near the support.

Grinding is not normally a large volume metal removal process, but is used primarily for finish and accuracy improvement following some other machining process. For cylindrical surfaces, grinding machines are available that use most of the motions used on lathes, except that the rotation of

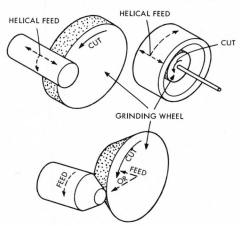

FIG. 19–12.   Cylindrical and conical surfaces by grinding.

the work becomes a feed motion, and the cutting motion is provided by the rotation of the wheel. Grinders are used for generating both internal and external cylinders and cones, using a helical feed consisting of the combined rotation and axial movement of the work. A straight edged grinding wheel may be plunged into the rotating work without axial feed to produce a formed cylinder or cone. Fig. 19–12 shows internal and external cylindrical generating and external conical forming by grinding.

Theoretically it would be possible to make a cylinder or cone by use of a multiple toothed milling cutter with motions similar to those in grinding. In practice, no standard, and few special, milling machines use milling cutters to produce entire cylinders. In the few applications that exist, the cutter is usually given a planetary motion with the workpiece held station-ary except possibly for axial feed.

The making of complete cylinders with straight line cutting motion is limited in practice to broaching with a form cutter, as in Fig. 19–13. The depth of cut is represented by the circumference of the hole. The feed, related to the chip thicknesses, is determined by the amount each tooth is larger than the preceding one. The shape and size of the last cutting tooth determines the shape and size of the finished hole.

Other possibilities exist for producing circular cylinders and cones. Abrasive finishing methods use either a lap with loose abrasive particles or a solid formed abrasive stick to finish cylinders with a combined forming and generating action. Reamers are used on drilling equipment and lathes for finishing both internal cylinders and cones.

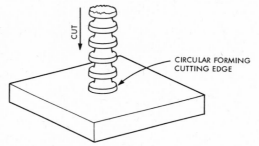

FIG. 19–13. Cylindrical surface by straight line cutting and form cutter.

Partial Circular and Noncircular Cylindrical Surfaces. Very few objects can be made up entirely of a single surface shape. It is true that many functional parts consist of a variety of only the very important flat and circular cylindrical shapes, but even these must frequently be combined with partial cylinders, noncircular cylinders, and certain curved surfaces. *Partial cylinders* and *noncircular cylinders* are particularly valuable for the design of moving mechanical parts whose function makes positive location or transmission of motion important.

Not to be considered here is the making of these surfaces as combinations of flat and circular cylinders produced by the methods already discussed. A cube is a noncircular cylinder that could be produced by machining the six faces separately by any of the methods used for flat surfaces, but the concern here is with methods that could produce four faces of the cube in one operation. Likewise, the partial circular cylinder on part A of Fig. 19–14 could be produced by a normal turning cut on a lathe, but the projection on part B would interfere with the cutter in the normal operation of a lathe. The reverse would be true if these were internal surfaces with the same shapes.

Partial and noncircular cylinders are made up of straight line elements that are parallel to each other, but not equidistant from a central axis, except for the partial circular cylinder which does not form a closed surface. These surfaces are most important in connection with the transmission of torque. Splines and gears are made up of a series of regularly spaced ridges and hollows, each of which can be considered to be a partial noncircular cylinder making up a closed group which is a complete noncircular cylinder.

These shapes, Fig. 19–15, can be made with straight line cutting motion on machines like the planer, shaper, and broach, using a cutter with the desired form. A single edged tool used on a planer or shaper would make a number of successive passes, with feed consisting of repositioning the tool for each cycle of operation to project the cutting edge deeper into the material for the next cut. Broaching would be similar except that a series of chips would be removed by successive cutting edges and the surface completed with one pass of the multiedged tool.

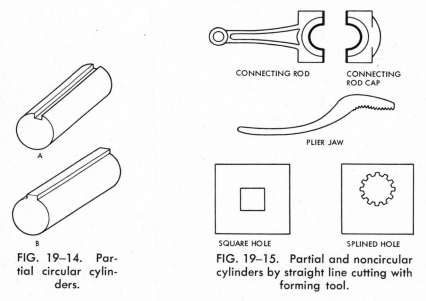

FIG. 19–14. Partial circular cylinders.

FIG. 19–15. Partial and noncircular cylinders by straight line cutting with forming tool.

Straight line cutting with a curved feed will also produce a series of straight line parallel elements which can be combined into any shape cylinder. The band saw with a series of like cutting edges can be used in this way to generate a surface. A shaper or planer would be capable of producing cylindrical surfaces with appropriate control of the feed path, but as normally constructed, these machines have only straight line feed motions that are used for producing flat surfaces. They are occasionally used for cylindrical surfaces in tool room work with manual control of the two different feed motions or a servo system that ties the feed motion to a curved template.

A much more important application of straight line cutting motion with curved feed is in the manufacture of gears. One important characteristic of correctly operating spur gears is that each gear of a pair is the *conjugate* of the other, and contact is maintained between the gear surfaces while a constant angular velocity ratio is maintained between the two rotating gears. If a cutter with the correct gear profile is used in conjunction with a straight line cutting action, and a rotary feed of both the cutter and workpiece establishes the correct angular velocity ratio, the workpiece will be shaped to the conjugate form of the cutter, as in Fig. 19–16. Even though the tool must have a particular shape, the surface is generated rather than formed. The final surface is the envelope of all the different cutter positions relative to the work and the final accuracy depends, in part, on the rate of rotary feed compared to the rate of the cutting strokes.

Partial cylinders, circular or otherwise, such as grooves and ridges, can be made with rotary cutting motion and straight line feed of the work past the cutter. In effect, the cutting stroke of a shaper can become a feed

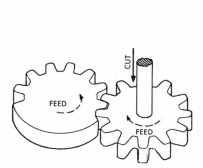

FIG. 19–16. Gear shaping.

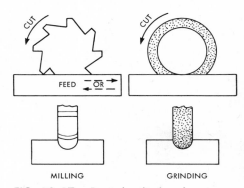

FIG. 19–17. Partial cylinders by rotary cutting with forming tool.

motion if the cutting tool is made multipoint and given a rotary cutting motion. This principle is used most with milling and grinding equipment fitted with a milling cutter or grinding wheel having a periphery profile corresponding to the desired cross-sectional shape. These operations, shown in Fig. 19–17, are forming operations since the profile of the work is a duplicate of the profile of the cutter. A rectangular groove produced by milling with a side milling cutter would consist of three flat surfaces, but it is actually a partial noncircular cylinder. In this case, the sides of the groove would be generated and the bottom formed.

Form milling is an important machining process. Many standard form milling cutters are available for corner rounding, for internal radii, for angular grooves that generally combine two flat surfaces with some radius, and for other common groove shapes. Grooves between the teeth of spur gears are generally produced most economically in small quantities by form milling each tooth space, one at a time, with appropriate indexing of the workpiece between cuts. With a relatively small number of cutters, it is possible to produce spur gears of almost any diameter or tooth size, using standard milling machines and attachments with low setup time and cost compared to that required for high production gear making equipment.

A special type of milling operation, known as hobbing, is used principally for the manufacture of gears with external teeth. A rotary cutting motion is used with a combined rotary and straight line feed, as in Fig. 19–18. The conjugate mating surface principle is again used, as in gear shaping. The profile of the cutter is that of a tooth from a rack or gear of infinite diameter. This profile travels relative to the work because of the helical shape of the cutter. Hobbing is ordinarily used only for high production because of the long setup time and special equipment requirements. With the proper cutter shape, it is possible to cut external involute splines. It would also be possible to cut a cylinder with square, rectangular, or other cross section, but these shapes are more economically produced by other methods.

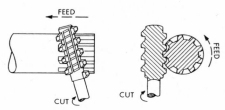

FIG. 19–18.   Noncircular cylinders by hobbing.

Certain types of noncircular or partial cylinders are best produced with a rotating cutter, either milling or grinding, and using a curved feed path, as shown in Fig. 19–19. Standard tool room and job shop types of milling

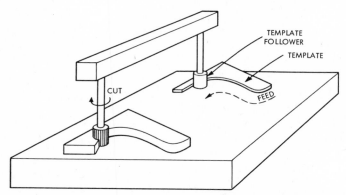

FIG. 19–19.   Partial and noncircular cylinders by rotary cutting and curved feed.

machines and grinders normally are constructed with only straight line feed motions, but standard machines may be equipped with special feeding fixtures. Also available are special production types that guide the work through the correct path, using a template and roller follower or a servomechanism. Machines of this type are especially useful for work such as making two-dimensional cams which are relatively thin compared to the profiled area.

A device called a *relieving* attachment is available for many tool room lathes that permits turning of some noncircular cylinders. The lathe is set up as for generating a circular cylinder but as the tool feeds parallel to the axis of the cylinder, a cam causes the distance of the tool from the axis to vary throughout each revolution of the work. This method is used most for providing the relief angle on milling cutters, threading taps, and other multipoint rotating cutting tools.

Double Curved Surfaces. A *double curved surface*, Fig. 19–20, is defined as a surface created by moving a curved line along curved directrices. The most common double curved surfaces produced regularly on

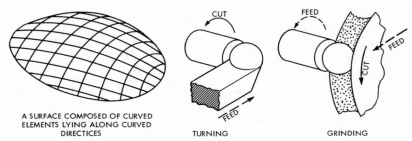

A SURFACE COMPOSED OF CURVED
ELEMENTS LYING ALONG CURVED
DIRECTICES   TURNING   GRINDING

FIG. 19–20. Double curved   FIG. 19–21. Double curved surface as a
surface.   surface of revolution with a forming tool.

standard machines are *surfaces of revolution*. A surface of revolution is obtained by rotating a plane curve about an axis lying in the plane. Cross sections normal to the axis are circles. These surfaces may be produced on lathes or cylindrical grinders by rotating the work and using a formed lathe cutter or grinding wheel, as in Fig. 19–21. The surface is formed since the profile is determined by the profile of the tool.

Surfaces of revolution may be generated on lathes by using a tracing attachment, as shown in Fig. 19–22. The path of the single point cutting

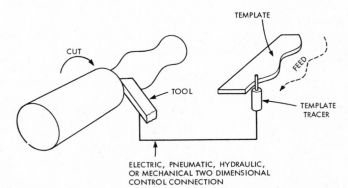

ELECTRIC, PNEUMATIC, HYDRAULIC,
OR MECHANICAL TWO DIMENSIONAL
CONTROL CONNECTION

FIG. 19–22. Double curved surface as a surface of revolution by generating with a tracing attachment.

tool is guided by a template having the correct profile. Such a machine is not limited to the production of double curved surfaces since circular cylinders and cones are also surfaces of revolution.

A lathe with a relieving attachment and the proper form tool or tracer control, or a milling machine with a form cutter and some means of providing a curved feed path, may be used to produce double curved surfaces other than surfaces of revolution. The need for such machined shapes, however, is small, particularly for parts produced in high quantities. When large quantity production is called for, special machines are often designed for the work.

Warped Surfaces. The majority of surfaces made by machining are the simpler types such as flat, circular cylinders and cones, and surfaces of revolution. Various combinations of these are designed into a great variety of useful articles. The shapes are relatively easy to produce with the mechanical motions available on common machine tools and can be manufactured accurately enough to serve satisfactorily as mating surfaces for other parts. Another surface type however, is needed to satisfy some functional and esthetic design requirements. The *warped surface*, Fig. 19–23, is defined as a surface composed of straight line elements, adjacent ones of which are nonintersecting and nonparallel. The two most used warped surfaces are those found on helical gear teeth and those used as threads.

The mathematical definition is somewhat misleading since, in practice, straight line cutting motion is not used for actual machining. Threads may be produced with a rotary cutting motion and a form tool. This combination occurs when a thread is *chased* on a lathe with the work rotating against a single form tool that feeds parallel to the axis of revolution as in producing a cylinder. For a thread, however, the feed is greater than it would be for a similar sized cylinder. The profile of the thread itself is formed by the shape of the cutting tool, but the overall helical shape of the thread is generated by the combined cutting and feed motions. Threading on a lathe is a versatile and accurate method but is slow compared to some other methods and is generally restricted to tool room use.

Ordinarily a thread can not be chased on a lathe with a single pass of the cutter along the work. The cutter must be withdrawn at the end of each pass, returned to the starting point, advanced to a new depth of cut, and the process repeated until the correct depth is obtained. For threads with large cross section, requiring a considerable volume of metal to be removed, milling with a revolving multitooth cutter may be used, as in Fig. 19–24, for increased rate of material removal. The thread is cut to full depth with a single pass of the cutter along the workpiece. A similar setup is used for milling one tooth at a time on a helical gear with a form cutter, but the helix angles of gears are quite different from those of threads.

Most threads machined in high quantities are cut with *taps* for internal threads, or *dies* for external threads. These are multitoothed and, while not usually described as such, are actually broaches that have many finishing teeth and are given a helical rather than a straight line cutting motion.

The straight line action of the gear shaper may be modified to produce helical gears by providing a helical guide to cause a twisting motion of the cutter and work spindles. Otherwise, the motions are the same as for straight spur gears. A hobbing machine may also be used to produce helical gears if the cutter is set at the correct angle and the proper synchronization exists between the different feed and cutting motions.

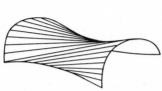

A SURFACE COMPOSED OF STRAIGHT LINE ELEMENTS ADJACENT ONES OF WHICH ARE NONINTERSECTING AND NONPARALLEL

FIG. 19–23. Warped surface.

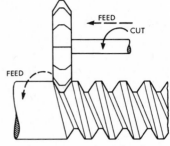

FIG. 19–24. Thread milling.

Complex Surfaces. In addition to the shapes discussed so far, all of which have rather precise and restricted mathematical definitions, many other shapes have usefulness either for functional or esthetic reasons. It is usually possible to build a machine with built-in mechanically controlled motions to produce any shape that can be described mathematically. However, such machinery can ordinarily be justified economically only when large numbers of parts are to be produced.

Typical of special purpose machines are those designed to produce bevel gears. A straight bevel gear is actually a noncircular cone with straight line elements intersecting at a point. Cross sections at right angles to the axis have a profile like that of a straight spur gear but the profile becomes smaller toward the point of intersection. Straight bevel gears are produced with a straight line cutting action in combination with a properly shaped cutting tool, and feed motions similar to those of a straight spur gear shaper.

Spiral bevel or hypoid gears bear the same kind of relationship to straight spur gears that helical spur gears have to straight spur gears. In addition to the decrease in the size of the teeth toward the small end of the gear, the teeth are twisted in a spiral. Such gears are produced on special purpose machines that use rotary cutters with formed teeth in combination with complex rotary feed motions of both the cutter spindle and the workpiece about several axes.

Most internal combustion engine pistons are produced with an elliptical rather than a true circular cross section on machines designed only for this purpose.

In addition to special machines with a single set of complex motions built in, others have the capability of being *programmed* for some variety of shapes. One older type in this class is a lathe used principally for glass bottle mold machining, that has a template control for the profile of the part along the axis of rotation and a cam control similar to a relieving attachment for the path of the tool throughout each revolution of the work.

Of increased importance in the last few years have been machines with feed motions controlled from information programmed on a magnetic tape, punched tape, or punched card. Such systems may be applied to lathes, drills, milling machines, or grinders to produce almost any shape that can be described mathematically and to which the cutting tool can be given access.

In addition to machines which are limited to producing shapes that can be *described*, other machines are capable of *duplicating* any shape that already *exists*. Duplicating machines are three-dimensional copying machines that can be used for any shape surface. One, or more, cutter spindles has its feed path controlled by a stylus that is moved over a master pattern. The pattern itself may be handmade from some easily fabricated material such as plaster. The cutters are of end mill type that can cut with any direction of feed movement. Their size and shape must be carefully related to the stylus and pattern for accurate duplication. The usual method of operation is to make many passes over the work, with two dimensional control in a plane for each pass and with a small enough separation between the planes to achieve the desired surface accuracy.

One of the large uses of the duplicating machine is for the making of dies for metals and plastics processing. Because of the high accuracy of duplication, thousands of man-hours may be saved in the making of this kind of product as compared to hand finishing after removal of most of the excess stock by conventional drilling and milling methods. Duplicating machines are sometimes used for high production of items containing warped or double curved surfaces that are important to the function of the part but are not easily produced by other methods. As an example, some turbine blades for use in aircraft jet engines are machined over the entire blade surface by use of multiple spindle duplicating equipment.

Surface Combinations for Design Reasons.   Surfaces discussed so far are single surfaces that by themselves may be produced by one or a variety of methods. As noted before, however, a sphere is about the only single surface closed shape of practical use. The process to be used for any particular surface is frequently dictated by the other surfaces that exist on the part. The flat end of a part that otherwise is made up of only surfaces of revolution that would be produced on a lathe would logically be produced by facing on the same lathe in the same setup. The end of a boss on a casting or forging could have the same size and shape but would more logically be machined by milling. In either case, the surface might have to be ground to achieve the desired accuracy; but again it might be on a cylindrical grinder in one case and a surface grinder in the other. If such a boss were to have a drilled hole in its center, it might well be machined by a spotfacing operation in a drilling machine.

The choice is properly based on the overall economics of producing the part. The quantity to be produced, as well as the surface relationships, has a great effect on cost per part. The teeth of a *single* spur gear would ordinarily be milled with a form cutter, one tooth at a time, but in large quantities hobbing or gear shaping would be more economical.

As a general rule, it is desirable to combine the production of as many surfaces as practicable into each setup. Not only may handling time be reduced, even at the expense of slightly increased machining time, but accuracies are generally improved. This is especially true of relationship accuracies between surfaces, such as parallelism, squareness, and concentricity.

QUESTIONS

1. What has led to the development of the standard machine tool types that are used today?
2. List the five basic groups of machine tools with the relative motions and tool types characteristic of each group.
3. What are the five surface types produced by machine tools?
4. Why would the production of a single part for which a die would be made nearly always exceed the cost of making such a part by machining?
5. What factors lead to the use of machining even for large quantities?
6. Distinguish between formed and generated surfaces.
7. Why is a flat surface produced by a cutter, as in Fig. 19–6, even when the cutting edges are helical rather than straight lines?
8. Does a face milling cutter produce a formed or generated flat surface?
9. What are the most common motions used for producing circular cylinders?
10. What restriction exists on the position of a straight edged cutting tool for producing a circular cylinder or cone as shown in Fig. 19–11?
11. What is the only standard method used for producing complete circular cylinders using straight line cutting motion?
12. Why is it not possible to produce generated partial circular cylinders on shapers or planers?
13. Is a rectangular groove produced by a side milling cutter formed or generated?
14. What is the principal use for a relieving attachment?
15. Why are most double curved surfaces produced as surfaces of revolution?
16. Is a thread chased on a lathe formed or generated?
17. What modification of broaching would be necessary for producing helical spur gears?
18. What is the difference between a duplicating machine and a tape controlled machine?
19. Why is it desirable to combine as many operations as practicable into each setup?

CHAPTER 20

Cutting Tools

A NUMBER of different elements are always involved in any machining setup. The *workpiece* is the material that is to be shaped. The *cutting tool* is the properly shaped, hardened material that applies the loads to the work material and forms the chip. The *machine tool* is the device which supports the work and cutting tool and provides the correct relative motions, as discussed in the previous chapter. Another term, *tooling*, is more loosely used to describe all the equipment, including the cutting tool, the work holding device, and special attachments, that are added to the basic machine tool to permit its practical use. The machine tools themselves, together with the work holding devices and special attachments of interest, will be discussed in the following chapters.

As was pointed out in Chapter 18, cutting tools may be made of any one of a number of materials, but they all have the identical function of loading the work to failure, with certain desirable values for rake angle, relief angle, and other tool geometry factors depending primarily on work material and tool material. In Chapter 19, it was shown that to achieve the desired surface, not only must the correct relative motions be established between the work and the cutting tool, but also that the tool must have the correct shape, which may differ depending on whether the action is forming or generating. In addition, it was pointed out that some tools have a single cutting edge, while some work more effectively with multiple cutting edges. In this chapter, it will be shown how the factors of work material, tool material, machining process, desired surface shape, and economic considerations affect the actual design of cutting tools.

SINGLE POINT LATHE, SHAPER, AND PLANER TOOLS

Whether used for forming or generating operations, only minor differences exist between the cutting tools used for lathes and those used for shapers and planers. During a normal lathe cut, the tool is in continuous contact with the work and little thermal or mechanical shock occurs, except at the start and end of cutting. On planers and shapers, the tool is

371

subject to shock each time it enters and leaves the cut, so that it is sometimes advisable to use lower values of rake angles, especially when tools are constructed from the more brittle materials.

A number of different mounting methods are used, influenced by the tool material, the machine tool, the nature of the operation, and the probable length of time the tool will be used. Most tool room lathe and shaper operations are done by use of standard high speed steel *tool bits* in sizes ranging from ¾₁₆ inch square by 1¾ inches long to ½ inch square by

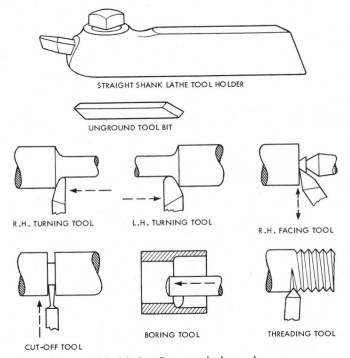

STRAIGHT SHANK LATHE TOOL HOLDER

UNGROUND TOOL BIT

R.H. TURNING TOOL   L.H. TURNING TOOL

R.H. FACING TOOL

CUT-OFF TOOL

BORING TOOL

THREADING TOOL

FIG. 20–1. Common lathe tools.

four inches long. Planer tool bits for large machines may be larger. These tool bits are normally purchased in the hardened condition from specialty manufacturers, shaped on the end to the desired form by grinding and supported for use in a tool *holder* that is then mounted in the machine tool. Fig. 20–1 illustrates a typical tool holder and some of the shapes that are commonly ground on the tool bits for the indicated applications.

Holders and bits have many variations. Cutoff operations may be performed with a tool bit or blade of rectangular rather than square cross section, held in a properly designed holder. In addition to straight holders, some are constructed with a bend, or offset, to present the tool in a more usable position.

Shapers and planers may use tool bits and holders of the same type as are used on lathes for most operations. Planers, however, are large machines and may use solid forged tools with the cutting edge ground on the end. Solid tools, rather than separate tool bits and holders, are also common for production applications because of their greater rigidity and heat dissipating ability.

High speed steel turning tools have been largely replaced by cemented carbides for high production applications, except for some complex form tools for which the cost of grinding carbide would be excessive or for which carbide would be too brittle in thin sections. Form tools are usually designed so they may be resharpened by grinding a simple flat face rather than regrinding the entire form. One such design is the *circular form tool*, as shown in Fig. 20–2. Not only are such tools relatively easy to grind, but producing the form originally as a surface of revolution is generally more economical than the making of some other shape. The tool shown is for thread cutting on lathes.

Cemented carbide tools are used to a limited extent in the tool room and for most production single point tools. This means primarily turning tools, since shapers and planers are seldom high production machines. The properties and high cost of cemented carbides have led to the use of different mounting methods than are used for high speed steel. The standard high speed steel tool bit is used as a cantilevered beam and has adequate strength for this type of

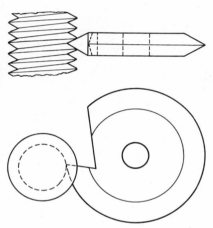

FIG. 20–2. Circular form tool.

mounting. Cemented carbides have extremely high compressive strength but relatively low tensile strength and would be subject to excessive bending loads if mounted in the same way. The first cost of cemented carbides is also high enough that mounting means which minimize the necessary material quantity are desirable.

Fig. 20–3 shows some of the methods that are used for mounting cemented carbides. The first tools were brazed to a medium carbon steel shank, usually in a milled recess so that the carbide was supported on the bottom and at least two sides. The steel shank was then mounted directly in the machine or in a standard high speed steel tool bit holder, depending on size. This method is still used for some tool room use and for form tools when space is insufficient to permit use of a mechanical clamp. Brazing has the required holding strength, but grinding of the finished tool is complicated by the need for different wheels to grind the carbide tip and the steel shank. Because of the different rates of thermal contraction between carbide and steel, high tensile stresses, which may contribute to fracture failure, may be introduced into the carbide during heating or cooling.

More recently, several types of mechanical mounting systems have been developed. Prismatic holders permit resharpening by grinding a flat face on the carbide insert with adjustment of the carbide in the holder to compensate for the reduced length. Most of the other mechanical holders are designed to use *throwaway* tool inserts. The tool may be used until one

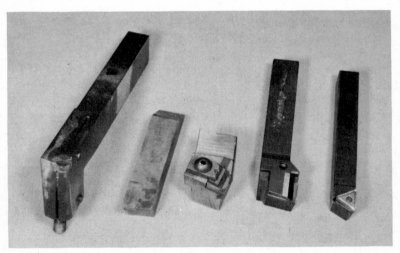

FIG. 20–3. Cemented carbide tool mounting methods. (Left to right) prismatic, brazed, clamped square with chip breaker, clamped triangle with chip breaker, cam locked triangle with molded chip breaker.

cutting is worn, then indexed to present a new cutting edge. This method permits at least three corners on a triangular and four corners on a square insert to be used. If the insert and holder combination are designed to let the tool cut with a negative rake angle equal to the relief angle, the angle between the flank and face of the insert will be 90 degrees. It will also be 90 degrees with the insert inverted, so that a square insert will have eight possible cutting edges. The relatively low cost of the inserts, combined with the high cost of regrinding and the change of size that would accompany regrinding, makes it practical to discard the insert after it has been used in all the possible positions. Ceramic cutting tools are used very little for any cutting other than single point turning in similar clamping type holders.

Special mechanical devices are often found between the mounting of the actual cutting edge and the machine itself, especially on production types of lathes. These may incorporate work support, tool adjustment, or feed motion in addition to those that are standard on the machine. The need for many of these special devices will be more clear after a discussion of the actual machines.

Chip Breakers. From the discussion of Chapter 18, it may be remembered that chips can be either segmented or continuous depending on the type of work material. Segmental chips seldom present any disposal problems or safety hazard and continuous chips are "continuous" only so long as the tool is in contact with the work. Thus, on most milling operations no serious problems exist, since each tooth produces only a relatively short chip. However, for lathe operations, the single point tool is in continuous contact throughout most cuts, and with some materials the chip is pro-

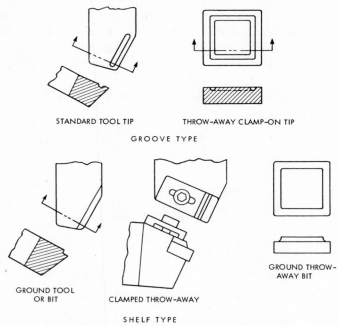

STANDARD TOOL TIP   THROW-AWAY CLAMP-ON TIP

GROOVE TYPE

GROUND TOOL
OR BIT

CLAMPED THROW-AWAY

GROUND THROW-
AWAY BIT

SHELF TYPE

FIG. 20–4. Chip breakers.

duced as a tough, stringy rough edged ribbon or wire. Not only does such a chip present a hazard because of the rough edges, but under most conditions of cutting it is also quite hot. In addition, the chip often curls about the work or tool holder and presents a problem in disposal. This is especially undesirable on automatic machinery where it might interfere with the continued operation of the machine.

Fig. 20–4 shows the different methods that are used to provide a *chip breaker* on the tool. The action of the chip breaker, either groove or shelf type, is to force the chip to turn a sharp corner. This action itself may break the chip or it may be spiraled into the uncut shoulder of the work and broken into short segments. By varying the width of the shelf along the tool edge, the chip may be made to curl in a spiral form and its direction can be controlled.

MULTIPOINT BROACHING AND SAWING TOOLS

Broaching.   In practice, broaches are described as either *internal* or *surface* broaches. An internal broach is one that cannot be supported throughout its length by the machine and during use must be either pushed or pulled through the work from one end only. In most cases, the workpiece completely surrounds an internal broach. The machine connections to an internal broach cannot be fixed since a pull type broach must be started through the workpiece before the pulling mechanism may be attached, or the workpiece must be removed from the final end of a push broach before the tool may be returned. Most internal broaches are pulled rather than pushed. This subjects them to tensile loading so they are not subject to columnar buckling as they would be under compressive loading.

Although any cutting tool plays a very important part in a machining

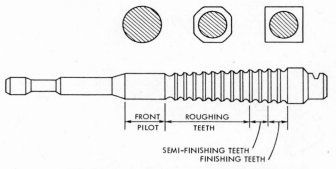

FRONT PILOT   ROUGHING TEETH   SEMI-FINISHING TEETH   FINISHING TEETH

FIG. 20–5. Pull type internal broach.

operation, a broach assumes a greater relative importance than most because it is designed for a specific operation. Although broaches may sometimes be used to produce similar surfaces on different workpieces, usually the tool must be designed not only for a specific surface producing operation, but also for a particular workpiece. Fig. 20–5 shows a broach designed for producing a square hole. The tool design must take into account the material of the workpiece which will determine the rake angle; the length of surface to be produced with will determine the length of chip for which space must be provided; the amount of material to be removed which, combined with the amount of step in each tooth, determines the number of teeth required; and the quality of finish desired. Several teeth, usually three or more, must be in contact with the work surface at all times in order to control the depth of cut and prevent straddling of the work. At the same time, the space between teeth must be large enough that the chips produced by each tooth can be curled and carried throughout the length of cut. The choice of tooth pitch then becomes a choice between two opposing influences which may result, especially for internal broaches, in borderline tooth strengths which will stand little abuse. Fig. 20–6 is a sectional view showing the details and terminology of broach design.

The accuracy of surfaces produced by broaching can often be held within a few ten-thousandths of an inch. Relationship accuracy between a broached surface and another surface already in existence may be more difficult. With surface broaching, the lateral supporting surface for the broach is actually the surface being machined and the broach is subject to some side drift. The shape and size of a broached hole can be held to extremely close limits but the location of the hole with respect to other surfaces of the part is more difficult.

Quality of work finish can be made very high by reducing the step per tooth on the last few teeth and providing several final teeth of the same size on the tool. For some shapes, the final surface may be burnished with a

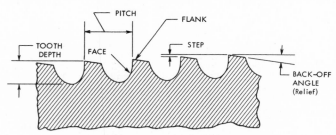

FIG. 20–6. Broach tooth design.

deforming action provided by oversize rounded projections on the broach following the last cutting teeth.

The cutting speed used with broaching is usually lower than would be used for the same materials in some other kind of cutting operation. The large contact length of cutting edge with the work, combined with high speed operation, would call for excessive and uneconomical size in the power equipment used to operate the tool. In addition, high speed would possibly increase the shock loading on relatively weak teeth, increasing the probability of breakage. But most important, economical operation requires that the costly tool have long life. Even with relatively low cutting speeds, however, the productivity of broaching is very high. A single pass of the multiedged tool across the workpiece roughs and finishes to a high degree of accuracy, keeping handling time at a minimum.

The design and manufacturing costs, together with the fact that the tool usually has very limited application, cause flat surface broaching to be restricted to those applications calling for high quantities. This is somewhat less true for some complicated external and most internal shapes such as splines, for which broaching may be the only practical way of producing the required shape, in any quantity, with the necessary accuracy.

Broaches are usually made with a number of finishing teeth of the same size to permit resharpening. Except for flat surface broaches which may be ground on the flanks of the teeth, broaches are ordinarily resharpened by grinding the same amount from the face of each tooth, including the first finishing tooth. Even though the flank of the tooth is not ground, tooth height will be decreased as its thickness is decreased because of the relief angle. After resharpening then, an original finishing tooth becomes smaller and acts as an intermediate tooth so that the next finishing tooth takes over for the making of the final surface and the same size and shape will continue to be produced.

Saws. The action of a saw blade in operation is similar to that of a broach except that the advance of each tooth into the work is obtained by feeding the entire blade rather than by a fixed step for each tooth as in a

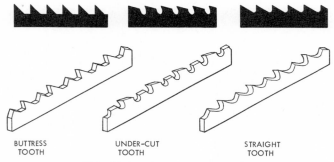

BUTTRESS   UNDER-CUT   STRAIGHT
TOOTH   TOOTH   TOOTH

FIG. 20–7.   Common saw teeth.

broach. The feed is usually obtained by maintaining pressure on the blade rather than by a fixed linear motion. Such feed systems are not only simpler to design and build, but permit the feed rate to adjust itself to the cutting conditions.

Saw blades are among the few metal cutting tools of which a large percentage are made of carbon tool steel or low alloy steel rather than high speed steel or one of the higher quality cutting tool materials. Some blades for special applications are made of high speed steel but seldom of the other materials. Saws are frequently used at higher cutting speeds than might be used for the same tool materials as single point tools. Any individual tooth is normally in contact with the work only a small percentage of the time and, particularly on band saws, the wear is distributed over a very large number of teeth.

Fig. 20–7 shows the three most common types of tooth design used for both hack saws, which operate with a reciprocating motion, and band saws, which use a flexible blade that operates continuously about wheels or pulleys. The cutter problems are similar to those of broaching. A number of teeth must be in contact with the work to prevent straddling which could result in excessive feed and breaking of the teeth. The teeth must have sufficient space between them to carry the chip throughout the cut. In addition, the actual width of the cut (the *kerf*) must be wider than the body of the saw to prevent rubbing and to permit the saw to cut a curved path where this is desired. This additional width of cut is obtained by bending the teeth alternately to one side and the other to provide *straight set* to the teeth. In a *wavy* set blade, groups of several teeth are alternately bent to the sides. In a *raker* set blade, a straight tooth is left between individual bent teeth.

The tooth profile is determined both by purpose and economics. The straight tooth is cheapest to manufacture and is used for most general purpose work. The undercut tooth can be made with more favorable rake and relief angles but is a more complicated shape. The buttress tooth is useful in providing additional chip space for aluminum and other soft ductile materials that are easy to cut. All types of teeth are available with different tooth size or pitch.

Hack saw blades are used primarily for straight sawing and are made in only a few standard widths but band saw blades are made in a variety of widths. The wide bands are stronger but allow only gentle curvature of the feed and are intended primarily for straight sawing. Narrow bands are made for sawing small radii and sharp curves.

DRILLING TOOLS

The importance of drilling is based on the importance of the circular cylinder to design and manufacturing. Where turning and cylindrical grinding are the most important process for machining external cylinders, drilling and allied operations are the most important for internal cylinders. On many workpieces produced in quantity, the external cylindrical surfaces may be given sufficient accuracy for use by a method such as die casting, and machining is unnecessary or used only for finishing. Most holes, however, especially small ones, are drilled rather than cast or forged. Even for pressworked sheet metal it becomes desirable to drill instead of punch holes when their diameter is less than the thickness of the sheet.

Some misuse of the terms *drilling* and *boring* is frequent. Drilling is the only practical means of originating a hole by machining, except for some low use special purpose methods. Common drilling tools are multiedged with a balanced cutting action, and they are not extremely rigid in the directions perpendicular to their axis. Consequently, holes drilled with standard drills may not have a high degree of straightness. Boring is normally a single point generating method used for removing material from a hole that already exists. Within the limits of the rigidity of the setup, the finished surface depends only on the axis of rotation of the tool, or work, and the feed path. The combination of drilling and boring is frequently used where better straightness and location accuracies are desired than can be obtained by drilling alone.

Twist Drills. Cutting tools used with drilling machines are in many forms. The most common tool is the *twist drill* designed for most hole origination in solid material. The cutting end of a twist drill is illustrated in Fig. 20–8. Located on the cone point end of the tool are two cutting edges, or lips, which like all cutting edges must have the material relieved behind them for controlled cutting. The end of the tool therefore is not truly conical in shape. The rake angle of the lips is the angle of helical twist of the flutes, or grooves, that carry chips to the surface of the work. The rake angle varies along the length of the cutting edge, being greatest at the outer diameter.

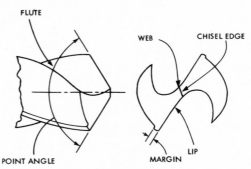

FLUTE

WEB   CHISEL EDGE

POINT ANGLE   MARGIN   LIP

FIG. 20–8.   Common twist drill point.

The flutes cannot exist to the center of the drill since they would intersect, robbing the tool of its strength. The supporting center structure, called the web, prevents the cutting lips from meeting at the center of the point. The resulting ridge at the tip of the tool is called the chisel point and, with conventional sharpening, serves as a high negative rake angle cutting edge to produce a small chip separate from that produced with the main cutting lips. The high negative rake angle of the chisel point combined with the low cutting speed in this area (actually zero at the center) requires a large feeding force. Of the total feed force, for most twist drilling operations, approximately 75 per cent is required by the chisel point.

The chisel point has an undesirable action when a drill is started. When it is brought against a flat surface, there is no stable point of rotation. Since the drill is not extremely rigid, it can rotate first about one corner of the chisel point and then the other with a walking action that not only makes accurate hole location difficult but can lead to drill breakage. To overcome this tendency, it is generally necessary to provide some guiding means for a standard length twist drill while the hole is being started. This may consist of a small conical depression made with a center punch and hammer, a small cast depression on castings, a short starting hole made with a shorter, more rigid tool, or a guide bushing of hardened material through which the drill passes before it enters the work.

Special *spiral point* drill grinding equipment is available which produces a complex shape on the cone point with less negative relief on the chisel point and a curved line for the end of the web. Contact with the work is established only in the center rather than along a straight line as with the ordinary chisel point.

The accuracy of hole size produced and the useful life of the cutting edges on drills are both influenced to a large extent by the quality of grinding the cutting edges. In addition to the need for a small but positive relief angle, the cutting lips must be equal in angle and equal in length to cut close to size. Error in either of these qualities will cause the drill to revolve about an axis different from its own and cut an oversize hole, as shown in Fig. 20–9. Although experienced mechanics can often grind

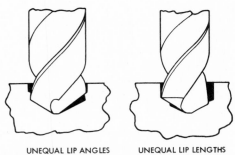

UNEQUAL LIP ANGLES   UNEQUAL LIP LENGTHS
FIG. 20–9. Effects of unequal drill lips.

drills *offhand* on a bench grinder, to cut satisfactorily, consistent results and good tool life can be obtained only by the use of special drill grinders designed for this purpose.

Torque for cutting power is transmitted to drills by several methods. Small drills are usually made with straight (cylindrical) shanks which may be gripped in drill chucks which are a special type of three jaw chuck with self-centering action. The maximum size drill that can satisfactorily be driven by three jaws contacting a straight shank is about ¾ inch in diameter. Most drills over ½ inch in diameter, and smaller ones when it is economically feasible, are constructed with Morse taper shanks which directly, or through adapter sleeves, are connected to the driving spindle of the machine. Tapered shanks are held and centered when pressed or driven into the mating internal taper of the machine, but can be easily removed with axial impact in the reverse direction. Special shanks of various kinds to permit fast tool removal are sometimes used on production jobs where the savings of a few seconds time will more than pay for the additional equipment costs.

Sizes of common twist drills are disignated by number, by letter, and by common fraction. Numbers from one to eighty are used for drill sizes of from 0.228 inch to 0.0135 inch diameter respectively. Drills numbered one to sixty (0.040) are commonly used as a set, with sixty-one to eighty used as another set sometimes called jewelers drills. Two consecutive numbers in the small end of the range represent only 0.0005 to 0.002 inch difference in size; but at the large end of the range, two consecutive numbers will represent 0.007 to 0.008 inch difference of drill diameter.

Except for being larger in size, letter drills are similar to number drills. The letter "A" is used to designate a drill 0.234 inch in diameter, with the other letters of the alphabet assigned to increasing sizes up to the letter "Z" for 0.413 inch diameter. Number and letter drills are used for drilling holes to be tapped for small thread sizes as well as thousands of other needs for small holes.

The size of most larger drills is described by common fraction. Although sizes as large as six inches in diameter have been made, fractional size drills are commonly used for $\frac{1}{64}$ inch to about three inches in diameter in $\frac{1}{64}$ inch increments. Large size drills are usually impractical because of small need and the large sized equipment needed to drive them. Also, large sized holes often have accuracy requirements than cannot be consistently obtained directly by drilling operations, so most are finished by boring type operations following the drilling of a smaller initial hole. Drills smaller than a number eighty drill, and some special larger sizes, are described in size by decimal fractions. Drills as small as one or two thousandths of an inch in diameter have been made, but because of their low strength, are used only when their need is essential. Suitable cutting speed is usually provided by special high speed machines with sensitive feed control. The use of large size drills, manufactured to decimal dimensions between the sizes that are commonly available, is often unrealistic since the common twist drill can seldom be depended upon for consistent, accurate hole sizing.

Core Drills.   The enlarging of holes that are not truly round, that vary in dimension or alignment, that have a hard scaly finish, or must be shifted to a new axis cannot be easily accomplished with the common twist drill. Even where these inaccuracies do not exist to any large degree, if the only purpose is enlargement of an existing hole, the rate at which a common twist drill can be fed is controlled by the thin web that limits its torsional strength. This kind of work can be done better with another tool design known as a *core drill*, Fig. 20–10. The name is derived from the fact that the tool is used mainly for truing cored holes in castings.

Without the restriction of being sharpened completely to the center of rotation, core drills may be designed with three, four, or more flutes and lips to divide the work into smaller increments. The flutes are shallower

3, 4, OR MORE FLUTES

FIG. 20–10. Core drill.

than in the common twist drill, resulting in shorter length of lips and heavier web section. While not like a single point boring tool, the greater stiffness of the core drill helps to maintain its rotational position about a single axis with less deflection than would be experienced with the two fluted twist drill. The increase of the number of lips, together with the shallower flutes, eliminates the chisel point; instead, the end of the drill includes a large flat area known as the *dead center* which has no cutting action whatever. The tool therefore cannot originate a hole and must always be used in such a way that the dead center does not contact solid material.

Deep Hole Drills.   One of the important functions of the drilling process is the making of long holes which often must also be comparatively straight. While a "deep" hole has no clear definition and a common twist drill design will drill deep holes if the length of the tool is great enough, it is generally feasible to use some special type of drilling tool when holes with lengths greater than eight or ten times their diameter for

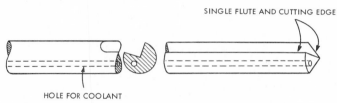

SINGLE FLUTE AND CUTTING EDGE

HOLE FOR COOLANT

FIG. 20–11.   Gun drill.

small drills, or even less for larger drills, are to be drilled. As deeper holes are required and longer drills are used, problems arise from drill deflections, the removal of chips from the cutting area to the surface, and excessive heating of the cutting edge. For these reasons, a number of special design drilling tools have been developed for producing deep holes under various conditions.

Deep holes requiring good straightness are often produced by use of *gun drills* as shown in Fig. 20–11. These tools have only a single cutting edge which precedes a relatively long guide section for maintenance of straight cutting progress. The body of the tool is in the form of a flattened tube through which coolant can be supplied to exit through a small hole immediately behind the cutting lip. After helping to reduce the coefficient of friction in chip formation and picking up heat in the cutting area, the coolant combines with and helps the flow of chips along the flattened portion of the tube out to the work surface. In order to facilitate the connection of a coolant supply through the shank of the tool, drills of this kind are usually held stationary while the workpiece revolves to produce cutting motion.

On standard gun drills, the cutting lip runs from the center of the tool to the outside edge. For larger sized holes, ⅜ inch minimum, another design known as a *target drill* has a central opening running the length of the tool with the cutting edge reaching only to the edge of the opening. This shorter cutting edge leaves a plug in the center of the cut which provides some support for the tool as well as reducing the work energy required for removing material. The elimination of the zero cutting speed area at the center of the cut makes greater tool feeds possible.

The *oil hole drill,* Fig. 20–12, is constructed the same as a common twist

HOLES FOR COOLANT

FIG. 20–12.   Straight shank oil hole drill.

drill except for the existence of two holes from the shank through the body of the drill to the cone point behind the lips. Coolant supplied under pressure improves cutting action, increases tool life by reducing the temperature to which the tool is subjected, and results in better dimensional accuracy because of reduced thermal effects on both the tool and the work. A variation of the oil hole drill is the *oil tube drill* which has small coolant tubes laid in grooves paralleling the flutes in the body of the drill. Theses drills are useful for holes that are longer than two or three times their diameter, especially on turret lathes, automatic screw machines and other machines that hold the tool stationary while the work revolves.

Oil groove drills are used in the vertical position and make use of gravity to cause coolant to flow through additional flutes in the body of the drill. Small notches near the drill tip allow the coolant to flow into the main flute to return to the surface with the chips. Since the extra flutes do not result in cutting edges, no chips enter these flutes to restrict the downward flow of coolant.

Since gun drills, oil hole drills, and oil groove drills, must all supply space for coolant channels, none of these designs can be used for very small drills and still leave sufficient strength in the tool to resist cutting forces. Small diameter, deep holes are made with standard twist drill tools. However, if the hole length requires drills much longer than normal, it may be beneficial to use a series of drills of increasing lengths. The hole is started with short drills that are relatively stiff and as the longer tools become necessary, the hole itself provides lateral support for most of the drill length. This process can be termed *progressive drilling* and coolant can be supplied only periodically by removing the drill and applying coolant in the hole and on the tool. Longer drills often have heavier web sections which may require special sharpening techniques to keep the chisel edge in reasonable bounds. Even with drills carrying coolant channels, it is frequently necessary when drilling deep holes to remove the tool periodically from the hole to clear the chips and prevent their increasing the rubbing friction.

Reamers. Holes made with standard twist drills have limited accuracy of diameter, straightness, and roundness and may have poor surface finish. Even with these faults, no further finishing is necessary for the great majority of drilled holes. When improvement is necessary, the most common method, particularly for diameter and finish qualities, is to use a multiple edged cutting tool called a *reamer*. The reamer provides a means of finishing a drilled hole in a short time, to within a few ten-thousandths of an inch tolerance, with good surface finish. While reaming is not a single point generating operation such as boring, and the reamer will tend

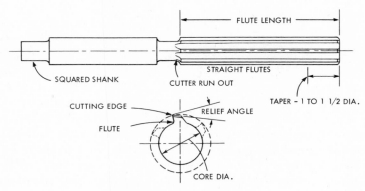

FIG. 20–13. Hand reamer.

to follow the drilled hole, some improvement occurs in the straightness of a reamed hole because of the stiffness of the reamer and the action of the long straight cutting edges. If properly guided, a reamer may be used for minor shifts in the location of holes in relatively thin workpieces.

Hand reamers, Fig. 20–13, are used only for small amounts of material removal. These tools can be recognized by the square end on the shank, suitable for gripping with a wrench. The cutting end of the tool is slightly tapered for a length of about one to one and one-half times the diameter of the reamer to allow entry into an undersized hole and provide some alignment with the hole axis. Most of the cutting occurs on this tapered section. The remaining part of the cutting edges serves mainly for guiding and some small amount of metal removal for the final finishing. Hand reamers are used to remove only from about 0.003 to 0.005 inch on the diameter when used in steel, but with nonferrous and other materials that are relatively easy to cut, may be used for greater stock removal. Long hand reamers, called line reamers, may be used in contact with several surfaces at one time for the final machining of bearing surfaces intended to be concentric with a single straight line axis.

Machine or *chucking* reamers are constructed with a steep chamfer on the end, as shown in Fig. 20–14, instead of a long shallow taper. With suitable relief angles, these chamfer edges become the principal cutting edges that remove most of the material. As with hand reamers, the long edges serve mainly as guides for the tool. Fig. 20–15 illustrates the difference between a standard machine reamer and a *rose* reamer. The rose reamer is circumferentially ground on the side edges and is thus similar to a

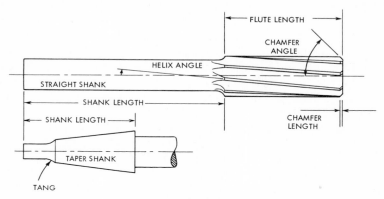

FIG. 20–14. Chucking reamer.

core drill. All the cutting must occur on the front end of the tool and it cannot provide as high quality finishes as a standard reamer with relief angle on the side edges, but it is a more rugged tool. Machine reamers may be used to increase the diameter of a hole as much as 0.015 or 0.030 inch in steel.

With any reamer, the accuracy of the hole produced will depend on the accuracy of alignment of the tool with the previously drilled hole. When hand reaming, and with many small workpieces when machine reaming, the tool is aligned manually with the workpiece. If the tool is limber enough that it can spring readily, or if it is mounted in a floating support so its axis can shift to line up with the previously machined hole, the need for extreme care in setup can be eliminated. Many larger diameter reamers are

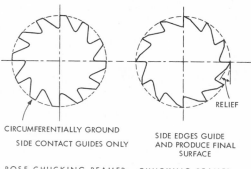

CIRCUMFERENTIALLY GROUND
SIDE CONTACT GUIDES ONLY

SIDE EDGES GUIDE
AND PRODUCE FINAL
SURFACE

ROSE CHUCKING REAMER   CHUCKING REAMER

FIG. 20–15. Reamer cutting edge design.

made of shell type design with separate shanks, as shown in Fig. 20–16.
Only the cutting portion need be replaced when the tool becomes worn
out.

Reamers tapered for their entire length may be used to form internal
conical surfaces. Many internal cylindrical tapers, especially in small sizes,
are made by first producing a cylindrical hole, then enlarging one end of
the hole with reaming. Fig. 20–17 illustrates one such class of taper reamers

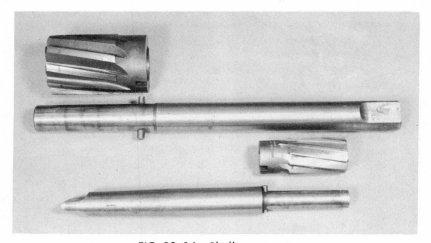

FIG. 20–16. Shell reamers.

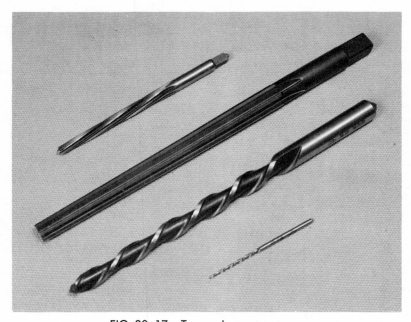

FIG. 20–17. Taper pin reamers.

used for finishing holes with which a tapered pin mates for assembly purposes. Spiral fluted reamers with left hand helix angle tend to overcome the natural tendency of the reamer to seize in the hole it is making and provide better finish than straight fluted reamers.

Miscellaneous Drilling Tools.   In addition to standard drills and reamers which make up the vast majority of tools used for drilling operations, a number of other tools, both standard and special, may be used. Fig. 20–18

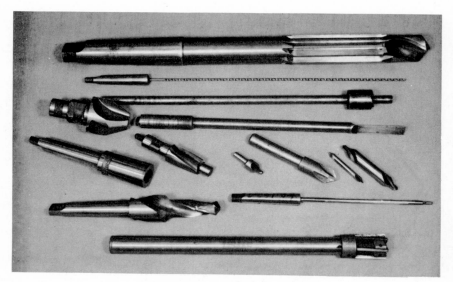

FIG. 20–18.   Miscellaneous drilling tools.

shows a few such tools. The countersink is used for making short steep tapers for recessing screw heads, for preventing burrs on threaded holes, and similar uses. Counterbores are used principally for making recesses for socket head screws. The combination drill and countersink is used primarily for making recesses to fit the work supports for certain types of lathe and grinding work. Step drills with two or more diameters are always special tools with high costs, but their use may be justified in some cases because of reduced handling time. Combined drills and reamers are likewise high cost tools and are difficult to resharpen. They may be used only on relatively thin work in which the drill portion of the tool passes completely through the work before the reamer portion starts to cut.

Reamers are ordinarily produced with a diameter slightly greater than nominal fractional sizes. They are available as standard increments of $\frac{1}{64}$ inch. For other sizes solid reamers are special. In tool room work, however, the need frequently arises for finishing one, or a few, odd-sized holes for which the cost of a special reamer could not be justified. There are two different designs of reamers whose size may be varied over a small range.

The diameter of a solid *expansion* reamer may be varied over a small range by means of the tapered plug which engages an internal taper in the body of the tool to spring the slotted tool body. A similar tool with greater range of adjustment is the *adjustable* reamer, which has separate blades or cutting edges and whose position in tapered slots may be varied to control the external diameter.

TAPS AND DIES

The majority of mass produced threaded fasteners and a smaller percentage of special parts have external threads produced by rolling, a deformation operation with no metal removal. Other than these, external threads and practically all internal threads are made by machining. A relatively small number of external threads are cut by milling or grinding, and a still smaller number of both external and internal threads are cut with single point generating type tools on lathes. The majority of machined threads are produced with taps and dies, both of which are one pass forming type tools with multiple cutting edges operating much like the teeth of broaching tools.

Taps. Practically all internal threads are cut with *taps*. In principle, a tap is an external thread with grooves or flutes cut either parallel to the axis or at a small helix angle. The intersection of the thread profile with the flutes provides cutting edges. To prevent a single intersection from having to do all the cutting, the end of the tap is given a conical or tapered shape so that in use the thread groove is cut progressively deeper by successive teeth on the conical end. A tap with four flutes and tapered for a distance of three times the thread lead would have twelve active cutting edges, each of which would remove a small amount of material so that the last would produce the final thread size and shape.

The rake angle of the cutting edges depends on the shape and placement of the flutes. On most taps, the angle is near zero. Relief angle may or may not be provided back of the cutting edges on the thread profile.

The biggest difference between taps is in the length of the cutting taper. The three principal types are shown in Fig. 20–19. A *taper* tap gives better alignment with the hole when the tap is manually guided. It has a taper with a length of one to one and one-half times the diameter of the tap. The standard tap for use in machine tapping, where the tap is positively guided by the machine, is the *plug* tap which is tapered for about three or four threads. Where a full thread is required as close to the bottom of a blind hole as possible, a *bottoming* tap with a taper of only about one full thread is used. The bottoming tap should be used only to finish the last few threads left uncut by a plug tap. If used to cut complete threads the life of a bottoming tap will be quite short.

Taps may be made of carbon tool steel, high speed steel, or cemented carbide. Most are presently made of high speed steel. Cheaper taps may be completely shaped before hardening, but for high accuracy it is necessary that the tap be ground after hardening.

In addition to the difference in taper, the material used, and the method used in manufacture, taps may differ in other respects. *Pulley taps* with longer shank lengths are available for reaching places that would be inaccessible to a tap of standard length, such as a set screw hole in the hub of a large diameter pulley. Long shank taps with the shank diameter less than the root diameter of the thread are also used for the special work of tapping nuts and other fastening devices. This type of work may also be performed on special nut tapping machines that use curved shank taps which permit continuous feeding of nuts over the cutting portion of the tool.

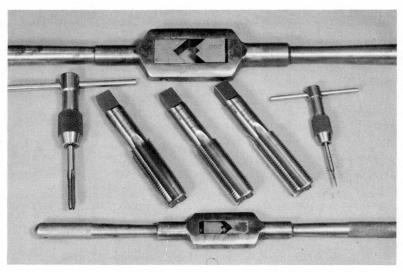

FIG. 20–19. Threading taps and wrenches. The large taps in the center are (left to right) taper, plug, and bottoming.

Except for the special work of nut tapping, it is generally necessary to reverse the rotation of the tap or the workpiece to back any standard solid type of tap from the hole after the thread is cut. The time required for backing the tap out can be reduced by use of *collapsing* taps which consist of three or more separate thread chasing elements supported by a steel frame. The chasers can be tripped at the completion of the threading operation to collapse below the root diameter of the thread and permit tool withdrawal from the hole without reversal of rotation. In addition to time saving, these tools have the added advantages of being easier to resharpen than solid taps and of being adjustable for thread size. However, their high initial cost limits their economical use to quantities in which substantial time savings can be accumulated. The minimum practical size is approximately one inch pitch diameter because of the space needs of a collapsing mechanism with adequate strength.

Dies. For cutting external threads, there are several types of *dies*. In principle, a die operates in much the same manner as a tap, the die having a standard thread profile interrupted by flutes to provide cutting edges and being tapered on the end to distribute the cutting over a number of teeth.

Because a tap must enter the hole it is to cut threads in, its size is restricted and for adequate strength most taps are of one piece solid construction. Dies, however, surround the workpiece and the lack of size

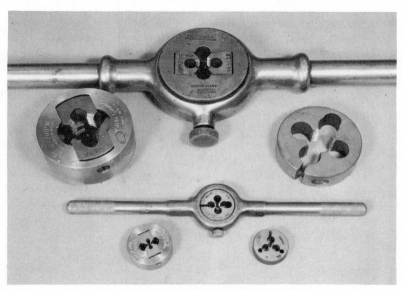

FIG. 20–20.   Hand threading dies and stocks.

restrictions permits some variations in types of construction. A few hand dies are made solid and nonadjustable but most hand dies are made as one of the types shown in Fig. 20–20. The split adjustable type has a simpler holder and may be adjusted for thread fit and to compensate for wear but is not ordinarily resharpened. Chaser type dies may also be adjusted and in addition may be resharpened although replacement of the cutting elements is commonly practiced after wear or damage has occurred.

Hand dies are ordinarily used by turning the tool over the work until the desired thread length is established, then reversing the rotation to back the die off. About as much time is needed for die removal as for the work of cutting the thread. Practically all external die threading in production is done with *expanding* die heads in order to reduce this lost time. These make use of three or four individual chasers. The operating principle is similar to that of a collapsing tap. However, the size restriction on taps is not present and expanding dies may be used for threads of any sizes. They are made in nonrotating types for use on turret lathes, automatic screw machines, and special threading machines, and in rotating types for use where it is impractical to rotate the work.

The accuracy of machined threads depends on a number of factors, first of which is the accuracy of the cutting edge shape. In addition, the tool must be properly aligned with the work. The lead of the finished thread will depend on the manner of regulating the feed of the tool. In most cases, the feed is regulated by the natural guiding action of the tap or die following the threads it has already cut, but if incorrect feeding pressure is provided, the lead may be distorted. For very accurate threads, either internal or external, the feed should be regulated by the machine. This may be by a lead screw arrangement as is used for single point thread chasing on a lathe or a *leader* and *follower* arrangement which consists of accurate internal and external mating threads on the spindle on the threading machine.

MILLING CUTTERS

Much of the value of milling as a process is due to its wide versatility which comes largely because of the many forms, shapes, and sizes of milling cutters that are manufactured as standard items in relatively large quantities and are readily available from distributors at reasonable cost. Because of this wide variety of cutters, it sometimes appears that the operation of different types of cutters may be basically different. Actually however, with the possible exception of a milling cutter being used as a drilling or reaming tool, all milling cutters operate with the feed motion at right angles to the axis of rotation of the cutter and all the cutting takes place on the periphery of the cutter. Fig. 20–21 shows the possible location of the cutting elements on milling cutters and the two common methods of mounting.

Milling operations normally produce only two types of surfaces. One is a generated flat surface produced normal to the axis of the rotation by a cutter as noted at "B." It is not, however, the end or face of the milling cutter which produces the surface and in fact few milling cutters are sharpened with cutting elements in a plane exactly perpendicular to the axis of rotation. The second type of surface is that formed by the profile of the cutter. This may be flat if the cutter has cylindrical cutting elements as with cutter "A" and the feed is in a straight line. With a type "A" cutter and curved feed or a type "C" cutter and straight line feed the resulting surface would be a portion of a noncircular cylinder. With a type "C" cutter and curved feed the surface would be double curved. Cutters of type "B" or "C" are frequently used to produce two surfaces simultaneously, one formed by the profile of the cutter, the other generated normal to the axis of rotation.

While there are a large number of different names for specific milling cutters, they are frequently based only on differences in the proportions of length to diameter of the cutter, the method of mounting the cutter in the machine, or the particular surface or operation for which the cutter is designed.

Cutters may be mounted on an arbor that passes completely through the cutter and is supported on both ends or they may be mounted from one end only. Cutters of the latter type are called *end* or *face mills*, and the shank may be integral with, or separate from, the cutting elements.

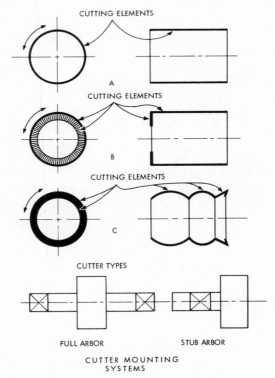

FIG. 20–21. Milling cutter principles.

Plain Milling Cutters. Arbor mounted cutters having cylindrical cutting elements only are usually called *plain* milling cutters, Fig. 20–22. If a cutter of this type is used to cut a slot, in which the sides of the slot would be generated, rubbing and heat generation is excessive, the finish created is very poor, and the corners of the teeth dull very rapidly. Plain cutters are normally used to produce only a single flat surface that is narrower than the length of the cutter. The cutting elements may be either straight or helical.

Specific names for plain milling cutters depend primarily on proportions. A cutter that is long compared to its diameter is called a *slab* milling cutter. With teeth having a helix angle greater than 45 degrees, the cutter may be called a *helical* cutter. One that is very narrow in width may be called a *screw slotting* cutter. A screw slotting cutter presents one minor exception to the rule, in that it is used to cut slots, but they are of shallow depth not exceeding the depth of the teeth on the cutter and the total amount of metal to be removed is quite small during the life of the cutter.

FIG. 20–22. Plain milling cutters.

Side Milling Cutters. An arbor mounted cutter of the type shown at "B" in Fig. 20–21 is one type of *side* milling cutter. Others are shown in Fig. 20–23. The principal use for full side milling cutters is the cutting of slots. When two or more, full or half, side milling cutters are mounted on the same arbor with spacers between the cutters and used to cut two or more parallel flat surfaces in one pass, the operation is called *straddle* milling. Staggered tooth side milling cutters have fewer teeth than standard with alternate teeth projecting on the sides of the cutter. They may be used with greater feeds than standard cutters because of the increased chip clearance and are designed primarily for roughing cuts.

When the width of a milled slot must be held to a close tolerance, a problem arises after the cutter is worn or resharpened and its width is reduced. For this application, *interlocking* side milling cutters permit the restoration of the correct width by inserting shims between the cutters.

For very narrow slots of considerable depth, a side milling cutter called a *slitting saw* is used. It may be a conventional side cutter design with teeth sharpened on the sides or it may be sharpened on the periphery only, in which case side clearance is obtained by hollow grinding or reducing the width of the cutter body below the cutting edges of the teeth.

End and Face Mills. The distinction between most end and face milling cutters, Fig. 20–24, is largely in the dimensional proportions between the side and end cutting edges. In principle, the standard cylindrical types are half side milling cutters mounted from one end only. End mills are relatively long compared to their diameter and may have integral shanks or, in the *shell end mill* type, have separate shank and cutter body. Integral shank cutters are made with diameters from $\frac{1}{16}$ to 2 inches and shell end mills from $1\frac{1}{4}$ to 6 inches.

FIG. 20–23. Side milling cutters (top) half side (left) staggered tooth (right) full side (bottom) slitting saw.

End milling cutters are used for a wide variety of operations. Grooves that extend completely through a workpiece are usually cut more efficiently with an arbor mounted cutter but end mills are the only practical tools for many recesses, grooves that extend only partially through a workpiece and must end abruptly, curved grooves except when the groove is circular, and profiling work on thin material. Typical operations of these types are shown in 20–25. In the toolroom, they are frequently used for operations that in production might be done by some other method or cutter because of the simple setups required and the wide variety of surfaces that can be finished with only a few cutters.

No sharp dividing line exists between end mills and face mills. The latter are relatively large in diameter compared to their length, are made

FIG. 20–24. End and face milling cutters.

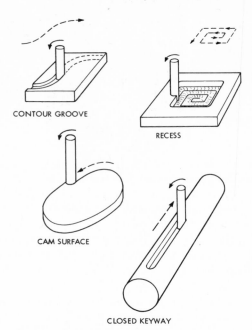

CONTOUR GROOVE

RECESS

CAM SURFACE

CLOSED KEYWAY

FIG. 20–25. Typical end mill applications.

in much larger diameters than end mills, and are used for the principal purpose of generating flat surfaces. Standard cutters are available from one to eighteen inches in diameter. Face mills are usually made with a carbon or low alloy steel body and inserted or brazed teeth made of high speed steel or cemented carbide. Face mills may either be mounted on a stub arbor or bolted directly to the end of the milling machine spindle.

Form Milling Cutters. The cutters discussed so far have all been those with cutting elements that are part of a circular cylinder. Except when a curved feed is used, as in profiling with an end mill, or in a few cases where a side milling cutter might be plunged into the work to make a semi-circular recess with flat sides, such cutters are used only for machining flat surfaces, either formed by the cylindrical cutting elements or generated by passing the work over the end or side of the cutters. When the cutting elements are part of a noncylindrical surface of revolution the general

FIG. 20–26. Form milling cutters. (Left to right) double angle, convex, special form, involute gear, corner rounding.

term *form* milling cutter is used to describe the tools. The profile of a surface made by such a cutter, in a plane at right angles to the direction of feed, will be determined by the shape of the cutter. The profile will otherwise depend on the direction of feed although straight line feed is by far the most common. The surfaces produced by form milling cutters are usually partial noncircular cylinders.

Single angle and double angle cutters have cutting edges that are elements of a cone and produce flat surfaces with straight line feeds. Such surfaces may also be made with end mills or side milling cutters. Angle cutters, however, simplify setups when the surfaces are at odd angles to the major locating surfaces of a workpiece and they are the only types of milling cutters that can cut acute angle grooves. A double angle cutter, together with other types of form milling cutters, is shown in Fig. 20–26.

A form milling cutter can be made for almost any shaped groove. A number are in sufficient demand that they are made as standard. These include radius, (concave and convex), single angle, double angle, involute gear, (roughing and finishing), roller chain sprocket, ball end mill, and tapered end mill. Ball end mills are in wide use for cavity shaping operations where the cutter is guided by a tracing device or by information programmed on a tape.

Miscellaneous Milling Cutters. A number of special purpose cutters are shown in Fig. 20–27. Threads may be milled on a machine designed for this purpose using a single-form thread milling cutter and rotating the work a sufficient number of times to produce the complete thread. Using a

FIG. 20–27. Miscellaneous milling cutters. (Top) hollow milling cutter, hypoid gear cutter, hob, (bottom) Woodruff keyseat cutter, dovetail cutter, multiple form thread milling cutter.

multiple form cutter as shown in the figure, the thread may be completed with only one revolution of the work. The Woodruff key seat cutter is an example of a plain milling cutter with shank mounting. A similar appearing tool, called a T slot cutter, uses a double side milling cutter form to cut the wings of a "T" slot after the leg has been cut with a standard end mill or side milling cutter. Hobbing cutters are used primarily for cutting gear teeth and splines. A fly cutter is a tool room cutter, used when demand exists for some special form for a limited amount of work. The toolmaker shapes a standard lathe type cutting tool to the correct profile and mounts it in either an arbor type or a single shank type holder depending on the particular job. The cutter has only a single tooth and must be used with a low feed rate but permits many jobs to be finished at less cost and in less time than would be required if a special multiple toothed form milling cutter had to be made. Fly cutters are also useful for boring holes when this operation needs to be combined in a setup with other milling work.

GRINDING TOOLS

In many respects, grinding wheels are like milling cutters. They are both multiedged rotating cutting tools. In use, most grinding wheels cut on the periphery as do milling cutters. However, the selection of a grinding wheel may be more involved than the selection of a milling cutter because of the great number of variables in its design and manufacture. Relatively few variables must be considered for milling cutters, other than shape and the material of which the cutter is to be made, which may be dictated by the shape. For grinding wheels, not only must the shape be specified, but also the type of abrasive, the type of bond, the hardness of the bond, and the spacing of the grains, known as structure. The size of the abrasive grains must be correctly chosen if the tool is to function properly.

Abrasives. A good abrasive has strength and brittleness balanced so that when used on the work material for which it is meant, it has the ability to fracture before excessive dulling of the grains occurs. The most common abrasive in use is aluminum oxide which, although it exists in a natural state, is used almost entirely as a synthetic product because of the greater control of purity and crystalline shape. Sapphires and rubies are large single crystals of aluminum oxide containing small amounts of impurities. This material has rather high toughness although it is not as hard as some other abrasives. It is used for most grinding of steel, malleable iron, and the harder bronzes and other nonferrous alloys. If used for grinding gray cast iron, softer nonferrous alloys, or other materials of relatively low tensile strength, the wheel tends to become loaded or glazed on the surface with particles of work material. The strength of the work material in this case is not sufficient to cause dull grains to fracture and present new edges for work material removal.

Silicon carbide is a harder material than aliminum oxide; but it is also more brittle or of less toughness. Most grinding of gray iron, nonferrous metals, and nonmetallic materials such as glass, rubber, and stone is done with silicon carbide. Even weaker work materials can cause fracture of the brittle grains and promote self-sharpening of the wheel. In addition, silicon carbide, because of its high hardness, may be used for rough grinding of cemented carbides although wheel wear rate is high. Aluminum oxide is worn much too rapidly by cemented carbides to be used for practical grinding of these materials.

For most grinding of cemented carbides and for many operations on glass and ceramics, diamond abrasives are used. The diamonds are of the same composition as gem stones, but are of dark color, contain flaws, or are too small for gem use. In more recent years, synthetic diamonds have been developed and used in competition with the natural materials. There appears to be little difference between the grinding ability of natural and synthetic diamonds so long as the particle shapes are the same.

Bonds. Most grinding wheels are made by mixing the proper amounts of abrasive particles or grains with a bonding material which will set and develop high hardness and strength, either by heat or a thermosetting reaction. The most common bond, used for over 75 per cent of all wheels manufactured, is *vitrified* clay, produced by firing mixtures of abrasives and clays. Vitrified wheels may be made with a more porous structure than other types, resulting in fast cutting action and their rigidity helps in attaining high precision. They are affected very little by water, oil, acid, or ordinary temperature variation.

Silicate bonded wheels are made with sodium silicate as the bonding material. After mixing with the abrasive, the material is dried at much lower temperature than that used for firing vitrified wheels. This bond is much weaker than a vitrified bond and breaks down to release dull grains more quickly. As a result, silicate bonded wheels wear faster than vitrified wheels but stay sharper and generate less heat in cutting. They are preferred for grinding cutting tools and for other uses where heat generation must be kept to a minimum.

Several different types of thermosetting organic materials are used for bonding, generally for somewhat special purposes. *Shellac* bonded wheels are not intended for heavy stock removal but are capable of producing high quality finishes on mill rolls and similar workpieces. *Resinoid* (phenol thermosetting plastic) bonded wheels have high strength and shock resistance and are used primarily for roughing work in foundries and for other applications where they may be subjected to shock loading. *Rubber* bonded wheels are used as feed wheels in centerless grinding machines and as thin wheels for cutoff or sawing operations. Rubber bonded wheels as thin as $\frac{1}{32}$ inch are used as cutoff wheels.

Grain Size. The finish produced by a grinding operation depends to a great extent on the size of the abrasive grains, although it is influenced by other factors such as wheel diameter and width, wheel speed, vibration, coolant, and work material. Because of the great number of grains which serve as cutting edges, a wheel with relatively large grains is capable of producing fine finishes. The metal removal rate is also controlled to a large extent by the abrasive size. Abrasives, whether natural or synthetic, are first crushed, then graded for size. Abrasive sizes are designated by screen numbers such as are used for foundry molding sand. Sizes used in grinding range from ten, very coarse, to six hundred, very fine.

Grade. The term *grade* is used to denote the hardness of a wheel. It is dependent on the bond of the wheel since the hardness of the abrasive grain is determined by the type of grain itself. The grade of a grinding wheel controls the amount of dulling of a wheel necessary before the forces become high enough to make the bond break down to release the grain. Soft wheels cut faster with less heat generation than hard wheels with the same type of abrasive but wear faster. Because of the change of shape and size effect caused by wheel wear, it is often necessary to use a harder wheel than might otherwise be desired when form grinding. Grade is designated by letter, with "A" being soft and "Z" being hard.

Structure. The *structure* of a wheel refers to the spacing of the grains in the wheel. Some correspondence exists between grade and structure in the action of grinding wheels. An open structure leads to faster cutting but faster wear, while a dense or closed structure reduces cutting ease but gives the wheel better shape retaining ability. The number zero designates the most dense structure and twelve the most open.

Fig. 20–28 gives an example of the use of the standard wheel marking system for identifying grinding wheels, which is used by different manufacturers. Although theoretically a wheel with similar markings would have the same characteristics, some variability occurs. Some trial and error is frequently involved in the optimum choice of grain size, grade, and structure, when a new operation is set up.

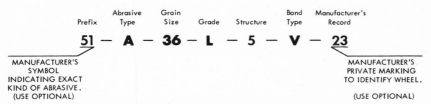

FIG. 20–28. Standard grinding wheel marking.

Wheel Shape. Most grinding wheels are straight wheels with cylindrical faces. Such wheels are used for the great majority of both cylindrical and flat surface grinding. The shape of the face may be altered by the manufacturer or the user of the wheel to various angular or curved forms for particular applications. Fig. 20–29 shows some of the other common wheel shapes. The principal reason for using other than straight shapes is for better access to the surface to be ground. A saucer or dish-shaped wheel, for example, may be used to reach between two teeth of a milling cutter or broaching tool to grind the face of the teeth. Diamond wheels are made with similar shapes, but for all except very small wheels, the major portion of the wheel is constructed of metal or standard grinding wheel materials. Bonded diamond abrasive is applied as a thin ($\frac{1}{32}$ to $\frac{1}{4}$ inch) strip or band to form the face of the wheel.

Wheel Dressing. As has been pointed out, a grinding wheel wears in normal use with a self-sharpening action. If it does not wear properly, the surface becomes "loaded" or glazed with particles of work material which fill the spaces between the abrasive grains and lead to reduced cutting action and increased heat generation, or the surface particles may be released so easily that the wheel very quickly loses its size and shape. In some types of generating operations, the wheel tends to retain a correct shape with wear rates chosen to prevent loading. If loading does occur, or if the wear destroys the proper shape, it becomes necessary to *dress* the face of the wheel to restore proper shape and expose new sharp grains.

Dressing may be accomplished by one of two methods. For aluminum oxide and silicon carbide wheels, a diamond or other hard material may be used as a single point tool to actually machine the wheel. The second method is based on the fact that the abrasive particles and bond of a wheel are brittle materials with relatively low tensile strengths. If sufficient pressure is exerted on the face of the grinding wheel, the abrasive grains and bond are crushed and released creating a new surface and exposing new grains. A common hand wheel dressing tool is made with free spinning washers, some of which are notched, which set up high pressure loads on the wheel surface when rotated by contact with the revolving grinding wheel. In *crush dressing*, a formed steel or cast iron roller is driven by a grinding wheel and rotated at reduced speed while high pressure is applied between them. The roller gets relatively little wear because of little relative motion, and wheel grains will break free until the wheel's surface assumes the shape of the roller surface.

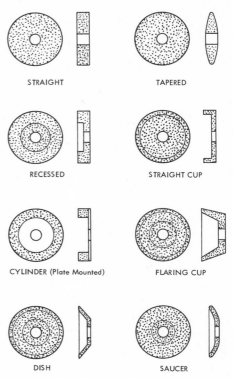

FIG. 20–29. Some standard grinding wheel shapes.

Other Abrasive Forms. In addition to their use in grinding wheels, abrasives find wide application in other forms. Loose abrasive particles, usually mixed with water or oil, are used in the lapping process for fine finishing. Solid sticks of bonded abrasives are used for *honing* to remove small amounts of material for finishing and sizing operations. Close tolerances and high quality finishes can result from small chips removed at relatively low rates. Deburring and corner rounding can be accomplished by manual honing but the process is used primarily for finishing accurate cylindrical holes.

Abrasive particles may be cemented to a cloth backing and used as belts, discs, or sleeves. At one time coated abrasives were limited to use on wood, but the development of high strength cements and electrostatic methods of depositing the abrasive particles with optimum orientation for cutting, has broadened their use to include plastics and metals. In some specialized applications, abrasive belts can provide higher metal removal rates than conventional wheels. They are also used for finish improvement either alone or as a preliminary step to final polishing, especially on parts with curved surfaces.

QUESTIONS

1. What is a cutting tool and its function?
2. What advantage is derived from using a holder and bits for single point tools?
3. How is a solid tool better than a holder and bit?
4. Describe a circular form tool.
5. What are the advantages and disadvantages of mechanical mounting versus brazing of carbide tool tips?
6. What is a throw away tool insert?
7. What is the purpose of a chip breaker and how does it work?
8. Why are most broaches designed for specific jobs?
9. What makes it possible for an internal broach to produce the same size surface after resharpening as that for which it was originally designed?
10. In connection with saw blades, what is "set" and its purpose?
11. Why is an internal cylindrical surface frequently drilled, then bored?
12. What determines the rake angle of a twist drill?
13. With a common twist drill, what in addition to its diameter will affect the diameter of the hole the drill produces?
14. How does a letter drill differ from a number drill?
15. Briefly describe a core drill.
16. Name the special drills designed for deep hole drilling.
17. What is the usual purpose of the use of a reamer?
18. Describe a tap and its use.
19. How do collapsing taps and expanding die heads contribute economic value in thread cutting?
20. Upon what is the feed of a tap dependent?
21. What is one of the greatest contributing factors to the versatility of the milling process?
22. Why is the choosing of a grinding wheel more difficult than choosing a milling cutter?
23. What is different about the wear of a grinding wheel from other types of cutting tools?
24. Name the five most commonly used abrasive bond materials.
25. What are the objects of grinding wheel dressing?
26. In what forms other than grinding wheels are abrasives used and to what processes are they valuable?

CHAPTER 21

Machine Tools

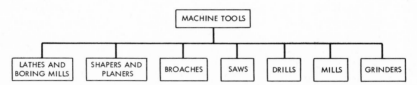

IT WAS pointed out in a previous chapter that the essential elements of machining include the workpiece, a *cutting tool* which is harder and stronger than the workpiece, and some means of providing a controlled relative motion between the workpiece and the tool. The present chapter will deal with the *machine tool* which is the device that provides the correct relative motion. In all but a few cases where support is provided by hand, the machine rigidly supports the tool and the workpiece.

In Chapter 19, it was noted that certain combinations of tool shapes and relative motions have proven to be more useful and desirable than others. This has led to the development of different groups or classes of machine tools with certain common features for each group, although a machine tool may be used with cutting tools and for operations more characteristic of some other group in some cases. Lathes or milling machines, for example, are frequently used to do drilling type operations.

Most machine tools were developed to their present form by the time of the Civil War, and the names that are used now were in use by that time. The improvements have come in accuracy, ease of control and operation, rigidity, power, and quantity production. Engine lathes may cost from under one thousand dollars to over one hundred thousand dollars and, for some types of work, the cheaper machine can perform as well as the more expensive.

Power Systems. Regardless of the size and complexity of a machine tool or the motions it is designed to produce, it will be similar to other machines in a number of respects. Practically all machine tools today use some type of electric motor as the primary power source. In the past it was common to provide one, or a few, very large electric motors to drive a number of machine tools by means of an overhead line shaft system. Individual belts were used at each machine to obtain power from the line shaft. From an economic viewpoint, line shaft drives are desirable for some constant load applications, but most machining operations do not fall in this category. Some line shaft systems are still used, but most are for supply of power to other than machining equipment. Individual drives provide greater flexibility of operation with freedom to locate the machine as needed, lower maintenance costs, and open the space above the machines for overhead conveyor systems.

Most machine tools must incorporate some system for altering the speeds of the cutting and feed motions. An engine lathe, for example, might be used with a high speed tool to turn a ten inch diameter rough cast iron workpiece, in which case the rpm of the rotating workpiece should be about 20 to give a cutting speed of 50 fpm. The same lathe might be used with a cemented carbide tool to turn aluminum workpieces ¼ inch in diameter, in which case the rpm would need to be over 15,000 for a cutting speed of 1000 fpm. In a practical machine built for this range of cutting conditions, the lower speed might be 20 rpm, but the upper speed would likely be limited to about 2,000 rpm because of problems of bearings and balance introduced at high speeds. A machine with such a speed limitation could be used to machine small diameters, but only at some sacrifice in efficiency. The same engine lathe would need feeds of from about 0.002 inch for fine finishing cuts to perhaps 0.250 for cutting a thread with that lead. Milling machines and drills likewise need wide range drives since they may use different diameter cutters made of different materials on different kinds of work materials. Shapers, planers, broaches, and saws need somewhat less range since the speed of the straight line cutting motion is not affected by the diameter or size of the workpiece or tool, but they still must be constructed with speed ranges to accommodate the different tool and work materials.

Speed variations may be achieved in a number of ways. Flat or vee belts may be used between stepped cone pulleys and speeds shifted by moving the belt from one set of steps to another. In practice, the number of steps with this arrangement is limited to four or five because of space and bearing limitations. A similar drive uses a special vee belt that operates between variable grooves (width) in the driving, and driven pulleys to give a continuous range of ratios over about the same total range as with stepped pulleys. With either type of belt drive, the total range is not usually great enough, except for small drilling machines, and at least one gear change is combined with the belt and pulley system, giving the machine a high (direct drive) range and a low (back geared) range with variations within each range obtained from the pulleys. Belt drives have the lowest first cost but may require considerable maintenance and can transmit only a limited amount of power.

Most machine tools have geared transmissions similar to the manual transmission of an automobile but nearly always having six or more steps. The range and the number of steps in such a transmission is limited primarily by the cost. Engine lathes may have as many as thirty-six speeds. Shifting gears is also the common method of obtaining changes in the feeds on a machine tool, even when the cutting or spindle speed may be varied by other means. The feeding mechanism transmits relatively low torque which permits small gears to be used. For a machine which depends on a accurate ratio between the rotation of the workpiece and the feed of the tool, such as needed in establishing the lead of a thread, gears offer the simplest means of obtaining this accuracy.

Variable speed direct current motors may be built with a range of about 100 to 1 and are desirable for many machine tools. The principal deterrent is the cost of obtaining direct current since most industrial current supplies are alternating current. For some equipment, the control provided by direct current power systems is important enough that rectifier or motor generator conversion units are built into the machines. Direct current drives also may require gear change since the natural torque output of a direct current motor is low at low speeds. Variable speed alternating current motors are either inefficient and limited to low power or are more expensive than direct current motors. However, alternating current motors may be built so that the effective number of poles may be altered by switching to obtain two or four speeds. Such a motor is called an adjustable speed motor and is used in combination with some gear changes to obtain the required number of speeds for a few machine designs.

Hydraulic systems are regularly used on many machine tools. High cost has limited their general use to straight line piston and cylinder drives used for feed motions or for driving shapers, broaches, and small planers. Rotary hydraulic motors are used in a few cases for driving feed screws. Hydraulic drives offer a wide range of infinitely variable and easily selected speeds or feeds but initial cost is high and maintenance cost is higher than with most other systems.

The inclusion of two separate speed changing mechanisms in most machine tools, one for cutting speed and one for feeds, leads to some confusion in names. In the most common usage, the term *head* or *headstock* includes the spindle and its speed changing system on lathes, milling machines, and drilling machines and the term *gearbox* refers to the speed changing system used for varying the feeds.

Design. The problem of vibration, together with the requirement of holding deflections to very low values for high accuracy, has led to machine tool structures that are much heavier than are usually found in other types of machinery that handles comparable loads. A machine tool transmission designed to handle 20 horsepower will be much larger than an automotive transmission in a car with a 200 horsepower engine. However, the machine tool operates at lower speeds and higher torques, it will be operating near rated load a high percentage of the time, and it will be expected to have a relatively maintenance free life of ten to twenty years, during which it may be used eighty hours a week or more. An auto given the same amount of use could be driven over four million miles.

It would be possible to build a machine tool structure of welded or cast steel that would be lighter and have greater rigidity than those used, but when such attempts have been made they have usually failed because of excessive vibration or chatter. Most machine tools are made with heavy gray cast iron bases and other major parts. Gray iron has high natural damping capacity, particularly for high frequencies, tending to decrease problems from this source.

Machines of all types are built with various degrees of automatic control of speeds and feeds. The first powered machines were manually fed, and many tool room operations now are more quickly done using manual feeds. Some small production machines also use manual feeds, either because the total cycle time may be reduced if the operator does not have to go through the motions of engaging a power feed, or because it may be desirable to let the operator have a greater control over the feed rate as the cut is being made. Manual feeds are often used on drilling operations, during which an experienced operator can determine when the flutes of the drill are becoming clogged with chips by the feel of the resistance to feeding. Most standard tool room types of machine tools are constructed so that the feed motions may be operated either manually or by power. Almost constant attention by an operator is required in nearly all cases for machines of this type, since the feeds and spindle rotations must be started and stopped by hand.

Machines intended for higher production rates usually have, in addition to higher power and greater rigidity, some degree of automatic control over the stopping of the feed motions at preselected points. This feature relieves the operator from constant attention and increases the duplication accuracy of the work, but the operator is still required for changing workpieces. Still higher degrees of automatic control involve changing or indexing tools, adjustment of tool position for cuts of different sizes, and variation of the cutting speed or feed rate.

Machines that are called *semiautomatic* generally require an operator only for changing workpieces at the end of a machining cycle, after which he engages a start mechanism and the machine will go through some fixed cycle of operations, including spindle starting, stopping, speed changing, feeding, and tool indexing. Although the term *automatic* has also been applied to many such machines, it is most often interpreted to mean a machine that can go through a number of cycles of operation, including changing of the workpieces or advancing bar stock from which parts are machined, without the attention of an operator. Even higher degrees of control are possible in which machined parts may be automatically measured and the tool repositioned to compensate for wear.

The design of machine tools is always affected by the type of use for which they are intended. If they are to be used in a tool room, job shop, model shop, or experimental laboratory in which only one or a very few parts of the same type are likely to be made, the principal aim will be to reduce the setup time required, even at some sacrifice in machining time. Machines of this type are usually designed with universal types of work and tool holding devices, manual or power feeds, and a number of movable components to permit the easiest positioning of the workpiece for a given cut. Available power is usually low on such machines, since the large number of movable components leads to less rigidity and a greater tendency for vibration that limit the size of cut which can be satisfactorily made.

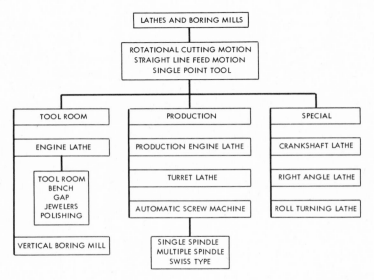

Many standard machines are designed with the capability of doing repetitive work of somewhat specialized nature, or limited range, with greater dependability than usually expected from multiple work with tool room equipment. Such machines have less versatility, fewer adjustments, greater rigidity, higher power, and often require longer setup time than tool room machines; but once the setup has been made, they turn out work at faster rates.

Even greater specialization in order to gain decreased operating time is present in special machines of low versatility designed for specific products. These special machines range from those that may be able to do a number of operations on a specific type of product, such as a railway carwheel lathe, to those that can machine only a single surface on a specific workpiece, such as a milling station in an automotive engine transfer machine.

Classification.   Machine tools could be grouped for discussion in numerous ways. They might be grouped according to their ability to produce surface types such as flat, cylindrical, double curved, etc. Many machines would fit in all the groups, as they would for a system based on work holding methods, tool holding methods, or tool types. In this chapter, machines will be grouped according to a combination of features, including the names that are used for the machines in practice but primarily the combination of cutting motion, feed motion, and tool type. The seven groups are those shown in the chapter heading. Within each of

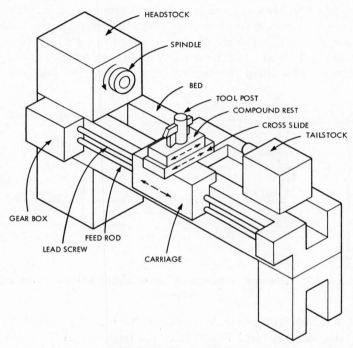

FIG. 21–1. Engine lathe.

these groups, machines can usually be identified as either tool room, standard production, or special, depending on the purpose for which the machine is built.

The oldest, most highly developed, and most widely used group of machine tools are those which rotate the workpiece and normally use single point cutting tools. Their wide use is due to the great need for circular cylinders and other surfaces of revolution.

Toolroom Types. The principal machine of this type is the *engine* or *toolroom* lathe shown schematically in Fig. 21–1. The figure does not show the controls on the headstock, gearbox, carriage, and tailstock for gear changing, manual feeding, and engaging power feeds. The names engine lathe and toolroom lathe are used somewhat interchangeably although, if a given manufacturer makes two lathes of similar size, the simplest of the two may be called an engine lathe and the one with more controls or greater versatility, a toolroom lathe.

Fig. 21–2 is a schematic diagram of the power supply to the cutting and feed motions on an engine lathe. The motor must either have variable speed, or drive the spindle through some speed changing mechanism using belts or gears. The workpiece is either held on the spindle alone, or additional support may be provided by the tailstock. The spindle is tubular to accommodate long bar stock through its center when this is desired. The gearbox takes power from the spindle, and after the appropriate speed conversion, transmits it to the carriage assembly through the feedrod or leadscrew. As indicated in the figure, crossfeed motion may be obtained only from the feedrod which is normally a rod over which a keyed gear in the carriage slides when the carriage moves along the bed.

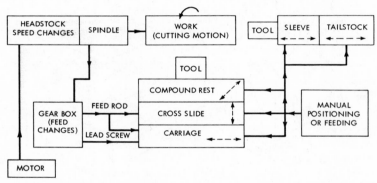

FIG. 21–2. Schematic diagram of power supply to lathe machining motions.

Two methods will provide power feeds for the longitudinal motion of the carriage along the bed. Power from the feedrod may be used to drive the carriage by means of a rack recessed in the front of the bed contacted by a pinion gear projecting from the carriage. This is the feed motion normally used for generating cylinders. For the more precise longitudinal feed required for chasing screw threads, the leadscrew (an accurately threaded rod) is engaged by a split nut on the carriage. The leadscrew then pulls the carriage along at a rate determined by the spindle speed, the setting of the gearbox, and the lead of the leadscrew. Since the power for feeding is obtained from the spindle, any variations in the spindle speed cause a corresponding variation in the feed rate, but the feed remains constant.

The compound rest is mounted on a vertical pivot on the cross slide and its position may be adjusted to provide straight line feed motion in any horizontal direction for generating conical surfaces. Because of the somewhat limited use of the motion of the compound rest, and the difficulty of providing it with power feed, most engine lathes are built with only manual feed for the compound. A single point cutting tool is normally held in a *tool post* which is clamped in a tee slot on the compound.

The *tailstock* may be roughly positioned and clamped at any point along the bed. A manually fed spindle in the tailstock provides fine motion for final adjustment when the tailstock is used to support one end of the work or to feed drilling type tools when the lathe is used for this operation. There is also a fine adjustment in the direction of the cross slide motion to permit aligning of the tailstock center with the headstock spindle center, or to permit intentional misaligning for taper turning.

Engine lathes are among the most versatile of all machine tools. The majority of work done on them consists of cylindrical turning or boring, and flat facing operations to produce flat ends and shoulders on cylindrical parts. Threads of almost any type can be machined to almost any required degree of accuracy. An experienced machinist can quickly grind a single point tool to produce grooves of the required shape.

Because of the wide variety of highly versatile work holding devices available, and the short setup time required for their use, the engine lathe can often be used on small quantities for operations that on large quantities of parts would be done by some other method. Flat surfaces may be machined by facing on square, rectangular, or irregular shaped parts as well as on cylinders. Such a surface produced on a lathe is normally as accurate as can be obtained by shaping, planing, or milling, although the circular cutting pattern is usually evident. A part having a flat surface to be machined with a hole to be drilled and reamed perpendicular to the surface could be done in a single setup on an engine lathe but might require separate setups on a milling machine or drill press.

Two dimensions are required to describe the size of an engine lathe. The first is the diameter, in inches, of the largest diameter of workpiece that may be turned without interference with the bed of the machine. The second is the length of workpiece that may be mounted between the headstock and tailstock. A workpiece with both maximum *swing* and length may not be used since its diameter would interfere with the cross slide.

A number of special purpose variations of the engine lathe, generally simplified, have been developed. A *bench* lathe may have all the features of a floor mounted engine lathe but is of smaller size. A *jewlers* lathe is a small, simplified bench lathe, frequently with no power feeds at all. A *polishing* lathe is primarily a headstock and spindle that may be used for holding and rotating work while manual deburring and polishing operations are performed. Polishing lathes may also be equipped with simplified carriages and tailstocks. When only occasional work of large diameter and short length is to be machined, a *gap* lathe may be used. It is an engine lathe with a two piece bed, the top half of which may be moved away from the headstock, or opened by removal of a section, to provide space for large diameter work.

A *vertical boring mill*, as illustrated in Fig. 21–3, is quite similar to an engine lathe in function, but different in appearance and name. The need for such a machine arises when turning, boring, facing, and drilling operations are to be done on work of large diameter and relatively short length. An engine lathe built to handle such work faces two problems. The centerline of the spindle would of necessity be at an awkward height above the floor level and, since the workpieces of large size are generally also of large weight, supporting the work would be a problem. In principle, a vertical boring mill is an engine lathe turned 90 degrees in a vertical plane, with the headstock set below floor level. The end of the spindle is equipped with a circular table on which the workpiece may be mounted and the weight of the workpiece assists its own holding.

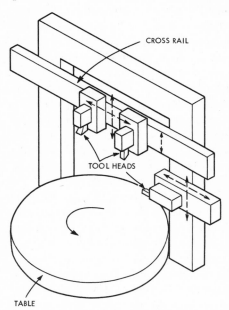

CROSS RAIL

TOOL HEADS

TABLE

FIG. 21–3.   Vertical boring mill.

The tool feed motions possible and the operations that can be performed on a vertical boring mill are similar to those for an engine lathe. Cylindrical turning or boring makes use of a vertical motion of the cross rail on the housing, or of the tool head in its own compound slide. Feed of the tool heads along the cross rail is equivalent to the cross feed on an engine lathe for producing flat surfaces.

Vertical boring mills are built with table diameters ranging from about two to thirty feet or more. Larger sizes are usually equipped with more than one tool head on the cross rail and may have additional tool heads, for turning only, mounted directly on the housing.

Production Turning and Boring Machines.   A standard engine lathe is capable of almost any operation that can be performed on any other turning and boring machine of equivalent size. In nearly all cases, however, the constant attention of an operator is required and the machine can normally be set up for performing only one operation at a time. If a part has a groove to be cut, a diameter to be turned, and a hole to be drilled and reamed from the tailstock, the operator would have to insert one tool in the tool post for the groove, make trial cuts to determine the setting of the tool, cut the groove, then change tools for the turning operation. A similar procedure would be required for the drill and reamer in the tailstock. For a single workpiece this procedure would be acceptable. If duplicate parts are to be machined on an engine lathe, the operator would either have to change tools for each operation, or do each individual operation on each workpiece before changing tools. Changing workpieces or tools would be time consuming, and for each operation the same need for trial cuts to determine the exact relationship between the tool and the work would occur.

Various approaches have been made to reduce the time required to machine duplicate parts. In most cases the cutting tools, cutting speeds, and actual cutting times are not greatly different than those for an engine lathe and the time saving is in handling, measuring, and adjusting. While sharp dividing lines do not always exist between tool room and production types of machines, production turning and boring machines are of three general types. First, direct modifications of engine lathes have automatic controls for tool positioning, feed stopping points, and spindle speeds, but are limited to a single tool setup as is the standard engine lathe. Second are *turret lathes* and single spindle *automatic screw machines*, which are equipped with indexing tool carriers in which a number of tools may be mounted and brought into cutting position when desired, then left set up but swung out of the way for the rest of the operation. The third type, which is the most suitable for high production quantities, are *multiple spindle* bar or chucking machines that do a number of operations simultaneously on different workpieces, then index the workpieces and repeat the cycle.

Machines of the first type are generally similar in appearance to a standard engine lathe. A *production engine lathe* may be heavier, more rigid, and more highly powered than an equivalent size tool room lathe, frequently has no compound rest for generating conical surfaces, may not have a leadscrew for thread chasing, and usually has adjustable mechanical stops for the carriage travel. The term *automatic lathe* is frequently used for similar machines that have a mechanical, electrical, or hydraulic control system that governs tool motion, speeds, and feeds during the machining of each part. Such machines require an operator only for setup, checking, and changing workpieces. Either of these machine types is frequently equipped with a tool post at both the front and rear of the cross slide, permitting multiple operations without tool changing. Automatic lathes are often set up with a number of single point tools carried in a single tool holder, properly positioned to machine a number of different surfaces during a single motion of the tool slide.

Fig. 21–4 shows an engine lathe equipped with a template tracer. As the carriage moves toward the headstock at a uniform feed rate the tracer finger rides along a flat template. When the finger reaches a shoulder or other shape change in the template, it actuates a hydraulic servo and the tool slide moves to a new position. Such machines may be used for cylindrical work with square shoulders, as indicated, or for tapers and contours.

The turret lathe shown in Fig. 21–5 is the most common example of a

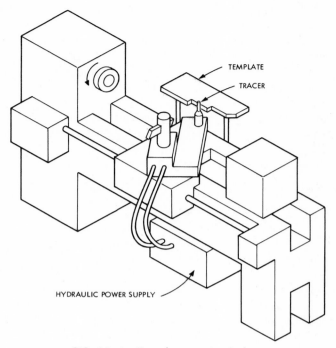

FIG. 21–4. Template tracing lathe.

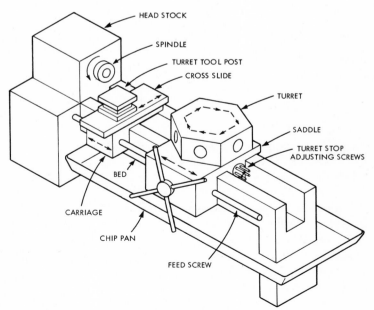

FIG. 21–5. Turret lathe (saddle type).

tool indexing machine. Both the saddle and carriage may feed parallel to the axis of rotation. A standard single point turning tool may be mounted in each of the four positions of the cross slide square turret and indexed into cutting position when needed. Six or more tools may be attached to the hexagon turret. These may be either drilling type tools or, since a need for more than four single point turning tools is frequent, tools in specialized holders that have been developed for turning or boring from what would be the tailstock position of an engine lathe.

Each of the turret positions has an adjustable stop that limits the feed travel of each tool to a preset position.

Fig. 21–6 shows the tool setup that might be used for a typical part.

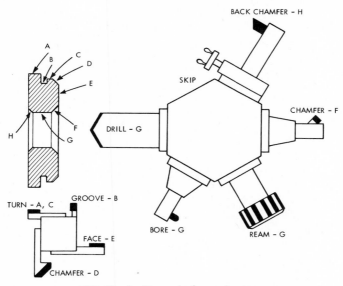

FIG. 21–6.   Turret lathe tool setup.

There would be no advantage to using a turret lathe for the production of a single such part. The tools would be similar to those used on an engine lathe and each tool would have to be individually positioned as it would on an engine lathe. In most cases, the setup for the first part on a turret is even longer than that required for a single part on an engine lathe. The advantage comes with the second and succeeding parts. In practice, turret lathes are used for the production of from as few as five to as many as several thousand duplicate parts.

Once the setup has been made on a turret lathe, a relatively unskilled operator can operate the machine since the dimensions are controlled by the tool positions and stops that are fixed in the setup. The operator's actions are a relatively simple series of motions that are repeated on each part. On most *single spindle automatic screw machines*, the repeated motions are controlled by a series of rotating cams that govern the feed of the cross slide, the feeding and indexing of the turret, the starting, stopping, and speed changing of the spindle, and the feeding of bar stock through the spindle. An operator is required only for inspection, tool changing when the tools become dull, and replenishing the bar stock.

On either a turret lathe or on a single spindle automatic screw machine, the total cutting time is usually the sum of the cutting times of all the individual tools, although it may sometimes be reduced by overlapping cutting times between cross slide tools and main turret tools. On a *multiple spindle automatic screw machine*, shown in Fig. 21–7, each of the tools is

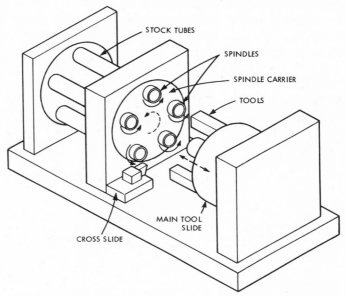

FIG. 21–7. Multiple spindle automatic screw machine.

operating at the same time on a different workpiece and the cycle time is simply that required for the longest operation. The tools retract and the spindle carrier indexes at the end of each cycle, bringing each spindle in line with the next tool slide. One finished part is produced each cycle of operation. Tools may be mounted on the main slide which has a motion parallel to the axis of revolution, or on individual cross slides at each spindle position. The spindle speed may be different at each position, or the spindle may be stopped in one or more positions for drilling or milling operations. The tool motions are controlled by cams as on a single spindle machine. For both machines, these cams are usually custom designed and manufactured for each new workpiece, causing the setup time to be long. Thus, the machines are not economical for any but large lot sizes.

Similar machines are sometimes known as multiple bar machines, or as multiple spindle chucking machines if designed to work on individual hopper-fed workpieces rather than from bar stock. A multiple station, vertical chucking machine operates on similar principles but is designed for larger workpieces. One of the stations is ordinarily used for manual loading and unloading.

Special Turning and Boring Machines.　Engine and tool room lathes, turret lathes, and single and multiple spindle automatic bar or chucking machines are made as standard machines in a wide variety of sizes and prices by a number of different manufacturers. While the features on one machine may differ from those on another, all these machines are designed and built for high versatility and, with the proper tools, may be used for a wide variety of workpieces. Although standard machines can be used for practically any turning operation, in many cases a special machine may be built with features that give greater efficiency for some limited range of operations or on some limited type of product.

Special machines may be either job shop types designed to do a variety of operations on some special class of workpieces in low quantities, or very high production types, often designed to do a particular operation, on one product in large quantities. Gun turning, steel mill roll turning, and car-wheel lathes are examples of the job shop types that are basically engine lathes that have been modified for particular sizes or shapes. A gun

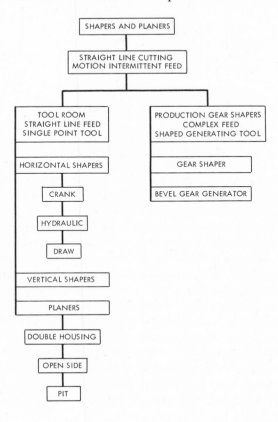

turning lathe, for example, usually has two or three carriages that can operate smultaneously, each controlled by a template tracer.

With the exception of a few production gear cutting machines, shapers and planers are strictly tool room types of machines with wide versatility for producing mainly flat surfaces, usually with low setup times. In nearly all cases, a more efficient method exists if large quantities of parts are to be produced.

All the machines of the tool room type make use of straight line cutting motion, intermittent straight line feed occurring between cutting strokes, and single point tools. This combination is most often used to produce flat surfaces but may be used for small formed grooves with appropriate tools. The wide use of these machines for tool room work is due largely to the

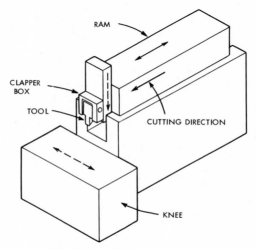

FIG. 21–8.   Horizontal shaper.

simplicity of the tooling. Cutting tool design requires that the tool be drawn back across the finished surface at the completion of each cutting stroke. To prevent rubbing of the tool flank on the tool surface, which would be detrimental to both the tool and the finished surface, the tool is mounted in a *clapper box*. This arrangement permits the tool to rub only lightly on the return stroke or to raise over a chip when necessary. On some large machines the tool may be mechanically lifted from the surface each return stroke.

The most common type of shaper and the one to which the term shaper *normally* refers is the type shown in Fig. 21–8 with the ram moving in a horizontal plane. One of the reasons for the inefficiency of any shaper is the loss of cutting time during the return stroke. Two different driving mechanisms have been developed which permit a higher speed during the noncutting return stroke so that the cutting portion of the cycle requires more than half of the total time. Crank shapers are driven by a *Whitworth* mechanism that gives a return to cutting speed ratio of about 1.4. This drive also provides very rapid acceleration and deceleration at the ends of the stroke with nearly constant speed during most of the cutting stroke instead of a sinusoidal motion as is common with most crank mechanisms. A hydraulic drive provides even greater efficiency, more uniform cutting speed, and more rapid adjustment, but it is more expensive initially and requires greater maintenance.

Horizontal shapers are used almost exclusively for flat surface production on tool room work. The knee is equipped with Tee slots to permit clamping the workpiece. In many cases, setup time is held to a minimum by keeping a large vise semipermanently attached to the knee.

The draw cut shaper shown in Fig. 21–9 offers some advantage in rigidity over the more common push cut type. On a draw cut shaper, the ram is in tension rather than compression during the cutting stroke. The ram is supported by an overhanging arm. In addition the knee is pulled tightly against, rather than away from, the column of the machine during the cutting stroke. Combination of these features permits heavier cuts than possible with the conventional machine.

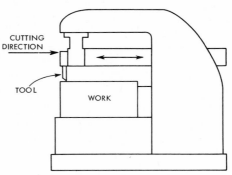

FIG. 21–9.   Draw cut shaper.

Shaper size is described by the stroke length through which the tool can be moved. The maximum practical size, because of the difficulty in obtaining the necessary rigidity for support of the tool at the end of the stroke, is about five feet. The vast majority of shapers used in industry— mainly in job shop operations—are not over three feet in length of stroke.

The vertical shaper is similar in principle to the horizontal type but differs considerably in appearance. The work support consists of a table that can be rotated as well as fed in two perpendicular directions in the horizontal plane. The tool carried on the end of a vertically moving ram approaches the table as it cuts and must be designed so that the face over which the chip slides is on the end of the tool, interchanged in position with what would normally seem to be the flank behind the cutting edge. The ram of the machine can be set at small angles with the perpendicular to the table so that draft angle on dies, patterns, and like work can be produced almost automatically by positioning the workpiece properly on the machine table. Since the workpiece can be fed and repositioned by table movement, the accuracy of relationship between various surfaces can be the accuracy of the machine; thus, dependence on the ability of an operator to reposition a workpiece is reduced. The principal work of the vertical shaper is on internal surfaces, the making of keyways, the production of the sides of cavities in patterns, dies, and other work requiring good relationship between surfaces that can be indexed into cutting position under the tool.

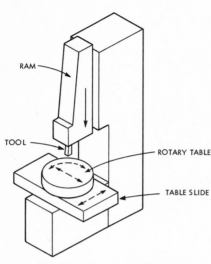

RAM

TOOL

ROTARY TABLE

TABLE SLIDE

FIG. 21–10. Vertical shaper.

The tools used with shapers are mostly of the simple, single point type, similar in shape to those used for turning work on a lathe. The side relief angle can usually be smaller than that on lathe tools, because the tool moves in a straight line while cutting. The shape of the cutting edge, as with most tools, will be dependent upon the material of the work, the accessibility of the surface to be machined, the quality of surface desired, and other usual factors given consideration in tool design.

Shapers are primarily tool room or job shop machines. Simplicity and ease of setup compensate for rather poor operating efficiency for short runs. Accuracies closer than one to two thousandths of an inch are seldom attempted with the shaper; and since the human element in both setup and operation is rather large, skilled personnel are required to perform accurate work.

Planing. Except for being of larger size, the work performed on a planer is similar to that done on a shaper. Cutting motion is produced by the work fastened to the table, or platen, moving back and forth in straight line. Feed of the tool into new material is accomplished by moving the tool in a path perpendicular to the cutting motion. As with the shaper, the machine is usually set up so that cutting occurs only when the table is moving in one direction and the tool can be fed during the return stroke portion of the cycle.

Although some old planers still in use are powered through a belt system, most of the machines are driven by directly connected reversing motors. The motor drives a shaft carrying a gear in contact with a rack fastened to the underside of the platen. This system minimizes the distance required for reversal at the ends of the table travel and is simple enough that it creates few maintenance problems. Some small planers are powered with hydraulic systems, but the cost is prohibitive for most large applications. With the usual single direction cutting, productive work is accomplished for only part of the time the machine is in operation, so the return stroke is speeded to reduce the lost time.

Planers are of two main kinds or styles. The double housing planer, shown in Fig. 21–11, has a vertical column on each side of the table to support the cross arm and tool supporting head. This type of construction provides rigid support for the tool but limits the size of workpiece that can pass through the machine. Open side planers, as in Fig. 21–12, are more popular because of their improved versatility. A single vertical column on one side of the machine supports the cross arm as a cantilever beam, thus leaving one side of the machine open. With this open side, larger workpieces can be permitted to over-hang the table, thereby increasing the machine's versatility for size and shape work.

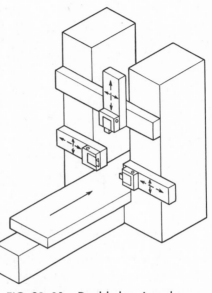

Pit planers and edge planers are specialized types of machines that carry the name planer mainly because of their large size. Their cutting ac-tion resembles that of a shaper in that the work remains stationary on a shelf or platform and the tool is car-ried back and forth by a carriage rid-ing on rails. Their use is limited mainly to the machining of flat sur-faces on large sheets of material.

FIG. 21–11. Double housing planer.

Most of the tools used for planing operations are of the simple, single point variety and are much like lathe tools. They must be mounted on a clapper box to permit lifting over ob-structions on the return stroke. Since they are often heavy enough that being lifted by dragging over solid obstructions would damage the cutting edge, they frequently are power lifted by mechanical, electrical, or hy-draulic means during the return stroke of the machine.

The principal value of the planer is that it can easily be made in large sizes and can be used for machining large and heavy workpieces. Although its principal work is that of making flat surfaces on large pieces, it may be used occasionally to machine a number of small workpieces set in line on the table. This kind of setup is referred to as string planing. Machines that are over one hundred feet in length have been constructed, but the more common sizes are from six to twelve feet in width and from twenty to forty feet in length.

Accuracies that may be expected in planing are in the range of from one to five thousandths of an inch, but they are dependent to a large extent upon the application and the ability of the operator to set the piece up properly, in addition to the design and condition of the machine. The human element is large in the setup of the work; in many cases, the setup time required to position a workpiece properly and provide it with suitable support is longer than the actual machining time.

Gear Shapers.   Most of the gears made in production quantities that are not machined by hobbing are cut on the gear shaper. This is a special machine designed for this purpose and has the straight line cutting action

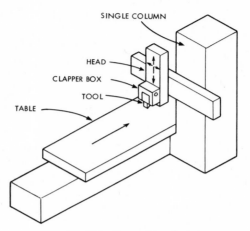

SINGLE COLUMN

HEAD

CLAPPER BOX

TOOL

TABLE

FIG. 21–12.   Openside planer.

of all shapers, with the tool moving back and forth in straight line. Feed is a rotational movement of the work, with the gear shaped cutter rotating at the same rate to produce a generated mating surface.

Power is supplied by the machine to the cutter spindle and the work spindle which are related to each other through a train of gears. Change gears in the train allow the relationship to be varied for cutting different sized gears. The combination of cutting and feed motions on the gear shaper is rather complex. The cutter spindle reciprocates to produce cutting motion at the same time it is slowly revolving to present new portions of its cutting edges to the work. The work spindle rotates with feed motion and backs away to cause clearance between the work and cutter during the return stroke, then resumes its original spacing for the cutting stroke. The machine is semiautomatic in operation and is started with the spindles retracted from each other. In addition to the regular operating motions, the work spindle feeds toward the cutter spindle slowly to a predetermined center spacing and holds this position until a complete revolution of the work spindle has caused the gear to be machined all the way around. After completion of the gear, the machine shuts off for unloading and the start of another cycle. Some gear shapers are designed for a double cycle of cutting and can be set to remove most of the excess stock during the first revolution of the work and then advance the work spindle a short distance for another revolution of finishing cut.

Although certain other shapes can be made with special cutters, almost the entire work of a gear shaper is the manufacture of gears. The tool is of gear shape, ground on one side to produce sharp edges to cut chips as it is moved with an axial straight line shaper action. The rotational feed as the cutter reciprocates causes a blending of the successive cuts by different portions of the cutting edges, to produce a generated surface. Since this is a mating surface operation, the same cutter can be used for all gear sizes of the same pitch.

The accuracy of gears produced by gear shaping is good, particularly when the machine is set up for the combination of rough and finish cycles. Normal cutting speeds provide high productivity. Once the machine is set

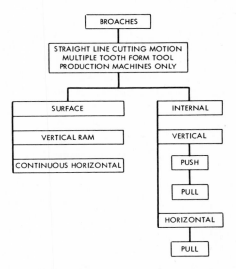

up, it is almost entirely automatic in its operation and requires only little attention from the operator.

One principal advantage gear shaping has over other gear manufacturing methods is that it can be used to cut internal and cluster gears. The cutter mounted on the end of the spindle can be inserted through an opening just as easily as it can be used on the outside of the work. The straight line cutting stroke allows completion of work close to an obstruction, such as a shoulder. A small relief groove, usually not more than about $\frac{1}{8}$ inch in width, is necessary so the chip can be completed and detached from the parent stock. Cluster gears, consisting of a number of gears of different diameter attached together, can be made in one piece by this method.

Most straight bevel gear teeth are cut on a specialized gear shaper similar in principle to that used for spur gears. The usual machine uses two tools mounted on a cradle. As the gear revolves, the cradle reciprocates for cutting motion and feeds with a motion simulating a crown type of bevel gear. At the completion of each tooth, the tools are withdrawn and the cradle and work spindle indexed to new starting positions for the next tooth.

As indicated in Chapter 20, broaching cutters are designed and built for machining a particular surface shape on a given workpiece. For such a cutter to be economically feasible, it is necessary that it be used as a production tool on a number of workpieces.

Compared to most other machine tools, broaches are relatively simple machines. Most are powered with hydraulic systems which are easy to control and can provide smooth, uniform power for straight line operation. It is common to run broaches at somewhat lower cutting speeds than are used with other machine tools. There is often little to be gained from high speeds, since the cutting time is a small percentage of the total cycle time even with low speed because of the single pass required. In addition, the low cutting speed results in very long life for the expensive form cutter.

Most surface broaching is done on a vertical machine such as shown in Fig. 21–13. The cutter is mounted directly on the face of the slide and the workpiece in a fixture on the platen. Surface broaches are used most for cutting single flat surfaces, grooves in which three surfaces are cut and other applications in which the forces on the workpiece are not balanced in a plane perpendicular to the axis of the cutter, as they are in internal broaching. As a result, there are usually large separating forces between the broach cutter and the workpiece, which must be resisted by rigid cutter mounting and workpiece fixtures.

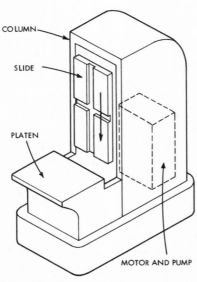

FIG. 21–13. Vertical ram type broach.

In order to permit increased operator efficiency, surface broaching machines are often equipped with two slides. With two identical fixtures the operator can change workpieces in one fixture while the machine is cutting the workpiece in the other. A single hydraulic system can supply both slides. A similar effect may be achieved on a single ram machine by providing the machine with a receding table, so that the fixture can be unloaded and reloaded while the ram is returning to broaching position.

On a *continuous* broaching machine, the broach is mounted in a fixed position, the necessary distance away from a flat roller table. In operation, the workpieces are pulled along the table and past the broach cutter by a chain or other means.

Internal broaching, in which the workpiece completely surrounds the cutter, presents a different problem. Whether the broach is pushed or pulled through the work, it is necessary at the end of the cutting stroke to disengage the broach from the driving means in order for the workpiece to be removed. During the workpiece removal, the cutter must be supported at the opposite end. This second support must be released for starting a new workpiece after the broach is returned to the starting position. Because of the relatively high length to diameter ratio with which most internal broaches must be designed, pull broaching is much more common than push broaching.

In a *vertical pull-up* broaching machine the operation is as follows. The workpiece is dropped over the pulling shank of the broach which is supported at its lower end in a separately driven elevator mechanism. As the elevator raises the broach, the pulling end of the cutter passes through a hole in a fixed table and is automatically engaged by a pulling slide mounted above the table. The elevator mechanism releases the broach and the pulling slide raises, pulling the cutter through the workpiece which is retained by the fixed table. At the completion of the cut, the workpiece falls from the cutter onto a deflector table and then away from the machine. The pulling slide then returns the broach to the lower elevator mechanism for the next cycle of operation. Machines of this type may operate as many as eight separate cutters at the same time.

Pull-down broaching machines are similar with the pulling and handling slides reversed. Large parts may be handled with greater ease than on a pull-up machine, but the workpiece does not automatically fall from the machine at the end of the working stroke.

Horizontal broaching machines are very common for broaching of round holes, keyways, and splines, especially for lower production and when the cutter is very long, which would require excessive headroom if a vertical machine were used. The operation is similar to that on vertical machines but the broach is often handled manually except for the actual cutting stroke.

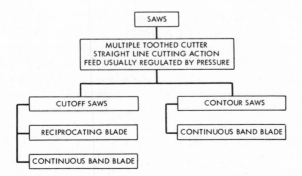

Saws are among the most common of machine tools, even though the surfaces they produce often require further finishing operations. Saws have two general areas of application. Contour saws are used for producing generated forms or outlines with accuracy requirements which need little or no finishing. Even more numerous are those applications which initiate machining processes by cutting short lengths of stock from long bars or rods with a *cutoff* saw.

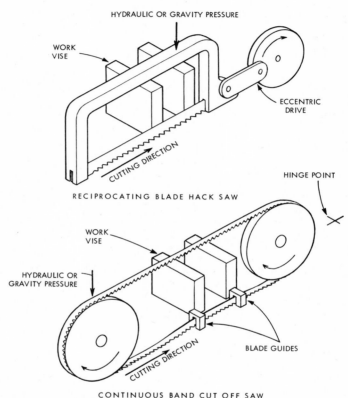

FIG. 21–14. Cutoff saws.

Cutoff Saws. As indicated in Fig. 21–14, cutoff saws may use either a continuous band that travels constantly in one direction over wheels, or a relatively short straight blade that reciprocates. Hack saws are slower than band saws because of the time lost during the return stroke, but they can use a stiffer blade since it does not have to bend around wheels.

Hack saws are driven by a crank mechanism and the principal differences between different machines are in size and the way the blade is held and fed. In light duty saws, the blade is held in a "U" shaped frame that is pivoted at one end with feed through an arc. Heavier duty saws have a four sided frame in which the blade may be held more tightly with greater rigidity. The frame is held in vertical guides which control the feed direction.

Hack saws are usually provided with a hydraulic feed regulating mechanism that controls the pressure on the blade rather than the rate of advance into the work. The pressure must be relieved on the return stroke to prevent damage to the teeth. On some saws the blade is actually lifted free of the work on the return stroke.

Although band saws are faster than hack saws the time savings may be offset by the additional cost of blades. In many cases, time for sawing is of minor importance since the saw is set up in an area where it may be operated by a stockroom attendant who has other duties to perform. For cutting off large numbers of pieces, the stock may be bundled together and the saw permitted to operate with only occasional attention.

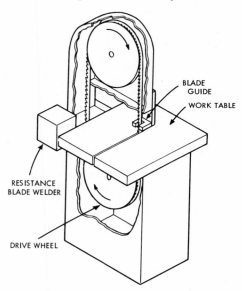

FIG. 21–15. Band contour saw.

Contour Saws. While contour or table band saws may be used for straight cutoff work, their greatest value is in their use for cutting non-circular cylindrical shapes that would be difficult to produce by other machining operations from flat plate. Fig. 21–15 illustrates the general construction which is similar to that of a wood cutting band saw. The cutting speeds must be much lower for metal cutting, however, and some speed control is necessary for the wide variety of materials that may be cut. The utility is further increased by the resistance butt welder, usually built as part of the machine, which permits cutting and rewelding of the continuous blade for sawing internal shapes with the aid of a drilled starting hole.

Contour saws are basically tool room machines. If larger quantities of the shapes they produce are required, they can often be produced more economically by pressworking, forging, or casting, although thin sheet metal is sometimes ganged for multiple production by sawing. For a single part, however, sawing has little or no tooling or setup cost. The finish and accuracy that are obtained are limited by the flexibility of the blade and the manual control of the workpiece. Continuous band files and abrasive bands are available for use on the same machine for finishing operations.

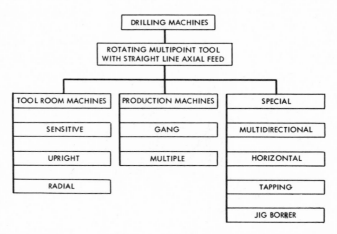

Drilling machines are the most common of all machine tools because they can be used to produce round holes which are among the most important of surface shapes. The greatest need for round holes is for assembly purposes with bolts, screws, rivets, and other mechanical fasteners. Such fasteners are used with products made by nearly all manufacturing processes, including casting, forging, sheet metal stamping, rolling, and even welding. It is usually more economical to drill small holes than to make them by some other method, even though no other machining is required. Because of the wide use, drilling machines, especially the commoner tool room types, are made in a great variety of sizes and price ranges.

Drilling machines have a simpler function to perform than most other machine tools. They must provide rotational power to the tool and straight line feed motion along the axis of the tool. Most drilling tools are by nature only semirigid in the radial direction and must be guided into the work by a starting depression or a bushing around the drill. As a result, the drilling machine spindle is not subjected to heavy radial loads and is therefore not designed with great rigidity, except in the axial feeding direction. Because of this construction, drilling machines are not meant to be used for milling or boring operations unless some special device is used to provide additional rigidity for the tool. Since the position of the tool relative to the work must be established by some auxiliary means, little need exists for accurately calibrated table movements. Most drilling machines are made with flat tables having no operating movements, and the correct position of the work is obtained by sliding the work or work holding device on the table, or in some cases by moving the spindle of the machine to the correct position.

Tool Room Machines.   The common characteristic of tool room drilling machines is a single spindle. Holes that are drilled are often reamed, tapped, counterbored, or countersunk, and with a tool room machine it is

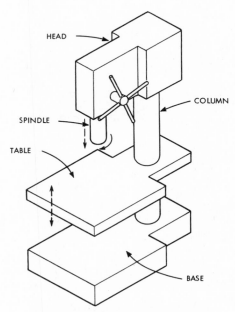

FIG. 21–16. Sensitive drill press.

necessary to change from one tool to another for each different operation. The principal differences in the machines are those permitting work with various sizes of workpieces and drilling tools.

For small hole operations on light workpieces, a *sensitive* drill press as shown in Fig. 21–16 is most often used. The distinguishing feature of the machine is the manual feed mechanism. The workpiece is positioned on the flat table and either clamped or held manually, depending on the size of the work and of the tool. Because of the excessive feeding force that would be required for larger drills, sensitive drill presses are intended for drilling holes up to about ¾ inch in diameter only. The machines are built in a wide range of sizes from light duty bench mounted models to heavier duty floor models. Spindle speed changes are obtained by shifting belts to different pulley diameters on most models, but on some of the more expensive designs changing speeds is accomplished with gear shifting. The manual feed arrangement not only results in cheaper construction for the machine, but also in improved control for most small drilling operations. A skilled tool room operator may not know exactly what feed to set on a machine, but when manually feeding he can feel the action of the drill and regulate the feed accordingly. In addition, he can sense when the flutes of

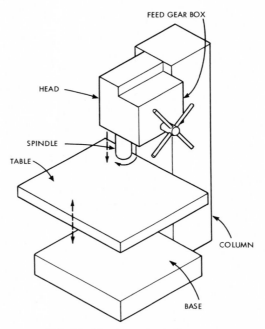

FIG. 21–17. Upright drill press.

the drill are becoming clogged with chips and retract the drill periodically more quickly than he could with power operated feed.

An upright drill press, as shown in Fig. 21–17, may be fed by hand but is also equipped with power feeds. Because it is intended for drilling operations up to about two inches in diameter, it is of heavier construction than a sensitive drill press. The table is often mounted on a dovetail slide constructed on the side of a heavy box-shaped column instead of on a round column. Because of the heavier torques transmitted, the spindle is more commonly driven through gears instead of by belts.

Theoretically, a sensitive or upright drill press could be built in any size desired, but a practical limit exists so far as the workpiece is concerned. On either of these simpler types of machines, the workpiece is positioned for drilling by sliding on the flat table. Such a procedure becomes difficult for very heavy workpieces, for which it is more practical to use a machine such as the *radial* drill press shown in Fig. 21–18. On this machine, the workpiece is positioned only roughly on the table and the spindle is moved to the correct position for the drilling operation. For additional holes, the spindle may be moved to the new positions. Since large workpieces may contain both large and small holes, radial drill presses are equipped with

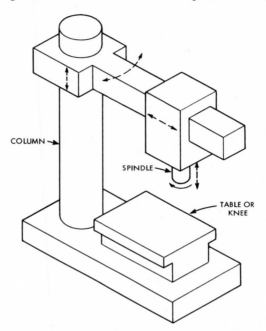

COLUMN →

SPINDLE →

TABLE OR
KNEE

FIG. 21–18. Radial drill press.

both manual and power feeds and with a wider range of spindle speeds than other drilling machines.

Production Drilling Machines. For many tool room and job shop drilling operations more time is spent in locating the operations and setting up the machines than in actual drilling. One aim in production work is to reduce setup time that must be paid for by the product. Production machine requirements vary widely depending on the number of holes to be produced in each workpiece, the number of different sized tools to be used, the size of the workpiece, and the number of parts to be produced. Even for large quantities of workpieces, if only a single drilling operation is required on each, a single spindle sensitive, upright, or radial drilling machine could be satisfactory. The workpiece would, however, likely be held in a special device called a *jig*, which properly locates the operation and guides the tool.

Fig. 21–19 illustrates a *gang* drill press which is most useful when a sequence of operations requiring different drill tools is to be done. The sequence can include various operations including drilling, reaming, tapping (with the proper attachment for reversing the tap), countersinking, counterboring, or spotfacing. The drilling heads on a gang drill press are identical to those which might be found on a single spindle machine, each with its own drive motor, spindle speed control, and feeding mechanism, which may be either manual or power operated. Time savings in the use

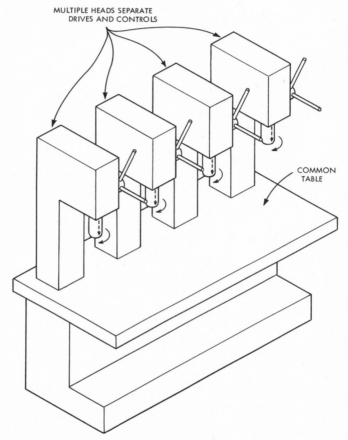

MULTIPLE HEADS SEPARATE
DRIVES AND CONTROLS

COMMON
TABLE

FIG. 21–19. Gang drill press.

of a gang drill come only with multiple production, since the setup time for each spindle is as long as that on a single spindle machine.

Fig. 21–20 shows a *multiple spindle* drill press. On this machine a single driving motor is connected to a number of individual spindles. The positions of the spindles may be varied within limits and remain connected to the driving power through universal joints or a train of idler gears. With a number of drills set in the correct pattern, the holes may all be drilled in the time that would otherwise be required to drill only one. It is still frequently necessary to hold the workpiece in a jig with bushings to insure that the drills start in the right location without walking on the surface and to provide support for longer longer tool life. The setup time for a multiple spindle machine is always longer than for a gang drill because of the relationships that must be established between the tools. The types and size variations of tools that can be used together are also limited because of the common power source and feed rate.

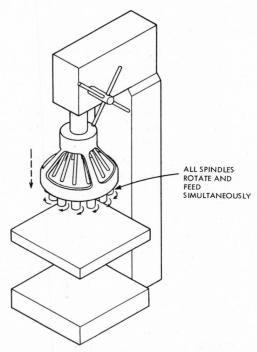

ALL SPINDLES
ROTATE AND
FEED
SIMULTANEOUSLY

FIG. 21–20.   Multiple spindle drill press.

Special Drilling Machines.   Drilling is the most common machining operation used in high quantity production, especially since it is the only machining operation performed on many parts that have their basic shapes established by casting, forging, or press working. Consequently, a high degree of specialization has been developed for some types of work. Multiple spindle machines are often designed for a specific workpiece, with the workholding device incorporated as part of the machine. Such machines often operate completely automatically, including loading and unloading. Under these conditions, a probing device or other means is desirable for detecting drill breakage.

Even more specialized are multiple axis machines for drilling simultaneously on more than one face of a workpiece. The individual slides on such a machine may carry either single or multiple drill heads, with the number of tools operating simultaneously, some times totaling as much as one hundred.

Several other drilling machines are not special in regards to specific workpieces but in the types of work they do; they are much less common than the standard tool room and production types of machines. Horizontal machines offer advantages when long holes are to be drilled through workpieces such as gun barrels or lathe spindles. The head and controls on a vertical machine with the capacity for such work would be at an awkward height, and the machine itself would create headroom problems. In addition, chips flow more freely from the hole in the horizontal position than in the downward vertical position when drilling deep holes. Horizontal drilling machines are usually powered at both the drill spindle and the work holding spindle, and either or both may be rotated during operation.

For tapping to be done in a conventional drill press, either an attachment must be used that reverses the tap at the proper time while the spindle continues to rotate in the forward direction, or the entire spindle must be reversed by reversing the machine motor. In either case, the lead of the thread being cut depends only on the lead of the tap for accuracy. Without positive advance a tap may lag or go ahead of the true thread lead, depending on the feed pressure. A tapping machine is similar to a drilling machine but is usually designed with threaded leader and follower at the top of the spindle to provide the correct axial advance of the tap. Tapping machines are ordinarily equipped with a reversing duty motor drive, which may be reversed quickly and often, without overheating or other damaging effect on the motor. Tapping machines must be fitted with a different leader and follower for each tap that is used, so the setup time limits use of the equipment to reasonable quantities.

The special requirement of locating holes very accurately with respect to other holes or surfaces on a workpiece has led to the development of special machines called *jig borers*. The two most common designs use either a vertical spindle with the workpiece mounted on a table having two orthogonal movements, or a horizontal spindle which can move along a cross rail that moves vertically on side posts. In either case, the distance or relative movement of the workpiece in a plane perpendicular to the axis of the spindle can be very accurately measured. On most machines the feed screws are used to provide motion only, and the measuring is done by an independent system that has constant controlled loads applied to it and uses gage blocks or other precision standards as the measuring elements. In other cases, measuring screws may be used but are so constructed that lost motion or play is not an error-contributing factor.

In any review of machine tools where all types are listed with equal weight, it is easy to overlook the importance of some type. With no explanation, this would be true of milling, since most of the surfaces that can be milled can be produced by other methods. In practice, however, milling is the standard method for producing the majority of flat surfaces and grooves defined as partial cylindrical surfaces. It is only when some special circumstances exist that other methods are used. As examples, simple flat surfaces may be shaped *if* there are very few parts and the part can be simply held in a vise; similar surfaces may be broached *if* there are sufficient parts to justify the tooling cost, *if* the depth of metal to be removed is not too great, and *if* there is straight line clearance for the broaching cutter; many surfaces may be ground *if* high precision is required *or* the material is too hard for milling; and some flat surfaces may

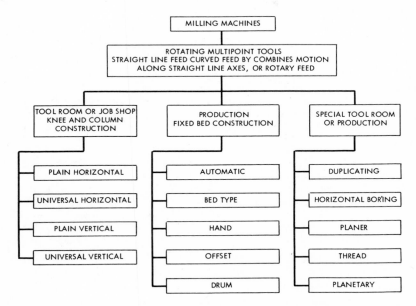

be faced on a lathe *if* they are combined with a surface of revolution so that both surfaces may be produced in a single setup. In the great majority of cases these special circumstances do not occur, and milling is the most common and economical method for making flat, partial cylindrical, and noncircular cylindrical surfaces.

It was pointed out in Chapter 20 that much of the versatility of milling is due to the large number of standard cutter shapes that are available. Because of the large number of cutter shapes and the wide range of conditions in which milling is used, a large number of machines have been developed, some definitely toolroom in nature, some useful only in production, and, as with drilling machines, some that may be used in either way.

Tool Room and Job Shop Milling Machines. Although milling cutters may be used with an axial feed like a drilling tool in a few instances, the workpiece is normally fed in a plane that is perpendicular to the axis of the cutter. For arbor mounted cutters the cutter axis passes over or past the workpiece and with shank mounted cutters the axis of the cutter often intersects the workpiece; but in either case a simple straight line feeding

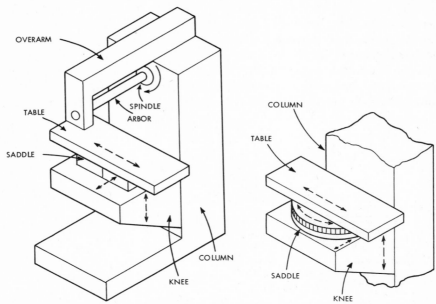

FIG. 21–21. Plain horizontal milling machine.

FIG. 21–22. Table swivel feature of universal horizontal milling machine.

motion is most common. In addition to this feeding motion, at least two other motions are needed in order to obtain the correct relative positions of the cutter and workpiece before the feed starts.

This combination of motions is achieved in tool room type milling machines with a *column* and *knee* construction, as shown for the *plain horizontal* milling machine in Fig. 21–21. This machine is normally used with arbor mounted cutters for which the overarm provides additional support to that of the driving spindle. The elevation of the knee on the column and the motion of the saddle on the knee are most often used for positioning and the feed motion is that of the table on the saddle.

Fig. 21–22 shows one variation that is used on a *universal horizontal knee and column* milling machine. The saddle is split along a horizontal plane and provided with a vertical pivot about which an additional motion can occur. In practice, this motion is used only to adjust the table position for the milling of helical surfaces for which it is necessary that the feed motion of the table be at other than 90 degrees with the axis of the cutter.

With the horizontal machines it is possible to hold practically any milling cutter and produce any surface that can be milled. In many instances, however, the setup can be simplified by using a similar machine with a vertical spindle, such as the *plain vertical knee and column* machine shown in Fig. 21–23. As with the plain horizontal machine, it has three mutually perpendicular motions, one of which is parallel to the axis of the spindle. A second, horizontal motion of the table on the saddle, is the normal feed motion. This machine is provided with a vertical motion of the spindle which duplicates the motion of the column on the knee. In practice, the movement of the knee on the column is used for positioning and the spindle motion is used for feeding cutters when using the milling machine for drilling type operations. Arbor mounted cutters are seldom

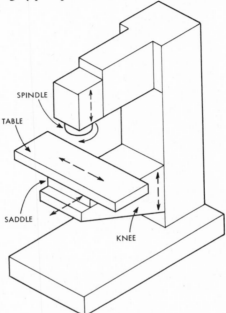

SPINDLE

TABLE

SADDLE

KNEE

FIG. 21–23. Plain vertical milling machine.

used on a vertical machine because it has no overarm support, but the setup and use of end milling cutters and face mills are usually more convenient than they would be on a horizontal machine.

Fig. 21–24 shows an even more versatile form of machine called a *universal vertical* knee and column milling machine. In addition to the motions of a plain vertical machine, the head which carries the spindle is adjustable about two angular axes. The principal value of these extra adjustments is to simplify milling and drilling setups that otherwise would require setting the workpiece at an angle on the table. Although the machine is extremely versatile, it is lightly powered and only used for toolroom and job shop work because of reduced rigidity from so many adjustments.

Production Milling Machines. As with other types of machine tools, standard types of job shop milling machines may occasionally be used for machining large quantities of parts when equipped with special workhold-

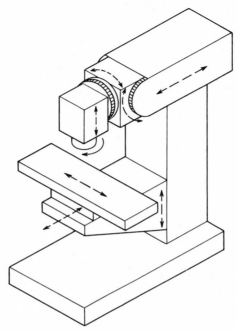

FIG. 21-24.   Universal vertical milling
machine.

ing devices or other attachments that increase the rate of production.
However, such machines have inherently limited capabilities because of
the reduced rigidity resulting from the knee and column construction and

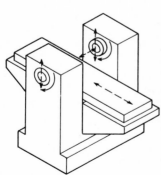

FIG. 21-25.   Duplex fixed
bed milling machine.

the relatively small motors with which they
are normally supplied. True production milling machines differ in two important respects
from tool room or job shop machines. The
higher degree of rigidity built into production
machines increases the size of cut that can be
made without chatter; and the degree to which
they are made automatic by providing some
mechanism for controlling part or all of the
cycle of operation decreases the effect of
human element on the product.

Greater rigidity is achieved by reducing the
number of adjustments possible or at least
changing the manner of making the adjustments to permit more rigid clamping once the
adjustment has been made. Fig. 21-25 shows one example of fixed bed
construction in which the only motion of the table is feed motion normal
to the axis of the cutter. The duplex machine shown in the figure has two

spindles, each of which has a limited adjustment along two other axes. These adjustments are less convenient than on a knee and column machine, but may be locked more rigidly once they are made. Fixed bed construction may be used with single or multiple spindles in either horizontal or vertical planes.

The term "automatic" is used for milling machines in much the same way as for lathes. It refers to some means of cycle control rather than to a specific machine type. Many knee and column machines that would otherwise be strictly tool room types are used as production machines when equipped with some means for reducing the operator's work to loading and unloading the workpieces. Most fixed bed machines are fitted

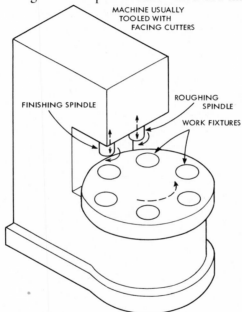

FIG. 21–26. Rotary milling machine.

with some type of automatic control. Mechanical, electric, and hydraulic controls are often actuated by trip dogs operated by the movement of the table. These trip dogs may be preset to control the distances of rapid table advance and feed motion, stopping and starting of the spindle, and even the raising and lowering of the cutter on *rise and fall* machines.

Small bed type machines with either a vertical or horizontal spindle are often built with a manually operated feeding mechanism, usually a quick acting rack and pinion rather than the screw and nut feed found on most other machines. While the use of hand operation for high production appears to be a contradiction, in many cases an operator can go through the cycle faster than an automatic machine. Not only does the operator save the time of operating a lever or switch to initiate the feeding motion, but also he is not limited by preset feeding rates and can compensate for varying depths of cut in a fragile workpiece.

On any milling machine with a straight line table feed, lost time while the table is returned to the starting point after the completion of the cutting cycle is often considerable. The problem may be lessened to some extent by providing two fixtures, one on each end of the table so that the operator may load one while the other is in the cutting position. Nevertheless, lost time is not completely eliminated and trouble may develop since the operation involves down milling in one direction and up milling in the other. A different solution is to provide the machine with a rotary feeding motion as on the *rotary* or *offset* milling machine shown in Fig. 21–26 or the *drum* machine in Fig. 21–27. With proper spacing of the fixtures, the cutting action is almost continuous and the operator can continuously unload and reload the fixtures. The versatility of the machines is obviously limited.

Special Milling Machines.   A number of milling machines may be classified as special either because they are designed to work on only certain types or sizes of workpieces or because they are restricted to producing certain kinds of surfaces. They may be either tool room or production types, although the economic justification for tool room types is valid only for applications that are impossible or extremely difficult by use of conventional equipment.

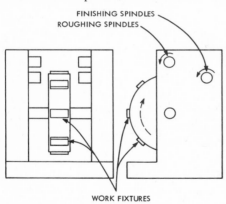

FINISHING SPINDLES
ROUGHING SPINDLES

WORK FIXTURES

FIG. 21–27. Drum type milling machine.

Fig. 21–28 shows a machine most commonly called a *horizontal boring mill* and often classified with turning and boring machines rather than milling machines. The machine has the motions of a plain horizontal or vertical knee and column milling machine and could conceivably be used for various milling operations. In practice it is used specifically for drilling, boring, and reaming operations on large holes, together with some face milling operations, that on smaller workpieces might be done by spotfacing. For boring operations, the workpiece is fastened to the table and the spindle axis aligned by raising or lowering the spindle and moving the table on the saddle. With a boring bar between the spindle and the end support and a single point cutting tool projecting the proper distance from the bar, the workpiece is fed along the bed toward the spindle. The relative motion between the tool and workpiece is identical to that which would be obtained on a lathe with the workpiece fastened to the spindle and the tool fed in a straight line parallel to the axis of rotation of the spindle.

For extremely large workpieces a *planer mill* is often used. The

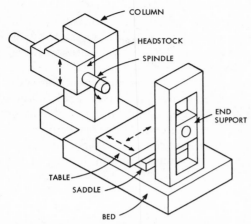

FIG. 21–28. Horizontal boring milling and drilling machine.

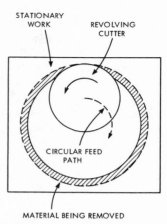

FIG. 21–29. Cutter-work relationship in planetary milling.

machine is named because of its resemblance in appearance to a planer. It is essentially a large bed type milling machine with either vertical or horizontal spindles mounted in positions corresponding to those of the tool holders on a planer.

A *thread mill* is a very specialized machine used for cutting threads which involve the removal of a considerable quantity of metal. The operation is similar to that of chasing a thread with a single point tool on a lathe, except that the rotation of the workpiece becomes part of the feed motion and the single point tool is replaced by a revolving form milling cutter. The thread can be cut to full depth in a single pass and, with a multiple form cutter having a length as great as the thread to be cut, with only a single revolution of the workpiece. The greatest use for thread mills is for cutting acme threads for use as leadscrews and jack screws.

The *planetary mill* having the action illustrated in Fig. 21–29 is also a highly specialized machine. Many grooves in circular workpieces lead to chatter when cut with a form tool in some type of lathe but can be produced more accurately and with better finish by milling, especially when the groove is internal. This type machine can also be used to mill grooves that do not go completely around the circumference of the workpiece.

Duplicating milling machines form one of the most important classes in modern production. When objects are made up only of simple flat surfaces and complete circular cylinders, they are usually made with conventional machines of various types. However the conventional machines are limited in their abilities to produce combination surfaces, partial cylindrical surfaces, especially when they are internal, and surfaces that cannot be described mathematically as planes or cylinders. Fig. 19–19 shows the action required for profile milling in which an end milling cutter is guided by a template follower device. Such a machine can produce partial and non-circular cylinders in a single pass; but for surfaces that are contoured in three dimensions, a different type machine is required. Complex three dimensional surfaces are common on dies or molds for forging, pressworking, die casting, permanent molding, and plastic molding.

Fig. 21–30 shows the action involved in producing surfaces of this type. A spherical ended milling cutter is guided through a curved path lying in a single plane by a follower device similar to that of a profiling machine, but regulating the cutter along its axis. After the completion of the pass, the cutter and tracer are moved a short distance normal to the plane and a new curve is traced and cut. The process is slow, and the finish is limited by the

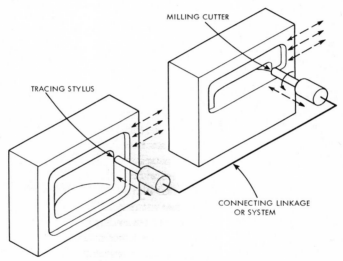

FIG. 21–30. Three dimensional duplicating.

diameter of the cutter and the size of the steps between passes. Dies produced by this method often require considerable hand work for finishing, but the man hours required for producing accurate complicated shapes is only a fraction of that necessary before the development of the duplicating machines.

The master which guides the follower may be another workpiece but is more commonly a model made of wood, plaster, or some soft metal that has been shaped by manual processes. Some duplicating machines are equipped with pantograph mechanisms which reduce the scale between the master and the workpiece while retaining the same proportions. With such a machine it is possible to obtain greater absolute accuracy in the workpiece than exists on the pattern, as well as work on parts too small to easily machine directly by more conventional methods.

Surfaces with two, or three, dimensional contours may also be produced on *numerically controlled* machines that guide the cutter from information supplied on a punched tape. Such machines will be discussed in some detail in a later chapter.

Grinding as a process offers distinct advantages over other machining processes. The first is the possibility of grinding hard materials. In practice, material with hardness up to about 35 Rockwell "C" can be turned, drilled, milled, broached, or cut by other processes using steel or cemented carbide tools with little difficulty so far as tool life is concerned. On the other hand, for materials with hardness above about 50 Rockwell "C," grinding is usually the only practical method of machining, although hard materials are occasionally cut with cemented carbide or ceramic tools. For

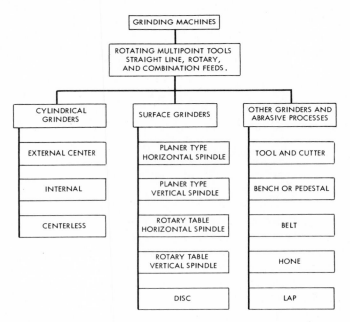

materials with hardness in the range 35 to 50 Rockwell "C," the economics of each situation govern the choice of machining method, with grinding frequently being used. When dimensional tolerances or finishes are not critical, it is possible to machine many parts to finished shape in an annealed condition, then harden and use without further machining. In most cases, however, the distortion that occurs during heat treat hardening is sufficient to require additional metal removal for suitable size or finish and the part must be left oversize for finishing after heat treatment.

The second and third advantages of grinding, the ability to produce good surface finish and the ability to machine to close dimensional tolerance, are related because both depend on the ability of abrasive grains to remove much smaller chips than other types of cutting tools. Grinding can produce good finishes and hold close tolerances on both hard and soft work material, but in many cases workpieces which must have close tolerances and good finishes are also hardened.

Whatever the reason for grinding, it is usually a slow process in relation to the volume of material removed. In most cases, parts that are to be ground are first machined by turning, milling, and other nonabrasive processes to leave as little material as practicable for finishing by grinding. Since grinding is in most cases used to remove only the final material from a surface that has already been shaped, it is logical that grinders that are similar in many respects to other machine tools would have developed. One class, called *cylindrical grinder*, is similar to turning and boring machines and is used to finish the surfaces that are usually started by turning and boring. In some instances, grinding would be desirable on holes which are first produced by drilling but are too small to be easily finished by standard procedures using grinding wheels. Internal *honing*, an abrasive process roughly equivalent to reaming, is often used for these.

No grinders are directly equivalent to shapers, planers, or broaches which are used primarily for producing flat surfaces. However, a large class of grinders are similar in form, appearance, and motions to milling machines. These are used for finishing flat surfaces and partial or noncircular cylinders that may have been rough machined by one of the flat surface machining procedures. The general term *surface grinders* is used for machines of this type.

Cylindrical Grinders.   A lathe may be used as a cylindrical grinder by mounting a grinding spindle and drive on the compound rest or cross slide in place of a tool post for a single point tool. Engine lathes are sometimes used in this manner for tool room work, but the setup usually lacks rigidity and the machine is subject to damage because the ways of the lathe bed are not protected from the abrasive action of the grinding wheel particles that are released from the wheel. Cylindrical grinders do have relative motions that are quite similar to those of a lathe, but the rotation of the work becomes part of the feed motion and the cutting motion is derived from rotation of the grinding wheel.

One practical design difference arises between lathes and grinders. Lathes are all universal in the sense that they may be used either for turning external surfaces or boring internal surfaces. The single point cutting tool would be identical except for the mounting position and tool wear rates have relatively small effects on work dimensions. The problem of wheel wear always occurs in grinding. For a given volume of wheel wear, the diameter of the wheel will be affected less as the size of the wheel is made larger. Thus, as large a wheel as is practicable is used for most grinding. External cylindrical grinders can use wheels of almost any diameter and in practice they usually range from six to twenty-four inches. The most efficient surface speed for the wheel is generally 5000 to

6000 feet per minute. For a twelve inch diameter wheel this requires about 2000 rpm. On the other hand, the wheel used for internal cylindrical grinding can certainly be no larger than the hole and in practice is made no larger than three fourths the diameter of the hole to keep the contact area relatively small. For a ½ inch diameter wheel used to grind a ¾ inch diameter hole, the most efficient speed would be about 50,000 rpm. Such speeds are feasible only with precision bearings and proper lubrication. A few cylindrical grinders are made that are called *universal*. These are equipped to do either internal or external grinding by use of different wheel spindles located in different positions and driven at different speeds. The majority of grinders are either equipped with a spindle and drive system designed to provide relatively low speeds efficiently to large diameter wheels with large amounts of power for external contact, or to provide higher speeds for smaller diameter wheels located for contact with internal work surfaces. The first are called *external cylindrical grinders* and the second *internal cylindrical grinders*. These types are shown in Figs. 21–31 and 21–32.

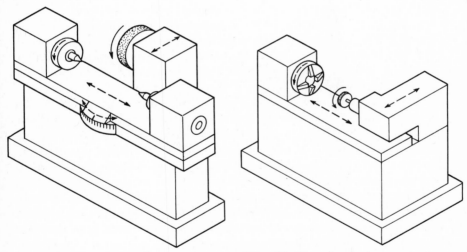

FIG. 21–31. External center type   FIG. 21–32. Internal center type
grinder.   grinder.

Although the relative motions between the workpiece and the cutting tool on a cylindrical grinder are similar to those on a lathe, there are differences in construction. Axial feed in grinding is obtained on external cylindrical machines by moving the workpiece and its driving spindle parallel to the wheel axis. On internal machines, the wheel is moved back and forth along its own axis with a feed motion at the same time it rotates with cutting motion. The combination of axial movement and rotation about an axis produces a helix which results in a generated cylindrical surface. If the grinding wheel is fed toward the workpiece with no axial feed, a formed surface of revolution results and the action is usually referred to as *plunge* cutting. For grinding tapers, the top half of the table carrying the work may be swiveled about a vertical pivot to the desired half angle.

The work may be held by any of the means used on turning and boring machines. In practice, however, the between centers method is most commonly used for external grinding and jaw type chucks are most common for internal grinding. Collet chucks are not often used since parts are seldom made completely from bar stock. Round bar stock itself may be ground more efficiently on a different type grinder.

The external grinder shown in Fig. 21–31 is often called a *center* type grinder to distinguish it from a *centerless* grinder which may also be used for certain types of external cylindrical grinding. The principle of operation for a centerless grinder is shown in Fig. 21–33. The work is supported between the grinding wheel, a regulating wheel—both made of abrasive material—and a work rest, usually faced with cemented carbide. The force of the grinding wheel on the work in combination with the slanted surface

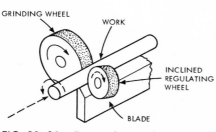

FIG. 21–33. **External centerless grinding.**

of the work rest produces a great enough force between the workpiece and the regulating wheel to "gear" them together effectively with little or no slippage. Although centerless grinders may be used for formed surfaces or for grinding cylindrical surfaces of different diameters by a forming action, the most efficient use occurs when the work is of uniform diameter, or at least the diameter to be ground is larger than any other part of the workpiece and accounts for most of its length. In these cases, the work may be fed continuously in an axial direction. This feed is provided by tilting the axis of the regulating wheel in a vertical plane and dressing its surface to provide line contact with the work. The contact path between the regulating wheel and the work thus becomes a helix and the work is "screwed" axially past the grinding wheel. The work has adequate support along the entire contact with the grinding wheel so that rigidity is much less of a problem than when supporting work between centers. Long bars of very small diameter may be centerless ground throughout their length so long as they may be adequately supported outside the grinder to prevent "whipping" of the ends.

Because of the relatively long setup time and the restrictions on the surfaces that can be ground, centerless grinders are strictly production tools and, except in very special circumstances, are used only for large quantities. For center type external grinders and chucking type internal grinders, no sharp dividing lines exist between toolroom and production types. Toolroom machines may have only manual axial feeds and the driving power is small. Production grinders have automatic feeds and may have automatic gaging, loading and unloading, and wheel dressing.

Surface Grinder. The similarities between surface grinders and milling machines are even more direct than those between cylindrical grinders and turning and boring machines. Both use multiple toothed rotary cutters. Both types of machines are built with either vertical or horizontal spindles and the feed motions are quite similar.

The most common type of surface grinder is the *planer* type shown in Fig. 21–34. This machine has motions identical to those of a horizontal fixed bed milling machine. Such a machine can be used for form grinding grooves or slots, but the most common use is for machining flat surfaces. The operation is somewhat different for this use than it would be on a milling machine. If 0.100 inch depth of material was to be removed from a two inch wide piece by milling, a slab milling cutter of any length greater than two inches could be used, and a single pass of the table at correct depth would be sufficient. Theoretically, the same setup and motions should be possible for grinding; but practical limitations would lead to difficulty. Because of the relatively inefficient chip production in grinding, a depth of cut of 0.100 would lead to excessive local heat generation with attendant warping and distortion. The usual depth of cut for surface grinding is on the order of 0.001 to 0.002 inches so that from fifty to one hundred passes would probably be required to remove 0.100 inch total. Furthermore, if the surface were ground by using a wheel with a width greater than two inches and down feeding between successive passes, the wear on the wheel would not be uniform across its face and the resultant surface would

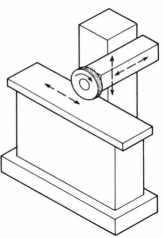

FIG. 21–34. Planer type surface grinder.

contain a series of grooves of various depth parallel to the direction of table feed. The problem of wear is partially solved by using a number of passes of the table at each depth with axial movement of the wheel between passes. The axial feed is usually about 25 per cent of the wheel width. The usual wheel width for a workpiece of this size would be about one inch. Therefore, the total number of table passes would be at least eight for each 0.001 downfeed and the total to remove 0.100 inch might be as many as eight hundred. Obviously, the removal of large amounts of metal in a precision grinding operation such as this should be avoided where possible. The usual amount to be left for grinding is 0.005 to 0.020 inch, depending on the material, initial surface conditions, warpage, and other factors.

Fig. 21–35 shows the relative motions used by the different types of surface grinders. The planer type shown at A in the figure is the only one used for form grinding of grooves or slots since the others all use a generating action that results in a flat surface. Types B and C are the least common of the group. The type shown at D in the figure is usually built only in large sizes with wheels of two to five feet in diameter being common. Large wheels are built up of truncated pie shaped segments fastened to a metal backing and operating effectively as a cup or saucer type wheel. Grinders of this type may be used for precision finishing operations with many small parts mounted on the table. With coarser wheels, they are used as an alternative to milling, shaping, or planing on large castings—especially those difficult to hold—for producing the first finished surface.

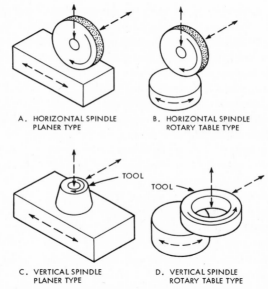

A. HORIZONTAL SPINDLE PLANER TYPE

B. HORIZONTAL SPINDLE ROTARY TABLE TYPE

C. VERTICAL SPINDLE PLANER TYPE

D. VERTICAL SPINDLE ROTARY TABLE TYPE

FIG. 21–35. Motions used for surface grinding.

Other Grinders and Abrasive Processes. Cylindrical grinders and surface grinders are almost directly comparable to turning machines and milling machines, respectively. A number of other grinding machines and abrasive processes are not directly equivalent to other machining processes. Most cutting tools themselves are finished or sharpened on special machines designed for specific purposes. The periphery of rose reamers or twist drills, for example, may be ground on standard external cylindrical grinders, since their lands are cylindrical surfaces without relief angles. The side cutting edges of standard machine reamers while similar in appearance to those of rose reamers, differ, however, by having relief angles. These must be gound one cutting edge at a time, with the wheel set to produce the correct relief angle and fed in an axial direction only, with only enough rotation to follow the helical form, if any, of the tooth. The cutting end of a twist drill also has a complex form that requires either manual control during grinding, or the use of a special grinder capable of guiding the work to produce the correct point angles.

Nearly all shops, especially tool rooms, are equipped with one or more *bench* or *pedestal* grinders. These may be only a motor with shaft extensions on one or both ends for the mounting of grinding wheels. They are usually also equipped with guards for the wheels and adjustable work rests. They are used with manual control of the work (*offhand*) for deburring, drill sharpening, single point tool sharpening, and some forming operations where tolerances are not critical. Grinding as a process has an advantage in forming type of work, since some cutting will occur with even light loads on the work and the tendency for chatter that would occur if milling were attempted with manual control of the work does not exist.

Cloth belts with abrasive grains bonded to the surface are used in several ways as grinding tools. They were first used only for sanding of work; but with the development of superior abrasives and adhesives, they have become important metal working tools. On one form of belt grinder, the belt runs over two drums and is backed up by a flat platen between the drums. It is useful for some of the same work that is done offhand on a bench grinder but is also capable of producing a reasonable flat surface, provided large amounts of metal do not have to be removed. With a curved or flexible backing or no backing at all between the drums, the belt grinder is useful for finish improvement and edge deburring on some castings or stamped parts.

Belts are also used in finishing some sheet and plate stock as a mill operation. The belt passes around a relatively small diameter roll or drum with the sheet passing between the drum and a small diameter pressure roll. Exact flatness is not produced, but thickness and finish can be controlled.

For first operations on castings, especially where only small amounts of metal are to be removed, and precision is not high, *disc* grinders may be used. The wheels are made with a relatively coarse abrasive, and grinding is done primarily on the flat face of the wheel. The work may be carried in a fixture that swings past the wheel or manually placed against the wheel with the grinding force against a fixed rest that supports the work near the surface of the wheel.

When *honing* is done as a high production operation, it is nearly always on special machines that are designed for a specific product. Job-shop type machines exist which are relatively simple in construction, with a horizontal spindle, coolant supply, and a means for feeding the honing stones against the work. *Lapping* is likewise a somewhat specialized process requiring equipment designed for specific products when used for economical manufacture of like parts in quantity.

QUESTIONS

1. In the machining process, what function does the machine tool serve?
2. What advantages are offered by individual motor drives for machine tools over the older line shaft system?
3. Why is it necessary for machine tools to be constructed to operate at various spindle speeds?
4. For what reason is the power transmission system of a machine tool much heavier in construction than a comparable system for automotive or similar use?
5. What particular advantage, other than economy, does cast iron offer for the principal structural material of machine tools?
6. In machine tool design, what are the usual aims of specialization?
7. Describe the different objectives of tool room, production, and special machine designs.
8. Sketch a schematic diagram of a lathe power supply.
9. Describe the two methods by which longitudinal feed motion is supplied to the carriage of an engine lathe.
10. How can the lathe facing methods of producing flat surfaces be identified as different from shaping, planing, or milling?
11. How is the size of an engine lathe specified?
12. Describe the three general modifications of engine lathes that are useful and economical for larger quantity manufacturing.
13. Under what conditions might the use of a turret lathe be economically justified for small numbers of pieces?
14. When are special machines, limited to a single kind of product, justified?
15. What are the most common reasons for use of a shaper?
16. Describe a clapper box.
17. What are the principal differences between a tool designed for a vertical shaper and one for a horizontal shaper?
18. What kind of surface is produced by a gear shaper?
19. Regarding product design, what advantage does gear shaping offer over most other gear manufacturing methods?
20. To what does the term "surface broaching" refer?
21. Why is pull broaching more common than push broaching for internal surfaces?
22. What are the two common applications for sawing?
23. What is the distinguishing feature of a sensitive drill press?
24. Describe the differences in design and use between gang and multiple drill presses.
25. What thread accuracy limitation usually exists when tapping is performed on a standard drill press?
26. How does the objective in use of a jig borer differ from that of most other drilling type machines?
27. How does an universal column and knee milling machine differ from a plain type and for what is it needed?

28. Why is a vertical milling machine important even though it is not as versatile as the horizontal type?
29. What are the two main differences between production milling machines and tool room or job-shop types?
30. In what way are the production characteristics of a rotary or drum type milling machine better than for other types?
31. Briefly describe the actions of a three dimensional duplicating machine when machining a surface.
32. Name the three principal advantages of grinding over other machining processes.
33. What is the range of cutting speed used for most grinding operations?
34. How is the work provided with feed motion on an external centerless grinder?
35. What is the general meaning of the term "surface grinder?"

CHAPTER 22

Auxiliary Machine Equipment

IN MANY RESPECTS, the purchase of a machine tool is similar to the purchase of an automobile. In both cases there are many different models to choose from, each of which was designed to perform the same basic function. Also in both cases, the "standard" machine often includes some minimum set of equipment which permits the machine to perform its function but to which most purchasers add from a list of available "optional equipment." Some of the options are even directly comparable. Both machine tools and automobiles are available with different motor sizes, both are available either with or without power brakes, power steering (template tracing devices for machine tools), or automatic transmissions.

Although many modifications of machine tools must be accomplished at the factory, some of the conversions and additions may be made after the original purchase. For example, mechanical stops may be added to a tool room type machine to simplify duplicate manufacturing. Most engine lathes are sold originally with three- or four-jawed chucks for work holding, extra cost options, but most may also use collet chucks without modification of the machine.

Standard machine tools are provided with attachments or auxiliary tools for several reasons. One of the most common is to increase the rate of production by providing workholding devices or machine attachments suitable for the product. These either simplify the operator's location and measuring problems or increase the rigidity of support for the work or tool to permit faster rates of metal removal. Other attachments may be designed primarily to permit maintenance of increased accuracy, either by providing for closer measurements of machine movements or by insuring increased accuracy for duplicate production. A number of attachments, particularly for tool room use, are designed to increase the versatility of a particular machine, permitting setups that would not otherwise be possible. In some cases, attachments of this type effectively convert a machine tool to one of a different type. A tool room lathe, for example, may be equipped with a "grinding" or a "milling" attachment.

452

STANDARD HOLDING DEVICES

Clamping of the workpiece is one of the areas involving a great number of possible choices. In many instances, the setup man has a wide choice of methods, any one of which would be satisfactory especially in tool room or job shop work. The method used is likely to be the one most available or one of personal preference.

Standard Clamps and Vises. Many workholding devices are comparable to standard tool room and job shop types of machine tools. They are designed with the greatest versatility practicable. Not only may they be used to hold many different workpieces, but they may frequently be used on different machines, including machines of different types. They may be used either for manufacture of single parts or, in some cases, as the best method for multiple production.

Milling machines, shapers, planers, and some other machines have tables that are produced with tee shaped slots running in one or two directions. On a milling machine, the slots are parallel to the direction of table travel. In practically all cases, the various machine tool builders have standardized to the size and location of the tee slots so that workholding devices making use of the slots on one machine may be transferred to another machine of the same type with a minimum of difficulty. The slots are used primarily for holding the heads of bolts which clamp the workpiece directly, a separate workholding device, or a machine attachment to the table of the machine.

When the workpiece is held directly to a machine table having tee slots, it is usually with standard clamps of the type shown in Fig. 22–1. Clamps such as these are used for holding a great variety of workpieces. When the only surface readily available for clamping is the surface that must be machined—for example, when one face of a flat plate must be milled or shaped—a restriction often arises. In these cases it may be necessary to place the clamps in one position, machine part of the surface, then move the clamps to new locations; normally this is not good practice. In some cases, the workpiece may have either no good natural clamping surfaces available or no good natural surface on which it can rest for clamping. In these cases it may be desirable to design extra bosses, lugs, or projections on the workpiece as aids to fastening. These extra surfaces may sometimes be left on or removed later by machining if necessary.

A number of standard items have been designed to simplify locating and clamping the workpiece. Some of these are shown in Fig. 22–2. Step blocks are useful as the supporting member when a standard clamp is used. V-blocks especially simplify holding circular workpieces.

Direct clamping to the table is often a time-consuming process and one which can be used only when a suitable base surface exists on the work. It is often much simpler to hold the workpiece in a standard vise which itself

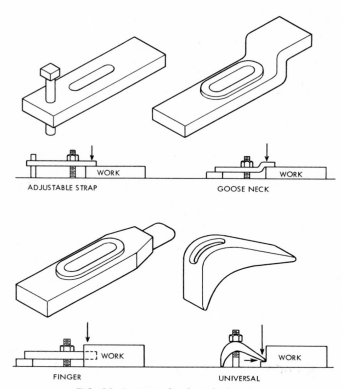

ADJUSTABLE STRAP

GOOSE NECK

FINGER

UNIVERSAL

FIG. 22–1. Standard work clamps.

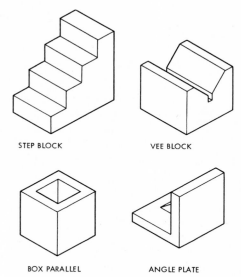

STEP BLOCK

VEE BLOCK

BOX PARALLEL

ANGLE PLATE

FIG. 22–2. Clamping auxiliaries.

is bolted or clamped to the table of the machine, although this too is limited to pieces with certain shapes and surface relationships. Fig. 22–3 shows a typical milling machine vise of one type. Others may incorporate quick adjustment features, have grooved jaws for aligning circular work-pieces, or keys on the bottom surface for alignment in the slots in the machine table. Vises may also be mounted on a base which permits adjust-ment about one or more axes for angular settings. Additional adjust-ment features are usually obtained only at some sacrifice in rigidity. Horizontal shapers are nearly al-ways equipped with a large capac-ity vise as a standard feature, al-though tee slots are available for use of other fastening methods.

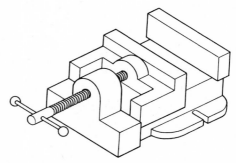

FIG. 22–3.   A simple milling machine vise.

Chucks. A wide choice of stand-ard holding devices exists for rotat-ing tools or workpieces. The term *chuck* is loosely applied to any de-vice that grips a workpiece, either externally or internally, with movable jaws. More specifically, the term refers most often to a three-jawed *drill chuck* with taper operated jaws or a *lathe chuck* (used also on other machines) consisting of a body with jaws that are moved radially in slots with screws, scrolls, levers, or cams.

Fig. 22–4 shows the most common types of lathe chucks. The jaws in a

FIG. 22–4.   Three jaw universal and four jaw independent lathe chucks.

three-jaw *universal* chuck are actuated by a scroll plate which rotates inside the body so that the jaws remain equally spaced from the axis of rotation. Universal chucks are used for holding round or hexagon bar stock or castings with appropriate shapes. The accuracy of a chuck deteriorates because of wear, dirt, and bending of parts from overtightening or excessive loads.

Independent chucks are most frequently made with four jaws, each adjusted with a separate screw. They may be used for holding odd or uniformly shaped workpieces about any axis of rotation. They may also be used for greater centering accuracy than is possible with a universal chuck, although precise centering with an independent chuck is a time-consuming process requiring considerable skill.

There are many special types of chucks. Two jaw chucks are similar to a vise and, when equipped with specially shaped jaws, permit rapid clamping and provide good support for duplicate part manufacture. For tool room and job shop use chucks are manually operated; for production use they may be operated by air, hydraulic power, magnetic force, or mechanical systems.

Collets, Fig. 22–5, are limited range chucks with jaws actuated by a taper or inclined plane mechanism. Most collets are made of a single piece of steel with the central hole finished to the size and shape of the material to be held. Longitudinal slots permit the jaws to spring open or shut a small amount, but since the jaws act as though hinged about the back end of the collet, they fit properly only when the work is within a few thousandths of an inch of the proper size. Collets for tool room work are generally made in sets, with an increment of $\frac{1}{16}$ inch between sizes and a range from $\frac{1}{16}$ inch up to a maximum determined by the spindle hole in which they will be used. Most collets are made for holding round bar stock, but are available in square, hexagon, and other shapes.

Various methods are used for operating the tapered section of the collet to provide the clamping action. The simplest, and most used in tool room work, is the draw type collet shown at "A" in Fig. 22–5. The draw type is undesirable for production machines on which the length of stock is set by feeding the bar against a fixed stop, since as the collet closes, it tends to draw the stock away from the stop. For these applications the push type as shown at "B," which tends to push the bar against the stop, or the stationary type as at "C" are used.

The rubber bonded collets shown at "D" in the figure are of greatest use in tool room work, where nonfractional sizes often must be held. The jaws remain parallel over a range of about $\frac{1}{8}$ inch, and a small number of different capacity can cover the desired sizes.

Between-Center Support.   Chucks or collets have a number of drawbacks. The work is supported from one end only and is subject to excessive deflection leading to chatter and inaccuracy if it projects several diameters from the chuck. The accuracy of centering in a chuck or collet

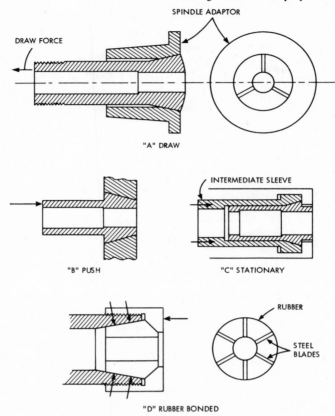

FIG. 22–5. Types of collet chucks.

is never absolute, so can lead to eccentricity under some conditions. An axis of revolution is fixed when a part is chucked, and surfaces produced while the part remains chucked will be as concentric as the spindle bearings of the machine permit. However, if the part is removed from the chuck and later installed in the same or a different chuck, the axis of revolution will be different from that of surfaces made in the first setup. Difficulties may often be overcome by mounting the work *between centers* as shown in Fig. 22–6. Driving torque is generally provided by a dog that has a tail engaged in a slot in a driving plate mounted on the spindle of the machine clamped on the work, but may also be transmitted by special design devices such as a serrated driver making contact with the inside of a tube.

The ends of the workpiece are usually prepared with a combination drill and countersink that leaves a conical seat. The axis of revolution of the work is therefore determined by the line between the conical seats and accuracy is limited only by the accuracy of the cones or *centers* on the machine that fit in the workpiece. The workpiece may be removed from the machine and replaced in the same or some other machine with the centers in the work providing a repeatable axis of revolution. One of the greatest uses of this method is on parts that must be rough machined in a lathe, then transferred to a grinder, usually after hardening by heat treat.

For most tool room work, solid hardened steel or cemented carbide centers are used in the machine. For lathe operations, the center in the headstock rotates with the work and can contribute to eccentricity if the

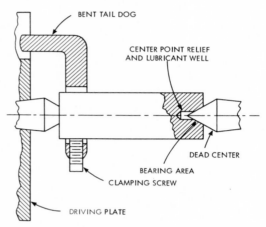

FIG. 22–6.   Between-center support.

axis of the cone of the center is not concentric with the axis of revolution of the center. The tailstock center is fixed and acts as a bearing surface for the rotation of the work. The tailstock center may be provided with antifriction bearings of its own to permit greater loads, but at the expense of possible inaccuracies in the bearings themselves. For most grinding operations, both centers are fixed, or *dead*, to provide the greatest possible centering accuracy, the axis of rotation being determined only by the two centers in the work. Some parts held in a chuck at the headstock are given added support from a center at the tailstock end, usually with the objective of reducing deflection and possible chatter.

Support may be given to many parts that do not have natural centers of chucking surfaces by using *mandrels*, which are themselves chucked or mounted between centers. The need for this type of support frequently arises when surfaces must be turned, ground, or milled to be concentric with a hole that already exists in the part. Typical operations would be the groove in a pulley or the teeth on a gear. Fig. 22–7 shows several common types of mandrels. Similar devices, referred to as *arbors*, are mounted directly on the spindle of the machine and are more commonly used for holding rotating tools such as milling cutters, although some confusion does exist regarding the use of the two terms.

Steady Rests. Deflection problems often exist when the workpiece is long and slender. In many cases, one end can be chucked but the other end must be available for a drilling or similar operation. In other cases, even with support at both ends, the part is still not sufficiently rigid to prevent chatter or inaccurate dimensions. For these cases, *center rests* or *follower rests* may be used to advantage. A steady rest is fixed to the bed of a lathe or other machine at some intermediate point of the workpiece and provides additional support with rollers or solid wear pads. A follower rest is mounted on the tool carriage itself and moves along with the tool, providing support directly adjacent to the cut.

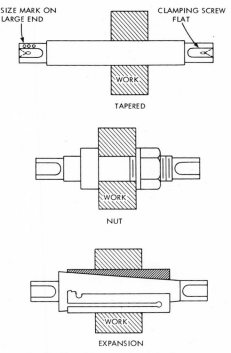

FIG. 22–7. Common mandrel types.

Magnetic Holders. One of the simplest holding methods involves the use of either permanent magnets or electromagnets for holding workpieces of iron or steel. Permanent magnet devices are made with "U" shaped magnets inside the body of the holder with the poles on the surface. The holder may be turned "on" or "off" with shorting bars that rotate inside the body. Electromagnetic holders operate on direct current and require a rectifier or other DC power supply. Electromagnetic chucks have greater holding power than permanent magnet types and may in addition be used for demagnetizing the workpiece by intermittently reversing the polarity during unclamping. The principal use for magnetic holders is for grinding where tool loads on the workpiece are generally lower than in other types of machining. Both rotating chucks and reciprocating or fixed tables are available. Similar devices, using vacuum, are available for holding brass, aluminum, plastic, or other nonmagnetic workpieces.

JIGS AND FIXTURES

Most clamps, vises, and chucks are designed primarily for tool room or job shop work where speed and accuracy of setup for a single or very few workpieces are the principal objectives. The two major problems in any setup are to clamp the workpiece securely enough to prevent movement or excessive distortion from the cutting loads, and to locate the workpiece correctly with respect to the cutter and the machine motions. For most tool room or job shop work, the workholding device must first be mounted on the machine in proper alignment. In some cases, a vise or chuck may be left on a machine for several setups, but this is the exception rather than the rule. After the holder and work are mounted, the cutter must be located with respect to the workpiece. The usual procedure when turning, facing, boring, milling, shaping, or grinding is to make a trial cut of shallow depth, measure, then use the calibrated feed screws on the machine to establish the position of the final cut.

For drilling operations, two general procedures are followed in small lot production. If the accuracy requirements are not too high, the locations of the hole centers may be established by *layout* on a surface plate and then centerpunched to provide a starting depression for the drill. If greater accuracy is required, the work must be rigidly mounted and aligned on a jig boring machine or milling machine, having calibrated feed screws. At each location to be drilled, a hole must first be started with a short rigid centerdrill to prevent walking of the drill.

For multiple production, where the cost of additional tooling can be prorated over a sufficient number of parts, use is made of *jigs* and *fixtures* to simplify the problems of holding and locating. Although definitions differ somewhat in other areas, particularly in joining, for machine tool work a fixture is a special device designed to hold and locate a workpiece for a specific operation. A jig is a special device designed to hold and locate the workpiece and guide the tool for a specific operation. The tool guiding characteristic is the most important for a jig, and in some cases the work locating and support characteristic is given up entirely with the jig being simply clamped to the work. In such cases, the work support must be provided in some other way. Of greatest significance in the definitions is the fact that a jig or fixture is ordinarily designed for a single machining operation on a particular workpiece; it is not normally useful for other operations or other workpieces.

Standard holding devices cause considerable sacrifices in operating speed in order to obtain the universality required for tool room and job shop work. Jigs and fixtures may use highly specialized clamps that are fast acting, although of limited range. With the workpiece properly located by the jig or fixture, the trial and error location, alignment, and measuring procedure must be performed only once during the original setup. Further workpieces may then be machined correctly at the same machine settings. Jigs are most commonly used for drilling operations with bushings that not only locate the operations correctly with respect to the workpiece, but eliminate the need for a starting depression on the surface and provide tool support, permitting faster work and better accuracy.

Location.   Although every jig or fixture is different from another, certain principles of workpiece location are common to all. Referring to Fig. 22–8, the complete location of any object in space requires that six different degrees of freedom be restricted. In the figure, these are shown as translation along the "X," "Y," and "Z" axes and rotation about the same axes. It is not necessary that the axes be mutually perpendicular, but only that they form three nonparallel planes. In practical jig and fixture designs, however, location on orthogonal planes usually gives greater rigidity and accuracy of location.

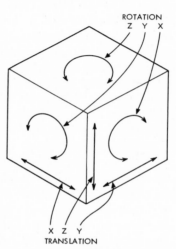

FIG. 22–8.   Object in space with six degrees of freedom.

An object could be completely located by fitting it into a cavity such as a casting mold or forging die that would be required to produce the object. However, variations in sizes will occur with a large number of parts, so that the cavity would have to be large enough to accommodate the largest variation and other parts would be free to move. In addition, any foreign objects left in the cavity would interfere with correct location. Such restriction is therefore seldom practical for locating purposes.

Many jigs and fixtures are designed with pin locators, so positioned that if contact is maintained with six pins, or their equivalent, the part is completely located. In Fig. 22–13, pins 1, 2, and 3 determine the XY plane and restrict the Z translation and rotations about the X and Y axes. Pins 4 and 5 fix the XZ plane and prevent Y translation and Z rotation. Pin 6 fixes the YZ plane and prevents motion along the X axis.

A number of principles apply to the use of pin locators. The pins should be spaced as far apart as possible in each of the planes. The wider the spacing, the greater the torque load that can be resisted with a given load on the pin. Also the wider the spacing, the smaller the angular error introduced by foreign matter between a pin and the work. The area of the pins should be as small as practicable to reduce the possibility of interference from dirt or chips without causing contact loads sufficient to produce permanent deformation.

If more than the minimum number of points are required in any of the planes to provide adequate support for a casting or forging, the extra pins should be adjustable or distortion may be introduced. Additional pins, or large area contact, may be used on finished surfaces provided any possible distortion is small enough to be tolerated. Additional points may be desirable on finished surfaces even when not needed for support. If a machined surface, that is assumed to be flat, is brought against four pins that lie in a common plane, any rocking indicates either an error in the surface or the presence of dirt on one or more of the pins. Drill jigs are often provided with four reduced area feet for contact with the table of the drill press to reduce the problems associated with chips accumulating on the drill table.

In many jigs and fixtures, the principles of pin location are used without the locating points having the physical appearance of separate pins. A cylindrical locator in a round hole provides the action of four pins in two orthogonal planes and restricts all degrees of freedom except rotation about the axis of the cylinder and translation along the axis. If the workpiece has two parallel holes, a full cylindrical locator may be used in one hole, but is not needed in the second hole since the second locator must restrict only a rotation about the axis of the first pin. Fig. 22–9 shows the use of a round pin in one hole and a diamond shaped locator in the second. The diamond locator tolerates considerable center distance variation between the holes but provides close control of the rotation about the round pin. A "V" locator provides four locating points as shown in Fig. 22–10.

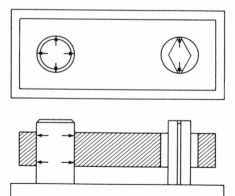

FIG. 22–9.   Round and diamond pin locators.

Simple *template* jigs for short-run production may be only flat, unhardened plates with holes located as necessary. The plate is clamped on the workpieces and the holes are used to locate and guide the drills. Such jigs have short life since the drills wear the holes oversize in the unhardened plate. In most drill jigs, hardened steel bushings are used to guide the drills or other tools. These drill bushings are standard items made in quantity by specialty manufacturers. Fig. 22–11 shows some of the different styles available.

Press fit bushings are used in jigs which are unlikely to need bushing

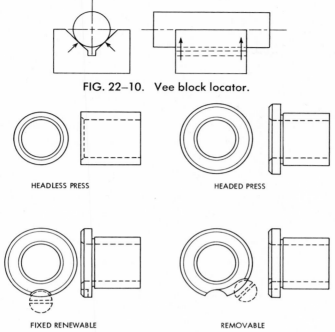

FIG. 22–10. Vee block locator.

HEADLESS PRESS   HEADED PRESS

FIXED RENEWABLE   REMOVABLE

FIG. 22–11. Types of drill bushings.

replacement. Headless bushings are simpler but headed bushings have less chance of being moved and are easier for the operator to spot visually during the drilling operation. Replacable bushings are used in hardened steel liners in jigs that are to have very long life and which will require that the bushings be replaced to maintain accuracy. Slip removable bushings are used when it is necessary to remove the bushing each drilling cycle to permit a secondary operation such as reaming or tapping with the workpiece still in the jig. Milling cutters are not directly guided by the fixture in which a workpiece is held for a milling operation, but the fixture may incorporate a locating *target* to assist in proper adjustment of the fixture relative to the cutter during the initial setup of the machine. Fig. 22–12

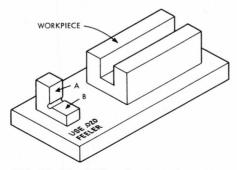

FIG. 22–12. Milling fixture with target.

shows the use of a target for setting a milling cutter to the correct depth and at the right location sideways. The setup man adjusts the cutter until it just makes contact with a 0.020 inch thick feeler gage placed on the target surfaces, using surface "B" for the depth and surface "A" for side location.

Clamping. In some cases with locating pins in three orthogonal planes, it is possible to supply a single clamping force having components directed toward all three of the planes. More frequently, however, the clamping forces must be directed parallel to the axes of the planes. For completely rigid clamping, three forces as shown in Fig. 22–13 would be required.

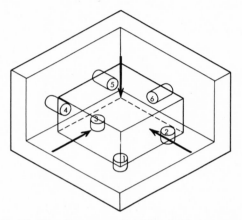

FIG. 22–13.   Forces required for rigid clamping.

Consideration of the forces to be resisted in the use of a jig or fixture may simplify the problem of clamping. For example, with the tool along the "Z" axis in drilling, a relatively large thrust force occurs along the "Z" axis, which frequently reverses as the drill breaks through, and a relatively large torque in one direction only about the "Z" axis. Relatively small forces, however, tend to rotate or translate the part along the "X" or "Y" axes. The part shown in Fig. 22–14 could rest on three pins or a flat surface for the XY plane with a rigid clamping force along the "Z" axis to prevent lifting when the drill breaks through. With conventional placement of pins at A, B, and C, a spring load at C' would be sufficient to maintain contact with pin C, but a rigid clamp would be required at A'B' to resist the torque from the drill. With the placement of the pins modified as in Fig. 22–15, a rigid clamp would still be needed along the Z axis, but spring forces at A', B', and C' would be sufficient since the torque of the drill would keep the work in contact with fixed pins A and B.

The designer of jigs and fixtures has a wide variety of clamps available. Standard strap and gooseneck clamps as shown in Fig. 22–1 are among the most frequently used, especially when equipped with a knurled knob or star wheel for direct operation instead of a nut which requires a separate wrench. With the clamp properly positioned, it is necessary for the thread

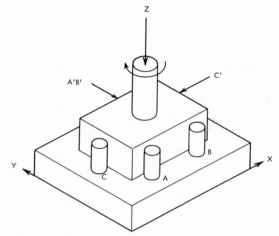

FIG. 22–14.   Clamping for conventional pin placement.

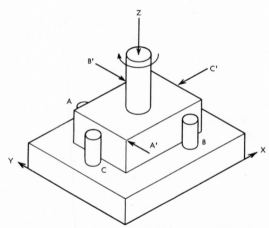

FIG. 22–15.   Utilization of cutting forces to aid clamping.

to be loosened only part of a turn since the slot permits the clamp to be moved back to clear the work. Standard vises are often used as the basis of fixtures by equipping them with special jaws that properly locate the workpiece.

Many quick-acting clamps designed for use on large numbers of parts, where the saving of a few seconds per part may justify the additional cost, may be used for jigs and fixtures. Fig. 22–16 shows a cam clamp that can be loosened by the movement of a simple lever. Fig. 22–17 shows a quick-acting nut that may be removed without unscrewing for the entire length of the thread. Toggle clamps as shown in Fig. 22–18 are available as standard items from a number of different manufacturers.

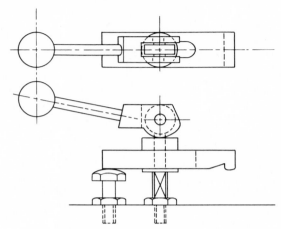

FIG. 22–16.   Cam clamp.

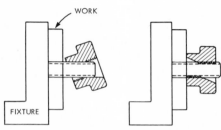

FIG. 22–17.   Quick-acting screw and nut.

Jig and Fixture Design.   The design of jigs and fixtures involves somewhat different considerations than that of most other products. Their accuracy must be quite high. As a rule of thumb, the tolerances on location points and the spacing of drill bushings must be from one tenth to one quarter of the tolerances for the same dimensions on the workpieces. Maintenance of accuracy throughout the life of the tool requires that they be very ruggedly constructed to withstand some abuse as well as the normal cutting loads.

Because of the high accuracy required and because jigs and fixtures are most often built as single items, most of the cost is in design and labor of manufacturing instead of in materials. Consequently, the usual practice is to make most parts of heavier construction than would theoretically be required if stresses or deflections only were the basis for design. Nearly all engineering materials are used in jig and fixture construction at some time. Cast iron and rolled steel shapes are common because of their ready availability. Aluminum and magnesium are often used where light weight is desirable, as in a drill jig for a large part. Plastics have more recently grown in importance for tooling construction, not only because of their light weight and high strength to weight ratio, but also because they may offer short cuts in construction that reduce the labor time. Simple drill jigs, for example, may be made by casting room temperature thermosetting plastics with the drill bushings in place around a workpiece as shown in Fig. 22–19.

For metal jigs and fixtures, three methods of construction are in general

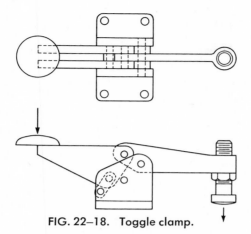

FIG. 22–18.   Toggle clamp.

use. Cast iron is often used where extreme ruggedness is required, where facilities for patternmaking and casting are readily available, and where the shape required is conducive to casting. Welding also offers ruggedness and is the fastest method of construction for many tools. Locating surfaces must usually be machined after welding because of the heat distortion that occurs.

Many jigs and fixtures are made by fastening the individual components together with screws and dowels. This method, while often less rugged than welding or casting, requires no special equipment outside the machine shop and offers some short cuts to obtaining high precision. With the parts screwed or bolted together

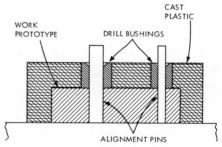

FIG. 22–19.   Cast plastic drill jig.

through clearance holes for the fasteners, final adjustments may be made in spacing and location, then holes drilled and reamed for dowel pins to insure that no further shifting between parts will occur.

Chip disposal and cleaning should always be considered in the design of a jig or fixture. During the cutting operation itself, there must be room for the chips to clear the cutting area and for coolant to be applied if necessary. After the workpiece is finished and removed, it is necessary to clear all locating points of chips before the next workpiece is inserted.

The term *foolproofing* is used to refer to design features which prevent the operator from making mistakes in the use of a jig or fixture. The part shown in Fig. 22–20, for example, could be sufficiently located by pins in holes "A" and "B," but the operator could insert a part in the fixture backwards or upside down if the holes were the same size. The addition of an extra pin in hole "C" would prevent these possibilities. The extra pin could be undersize and would not actually contribute to the location of the part.

Electrical interlocks may be provided that prevent a machine from operating unless all clamps are properly tightened. Many machine tools are equipped with electrical or mechanical interlocks that prevent some types

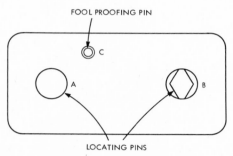

FIG. 22–20. Jig and fixture foolproofing.

of improper operation. These include mechanisms that prevent shifting gears with the spindle running or engaging more than one feed mechanism at the same time.

A problem occurs with a drill jig that is used for both drilling and reaming at the same locations. If the drill bushing is not removed before reaming, severe damage results to the reamer, the drill bushing, or both. One solution is to set the reamer at such a height that it will not pass over the head of the drill bushing. With one form of patented drill bushing, if the operator attempts to insert a reamer through the bushing, the bushing rotates with the reamer, preventing damage and giving an audible warning.

Applications of Jigs and Fixtures. By the definition which includes guiding of the tool, jigs are used almost exclusively for drilling, reaming, and other drilling type operations which involve nonrigid tools that need guiding. While the number of possible jig designs is virtually unlimited and many jigs are unlike any others, a few types have become somewhat standardized, at least as to name.

For large sheet metal parts, conventional jigs are often impractical because of the large sizes and the low production that may be involved. The problem is often to drill holes in two matching parts that are used for assembly with bolts or rivets. In these cases *template* jigs may be used. A template jig consists of a single plate or supporting structure that contains drill bushings at the required locations in a plane. The workpiece is clamped to the template, or for very large structures the template may be taken to the workpiece. The same template is often used for both parts of a matching set of workpieces.

For many parts, especially when their general shape is rectangular, a *box* jig as shown in Fig. 22–21 is used. As many sides of the structure are enclosed as are necessary for mounting drill bushings and for providing the necessary rigidity. Reduced area feet are provided on the sides opposite those having drill bushings. At least one side is left open for inserting the workpiece and removing chips.

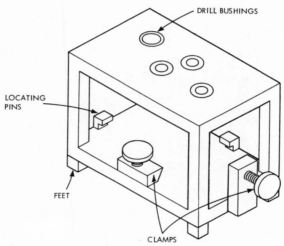

FIG. 22–21.   Box jig.

In many instances where a box design for a jig is the most practical, the box cannot be made completely fixed since the side through which the workpiece must be inserted must also carry either clamps or drill bushings. In these cases, one member may be hinged on one end and clamped on the other to form one face of the box. Fig. 22–22 shows such a *leaf* type jig.

Many jigs are given names corresponding to some locating or operating feature. A *rollover* jig is one that may be of box form but that is intended to be used in more than one position. If mounted in a carriage with end pivots it may be called a *trunnion* jig. *Indexing* jigs with provision for drilling holes at proper angular spacing have many forms.

A number of commercial designs exist for *universal* jigs which may be refitted for different parts after the production of one design part has been completed. In the *pump* type universal jig shown in Fig. 22–23, the base is fitted with appropriate locating pins for a workpiece and the head plate is fitted with a plate carrying drill bushings in the required pattern. Movement of the pump handle lowers the head plate which acts as a clamp for the workpiece. The operating mechanism contains a pair of one-way clutches which keeps the head in locked position until the handle is raised. Jigs of this type are useful for drilling in only one plane.

Fixtures form the second class of special workholding devices. While the area of greatest importance is milling, fixtures of some type are also

FIG. 22–22.   Leaf type box jig.

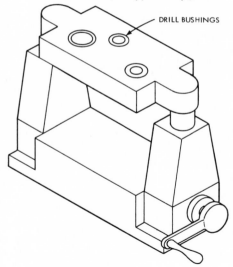

FIG. 22–23.   Pump jig.

needed for most broaching and for many production grinding and turning operations. In addition, they are used for some drilling type operations, where the guiding of the tool may be done by precast depressions in the work or a cored or punched hole.

With some exceptions, the problems of location and clamping in fixtures are similar to those for jigs. In jigs the workpiece may often be completely surrounded which simplifies the problems of location and clamping. In fixtures, at least one side of the workpiece must be exposed for the machining operation with the result that the surfaces available for location and clamping are limited. Jigs are usually not fastened to the drilling machine since the drill bushings establish the correct relationship between the tool and the work. Fixtures must ordinarily be rigidly fastened to the machine in the correct location, since the fixture is responsible for the correct relationship of the cutter to the workpiece although it does not directly guide the cutter.

MACHINE ATTACHMENTS

Jigs and fixtures, clamps, vises, and cutting tools are part of the group of components called tooling, but they are not considered attachments even when fixed to the machine. The term *attachment* refers to devices which modify speeds, feeds, motions, measurements, or other features of a standard machine tool to permit increased speed, accuracy, or versatility. Attachments fall into two principal classes: those which convert a machine to a different type, and those which establish motions not normal to any standard type of machine.

Conversion Attachments. Many of these attachments are strictly toolroom devices intended to permit occasional operations that would be done on a standard machine if the proper one were available. In small shops where the equipment is not in full use, the purchasing of additional low use equipment may not be justified where an attachment for some different type of standard machine will work. Nearly all shops, however small, contain at least a milling machine and an engine lathe, and most of the attachments in the tool room conversion class are for these machines.

The engine lathe can provide all the motions necessary for cylindrical grinding except the rotation of the grinding wheel, which may be supplied by an attachment mounted on the tool post in place of a single point cutting tool. Fig. 22–24 shows such an attachment being used for internal grinding. Grinding attachments are used, not only by small shops which do not have a cylindrical grinder, but also by larger shops as a means of handling overloads. They may also be used by large shops for occasional grinding of very large parts. One drawback to the use of this attachment is the lack of protection against abrasive wear of the bed-ways on an engine lathe. Some protection may be provided by a cloth cover.

Like the grinding attachment, a *milling* attachment for engine lathes uses those natural motions of an engine lathe which correspond to those of a milling machine and add what is necessary. A horizontal or vertical milling machine normally has three mutually perpendicular feed motions, one of which is parallel to the rotating cutter spindle. This combination can be obtained on an engine lathe by mounting the milling cutter in the spindle and adding an attachment in place of the tool post on the cross slide. The attachment consists of a vertical slide carrying a vise for holding the workpiece. This attachment is practical principally for end milling operations on small workpieces.

If a small shop is limited to a single milling machine, it must be a horizontal machine if arbor mounted cutters are to be used at all. However, spindle speeds on a horizontal machine are designed for large diameter cutters so that end milling cutters must generally be used at lower speeds than desirable. Furthermore, the setup for end milling most work on a horizontal machine is more awkward than on a vertical machine. A

FIG. 22–24. Engine lathe grinding attachment.

vertical attachment as shown in Fig. 22–25 converts a horizontal milling machine to a vertical by changing the spindle direction. Such attachments are often constructed to permit adjustment of the cutter spindle to any angle in a vertical plane and they may also contain speed increasing gears which provide speeds more suited to end milling and drilling operations.

One milling machine attachment is designed to increase the accuracy rather than the versatility of motion. Table movements on a milling machine are normally measured only by the rotation of the feed screws. The calibration of the screws is accurate for short distances, but this method of measurement is subject to several drawbacks. The screws are subjected to different loads at different points of travel so the accuracy is affected by compression or stretching of the screw. Backlash between the screw and nut must always be taken out in the same direction or compensated. The accuracy of the screw itself is limited, especially over large distances. Jig boring machines are designed to overcome these difficulties but these machines are quite expensive and many small shops cannot justify a jig boring machine for relatively small percentage use. Precision measuring attachments that permit the measuring to be done independently of the table feed screws by use of gage blocks or precision length standards as the measuring elements in a manner similar to that on a jig borer are available for standard milling machines. These attachments are most often used on vertical milling machines for the purpose of accurate hole locating.

FIG. 22–25. Vertical milling attachment.

A second group of conversion attachments is used when quantity production is of primary interest. These are attachments that add some element of a production machine to a standard tool room type, generally to simplify measurement or tool changing.

Engine lathes may have carriage stops that permit lengths to be duplicated on a number of cuts. Both single and turret type stops are available. On most engine lathes, however, the power feed must be disengaged manually before the carriage hits the stop and the final portion of the cut made with manual feed. Engine lathes may be almost entirely converted to turret lathes by replacing the tailstock with a turret and mounting a turret tool post on the cross slide. A four position turret tool post is shown in Fig. 22–26. As on a turret lathe, various tools for turning, grooving, threading, and cutoff may be set up only once, then indexed to the correct position for each duplicate part that is produced.

Fig. 22–27 shows one type of the production attachments available for drilling machines. Shown is a multiple drilling attachment that permits up to four holes to be drilled with a single feed motion of the spindle. With this type device a number of individual spindles are driven through universal joints, flexible shafts, gears, or cranks, which permit the pattern of holes to be changed within the size limits of the attachment. It should be noted that even with the drill spindles correctly positioned a jig is still necessary to insure that the drills do not "walk" on the surface of the part before starting to drill.

FIG. 22–26.   Turret tool post.

Tapping attachments are also available for drilling machines. These consist of a reversing mechanism carrying the tap and driven by the machine spindle. With feeding pressure in the normal down direction, the tap rotates in the same direction as the spindle and the tap enters the hole. When the tap reaches the correct depth, the feed pressure is reversed which actuates reverse gears and backs the tap from the threaded hole. Such attachments are useful primarily for smaller sized taps.

Attachments that Provide Special Positioning or Motions.   Attachments of the conversion type permit one machine to be used for operations that would be standard on some other machine without modification. Another class of attachments provides motions or positioning that are not normally available on any standard machine. Most of them are used to provide feed or cutting motions that cannot be obtained any other way. However, one of the more important, the *dividing head*, is a workholding device. Dividing heads may be used on many machines, but the most common use is as an aid to milling accurately spaced slots, flats, or grooves around the periphery of a workpiece. A typical use is for making one, or a small number, of spur gears as pictured in Fig. 22–28. In this application,

FIG. 22–27. Multiple drilling attachment.

the workpiece is held between centers and the space shape between two adjacent teeth is provided by a form milling cutter with the correct profile. The spindle of the dividing head is driven through a worm gear with a 40 to 1 ratio. The crankshaft is equipped with a plate containing holes in concentric rows in which a stop pin may be engaged. A series of plates having different numbers of holes is available, making it possible to divide the circumference of a workpiece into a large number of equal parts. To obtain eighteen equal spaces for the gear shown, the crank is turned two complete revolutions plus four spaces in an eighteen hole circle, six spaces in a twenty-seven hole circle, or eight spaces in a thirty-six hole circle for each cut. The driving shaft of a dividing head also may be geared to the feed screw of the milling machine for milling helices so that the head rotates as the table moves.

FIG. 22–28. Dividing head.

Except when used for milling helices, the dividing head is simply a positioning device and the cut that is made at each position is a partial noncircular cylinder made with a form cutter. Except for the use of the dividing head, such a cut would be considered standard for the machine. In Chapter 19, it was pointed out that the geometry of a machined surface depends on the relative interference path set up between the tool and the workpiece and that standard machines are those with motions that satisfy the functional product needs that have developed over the years. When a demand exists for a surface that cannot be produced by these standard motions, a special machine may be built if the demand is sufficient, or an attachment may be used if one exists. Several attachments for the engine lathe satisfy this need of nonstandard motions.

The engine lathe is capable of generating short tapers by use of the compound rest; for longer tapers a *taper attachment* as shown in Fig. 22–29 is used. The attachment consists of a bar which is clamped to the bed of the machine to prevent longitudinal movement and held parallel to the axis of the bed. Mounted on the bar is a guide which carries a shoe connecting it to the cross slide. The guide can be adjusted to the desired angle relative to the axis of the bed so that when the carriage moves longitudinally along the bed the tool will follow a straight line path at an angle determined by the setting of the guide bar.

The use of a template tracing mechanism was discussed in Chapter 19 in connection with the production of surfaces of revolution. Some special production lathes are built with tracers as part of the machine, but more

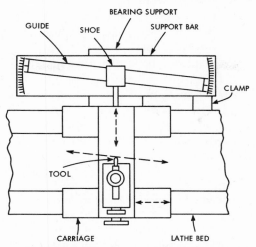

FIG. 22–29. Lathe taper attachment.

commonly they are added to standard engine or production lathes as attachments in the manner shown in Fig. 22–30. The template may be either a flat piece with the correct profile or a master workpiece. Tracers are not limited to cutting complex shapes, but also may be used for straight cylinders, shoulders, chamfers, or tapers.

Some of the attachments meet very highly specialized needs. A *relieving,* or *backing off,* attachment is used to produce the relief angles necessary on milling cutters and reamers. A cam, geared to the spindle of the lathe, is used to work the cross slide in and out as the workpiece rotates.

FIG. 22–30. Lathe tracer attachment.

The surface produced is a noncircular cylinder with as many lobes as the number of teeth on the tool being made. The flutes between the teeth are produced by a milling operation.

A *ball turning rest* replaces the standard compound slide on a lathe and provides a circular feed path. When properly positioned with respect to the work, the combined rotation of the work and curved feed motion of the tool produce a sphere or a portion of a spherical surface. The number of different attachments that can be designed has almost no limit, providing sufficient need warrants the time and cost for their production.

QUESTIONS

1. Name the three main objectives of auxiliary tools and attachments for machine tools.
2. What advantage does a gooseneck clamp offer over a plain strap clamp?
3. Why is it poor practice to shift clamps during a machine operation?
4. In reference to chucks, what does the term "universal" mean?
5. Name the advantages of an independent chuck over the universal type.
6. Why are collet chucks usually furnished in sets?
7. Under what condition is a "push" type collet better than a "draw" type?
8. In what ways are rubber bonded collets better than the all-metal types?
9. Why is the between-center method of support one of the most common ways to hold a workpiece for rotational machining?
10. What is a mandrel?
11. List the advantages and disadvantages of an electromagnetic chuck versus a permanent magnet type.
12. Why are jigs and fixtures limited to relatively large quantity manufacturing?
13. What six degrees of freedom may exist for an object in space?
14. Show by sketch how contact with six points will restrict the six degrees of freedom and fix an object in space.
15. Why should locating pins be separated as far as possible?
16. What is the purpose of using a feeler gage when setting a milling cutter in relation to a milling fixture target?
17. Name four clamp design features that are used for time saving when fastening parts in jigs or fixtures.
18. What is meant by "foolproofing" a jig or fixture?
19. What is a leaf type jig?
20. What two design features of fixtures are usually different from those of jigs?
21. When is the use of conversion type machine attachments justified?
22. What are the sources of position error for a table moved by the usual screw and nut method?
23. Of what does a tapping attachment essentially consist?
24. For what is a dividing head used?
25. Sketch a plan view of a lathe taper attachment.

CHAPTER 23

Numerical Control

NUMERICAL CONTROL systems are auxiliary machine equipment similar in some ways to those described in the preceding chapter. However, the importance of this relatively new development in the manufacturing field is sufficient to warrant individual treatment of the subject. The proportion of new equipment budgets used for this kind of equipment is steadily increasing. Expenditures for numerically controlled machine tools have approximately doubled each year since 1954.

The simplest definition for numerical control is: the control of a machine by numbers although this definition has been used often, it is not complete for machine tools because they are all controlled by numbers in a sense. For example, when the cross slide of a lathe is reset from one position to another manually, the operator notes the initial dial reading, then moves the proper *number* of turns or spaces of the dial. A more comprehensive definition is: numerical control is a form of tooling that controls the motions and actions of a machine by use of numerical (digital) values stored on a suitable medium.

The requirement that the values be stored on a suitable medium implies the absence of direct human control. A phonograph record fulfills this requirement since the music is stored as variations in the groove. However, the variations are continuous (analogue) and not numerical. The inclusion of the term digital is a practical matter. Theoretically, there is no reason a machine tool control system could not operate from information that varied in a continuous manner. In fact, a template tracer system for a lathe or a milling machine does this, but the template for such a system represents one step further in control than that required for numerical control systems. The shape of the template may first be described as a set of dimensioned points, but it is necessary for the template to be machined to correspond to these points. If the points describe a curve, some blending process is necessary to convert the points (digital), however close, to a smooth curve (analogue).

The complexity of numerical control systems depends greatly on their ability to convert from digital input information to smooth curves. Ulti-

479

mately this ability depends on how closely together the points may be plotted and still be resolved as individual points by the system.

Principles of Operation.　While many different machines are numerically controlled, the principles of operation have much in common. In fact, relatively few different control systems exist. It should be kept in mind that the subject is numerical *control* and that the systems being controlled are often conventional machines that might otherwise be controlled manually. Even when entirely new machine tools have been built with numerical control, they are still machines that do conventional machining operations and use the same cutting tools and motions that have been discussed in previous chapters.

Several different media have been used for input data, these include punched tape, punched cards, magnetic tapes, and direct input by dial and switch setting. At the present time only punched tape and direct dial inputs are used to any great extent. The progress in standardization, which usually accelerates the rate of adoption of new systems, has been much more rapid than in past machine tool developments. Even with the wide diversity of numerically controlled machines, general acceptance of one-inch wide, eight-channel tape as the standard input medium has occurred throughout industry. Fig. 23–1 shows a section of such a tape. The presence or absence of a hole in a particular location is referred to as a *bit* of information. A row of holes, or possible hole locations, across the width of the tape constitutes a *character* which is normally a number from zero to nine or one of the letters of the alphabet.

For forming the numbers, a standard binary code is used. A hole in the first channel has the value one, a hole in the second channel the value two, a hole in the third channel the value four, and a hole in the fourth channel the value eight. Tape readers can be designed to examine each character electrically to check whether an odd or even number of holes are read. Each character is made to have an odd number of holes on the tape so that if the reader reads an even number of holes the reading error can be appropriately indicated or the machine stopped automatically. In order to make characters have an odd number of holes when the binary code calls for an even number, a hole is punched in the fifth channel, as is done for the letters "X" and "Y," and the numbers "3," "5," and "6."

Letters are made of combinations of holes in the first, second, third, fourth, sixth, and seventh channels. A hole in the eighth channel is used only to indicate the end of one complete block of words, usually corresponding to one machine movement. Not shown in the figure is a row of smaller holes between the third and fourth channels that is used for feeding the tape.

At least three different types of tape readers are in use. Mechanical readers have spring loaded pins for every possible hole location. These contact a ground plate and complete an electrical circuit if a hole is present. Photoelectric readers have lights on one side of the tape and photocells on the other. Mechanical readers are somewhat slower and are most commonly used in *block* readers where an entire block is read at the same time. Photoelectric readers can be extremely fast and generally operate as *sequential* readers, reading one character at a time. Less common are the third type, pneumatic readers that operate much as the "reader" on a player piano which draws air through holes in the tape to actuate the mechanism.

Regardless of their complexity, most numerically controlled machines have somewhat similar control and drive systems. Most contain a number of independent elements, each controlled by one word in a block of taped

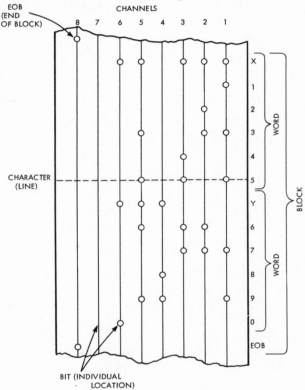

FIG. 23–1. Section of n/c tape.

information. These elements are of two distinct types. Auxiliary functions such as coolant supply, spindle rotation, spindle speed, and tool selection have a limited number of discrete values possible (coolant on or off, for example) and are controlled by open loop systems such as shown in Fig. 23–2. Some actions associated with driving an automobile may be compared to these open loop auxiliary functions. These would include: unlock the door, turn the switch key on, place the transmission in second gear, turn headlights on, or blow the horn. For each of these actions, a fixed set of motions must be performed and there is no other control. If the driver operates the light switch and the lights do not come on, he may operate as an interlock and stop the machine, but so far as turning on the lights is concerned, he has no corrective action to take other than repair.

The second type of numerically controlled function is much more complex. For machine tools, this is concerned with the variable motions of machine slides which position the workpiece for drilling or other point located operations, feed the slide for milling operations, feed the carriage or cross slide on a lathe, or control similar motions on other machines. Some machines have been built with open loop systems for control of these motions, but the great majority used closed loop systems such as shown in Fig. 23–3. Inherent in each closed system is a *transducer*, which is

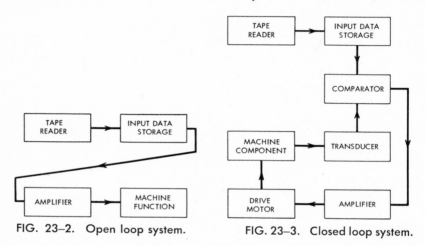

FIG. 23–2. Open loop system.   FIG. 23–3. Closed loop system.

connected to and driven by the machine component (slide) under control. Transducers are of several types, but most operate by generating an electrical pulse each time the slide moves some given increment of distance, the size of which is normally 0.001 inch or less with 0.0002 inch being most common. The polarity of the pulses is reversed when the direction of slide movement is reversed. The comparator in the system contains a counter which adds or subtracts pulses, so that it is constantly supplied with information as to the location of the slide. The actual location can be continuously compared with the desired location (tape information stored in the memory of the comparator) and corrective action taken until coincidence occurs. A single machine motion consists of the following sequence. The tape reader feeds a desired new location for the slide through the data storage section to the comparator. Since this new locaton does not correspond to the present position of the slide, an *error* signal is generated by the comparator. The error signal is fed through the amplifier to the drive motor and the machine slide travels in such a direction as to reduce the difference between the slide position and the desired new slide position. When the value in the comparator from the machine slide corresponds to the desired new value, the error signal becomes zero and the drive stops. The system is made more complex by the necessity of traveling at reasonably high rates of speed to the new position, but, stopping accurately at the position, preferably without overshooting.

Types of Control Systems.   As in conventional machine tools, the total relative motion between the cutter and the work on a numerically controlled machine is made up of a number of simple motions, either straight lines or rotation about axes. On an engine lathe, control of the cross slide on the carriage and the carriage along the bed is sufficient for all standard operations. Such a machine would be known as a *two axis* machine. Milling machines may have as many as five axes controlled: linear motion along three orthogonal axes, and rotation about two axes.

For dimensioning and programming purposes, it is common to refer to the linear axes as X, Y, and Z, with X and Y in the horizontal plane and Z in a vertical direction. Two different dimensioning systems are used. In the *absolute* system, dimensions are stated with reference to fixed base lines, one for each axis. The base lines normally have the value zero. Most machines using an absolute dimensioning system are equipped with *floating zero,* that is, the control system may be set so that the value in the comparator from the transducer may be made zero at any point within the travel limits of the table. With an *incremental* control system, the dimensions for each point must be stated with reference to the last point programmed. In effect, the base lines shift each time a new point is reached to correspond to that point.

Regardless of the number of axes, numerically controlled machines are classified either as *point to point* or as *continuous path,* depending on the way in which motions involving two or more axes are made. In Fig. 23–4, X_1Y_1 and X_2Y_2 represent two points on a workpiece between which a motion must be made. These points could represent hole centers for drilling, points along the contour of a part to be turned, or points on a path to be followed by a milling cutter. The X direction could represent the motion of the cross slide and the Y direction the motion of the carriage on a lathe. Since the line between the two points does not correspond

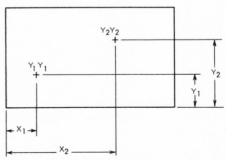

FIG. 23–4. Dimensioning for n/c.

exactly to a single motion of either slide, both slides must move for the cutter to travel from point one to point two.

In point to point machines, each axis has essentially independent control systems, with possibly an over-all control affecting the rate of travel, but the motion along any axis is independent of other motions and the rate of travel is approximately the same along all the axes. Consequently, the relative path of the cutter with respect to the work on a point to point machine would be as shown in Fig. 23–5. At the start of the movement, both slides would move to give a relative movement of approximately 45 degrees. The X slide would reach its dimension first, but the Y slide would continue to travel along the path shown. When the point X_2Y_2 was reached, the machine would be ready to perform an operation at that point.

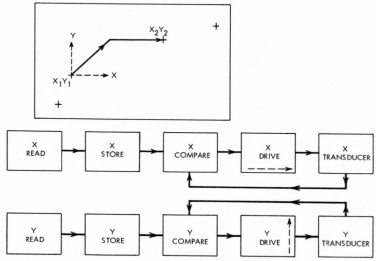

FIG. 23–5.   Point to point movement.

On continuous path machines, the movement is most used as a cutting path rather than a positioning movement, so the feed rate along the path must be controlled. Fig. 23–6 shows a simplified explanation of the way this move would be made by such a machine. Since as exact a straight line as possible between the two points is desired, the X and Y motions must be coordinated. This is done by computing the time required to travel the distance between the two points, then computing the rates for both the X and Y motions at which the table transducers must generate pulses in order for each to move the desired distance in the correct time. The pulse computer then generates these pulses at the required rate for each axis, and the X and Y comparators provide a signal as required to their respective drives to keep the pulse rate from the transducer synchronized with the pulse rate from the generator. In effect, the slide is moving point to point in the smallest steps the transducer is capable of resolving. Theoretically, a point to point machine could be programmed to make the same very small moves, but a block of information on the tape would be required for each step, the machine would have to stop at each point for the next block to be read, and the total motion would be a series of discrete steps rather than a smooth line.

On continuous path machines, the points X_1Y_1 and X_2Y_2 are usually points on some path for which a continuous motion is desired, rather than positions at which operations are to be performed with the machine slides

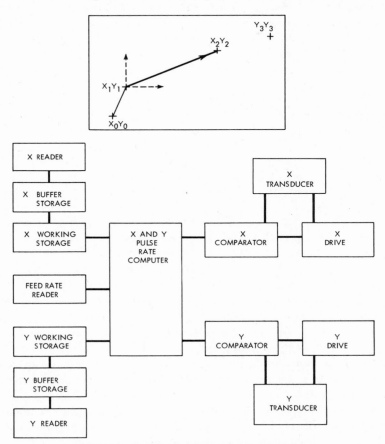

FIG. 23–6. Continuous path movement.

at rest as they would be on a point to point machine. In order to avoid stopping at each point for the tape to be read, the control unit for continuous path machines has an expanded input data storage section which permits the point X_3Y_3 to be read while the move from X_1Y_1 to X_2Y_2 is in progress. This data is immediately transferred to the pulse rate computer when needed.

Most continuous path machines work with *linear interpolation* as described, that is, the move between two adjacent points is made as a straight line connecting the points. Such a system requires a large number of points to be programmed for the final path to form a smooth curve but offers great flexibility. Some continuous path machines, particularly lathes, have been equipped with control systems capable of *circular interpolation*. With this system, given the dimensions of two points on the path and the center of a circle, the pulse rate computer generates pulses at the rate required to produce the desired circular path.

Machine Types. As with many other "new" developments, the history of numerical control reveals some very old attempts, many of which were quite successful. Evidence indicates that a card programmed lace making machine was built in England in 1611. At the Jacquard silk mill in France, card programmed looms were highly developed in the early nineteenth century.

The present period of development in machine tool controls started much more recently. Between 1948 and 1952, a three axis continuous path vertical milling machine was developed at the Massachusetts Institute of Technology. Since that time most of the major machine tool manufacturers have developed numerically controlled machines. The development has proceeded along several different lines. A number of different companies in the electronics field manufacture control systems which different machine tool manufacturers adapt to their machines. Most early machines were standard machines with control systems added. The present trend is to develop new machines specifically for numerical control. Such machines may have no manual controls at all, and they may have special provisions for automatic tool changing. Some of the machine tool manufacturers have developed their own control systems.

A distinct division has occurred along the lines of point to point versus continuous path control. During the first few years after the machine was developed at MIT, most machines built were continuous path. However, the average cost of these early machines was about $300,000, and the cost of the control units alone was over $50,000 each. The average cost of machines of this type is now about $150,000, with the controls representing about one third of the total.

The most spectacular gains have occurred in the point to point machines. Although much less capable than the continuous path machines, the average cost is less than $30,000. Presently, they account for approximately 90 per cent of all numerically controlled machines sold. A point to point drilling machine with control is available for approximately $10,000. Exact recent figures are difficult to acquire, but it is estimated that numerically controlled machines now account for nearly half of the total annual investment in new machine tools. By number of machines the percentage would be much lower.

Drilling machines with point to point positioning controls constitute by far the most important type of numerically controlled machine, so far as number of machines is concerned. These machines range from simple two axis machines with single spindles and manual control of the actual drilling operation to three axis machines with automatic tool changers. A number of turret drills have been built. These are actually two axis machines with the depth, spindle speed, and feed rate for each turret position being manually preset.

Milling machines constitute the next most important group. These range from three axis machines with point to point controls capable only of straight line milling corresponding to one of the major axes of the machine, up to five axis, continuous path, *machining centers*, with automatic tool changers.

Lathes have been built with both point to point and continuous path controls. At present, approximately 70 per cent of the lathes built have point to point control. Such machines are intended primarily for straight turning work. The machines are normally equipped with a turret tool post that can carry various tools for turning, facing, boring, and producing fillets. For contour work, these point to point machines may be equipped with tracers that operate from a template during the appropriate part of the cycle. Continuous path machines are more versatile but also more expensive.

In addition to drills, lathes, milling and boring machines, and grinders, numerical control has been applied to many nonchip forming machines. These include turret punches, tube benders, welding machines, wire wrapping machines, flame cutters, and panel wiring machines. The same control principles have also been used for many nonmetal manufacturing applications. A tape controlled mechanical handler can be programmed for loading, unloading, paint spraying, welding, or flame cutting. It can be programmed by manually running it through the desired set of motions. Inspection machines may incorporate only the transducer and feedback sections of a complete control system. On such a machine, the table is moved until the workpiece contacts a fixed probe and a reading obtained for this table position. The table is then moved until some new position on the workpiece contacts the probe and a second reading taken. The difference between readings indicates the dimension. Numerical control is used in bakeries to control the proportion of ingredients, dough mixing cycles, baking time, and oven temperature. It is used to control the mixing of concrete, the operation of entire petroleum and other chemical plants, and to control the light levels for proper balance in the printing of color movies.

Advantages and Disadvantages of Numerical Control. The adoption of any new machine, method, or process depends on its ability to produce acceptable products at lower cost than other procedures. The outstanding advantage for numerically controlled machines when compared with conventional ones is the reduced tooling costs.

Fig. 23–7 is a typical example of a part to be drilled. The tolerances on the hole spacing make hand layout, centerpunching, and drilling impractical. A number of methods could be used. On a jig boring machine, the operator would align the workpiece with the table, center the spindle over the lower left corner and, using this as a reference point, move successively to each hole location for centerdrilling and drilling. There would be no special tooling. As shown in Table 23–1, it may be assumed that the operator would spend about one-half hour gathering tools, studying the drawing, determining spindle speeds, and deciding on a holding method. He would spend about another one-half hour for the actual steps of aligning the work, moving the table, and drilling. He would save the tool gathering and other preparation time for subsequent parts, but little change would occur in the machining time.

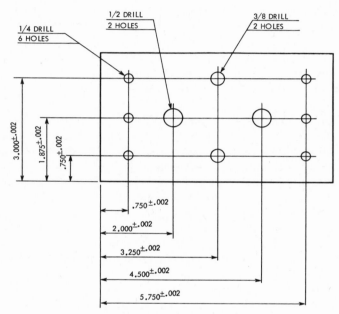

FIG. 23–7. Drilling example.

Until numerically controlled machines were developed, the only alternative to using the jig borer was to build a jig. Jigs themselves are special, requiring design, building, and testing. With a jig, the part could either be drilled one hole at a time in a gang drill, or all holes at once in a multiple spindle drill. The machining time would be less for the multiple spindle drill, but the setup time much longer.

Numerical control now offers other possibilities. Two different kinds of preparation are indicated in Table 23–1 for numerical control. In the first, a location and clamping fixture would be built. Its cost would be much less than the cost of a jig since it would not have drill bushings. It would insure that the workpiece was properly located and clamped with respect to the table of the drilling machine. However, the actual machine time would be longer than that required with a jig. At each location, it would be necessary to centerdrill or spot drill before drilling. Furthermore, the movements from hole to hole would likely take longer than they would when made manually using a jig. The second method indicated for numerical control would utilize standard locating and clamping means, as were indicated for jig boring. This would reduce initial setup cost but would add to the cycle time. In either case, the cost of preparing the tape would have to be included in the setup cost.

TABLE 23–1

Costs for Drilling Example

Machining Method	Setup costs	Cost/Part after Setup
Jig borer	$ 6	$6.00
Gang drill with jig	300	0.60
Multiple drill with jig	400	0.40
N/C with fixture	140	1.40
N/C without fixture	18	2.30

Fig. 23–8 shows how the unit cost for this example would vary with the number of parts produced. This example is typical of the economic standing of numerical control with present machines. Numerical control is cheaper for even a single part in many other instances, especially where three dimensional contours are involved. Numerical control has been misunderstood to some extent as competition for more conventional high production methods. Numerical control was developed originally to meet the needs of the aerospace industries. The largest users of the machines today are still job shop type manufacturers including the aerospace industries and machine tool manufacturers.

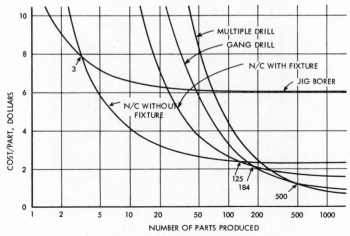

FIG. 23–8. Comparative drilling costs.

When larger quantities are involved, as in the automobile or home appliance industries, older methods are still used. With the older methods, the emphasis has been on mechanization of part handling between machines. However, even in the higher production industries, numerical control finds a place in the manufacture of jigs, fixtures, dies, and other tools. It is also likely that the range over which numerical control provides the lowest overall costs will increase in the future.

Other advantages may be cited for numerical control. Of great importance to many users is the reduced lead time possible with numerical control because of the reduced tooling needs. Lead time is the time between design and manufacture. In addition, quality is often improved and the need for inspection less, primarily because of the reduced human element when numerically controlled machines are used.

There are disadvantages as well. Many of these have resulted because of the increased complexity of numerically controlled machines as compared to more conventional ones. The control circuits for a single two axis point to point drilling machine may contain over seven hundred transistors and diodes. This leads to more and higher cost maintenance to prevent excessive down time. The machines require more floor space and may require air conditioning. Operators and maintenance personnel must be

FIG. 23–9. Numerically controlled drilling and
milling machine.

trained specifically for work on numerically controlled machines. When a company first introduces numerical control, special training or new personnel must often be added to handle programming, tape preparation, and the coordination with design that is required for most effective use of numerical control.

Example of Numerical Control. Fig. 23–9 shows a two axis point to point machine. It is a standard tool room type universal vertical knee and column milling machine. The machine as set up is intended primarily for drilling operations but is capable of straight line end milling operations that correspond to the saddle or table movements. The head is equipped with an air feed that can be manually preset for rapid traverse rate, rapid traverse distance, feed rate, and feed distance. Only one setting is possible for a given cycle of operations; to obtain drilled holes of different depths without resetting the feed stops, the tools must be mounted in holders of different lengths.

Fig. 23–10 shows one of the table drives. The standard feed screw of the machine is driven by a small direct current motor through a cog belt and one set of reduction gears. Concentric about the countershaft is an electrically operated clutch that engages the motor also to the viscous drag of

FIG. 23–10. X-axis drive motor.

a fan in an oil bath. In operation, the clutch is normally disengaged so that the table can be driven at high speed (120 ipm) until the desired point is reached. Normally some overtravel will occur. As the point is passed, the clutch is engaged and the motor reversed. The table then backs up more slowly (10 ipm) to remove the overtravel, and when the desired point is reached at low speed in the reverse direction the motor is shut off. The clutch is also engaged to obtain reduced speed table travel for milling operations.

Fig. 23–11 shows the transducer which responds to the motion of the

FIG. 23–11.   Y-axis transducer.

saddle on the knee ("Y" axis or cross slide motion). The transducer is carried by the saddle. A small pinion is engaged with a high precision stainless steel rack attached to the knee of the machine. Through step-up gearing, the pinion rotates the large gear at the top. On one side of the large gear are two light bulbs, and on the other two photocells in line with the teeth on the gear. Two cells are necessary for the transducer output to contain a direction sense. After amplification by transistors, the electrical pulses generated each 0.001 inch by the transducer are transmitted to the

FIG. 23–12. Control cabinet.

control cabinet, shown in Fig. 23–12, where they are registered on the appropriate counter tubes. The block tape reader is attached to the right of the control cabinet which also contains relays which act as the input data storage and a comparator which detects when the reading on the counter tubes corresponds to the setting of the relays.

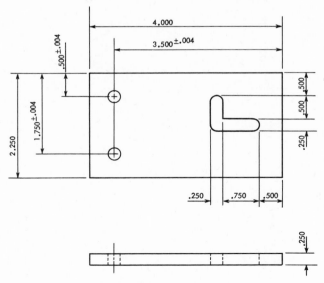

FIG. 23–13. Sample part.

In addition to direction signals and dimensions for the cross and longitudinal motions, one block of information for this machine contains a mode or sequence number. This number refers to the speed of travel (high speed for positioning or low speed for milling), to the action the air head is to take when the point is reached (no action, head down only, or head down and return), and to the action of the tape reader (no action, read with head down for milling, or read when head returns after drilling).

Fig. 23–13 shows a typical part that might be programmed for this machine. It contains two drilled holes with moderately close location tolerances and an "L" shaped milled slot. Assuming that some means of orienting and positioning the part were available, that tools of the correct length were available so that automatic operation of the head could be used, and that the upper right corner of the workpiece were selected as the zero point, one possible program for the part is shown in Fig. 23–14.

At the location where the milling cutter is to enter the work and at the centers of the two holes, a spot drill is used in the automatic drilling mode.

THE OHIO STATE UNIVERSITY
DEPARTMENT OF INDUSTRIAL ENGINEERING
NUMERICAL CONTROL PROCESS SHEET

PART NO.   PART NAME
                    Sample

REMARKS   Zero Set at Upper Right Corner
            Of Work

STEP NO.	HOLE NO.	MODE	"X" DIMENSION +0-	"X" DIMENSION VALUE	"Y" DIMENSION +0-	"Y" DIMENSION VALUE	REMARKS
1	1	5	+	00.625	+	01.125	SPOT DRILL IN TO START
2	2	5	+	03.500	+	01.750	
3	3	5	0	03.500	–	00.500	
4	3	1	0	03.500	0	00.500	CHANGE TO 1/4 DRILL
5	2	5	0	03.500	+	01.750	
6	1	5	–	00.625	–	01.125	
7		2	0	00.625	0	01.125	CHANGE TO 1/4 MILL
8		8	+	01.375	0	01.125	
9		9	0	01.375	–	00.625	
10		0	–	00.000	–	00.000	END

FIG. 23–14. Program for sample part.

With mode 1 called for in step 4, automatic operation stops. After tool changing, the operator has only to push the down control manually and the machine returns to automatic drilling. Mode 2 called for in step 7 also permits tool changing, but after the operator pushes the down control the head will stay down and the tape reader will operate for automatic milling (modes 8 and 9).

The example shown is for a very simple part programmed on a machine of limited versatility. With more complex machines, especially with continuous path controls, computer assistance is almost mandatory for calculating intermediate points. Several programming systems with appropriate computer languages have been developed to reduce the amount of work which must be done manually. These systems may also permit programming in a universal language which may then be adapted by the computer for a specific machine tool.

QUESTIONS

1. What percentage of new equipment money spent for machine tools is presently being spent for numerical control equipment?
2. Define numerical control as most commonly used.
3. What entirely new kinds of machining methods are added to the conventional ones by use of numerical control?
4. In what ways may input data be supplied to a numerical control system and which is most common?
5. In reference to punched tape for numerical controls, define bit, character, and block.
6. Why are characters always made to have odd numbers of holes in a tape?
7. Name the three types of tape readers that are in use.
8. Sketch a schematic diagram for a simple closed loop numerical control system for a machine tool.
9. What is a transducer?
10. In a numerical control stystem, what is the difference between an absolute zero and an incremental dimensioning system?
11. What is the principal difference in the design features of point to point and contour type numerical control?
12. Why are most continuous path control systems equipped with a larger input data storage section than are similar point to point systems.
13. Why are point to point machines much more popular than contour machines?
14. What is the outstanding advantage of numerically controlled machines over the older more conventional types?
15. Sketch curves showing the typical economic relationship between use of numerical control and common drilling procedures for producing a number of accurately spaced holes in a part.
16. What advantages, in addition to direct cost reduction, may numerical control offer?
17. What disadvantages are connected with the use of numerical control?

CHAPTER 24

Miscellaneous Processes

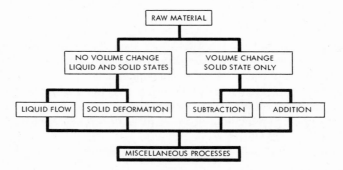

THE PROCESSES that have been discussed in previous chapters have all fit the conventional definitions for casting (melt and flow), deformation (plastic flow in the solid state), welding (bonds formed by heat and/or pressure), or machining (chip formation by a cutting tool). A number of other processes for shaping metal do not fit these standard categories. Most are new processes that are still undergoing development. Most are of importance primarily for some special purpose and do not compete economically with the more conventional processes on a wide scale. Several of them have been developed largely because of the need to shape new high strength and temperature resistant alloys that are not easily worked by the older processes.

METAL REMOVAL PROCESSES

Discussions of the processes to be covered here are often titled *nontraditional* or *nonconventional* machining. They are certainly nontraditional since they have all been developed since about 1950. Except for the introduction of new tool materials and more highly powered machines, traditional machining has undergone no fundamental changes in the last century. The new processes likewise are nonconventional when compared to conventional machining for they do not necessarily use a high strength tool to cause material failure by applying heavy localized loads to the workpiece.

None of these new methods can presently compete economically with conventional machining for shaping low and moderate strength materials when the surface to be machined is readily accessible and is composed of planes, cylinders, cones, or other simple geometric shapes. However it is only under special circumstances that materials with hardnesses above about 50 Rockwell "C" can be machined with single point cutting tools and even then tool life is likely to be quite short. In addition, while few shapes are absolutely impossible to machine, many are especially difficult and particularly uneconomical in small quantities. It is toward solving these two problems, high material properties and difficult shapes, that most of these new processes are directed. As with some of the newer low tooling cost pressworking processes, the aerospace industries have been the largest users of these new processes.

These processes are called machining for several reasons. They all remove material, most of them slowly and in small amounts, although not necessarily in chip form. Most of the machines used still have the appearance and general design features of conventional machine tools, since they must still provide for the proper positioning of a tool relative to the work and must still provide a geometrically controlled interference path between the tool and the work. The biggest difference occurs in the mechanisms used to produce material failure. With few exceptions, it is a chemical or thermal failure rather than mechanical.

Electrical Discharge Machining. The oldest, most successful, versatile, and widely used of the new removal processes is electrical discharge machining, often abbreviated EDM. As early as 1762, it was shown that metals were eroded by spark discharges. Electric arcs have been used to some extent for cutting operations in connection with welding for some time. Practical application to the controlled shaping of metals is much more recent however, although patents were applied for in the 1930's. The process in its present form dates from about 1950 in this country and a few years earlier in Russia.

EDM is based on the fact that if an electrical potential exists between two conductive surfaces and the surfaces are brought toward each other, a discharge will occur when the gap is small enough that the potential can cause a breakdown in the medium between the two surfaces. The temperature developed in the gap at the point of discharge will be sufficient to ionize common liquids or gases so that they become highly conductive. It is this ionized column which in the welding process permits a welding arc to be maintained at considerable length, even over short periods of zero voltage when alternating current is used. The condition of maintained ionization is desirable for welding but cannot be tolerated for controlled shaping, since the discharge would tend to remain at one place so long as a low conductive path were present.

For electrical discharge machining, the electrodes are separated by a dielectric hydrocarbon oil. The elements of the electrical circuitry are shown in Fig. 24–1. A capacitor across the electrodes is charged by a direct current power supply. With the electrodes separated by about 0.001 inch, a discharge will occur when the voltage reaches 25 to 100 volts, depending on the exact nature of the dielectric and the materials of the electrodes. The essential element of the process is the fact that the discharge will occur at the point where the electrodes are closest together. Whether the discharge should be defined as an arc or a spark is a matter of some debate, but the fact remains that small amounts of material are removed from both

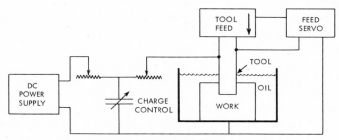

FIG. 24–1. Electrical discharge machining.

electrodes, probably largely as the result of surface vaporization caused by the high temperature developed locally. As soon as the capacitor is discharged, the oil extinguishes the arc (deionizes the path), and the capacitor is then recharged. Subsequent discharges will occur at other points which are then closer together. As material is removed from the electrodes the distance between them becomes greater and the voltage required to initiate a discharge rises. This rise in voltage can be used to actuate a servo control which feeds the electrodes together to maintain a constant discharge voltage, or stated another way, to maintain a constant distance between the electrodes. The amount of material removed by each discharge will be determined primarily by the amount of energy released from the capacitor. The rate of material removal will be determined by the individual quantity and the cyclic frequency. The frequency of discharges on most machines ranges between 20,000 and 300,000 cycles per second.

The applications for the process depend on the fact that one of the electrodes can be a workpiece, the other a tool that produces a shaped hole, cavity, or external surface in the work. The relative rate of material removal on the work and tool will depend on their melting points, latent heats of evaporation, thermal conductivities, and other factors. Ideally, the material of the tool would be eroded very slowly or not at all. In practice, wear ratios range from as low as 0.05 (twenty times as much workpiece material removed as tool material) for a steel workpiece and a silver tungsten alloy tool, to 2.0 or more when cutting cemented carbides. Because of its low cost and ease of shaping, brass is a more common tool material although wear ratios are much higher. Graphite provides very favorable wear ratios when used for cutting steel.

The process offers two principal advantages when compared to more traditional methods of machining; some shapes are more easily produced and workpiece hardness offers no problems. EDM may be used for producing almost any shape if the proper electrode can be made. Noncircular through holes which would otherwise require a broach or very time-consuming hand work are often made by first removing as much material as possible with a circular drilling operation, then finishing by EDM. The advantage comes in making the electrode, since the conventional machining can be done to an external shape. A square or splined electrode, for example, is more easily machined than a square or splined hole if a broach is not available.

If the hole goes through the workpiece, electrode wear creates few problems. The electrode is simply made with additional length which is fed through the work material to compensate for the wear. For a blind hole with straight sides, the electrode would also be made with additional length but would be removed periodically to have its forward end refaced. If the cavity is to have a three dimensional contour the problem is more severe. The number of electrodes required would depend on the materials used and on the geometrical precision required. As many as ten electrodes are often used.

Aside from its ability to cut complex two or three dimensionally contoured shapes, EDM has the ability to shape any material that has a reasonable amount of electrical conductivity. Hardened steels and cemented carbides present problems no greater than soft ductile materials that could easily be cut by machining. Materials are as easy to shape in a hardened state as they are in an annealed condition.

The process has one drawback in addition to relatively high equipment cost and the problem of electrode wear discussed before. An inverse relationship exists between the quality of the surface finish produced and the cutting rate. Surface finishes as good as ten microinches RMS are obtainable, but only with metal removal rates on the order of 0.0003 cubic inches per minute. Maximum metal removal rates at present are about 0.3 cubic inches per minute but when this rate is achieved, surface finish quality measures about five hundred microinches.

Electrochemical Machining. Electrochemical machining (ECM) is somewhat newer than EDM but has grown rapidly in the past few years. It offers great potential for the future, particularly because of the greater metal removal rates possible than with EDM. In this process, as in EDM, both the tool and the workpiece must be conductive, or at least the workpiece must be conductive and the tool must have a conductive coating. With a suitable electrolyte between them, the tool and workpiece form opposite electrodes of an electrolytic cell. The workpiece is connected to the positive terminal of a direct current supply and the tool to the negative terminal. The electrical circuit is identical to that used in metal plating where metal is removed from the anode and deposited on the cathode. There are two major differences. Different electrolytes are used so that the material removed from the anode forms insoluble oxides or hydroxides. In electroplating, the unagitated electrolyte permits metal ions to leave the anode only as fast as they can diffuse into the electrolyte. The low rate of diffusion restricts the maximum current flow that can be

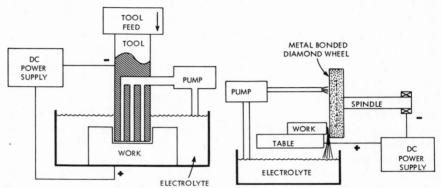

FIG. 24–2. Electrochemical machining.   FIG. 24–3. Electrolytic grinding.

efficiently used. In ECM the electrolyte is made to flow rapidly between the tool and the work by pressures up to 600 psi. Currents up to 10,000 amperes are used on a five square inch area with a resulting metal removal rate of about one cubic inch per minute. With adequate power supplies, there appears to be no reason that the metal removal rate could not be even greater.

Electrochemical machining is used for many of the same jobs that could be done by EDM, including the making of irregularly shaped holes, forming shaped cavities, and machining very hard or abrasive materials. Fig. 24–2 gives an outline of the process. Compared to EDM, tolerances must be greater, particularly in cavity shaping, and tool design is more critical to obtain proper flow of the electrolyte between the tool and the work. In addition, as much as 160 hp per cubic inch per minute of metal removal is required. This is about four times that required by EDM, and over one hundred times that needed by most conventional machining. On the other hand, tools do not wear and the metal removal rate is much greater than with EDM.

Electrolytic Grinding.   Fig. 24–3 shows the details of this variation of electrochemical machining. The cathode is a rotating grinding wheel, metal bonded to make it electrically conductive. The work and wheel are flooded with electrolyte while a direct current is passed between them. In operation, electrolytic action accounts for from 90 to 95 per cent of the work material removal and mechanical action of the abrasive particles in the wheel for the remainder.

The grinding process is much less versatile than EDM or ECM, being used primarily for cut-off operations done with thin saw type wheels and for flat facing. The largest single application, and the one for which the process was originally developed, is for grinding cemented carbides. The principal advantages when compared to conventional grinding are higher removal rates and lower wheel wear.

Chemical Milling.   This is a process for shaping of metals by chemical dissolution without electrical action. The name apparently originated from early applications where the process was used in aircraft manufacture as an adjunct to milling. It was originally used primarily to remove metal for weight reduction in areas of the workpiece that were not accessible to milling cutters and where work contours made following the surface with a cutter virtually impossible.

The procedure is relatively simple. The part is first masked in the areas where material is not to be removed with an oxidation resistant coating. The masking may be done by first coating the workpiece entirely, then removing the masking material from the desired areas by hand. Where production quantities warrant, silk screening may be used to apply the maskant only where needed. The part is then immersed in a suitable etchant which is usually a strong acid or alkalie. After the material has been etched to the required depth, the work is removed, rinsed, and the maskant removed.

One of the most widely used applications at present is in the manufacture of printed circuit boards for electronic assemblies. The process is also competitive with conventional press blanking for short runs, especially in thin material. One of the principal drawbacks is the undercutting that occurs along the edges of the mask. Depth control is reasonably good, but straight vertical sides or sharp corners cannot be achieved in the cavity produced.

Ultrasonic Machining.   The term ultrasonic machining is used to denote an abrasive machining process used for cutting hard materials by projecting tiny abrasive particles at the work surface at high velocities. Fig. 24–4 shows the details of the process. The abrasive is carried in a liquid flowing between the shaped tool and the workpiece. The tool is made to oscillate along its axis at a frequency of about 20,000 cps.

The heart of the equipment is the *transducer* which converts the high frequency electrical power to mechanical energy. Most transducers are made with nickel laminations which are placed in an oscillating magnetic field. Nickel has the property of *magnetostriction* and undergoes a change in length when placed in a magnetic field. The amplitude of vibration of the nickel is insufficient for practical use and must be amplified by attaching a suitable *horn* to one end. The tool is then brazed, soldered, or mechanically fastened to the end of the horn. The entire assembly must be mechanically tuned to resonate at the frequency produced by the electronic amplifier. When so tuned, the amplitude of the tool motion is from 0.002 to 0.004 inch.

The tool itself is most often made of soft steel and is given the negative shape of the cavity to be produced, as in EDM or ECM. The most common abrasive used is boron carbide in grit size ranging from 240 (coarse) to 800 (fine). The cutting rate and finish produced both depend on the size of the abrasive. With 800 grit abrasive, finishes as fine as ten microinches may be attained. Tolerances as close as 0.0005 inch are possible on size and contour with fine abrasives.

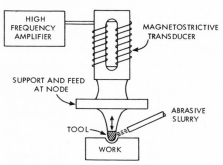

FIG. 24–4.   Ultrasonic machining.

Unlike conventional machining, which works only with material below a certain hardness, and EDM or ECM, which work with any conductive material, ultrasonic machining is best suited to materials that are both hard and brittle. However, the work material need not be a metal or otherwise conductive. The process has been used for engraving, slicing, drilling, and cavity sinking on hardened steel, gem stones, cemented carbides, ferrites, aluminum oxide, glass, and other ceramics.

Metal removal rate is presently the principal drawback, being only about 0.02 cubic inches per minute. It could possibly be increased considerably with better transducers but the process is likely to remain in the special purpose category.

Electron Beam Machining.   The use of a high energy stream of electrons as a power source was discussed in Chapter 16 in connection with welding and pictured in Fig. 16–10. The problems of generating and controlling the electron beam are more severe for machining than for welding. For welding, a continuous beam of relatively low intensity is sufficient. The problem in metal cutting is to vaporize a very localized area of material without melting or overheating the adjacent material. This is accomplished in *electron beam* machining by providing higher acceleration voltages than are used in welding, focusing the beam to a stream as small as 0.0005 inch diameter, then pulsing the beam on and off, subjecting the workpiece to short bursts of great energy. These short bursts are capable of vaporizing almost any known material. Damage to adjacent material is limited to a depth of about fifty millionths of an inch. Holes as small as 0.0005 inch and slots as narrow as 0.001 inch are possible.

The process has a number of drawbacks. As with electron beam welding, the operation must be carried out in a vacuum or with very low pressure inert gas. The equipment is quite expensive because of the precise apparatus needed to generate and control the beam. At present, the material removal rates are about the same as those achieved with ultrasonic machining. The potential removal rate appears to be much greater if adequate means of generating the electron beam can be designed.

The process is presently used only for very specialized applications. These include drilling small holes in stainless steel fuel-injection nozzles, sapphire bearings, and television gun assemblies. For milling slots or other shapes, either the workpiece must be moved or the beam itself deflected electrically. One of the more spectacular applications using the deflected beam is to cut complex shapes as extrusion dies for synthetic fibers.

Other Possible Material Removal Methods.   Electron beam machining, as well as EDM, ECM, electrolytic grinding, chemical milling, and ultrasonic machining, is presently a commercially used process for which equipment is available. Much development work still remains to be done on all these processes, but their present value is sufficient to warrant their existence. Other potential removal processes are now purely in the development stage but may offer competition in the future.

One that has received the most publicity is the *laser* or optical maser. This is a device for converting electrical energy into a narrow, high intensity beam of light or infrared energy. Used in short bursts, the beam has sufficient energy to produce local vaporization such as occurs with electron beam machining. A single burst may contain energy sufficient to produce a 0.015 inch diameter hole in metal 0.125 inch thick. Although a vacuum is not required as with an electron beam, costs are still prohibitive for commercial application.

The plasma arc was discussed in Chapter 16 together with electron beams as a heating source for welding. Plasma arcs are also capable of sufficiently localized energy inputs that surface material may be melted and vaporized with relatively small heating of the adjacent material. They are being used for some straight line cutting operations, where control is simple and tolerance requirements are not too high. Some experimental work has been done in lathe turning using a plasma arc as a cutting tool.

DEPOSITION PROCESSES

Of the more traditional processes, both welding processes using filler material and casting involve the deposition of molten material. The material is forced to conform to the desired shape by pressure provided by gravity, external pressure, or surface tension. One newer process of the same general type deposits material in controlled small amounts and permits a shape to be built up. Another new process is a variation of powder metallurgy that allows more complex shapes to be produced and does not require conventional dies.

Electroforming.   This process may be described as the reverse of electrochemical machining. When a direct current is passed between two electrodes immersed in the proper electrolyte, material is removed from the anode and deposited on the cathode. This action is the basis of electroplating which will be discussed later. For electroforming, however, coatings of much greater thickness (up to ⅜ inch) are built up.

For the production of an electroformed part, a master or pattern must first be produced with external shape and dimensions corresponding to the interior shape desired in the work. The pattern must have a conducting surface. If made of a nonconducting material, it must be coated with a conducting film of metal or graphite. The pattern is then placed in the electrolyte and the metal deposited to the required thickness. For certain shapes, the part may be stripped from the pattern and the pattern reused. Other shapes may require that the pattern be removed chemically or, if made of a low melting point material, by melting.

The process has a number of advantages. It is possible to produce complex internal contours with close dimensional control and surface finishes as good as eight microinches RMS. Because of these properties electroforming is used in making high frequency wave guides and venturis for nozzles and flow measurement. Parts may be made much thinner than by most of the conventional processes. It is possible to deposit most metals by the process. Parts with different metals on the interior and exterior surfaces may also be produced.

On the other hand, wall thickness is difficult to keep uniform so that exterior shapes and dimensions may not be controlled accurately. The rate of production is normally quite slow and the cost is high.

Slip Casting.   This process is both old and new. It has been used for many years in the ceramics industry, but the application to metals is more recent. The process consists of the preparation of a *slip* or slurry of very fine solid particles carried in suspension in a liquid. The slip is poured into a porous plaster mold which removes the liquid by capillary action, leaving the solid particles. As applied to metals, the process is essentially powder metallurgy. The green (wet) casting is first thoroughly dried in air, then sintered at the proper temperature and in the proper atmosphere to cause diffusion and bonding of the metallic particles.

As with conventional powder metallurgy, it is possible to process parts of almost any metal or alloy including tungsten, tantalum, columbium, titanium, and zirconium. These metals all either have very high melting points or they are so chemically active that they tend to unite with and be contaminated by any known crucible materials.

Unlike conventional powder metallurgy, the process does not require high strength pressing dies. In addition, shape possibilities are almost unlimited. Hollow shapes, re-entrant angles, internal and external threads, cored shapes, and thin walled shapes are all possible. Parts produced have ranged from tungsten X-ray targets weighing a fraction of an ounce to rocket nozzles weighing over one hundred pounds.

The process is primarily a low production process. It is slow and costly and like most of the other processes mentioned in this chapter does not compete economically with conventional processes when the latter can be used. Dimensional control is a problem because of the shrinkage that occurs during sintering. The shrinkage does tend to be quite uniform, however. The properties of sintered parts depend largely on the density of the final part; for slip cast parts, the ultimate density is only about 90 per cent of the theoretical density for a casting.

GROSS SEPARATION PROCESSES

The processes to be discussed in this section are somewhat different from the previous ones of this chapter. First, they are conventional in the sense that they are widely used and have been in existence for many years. They are "miscellaneous" only because they do not fit well in any of the esablished categories of casting, welding, machining, or deformation. In many applications, they are in competition with both sawing and shearing, both for straight line and for contour cutting.

Torch Cutting. This process depends on the fact that metals will combine with oxygen in an exothermic reaction if maintained above a certain kindling temperature. For iron, this kindling temperature is 1500°F. In normal atmospheres, oxidation is relatively slow because the amount of oxygen in the air is limited and because the oxides that form on the surface have some protective qualities. Even so, oxidation creates many problems in heat treating operations, particularly of ferrous alloys.

If pure oxygen is supplied as a high velocity stream to the surface of heated metals, particularly iron, oxidation becomes very rapid and large amounts of heat are generated. The success of torch cutting depends on sufficient heat being generated to keep the temperature of the unoxidized base metal above the kindling temperature. Whether or not this condition will prevail depends on the amount of heat generated by the reaction, on the temperature, melting point, specific heat, and thermal conductivity of the metal being oxidized, on the nature of the oxides formed, and on the geometry of the metal in relation to the burning surface. In practice, correct conditions are easily obtained with pure iron and low alloy steels, but very difficult to secure with cast irons, very high alloy steels including stainless steel, and nonferrous alloys.

Fig. 24–5 shows a mechanized setup for making straight line cuts in steel plate. Manually guided torches may also be used but considerable skill is required in keeping the speed and angle of the cut adjusted properly. If the speed is too fast, the cut does not proceed all the way through the material. If the speed is too slow, excessive burning and melting occur and the cut is not smooth. The tip of the torch is usually made with a relatively large central orifice for the oxygen cutting jet, around which are several smaller orifices for the preheating flames. Oxyacetylene is commonly used for the preheating flames but oxypropane or oxyhydrogen also work well. In use, the preheating flames are ignited first. After the work is brought up to kindling temperature, the oxygen jet is turned on and the cut started. Once the cut has started the preheating flames could be turned off, but it is common practice to leave them on, especially for manual cutting.

When properly applied, oxygen cutting is a very useful and versatile process. Accuracies compare with those obtained by sawing. Many parts require no further finishing after cutting. In addition to straight line cuts, contours may be made with proper guidance. Oxygen cutting machines are often equipped with photoelectric cells and servo drives for following black and white drawings of parts to be cut. Numerical control is used to

FIG. 24–5. Oxyacetylene cutting.

some extent and will undoubtedly be used to a greater extent in the future. Where quantities of parts are required, cutting machines may be equipped with a number of torches guided by a single control so that a number of duplicate parts may be cut from plate simultaneously. Oxygen cutting is widely used in connection with welding operations for the edge preparation required for bevel and vee welds.

The thicknesses which may be cut appear to be unlimited. Thin plate may be cut and production cuts have been made on steel up to sixty-two inches thick. However, the materials that can be cut are limited. Plain carbon and low alloy steels may be cut with no difficulty. If nickel is above 20 per cent, chromium above 5 per cent, or tungsten above 12 per cent, special techniques are required. With high percentages of these alloys, as normally exist in stainless steels, the oxides that form retard continuation of the cut. The problem may be overcome by introducing a fluxing agent with the oxygen. Nonferrous metals have such high thermal conductivity compared to the amount of heat generated by the burning that the metal may be maintained above the kindling temperature only by supplying heat in addition to that obtained from the burning reaction. Such heat is most commonly supplied by introducing powdered iron with the oxygen. As the iron burns, it adds heat to that obtained from the burning of the metal being cut. Because of the difficulties, oxygen cutting is not an important process for nonferrous metals.

A more recently developed method of cutting uses an electric arc. In *gas-shielded metal arc cutting*, a steel wire is fed at high speed while extremely high currents are used. The wire actually passes completely through the workpiece while the arc exists between the wire and the sides of the cut. The process is usable for cutting nonferrous alloys and stainless steels as well as plain carbon and low alloy steels. Argon is normally used as a shielding gas.

Friction Sawing.   Like torch cutting, friction sawing is not a new process although it is somewhat more special purpose and less widely used. It comes close to fitting the description for machining, but chips are not produced as they are in machining. Friction sawing depends on the generation of heat by the edge of a steel blade or disc in contact with the work moving at speeds of from 15,000 to 25,000 fpm. It is not necessary that the tool have any kind of cutting teeth, although it is usually equipped with shallow, square or vee shaped notches. The work is heated by friction and as it nears the melting point its strength becomes low enough that it is wiped from the cut.

Both rotary machines, similar to circular saws, and band machines, similar to upright band saws, are used. The tool is normally flooded with water as it leaves the cut to prevent its overheating. Relatively little wear on the tool occurs since it is in contact with the work only a small percentage of the time.

Friction sawing is used primarily for cut-off operations in connection with steel mill and warehouse operations for cutting bars, rods, and structural shapes to length. It is a fast operation, requiring large amounts of power. The finish and accuracy are equivalent to those obtained from oxygen cutting. Nonferrous metals are not normally cut because of their tendency to adhere to the tool and, as in torch cutting, the difficulty of maintaining high localized temperatures.

QUESTIONS

1. For what main reasons are new shape processing methods developed?
2. How do the majority of nonconventional shaping processes differ in load application to the work from the older more conventional methods?
3. Why are the majority of nonconventional processes little used?
4. How long before EDM was successfully put to work was it known that metals could be eroded with sparks?
5. Is a maintained ionized column of gas between the electrodes desirable or undesirable for EDM?

6. Sketch a schematic electrical circuit for EDM.
7. What is the purpose of a servo-control in the EDM electrode circuit?
8. What are the primary elements affecting rate of removal with EDM?
9. What are the two principal advantages EDM offers over traditional machining methods?
10. Why must EDM tool electrodes either be longer than the surface they are used to produce or be available in multiple quantities?
11. What main advantage does ECM show over EDM?
12. Describe the two major differences between ECM and electroplating.
13. How does ECM power efficiency compare with EDM and conventional machining?
14. By what action, or actions, is material removed in electrolytic grinding?
15. Describe chemical milling.
16. What material property is described by the word magnetostrictive?
17. Regarding work material, what advantage does ultrasonic machining offer over EDM and ECM?
18. Name three drawbacks to electron beam machining.
19. What is electroforming?
20. To what other process is slip casting most closely related?
21. What temperature condition is essential for torch-cutting to be successful?
22. What is the source of heat in torch cutting?
23. Why are nonferrous metals difficult to cut with a torch?
24. What range of speeds is used for friction sawing?

CHAPTER 25

Surface Finishing

Products that have been completed to their proper shape and size frequently require some type of surface finishing to enable them to satisfactorily fulfill their function. In some cases, it is necessary to improve the physical properties of the surface material for resistance to penetration or abrasion. In many manufacturing processes, the product surface is left with dirt, chips, grease, or other harmful material upon it. Assemblies which are made of different materials, or from the same materials processed in different manner, may require some special surface treatment to provide uniformity of appearance.

Surface finishing may sometimes become an intermediate step in processing. For instance, cleaning and polishing are usually essential before any kind of plating process. Some of the cleaning type procedures are also used for improving surface smoothness on mating parts and for removal of burrs and sharp corners, which might be harmful in later use. Another important need for surface finishing is for corrosion protection in a variety of environments. The type of protection provided will depend largely upon the anticipated exposure, with due consideration to the material being protected and the economic factors involved.

Satisfying the above objectives necessitates the use of many surface finishing methods which involve chemical change of the surface, mechanical work affecting surface properties, cleaning by a variety of methods, and the application of protective coating, organic and metallic.

CASE HARDENING OF STEELS

Some product applications require surface properties of hardness and strength to resist penetration under high pressure, and to provide maximum wear qualities. Where through hardness and the maximum strength associated with it are not necessary, it may be more economical to gain the needed surface qualities by a *case hardening* process. Case hardening involves a change of surface properties to produce a hard wear-resistant shell about a tough, fracture resistant core. This is usually accomplished by a change of surface material chemistry. With some materials, a similar condition can be produced by a phase change of material already present.

Case hardening may be more satisfactory than through hardening in those cases where a low carbon low cost steel with a hard shell, may be used instead of a higher cost high carbon or alloy steel needed for through hardening. The process is much less likely to cause warping or cracking and the product, because of its soft ductile core, is less subject to brittle failure than a through hardened product. Case hardening is often suitable for heavy sections which would require very special high alloy steels for through hardening to be effective.

Carburizing. Case hardening of steel may be accomplished by a number of methods. Choice between them is dependent on the material to be treated, the application, and the desired properties. One of the more common methods is carburizing, which implies an increase or addition of carbon which is actually the basis of the process.

Carburizing is usually performed on a low alloy or plain, low carbon steel. If an alloy steel is used, it usually will contain small quantities of nickel of some other element which will act as a retardant to grain growth during the heating cycle. Low carbon steels are commonly used to minimize the effect of subsequent heat treatments on the core material. It is possible to carburize any steel containing less than the 0.70 to 1.20 per cent carbon which is produced in the surface material.

Carbon is caused to diffuse into the steel by heating the material above its critical temperature and holding it in the presence of excess carbon. Temperatures used are usually between 1550°F. and 1700°F., with the choice most dependent on the desired rate of penetration, the desired surface carbon content, and the permissible grain growth in the material. Penetration is dependent upon both the temperature and time with variation of case depth from 0.010 to 0.040 inches possible in the first two hours by varying the temperature between the two extremes. The rate of penetration slows down as the depth increases as shown in Fig. 25–1, so that for large depths, relatively long periods of time are necessary.

The excess carbon for diffusion is supplied from a carbon rich environment in solid, liquid, or gas form. Parts to be carburized may be packed in carbon or other carbonaceous material in boxes which are sealed to exclude air, then heated in a furnace for the required length of time, in a process sometimes referred to as *pack hardening*. The liquid method makes use of molten sodium cyanide in which the parts are suspended to take on carbon. The cyanide method is usually limited to shallow case depths of about 0.010 inches maximum. The third method—often the most simple for production operations requiring heavy case depth—supplies gaseous hydrocarbons from an unburned gas or oil fuel source to the furnace retort in which the product is heated. The product is usually suspended on wires or rolled about in order that all surfaces will be exposed uniformly.

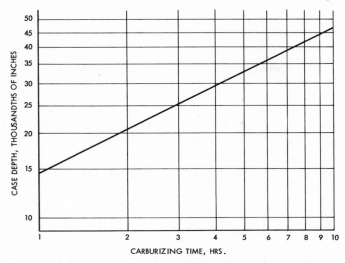

FIG. 25–1. Typical carburizing case depth-time relationship.

Carburizing steels containing grain growth inhibitors may be quenched directly from the carburizing furnace to harden the outside shell, but plain carbon steels must be cooled and reheated through the critical temperature range to reduce grain size. Even the alloy steels will have better properties if treated in this manner. Quenching from above the critical temperature will produce a hard martensitic structure in the high carbon surface material, but will have little or no effect on the low carbon core. As in the case of most through hardened steels, tempering is usually required to toughen the outside shell. The complete cycle for case hardening by carburizing is illustrated in Fig. 25–2.

Nitriding. Nitriding is another case hardening process by which the chemistry of the surface material is changed but in a different way than when carburized. The temperature of the product is raised to something less than 1000°F. in the presence of ammonia which causes very hard nitrides to form in the surface material. The process is very slow compared to that of carburizing and requires about seventy-two hours for development of approximately 0.025 inches depth of case. Despite the time requirement, nitriding is sometimes used for quality work because it makes a harder and more wear resistant surface than can be produced by carburizing. The surface does not require heat treating to develop its hardness and the lower temperature used in the process is less likely to cause warping.

Hardfacing. Although not usually referred to as case hardening, a result somewhat similar can be produced by depositing a hard alloy material on the product surface with welding techniques. Most commonly, materials that harden in the air as they cool, or materials that are hard in the solid state regardless of their temperature, are used for this purpose. Dimensions are changed by the application of the hard facing, and usually if a smooth surface is required, grinding or some other finishing procedure is necessary.

Hardfacing has advantages over carburizing: it is easier to treat surfaces on a product selectively, large depths of hard material are relatively easy to produce, different materials with different properties can be applied by the same process, and in many cases the deposition can be made in the field rather than in the factory. A typical example of its use is the coating of a plow point with a wear resistant metal alloy either originally to provide long life or later as a maintenance action.

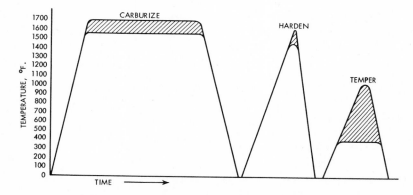

FIG. 25–2.   Heating cycle for case hardening by carburizing.

Flame Hardening.   Another case hardening process which does not require a change of composition in the surface material is flame hardening. This method can be used only on steels that contain sufficient carbon to be hardenable by standard heat treating procedures. The case is produced by selectively heating part or all of the surface with special high capacity gas burners or oxyacetylene torches at a rate sufficiently high that only a small depth from the surface goes above the critical temperature. Following immediately behind the torch is a water quenching head which floods the surface to reduce the temperature fast enough to produce a martensitic structure. As in the case of carburizing, the surface may be then reheated to temper it for toughness improvement. The depth of hardness is controlled by the temperature to which the metal is raised, by the rate of heating, and by the time that passes before quenching.

Flame hardening is used on materials of such composition that they could be through hardened, but if surface hardness is the only reason for treatment the case method is likely to be cheaper, particularly on large pieces. Also the chance of warping is reduced to a large degree. Flame hardening is used to produce hard, wear resistant surfaces on selected areas of large pieces such as machine tool beds that would be extremely difficult to treat by the more conventional heat treating procedures.

Results similar to flame hardening can be produced with induction heating and quenching. The part to be treated is encased in a coil of proper design for the work size and shape. High frequency electrical energy passing through the coil sets up magnetic fields in the work which cause eddy currents resulting in heat. The location and extent of heating is controlled by the coil design, and current flow, and the frequency of the power supply. Quenching from a water spray similar to that used in flame hardening may be automatically timed in production operations.

Few, if any, shaping and sizing processes produce products that are usable without some type of cleaning unless special precautions are taken. Hot working, heat treating, and welding cause oxidation and scale forma-

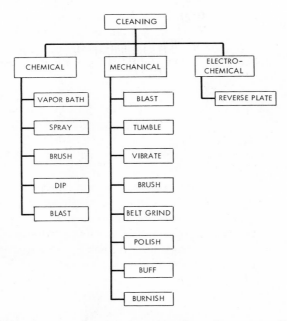

tion from high temperature in the presence of oxygen. For the same reason, castings usually are coated with scale or oxides. If made in sand molds they may have sand grains fused or adhering to the surface. Residue from coolants, lubricants, and other processing materials is common on many manufactured parts. In addition to greasy films from processing, protective coatings of greases, oils or waxes are frequently used intentionally to prevent rust or corrosion on parts that are stored for some period of time before being put to use. Even if parts are clean at the completion of manufacturing they seldom remain that way for long. After only short storage periods, corrosion and dust from atmospheric exposure necessitate cleaning for best condition or to permit further processing.

Cleaning sometimes has finish improvement associated with it. Some shape producing methods produce unsatisfactory surface characteristics such as sharp corners, burrs, and tool marks, which may effect the function, handling ease, and appearance of the product. Some cleaning processes at least partially blend together surface irregularities to produce uniform light reflection. Improvement of surface qualities may be accomplished by removal of high spots by cutting or plastic flow as cleaning is performed.

Choice of Cleaning Method. As indicated by the list at the head of this section, many different cleaning methods are available. The one most suitable for any particular situation is dependent upon a number of factors. Cost is of course always a strong consideration, but the reason for cleaning is bound to affect the choice. Convenience in handling, improvement in appearance, elimination of foreign material which may affect function, or establishment of a chemically clean surface as an intermediate step in processing might all call for different methods. Consideration must be given to the starting conditions and to degree of improvement desired or required. Methods suitable for some materials are not at all satisfactory for use on other kinds of material.

Some cleaning methods provide multiple benefits. As pointed out above, cleaning and finish improvement are often combined. Probably of even greater importance is the combination of corrosion protection with finish improvement, although corrosion protection is more often a second step which involves coating an already cleaned surface with some other material.

Liquid and Vapor Baths. The most widely used cleaning methods make use of a cleaning medium in liquid or vapor form. These methods depend on a solvent or chemical action between the surface contaminants and the cleaning material. Many cleaning methods and a variety of materials are available for choice depending on the base material to be cleaned, the contaminant to be removed, the importance and degree of cleanliness, and the quantity to be treated.

Among the more common cleaning jobs required is the removal of grease and oil deposited during manufacturing or intentionally coated on the work to provide protection. One of the most efficient ways to remove this material is by use of solvents which dissolve the grease and oil but have no effect on the base metal. Petroleum derivatives such as Stoddard solvent and Kerosene are common for this purpose, but since they introduce some danger of fire, chlorinated solvents such as trichloretholene which are free of this fault are sometimes substituted.

One of the most economical cleaning materials is water. However, it is seldom used alone even if the contaminant is fully water soluble, since the impurity of the water itself may contaminate the work surface. Depending on its use, water is treated with various acids and alkalies to suit the job being performed.

Water containing sulfuric acid in a concentration from about 10 to 25 per cent and at a temperature of approximately 150°F. is commonly used in a process called *pickling* for removal of surface oxides or scale on iron and steel. The work is immersed in the solution contained in large tanks for a predetermined period of time after which it is rinsed to stop the chemical action. Improper control of the timing, temperature, or concentration in the pickling bath is likely to result in pitting of the surface because of uneven chemical reaction. Most pickling baths are treated with chemical inhibitors which decrease the chemical effect of the acid on the base metal but have little effect on the rate at which the oxides are attacked.

Many of the common cleaning liquids are made up of approximately 95 per cent water containing alkaline cleaners such as caustic soda, sodium carbonate, silicates, phosphates, and borates. The proportions are varied for different purposes and are available under different brand names for particular applications.

Liquid cleaners may be applied in a number of ways. Degreasing, particularly on small parts, is frequently done with a vapor bath. This does an excellent job of removing the grease but has the disadvantage of not being able to remove chips and other kinds of dirt that might be present. Vapor degreasing is usually done in a special tank which is heated at the bottom to vaporize the solvent and cooled at the top to condense the solvent. Cold work suspended in the vapor causes condensation of the solvent which dissolves the grease and drips back into the bottom of the tank. The difference in volatility between the solvent and the greases permits the vapor to remain unchanged and to do a uniform cleaning job.

Spraying, brushing, and dipping methods are also used with liquid cleaners. In nearly all cases, mechanical work to cause surface film breakdown and particle movement is combined with chemical and solvent action. The mechanical work may be agitation of the product as in dipping, movement of the cleaning agent as in spraying or use of a third element as in rubbing or brushing. In some applications, sonic or ultrasonic vibrations are applied to either the solution or the workpieces to speed the cleaning action. Chemical activity is increased with higher temperatures and optimum concentration of the cleaning agent, both of which must in some cases be controlled closely for efficient action.

Washing and rinsing away of the cleaning liquids is usually necessary to prevent films and spots. Fast drying of water solutions on iron and steel products is sometimes needed to prevent the formation of rust. If the product mass is large enough, heat picked up from the cleaning bath may be sufficient to cause fast drying; otherwise, air blasts or external heat sources may be required.

Blasting.   The term blasting is used to refer to all of those cleaning methods in which the cleaning medium is accelerated to high velocity and impinged against the surface to be cleaned. The high velocity may be provided by air or water directed through a nozzle or by mechanical means with a revolving slinger. The cleaning agent may be sand, abrasive, steel grit, or shot, used either dry or wet, and liquid or vapor solvents combined with abrasive material.

The solid media are used for the removal of brittle surface contaminations such as the heat treat scale found on forgings and castings. Steel grit has replaced sand and other refractory type abrasives to some extent, because of the reduced health hazard (silicosis) and a reduced tendency for pulverization. Sand, however, can be used without danger to the operator when parts are small enough to be handled by hand inside a properly designed chamber fitted with a dust collector.

In addition to cleaning, solid particles can improve finish and surface properties of the material on which they are used. Blasting tends to increase the surface area thus setting up compressive stresses which may cause a warping of thin sections, but in other cases may be very beneficial by reducing the likelihood of fatigue failure. When used for this latter purpose, the process is more commonly known as *shotpeening*.

Liquid or vaporized solvents may by themselves be blasted against a surface for high speed cleaning of oil and grease films with both chemical and mechanical action. Water, containing rust inhibiting chemicals, may carry fine abrasive particles in suspension which provide a grinding cutting type action for finish improvement along with cleaning. The blasting method using this medium is commonly known as *liquid honing*.

Abrasive Barrel Finishing.   Barrel finishing, rolling, tumbling, and rattling are all terms used to describe similar operations which consist of packing parts together with some cleaning media in a cylinder or drum which can be rotated to cause movement between them. The media may be abrasives, either fine or coarse, metal stars, slugs or balls, stones, wood chips, saw dust, or cereals. In fact, any material capable of producing abrasive and polishing action can be used. The work may be done wet or dry depending upon the materials being worked with, the kinds of surface finishes desired, and the kind of equipment available. The time required to complete the work may vary from one to ten hours or sometimes even longer, but even so it is usually a cheap process since relatively large quantities may be treated at one time. The only human labor involved is for loading and unloading.

The process referred to as *tumbling* or *rattling* is most commonly a foundry cleaning process for removal of scale, adhering sand, and minor projection type faults from both ferrous and nonferrous castings. Small to medium size parts, usually in a variety of shapes and sizes, are packed to fill a tumbling barrel almost completely, as shown in Fig. 25–3. Metal stars, slugs, or loose gates and risers are usually added to aid in the cleaning action. As the barrel is slowly rotated, the parts slide against each other to produce a cleaning action. Care must be exercised not to place parts with too great variety of size in the same load to prevent damage to the smaller and weaker pieces. Some parts with thin weak sections may require the use of fixtures to prevent damage.

The term *barrel finishing* is most commonly used to refer to the rolling, deburring, polishing, and burnishing also illustrated in Fig. 25–3. The differences between all the barrel cleaning methods are rather small, consisting mainly of the medium used and the purpose of the work. As already pointed out, tumbling slides parts against each other. Rolling, deburring, and polishing are accomplished by using a relatively large amount of abrasive material to perform the cleaning, while burnishing depends upon the impact and high pressure sliding of balls or pins to clean, polish, and compress the work surfaces. Most rolling, polishing and burnishing is done wet with soaps, detergents, lubricants, or chemical inhibitors present in the mixture to speed up the operations and produce more uniform results.

Many manufacturers are now producing vibratory finishers in which small parts can be smoothed and polished with results similar to those of rolling or barrel polishing. Parts are mixed with abrasive materials in a

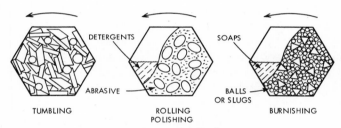

FIG. 25–3. Barrel finishing.

hopper which vibrates to provide motion to all of its contents. The ratio of abrasive to work is high. The vibratory motion causes the individual work pieces to move slowly about, rotate, and assume all positions, exposing their surfaces to the cutting action of the abrasive. As in barrel finishing, the operation is usually done wet to produce better and faster results.

Wire Brushing.   A number of cleaning operations can be quickly and easily performed by use of a high speed rotating wire brush. In addition to cleaning, the contact and rubbing of the wire ends across the work surface produces surface improvement by a burnishing type action. Sharp edges and burrs can be removed. Scratches, rough spots, and similar mechanical imperfections can be improved primarily by plastic flow which also tends to work harden the surface material. Most wire brushing is done under manual control, but where the surfaces can be made accessible and the quantity to be treated is sufficiently large for economic feasibility, machines for automatic brushing can be set up.

Common applications of wire brushing are the cleaning of castings, both ferrous and nonferrous, the cleaning of spatter and slag from weldments, and the removal of rust, corrosion, paint, etc. from any object whose base material is strong enough to withstand the brushing. Wire brushing produces a distinctive pattern on the surface and in addition to cleaning, it sometimes is used to produce a decorative surface.

Abrasive Belt Finishing. Continuous fabric belts coated with abrasive can be driven in several kinds of machines to provide a straight line cutting motion for grinding, smoothing, and polishing work surfaces. Plane surfaces are the most common worked upon. For these, a table or platen behind the belt provides support to produce a flat surface when work is held against the belt. Some curved surfaces can be worked on where the belt passes around a drum or pulley and edges are sometimes deburred against a loose belt having no backing support. Most abrasive belt polishing is manually operated, although large sheets of steel, brass, aluminum, plastic, and other materials may be finished in fully automatic machines.

The speed of cutting and the quality of surface finish obtained with coated abrasives is dependent mainly on the abrasive size used. The abrasive type and cutting speed also show some influence. Where fine finishes are desired, as in metallurgical polishing, a succession of finer abrasives is used with each one removing the scratch marks of the preceding abrasive until the desired quality is reached. Fine abrasives are used most where the principal objective is finish improvement. When coarse grains are used, significant amounts of material may be removed.

Initial flat surfaces on castings, forgings, weldments, and other type work objects are sometimes established by belt grinding. However, it is more common, when the objective is primarily that of material removal, to use grinding wheels of solid construction. Fins on castings and forgings are frequently removed in this way, and gate connections, imperfections, or rough spots on all kinds of parts smoothed by use of grinding wheels. Burrs and sharp edges also may be removed by grinding, although this is usually limited to small lot sizes since more economical methods are available when the quantities are large enough.

Polishing. The term polishing may be interpreted to mean any non-precision procedure providing a glossy surface but is most commonly used to refer to a surface finishing process using a flexible abrasive wheel. The wheels may be constructed of felt or rubber with an abrasive band, of multiple coated abrasive discs, of leaves of coated abrasive, of felt or fabric to which loose abrasive is added as needed, or with abrasives in a rubber matrix.

These wheels differ from grinding wheels only by being flexible, which enables them to apply uniform pressure to the work surface and permits them to conform to the surface shape.

Polishing is usually done off-hand except where the quantity is large. The process may have several objectives. Interest may be only in finish improvement for appearance. The surface finish may be important as an underlay for plating, which has only limited ability to improve surface quality over that of the surface on which it is placed. Polishing may also be important as a means of improving fatigue resistance for products subject to this kind of failure.

Buffing. About the only difference between buffing and polishing is that, for buffing, a fine abrasive carried in wax or a similar substance is charged on the surface of a flexible wheel. The objectives are similar. With finer abrasive, buffing produces higher quality finish and luster, but removes only minor amounts of metal. With both polishing and buffing, particularly of the softer metals, plastic flow permits filling of pores, scratches, and other surface flaws to improve both appearance and resistance to corrosion.

Electropolishing. If a workpiece is suspended in an electrolyte and connected to the anode in an electrical circuit, it will supply metal to the electrolyte in a reverse plating process. Material will be removed faster from the high spots of the surface than from the depressions, thereby increasing the average smoothness. The cost of the process is prohibitive for very rough surfaces since larger amounts of metal must be removed to improve surface finish than would be necessary for the same degree of improvement by mechanical polishing. Electropolishing is economical only for improving a surface that is already good or for polishing complex and irregular shapes, the surfaces of which are not accessible to mechanical polishing and buffing equipment.

COATINGS

Many products, in particular those exposed to view and those subject to change by the environment with which they are in contact, need some type of coating for improved appearance or for protection from chemical attack. All newly created surfaces are subject to corrosion, although the rate of occurrence varies greatly with the material, the environment, and the conditions. For all practical purposes, some materials are highly corrosion resistant because the products of corrosion resist further corrosion. For example, a newly machined surface on an aluminum alloy will immediately be attacked by oxygen in the air. The initial aluminum oxide coating protects the remaining metal and practically stops corrosion unless an environmental change occurs. Corrosion rates are closely dependent on environment. Rates increase with rise of temperature and greater concentration of the attacking chemical.

The need for corrosion protection for maintenance of appearance is obvious. An object made of bright steel will begin to show rust in a few hours time of exposure to ordinary atmosphere, unless protected. In addition to change of appearance, loss of actual material, change of dimensions, and decrease of strength, corrosion may be the cause of eventual loss of service or failure of a product. Material that must carry loads in structural applications, especially when the loads are cyclic in nature, may fail with fatigue if corrosion is allowed to take place. Corrosion occurs more readily in highly stressed material where it attacks grain boundaries in such a way as to form points of stress concentration which may be nuclei for fatigue failure.

The corrections for corrosion problems include choice of materials that resist attack from the environment to which they are exposed, selection or control of the environment to minimize corrosion effects, and the use of selective corrosion by placing materials with greater susceptibility to corrosion near those to be protected. The latter is illustrated by the use of magnesium rods in hot water tanks. The magnesium is the target for corrosion; as long as it is present, corrosion of the steel walls of the tank is insignificant. Another correction for corrosion, when the others are impractical, is the coating of the surfaces needing protection with a material that excludes the environmental elements that are harmful.

In addition to stabilizing appearance by resisting corrosion, coatings are often very valuable for providing color control, change in appearance, and variety, which may be important to sales appeal. Some coatings, such as fillers, paint, and others with substantial body, improve surface smoothness by filling pores and cavities. Some coating materials can provide uniform appearance for products made as assemblies of different materials.

Coatings of various types may be used to change or improve surface properties. Case hardening of steel has been discussed earlier and although it is a surface property changing method, in most of its forms case hardening does not consist of the addition of a coating. Hardness and wear resistance can, however, be provided on a surface by plating with hard metals. Chromium plating of gages subject to abrasion is frequently used to increase their wear life. Coatings of plastic materials and asphaltic mixtures are sometimes placed on surfaces to provide sound deadening. The additional benefit of protection from corrosion is usually acquired at the same time.

Friction characteristics of a surface can be varied in either direction by application of a coating. Rubber and some other plastic materials may be applied for increase of friction characteristics. An example would be the special compounds applied to the floor boards or bottom of small boats to decrease the chance of slipping. Other plastic materials, the fluorocarbons being good examples, are applied to surfaces where slipping is desired since they will provide a very low coefficient of friction. Plastics of many kinds, mostly of the thermoplastic type because they are easier to apply and also to remove later if necessary, are used for mechanical protection. Highly polished material may be coated with plastic which may be stripped off later to prevent abrasion and scratches during processing. It is common practice to coat newly sharpened cutting edges of tools by dipping them in thermoplastic material to provide mechanical protection during handling and storage. Multiple benefits are obtained in many cases. For example, the plastic coating on the wires of a dishwasher basket supplies corrosion protection for the wires themselves, mechanical protection for dishes that are placed in the basket, and sound deadening.

Preparation for Coatings.   Cleaning by one or more of the methods discussed earlier in the chapter is usually essential before any kind of coating can be applied. In practically every case, a clean dry surface is necessary for coating adhesion. The quality of surface finish before coating may vary through a wide range, depending on the kind of coating and its purpose. Whether or not a combination cleaning and smoothing operation should be used depends somewhat on the previous processing as well as the desired final finish. Some coatings, such as the heavier plastics, can hide large faults and imperfections but others, such as finishing lacquers and metallic platings, improve finish quality to only a very small degree. With the latter, scratches, surface faults, and even tool marks can continue to show on the final surface even though the coating tends to blend and soften them.

Coating Material and Method Needs. A large variety of coating materials and a number of methods of application are needed to supply all of the requirements. The variety of materials to be coated is, of course, great. Under some circumstances, any structural material may require coating. In a few cases, it may be desirable to coat a material without changing its appearance, but in most cases, the appearance, both texture and color, is changed to a large degree. Although affected some by coating, surface smoothness is usually a result of previous processing. However, without substantial change in surface quality, a number of different surface finishes can be provided with uniformity of appearance by application of a suitable coating.

Manufactured products show a need for a variety of surface properties, are subject to all kinds of environments, and must withstand wide degrees of exposure. Surface coatings may be expected to provide physical properties not already present and to provide protection from acids, alkalies, moisture, temperature, and other environmental conditions which may affect the function or life of the product. The expected life of a coating varies widely, with those providing the best life usually being of the highest cost. As in many other situations, the material used turns out to be a compromise choice of the cheapest one to provide satisfactory service. Desired life varies with the application. Sometimes temporary protection for transit or storage is all that is required. In other cases, for example, with chemical equipment, the entire life of the product may be dependent on the coating chosen.

Organic Coatings. Organic coatings are used to provide pleasing colors, to smooth surfaces, to provide uniformity in both color and texture, and to act as a protective film for control of corrosion. Organic resin coatings do not ordinarily supply any chemical inhibiting qualities. Instead they merely provide a separating film between the surface to be protected and the corrosive environment. The important properties, therefore, are continuity, permeability, and adhesion characteristics.

If the film is a mere mechanical barrier, it is obvious that *continuity* or lack of porosity is essential for corrosion protection. Different organic coatings and different work materials being covered require different thicknesses of the coating material for production of a pore free film. *Permeability* is a measure of the ability of a film to pass water vapor and other gases through itself. Coatings providing the best protection will have low permeability. Passage of gases is not dependent on porosity but instead is more likely to be a mechanism of absorption followed by diffusion through the coating material. The addition of pigments can materially alter the permeability characteristics of a particular vehicle. One of the most efficient in reducing permeability is leafing type aluminum.

The ability of an organic film to adhere to a metal surface (adhesion) is dependent primarily on the degree of cleanliness of the metal surface. However, some materials hold tighter on a surface that has been slightly roughened by some process such as sand blasting, while still others may require chemical treatment of the base metal for formation of an oxide or phosphate film for satisfactory adhesion.

Paints, Varnishes, and Enamels.   Painting is a generic term that has come to mean the application of almost any kind of organic coating by any method. Because of this interpretation, it is also used generally to describe a broad class of product. As originally defined and as used most at present, paint is a mixture of pigment in a drying oil. Color and opacity are supplied by the pigment. The oil serves as a carrier for the pigment and in addition creates a tough continuous film as it dries. Drying oils, one of the common ones of which is linseed oil, become solid when large surface areas are exposed to air. Drying starts with a chemical reaction of oxidation. Nonreversible polymerization accompanies oxidation to complete the change from liquid to solid. Paint is similar to a thermosetting plastic. Paint mixtures usually also contain driers and thinners. Driers are compounds of lead, manganese, and other metals which speed the drying action after the material has been spread. Thinners are liquids such as petroleum spirits or turpentine which are used to adjust the consistency of the paint mixture.

Varnish is a combination of natural or synthetic resins and drying oil, sometimes containing volatile solvents as well. The material dries by a chemical reaction in the drying oil to a clear or slightly amber color film. A solution of resin in a volatile solvent without the drying oil is called *spirit* varnish, or *shellac* varnish.

Enamel is a mixture of pigment in varnish. The resins in the varnish cause the material to dry to a smoother, harder, and glossier surface than produced by ordinary paints. Some enamels are made with thermosetting resins which must be baked for complete dryness. These *baking enamels* provide a toughness and durability not usually available with the ordinary paints and enamels.

Paints, varnish, and enamels are used for coating a wide variety of products. One of the biggest uses for paints is, of course, the coating of both exterior and interior structures. Varnishes are restricted primarily to finishing of wood where it is desired that the natural color show through.

Enamels are mixed to produce a variety of finishes, available in many colors, and may be used on almost any kind of product. Small products manufactured in quantity are likely to be coated with the *synthetic* (manufactured resin) baking type enamels because of the shorter drying time required.

Lacquers.   The term *lacquer* is used to refer to finishes consisting of thermoplastic materials dissolved in fast drying solvents. The most common combination is cellulose nitrate dissolved in butyl acetate. Present day lacquers are strictly air drying and form films very quickly after being applied, usually by spraying. No chemical change occurs during the hardening of lacquers so the dry film can be redissolved in the thinner. Cellulose acetate is used in place of cellulose nitrate in some lacquers because it is nonflammable. Vinyls, chlorinated hydrocarbons, and other synthetic thermoplastic resins are also occasionally used in the manufacture of lacquers.

Clear lacquers are used to some extent as protective films on such materials as polished brass, but the majority are pigmented and used as color coats. The pigmented lacquers are sometimes called *lacquer enamels*. Lacquers are widely used for coating manufactured products because of their ease of application and speed of drying.

Organic Coating Application.   Paint type materials are applied by dip, brush, and spray. Dipping is common for applying protective coatings to forgings and castings for prevention of rust during storage and processing and to serve as primers for the final finish. Many other products made in large quantities also are finished by dipping. Dipping may be done manually with parts hung on drying racks until finished. Frequently parts are hung on conveyors which dip down over paint tanks to immerse the product and then elevate again to carry the parts through an air dry cycle or sometimes through an oven for accelerated drying. Dip application is limited to parts that do not have recesses, pockets, or shapes that will hold the liquid paint or prevent its flowing to an even coat.

Brush painting is slow and used little in manufacturing work except on large, heavy, or odd shaped parts, that cannot be moved or manipulated in a spray paint area. Brushing and rolling are commonly used for coating structural surfaces such as walls and ceilings of buildings. Brushing does provide efficient use of coating material, since practically none of it is wasted and the mechanical rubbing of a brush or roller provides some cleaning action which may provide better adhesion.

By far the greatest amount of organic coatings are applied industrially by spraying. This method is used most with lacquers and fast drying enamels. The short drying time causes parts to become dust free very quickly so they can be moved away from the spray area and advantage can be taken of this fast application method. Spraying is done in booths designed for this purpose where adequate ventilation carries fumes and spray particles away from the operator. Large installations often use a water curtain in the back of the booth to collect for possible salvage the spray particles that do not strike the article being painted. Spray painting of automobile bodies and other large objects that are conveyorized is often done automatically with a number of spray heads, some stationary and some movable, adjusted to spray a uniform layer over the entire object.

Small objects, usually hanging on a chain conveyor, may be painted with an electrostatic spraying method for which the paint particles are sprayed through a high voltage electrostatic field. Each paint particle takes on an electric charge from the field and is attracted toward the grounded article to be painted. This method provides better efficiency of paint use than ordinary spraying, but even more important, causes the coating to distribute itself more evenly over the entire object. Electrostatic force can also be used to pull off drips or tears that form by gravity along the bottom edges of newly painted objects. This is done by passing the parts over an electrostatically charged electrode which exerts the force necessary to pull the heavy coating from the edge.

As indicated above, organic coating is often done in free air. Some solvents and vehicles are so volatile that drying is accomplished almost immediately. Others require several days for drying and still others require elevated temperatures for necessary polymerization to take place. Heat for drying and speeding chemical reaction may be provided by various types of ovens. Some ovens are batch types in which racks of parts are placed for specific periods of time. Others are continuous types built over conveyor systems which regulate the time of exposure by the length of oven and the speed of conveyor operation. Ovens that circulate hot air may be heated with any kind of fuel or electricity, with gas firing probably most common. Many coatings are dried by radiant heat from infrared lamps. These may be arranged to enclose the object in a manner similar to that of a hot air oven, or they may be set up in large banks or panels.

Vitreous Enamels.   Vitreous or *porcelain* enamel is actually a thin layer of glass fused onto the surface of a metal, usually steel or iron. Shattered glass, ball milled in a fine particle size, is called *frit*. Frit is mixed with clay, water, and metal oxides, which produce the desired color to form a thin slurry called *slip*. This is applied to the prepared metal surface by dipping or spraying and after drying is fired at approximately 1500°F. to fuse the material to the metal surface. For high quality coating, more than one layer is applied to guard against pinhole porosity.

Glass applied in this way has high strength and is usually flexible enough to withstand bending of the steel within the elastic limits of the base metal. The coatings have excellent resistance to atmospheric corrosion and to most acids. Vitreous enamels can be made suitable for use over a wide range of temperatures. Some special types have been used for corrosion protection on exhaust stacks for aircraft engines. Considering their high quality protection, vitreous enamels are relatively inexpensive and find many uses. At one time, many cooking pans were constructed of material of this type, but this use has been largely replaced by the use of stainless steels and aluminum. Linings for hot water tanks, containers for mild acids, and uses where materials must have corrosion resistance to high temperature fumes are important applications for this coating.

The advent of rockets and missiles has introduced an entirely new field where high temperature corrosion protection is essential. Porcelain enamel has been satisfactory in some of these applications but ceramic coatings with better refractory characteristics are more commonly used. Some are applied the same as porcelain enamel. Others are fused to the metal surfaces with the intense heat of a plasma jet.

Metallizing. Metal spraying, or *metallizing*, is a process in which metal wire or powder is fed into an oxyacetylene heating flame and then, after melting, is carried by high velocity air to be impinged against the work surface. The small droplets adhere to the surface and bond together to build up a coating. The nature of the bond is dependent largely on the materials. The droplets are relatively cool when they make contact and can in fact be sprayed on wood, leather, and other flammable materials so little, if any, liquid flow aids the bonding action. If, however, sufficient affinity exists between the metals, a type of weld involving atomic bonds may be established. The bond is largely mechanical in most cases, and metal spraying is usually done on surfaces that have been intentionally roughened to aid the mechanical attachment.

Zinc, aluminum, and cadmium, which are anodic to steel and therefore provide preferential corrosion protection, are usually sprayed in thin layers averaging about 0.010 inch thickness as protective coatings. Since sprayed coatings tend to be porous, coatings of two or more times this thickness are used for cathodic materials such as tin, lead, and nickel. The cathodic materials protect only by isolating the base material from its environment.

Another important application for metal spraying is in salvage operations for which a wide variety of metals and alloys may be used. Surfaces, usually after first being roughened, are built up to oversized dimensions with metal spray. The excess material is then machined away to the desired dimension. Expensive parts with worn bearing surfaces or new parts that have been machined undersized can sometimes be salvaged by this relatively cheap procedure.

Vacuum Metallizing. Some metals can be deposited in very thin films, usually for reflective or decorative purposes, as a vapor deposit. The metal is vaporized in a high vacuum chamber containing the parts to be coated. The metal vapor condenses on the exposed surfaces in a thin film that follows the surface pattern. The process is cheap for coating small parts, considering the time element only, but the cost of special equipment needed is relatively high.

Aluminum is the most used metal for deposit by this method and is used frequently for decoration or producing a mirror surface on plastics. The thin films usually require mechanical protection by covering with lacquer or some other coating material.

Hot Dip Plating.   Several metals, mainly zinc, tin, and lead, are applied to steel for corrosion protection by a hot dip process. Steel in sheet, rod, pipe, or fabricated form, properly cleansed and fluxed, is immersed in molten plating metal. As the work is withdrawn, the molten metal that adheres solidifies to form a protective coat. In some of the large mills the application is made continuously to coil stock that is fed through the necessary baths and even finally inspected before being recoiled or cut into sheets.

Zinc is one of the most common materials applied to steel in this manner. In addition to protection by exclusion, electrochemical protection (the source of the term *galvanized* iron) occurs when exposed steel and adjacent zinc are connected by conducting moisture. Zinc is one of the most favored coatings for corrosion protection of steel because of its low cost and ease of application. In addition to hot dipping, zinc can also be applied by electroplating, spraying, and *sherodizing*. Sherodizing is a process by which steel, heated in the presence of zinc dust, becomes coated with zinc.

Tin plating and terne plating, the latter using a mixture of approximately four parts lead to one part tin, are also done by hot dipping.

Electroplating.   Coatings of many metals can be deposited on other metals, and nonmetals when suitably prepared, by electroplating. The objectives of plating are to provide protection against corrosion, to improve appearance, to establish wear and abrasion resistant surfaces, to add material for dimensional increase, and to serve as an intermediate step of multiple coating. Some of the most common metals deposited in this way are copper, nickel, chromium, cadmium, zinc, tin, silver, and gold. The majority are used to provide some kind of corrosion protection, but appearance also plays a strong part in their use.

Fig. 25–4 is a schematic diagram of a simple plating setup. When direct current power of high enough voltage is applied to two electrodes immersed in a water solution of metallic salt, current will flow through the circuit causing changes at the electrodes. At the negative electrode or cathode (the work), excess electrons supplied from the power source neutralize positively charged metallic ions in the salt solution causing dissolved metal to be deposited in the solid state. At the positive electrode or anode (plating metal) metal goes into solution to replace that removed at the other electrode. The rate of deposition and the properties of the plated material are dependent on the metals being worked with, the current density, the solution temperature, and other factors. Thickness of plating is usually low, in the range of 0.0001 to 0.001 inches. Chromium applied for appearance only may be used in thickness of only about one tenth these amounts, but when used to provide wear resistance and for building up dimensions, as on gages, may be applied in thickness as much as 0.010 inches. Layers of different metals are sometimes plated for maximum properties. For example, an object such as a steel bumper for an automobile may first be copper plated for good adhesion and coverage of the steel and to facilitate buffing to a smooth surface necessary for high quality final finish. Nickel is then plated over the copper to serve as the principal corrosion protection. Finally, chromium is plated over the nickel to serve as a hard, wear resistant, bright, blue-white color coating over the softer, tarnishable nickel.

Some problems exist with electroplating. Deposit on irregular shapes may vary widely in thickness. Projections and exposed surfaces may plate readily but recesses, corners, and holes can sometimes be coated only by using specially located electrodes or electrodes shaped to conform to the

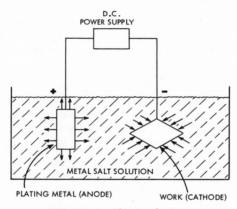

FIG. 25–4. Electroplating.

workpiece shape. Electroplating can be costly because it involves payment for considerable electric power and the metal plated and lost. Since plating thicknesses are usually very small, the coating has little hiding power and surface imperfections and roughness usually show through. Buffing and cleanliness before and during the processing are very important.

The equipment needed for electroplating is simple when compared with most other processing needs, but operations may require considerable space in production because of necessary cleaning and rinsing steps in addition to the plating itself. All electroplating operations require a source of direct current power. In most cases, 2 to 4 volts are all that is necessary but as many as 12 volts may be required when the work and anode cannot be placed close together. The current capacity of the supply is dependent upon the total surface area being plated at any one time. Larger areas require higher current flow to maintain sufficient current density. The power supply may be either a DC generator or a transformer-rectifier, either of which must have voltage control to permit adjustment for the amount of work being done. The tanks used for cleaning, rinsing, and plating are usually made of steel which may have to be lined with plastic, rubber, lead, or other material to prevent chemical attack or contamination of the electrolyte. Because of necessary cleaning and buffing operations, various mechanical equipment is often associated with the process.

Temporary Corrosion Protection. It is not uncommon in industry for periods of time, sometimes quite long, to elapse between manufacturing, assembling, shipment, and use of parts. During these periods some parts can be harmed or even destroyed by corrosion so far as their function is concerned. Unless a new processing schedule can be worked out, about the only cure for the problem is corrosion protection suitable for the storage time and exposure. The coatings used are usually nondrying organic materials called *slushing compounds* that can be easily removed, theoretically at least, with solvents.

The two principal types of compounds used for this purpose are petroleum base materials, varying from extremely light oils to semisolids, and thermoplastics. The latter may be used in sheet form for wrapping, or liquid form for dipping, spraying, or brushing. The kind of material to be protected and the conditions under which protection must exist will effect the choice of slushing material. Short periods of storage under reasonably good conditions indoors will probably require only light oils, which possibly can be supplied as coolants in the last step of manufacturing. Outdoor storage of such items as gears, bearings, chains, even on completed assemblies such as farm equipment, will require better protection with material able to withstand temperature changes and severe conditions. Such material usually will be more difficult to put in place and also to remove. Frequently, because of the difficulty of removal, the slushing compounds are lubricant type materials which will do no harm if mixed in service with regular lubricants.

Corrosion from atmospheric exposure is the principal protection problem for temporary coatings. Exclusion of the oxygen and moisture in the air is the usual protection method. However, the length of time protection is satisfactory may be increased by chemical inhibitors in the slushing compound.

The most common method of application of slushing compounds for small parts is by dipping. Larger parts that cannot be easily handled may be sprayed, brushed, or flow coated with the compound. It is important that any surface to be protected be clean and dry when the application is made to prevent trapping any harmful materials inside the coating. Good protection requires uniform thickness of coating with the actual thickness depending on the kind of exposure to be resisted.

CHEMICAL CONVERSIONS

A relatively simple and often fully satisfactory method for protection from corrosion is by conversion of some of the surface material to a chemical composition that resists attack from the environment. These converted metal surfaces consist of relatively thin (seldom more than 0.001 inches thick) inorganic films which are formed by chemical reaction with the base material. One important feature of the conversion process is that the coatings have little effect on the product dimensions. However, when severe conditions are to be encountered, the converted surface may be only partial protection and coatings of entirely different types may be applied over them.

Anodizing. Aluminum, magnesium, and zinc can be treated electrically in a suitable electrolyte to produce a corrosion resistant oxide coating. The metal being treated is connected to the anode in the circuit, thus providing the name *anodizing* for the process. Aluminum is commonly treated by anodizing which produces an oxide film, thicker than, but similar to that formed naturally with exposure to air. Anodizing of zinc has very limited use. The coating produced on magnesium is not as protective as that formed on aluminum, but does provide some protective value and substantially increases protection when used in combination with paint coatings.

Because of their greater thickness and abrasion resistance, anodic films offer much better protection against corrosion and mechanical injury than do the thin natural films. Aluminum is usually treated in a sulfuric acid electrolyte which slowly dissolves the outside at the same time it is converting the base metal to produce a porous coating. The coating can be impregnated with various materials to improve corrosion resistance. It also serves as a good paint base and can be colored in itself by use of dyes.

Chromate Coatings. Zinc is usually considered to have relatively good corrosion resistance. This is true when the exposure is to normal outdoor atmosphere where a relatively thin corrosion film forms. Contact with either highly aerated water films, or immersion in stagnant water containing little oxygen, causes uneven corrosion and pitting. The corrosion products of zinc are less dense than the base material so that heavy corrosion not only destroys the product appearance, but may cause malfunctions by binding moving parts.

Corrosion of zinc can be substantially slowed by the production of chromium salts on its surface. The corrosion resistance of magnesium alloys can be increased by immersion or anodic treatment in acid baths containing dichromates. Chromate treatment of both zinc and magnesium improves corrosion resistance but is used also to improve adhesion of paint.

Phosphate Coatings. Phosphate coatings, used mostly on steel, result from a chemical reaction of phosphoric acid with the metal to form a nonmetallic coating which is essentially phosphate salts. The coating is produced by immersing small items or spraying large items with the phosphating solution. Phosphate surfaces may be used alone for corrosion resistance, but their most common application is as a base for paint coatings. Two of the most common application methods are called *parkerizing* and *bonderizing*.

Chemical Oxide Coatings.   A number of proprietary blacking processes, used mainly on steel, produce attractive black oxide coatings. Most of the processes involve the immersing of steel in a caustic soda solution, heated to about 300°F. and made strongly oxidizing by the addition of nitrites or nitrates. Corrosion resistance is rather poor unless improved by application of oil, lacquer, or wax. As in the case of most of the other chemical conversion procedures, this also finds use as a base for paint finishes.

QUESTIONS

1. Name five possible objectives for surface finishing.
2. Define case hardening.
3. Upon what kind of material is carburizing performed?
4. Briefly describe carburizing.
5. For case hardening, what treatment subsequent to carburizing is required?
6. What are the advantages and disadvantages of nitriding compared to carburizing type case hardening?
7. How is hardfacing accomplished?
8. What kind of material can be flame hardened?
9. Why is cleaning frequently an important processing step?
10. What cleaning materials are most commonly used to remove grease, oil, and wax films?
11. What is pickling?
12. Describe the operation of a vapor bath cleaning operation.
13. List cleaning media used by blasting.
14. What benefit in addition to cleaning may be obtained from solid particle blasting?
15. Why is a tumbling barrel usually filled almost completely with workpieces and any cleaning media that may be used?
16. Discuss the effective differences of wire brushing and abrasive belt finishing.
17. What is the main difference between polishing and grinding wheels?
18. Why is electropolishing limited to improvement of surfaces that are already relatively good?
19. List four possible solutions to corrosion problems.
20. Why is a variety of coating materials necessary?
21. What would be the important properties of a good organic coating material?
22. What is the composition of paint?
23. How does enamel differ from paint?
24. Describe lacquer.
25. What is the principle of electrostatic spraying?
26. How does porcelain enamel differ from ordinary enamel coatings?
27. For what purposes is metallizing used?

28. How does zinc protect steel from corrosion?
29. Sketch a simple electroplating setup indicating the polarities used.
30. What is a slushing compound?
31. What chemical compound is formed on the surface of aluminum by anodizing?

Inspection

INSPECTION is an essential procedure carried on in connection with all manufacturing processes by which usable goods are produced. Inspection work, however, differs from that of all the processes discussed to this point. Unlike them, it does not add any quality to the product unless it is considered that the elimination of bad parts improves the average quality of those that remain. In general terms, inspection can be defined as an examination to determine the conformance of parts or assemblies to their specifications. The information gathered from such an examination may be used for several purposes. It is frequently impossible to manufacture articles within close enough limits that all can be used in exactly the same way. Sorting is frequently used to separate products into groups when the manufacturing variation is so great that all parts could not be used interchangeably. The information gathered from inspection is also used as an indication of need for adjustment of equipment or processes. A third objective of inspection procedures is to provide data for control of quality.

Although the term *quality control* is occasionally used synonymously with inspection, its meaning is sometimes different. The association between quality control and inspection is close. Quality control is often a second step, making use of inspection data for analysis and decision making for achieving, maintaining, and improving quality of products. In some manufacturing plants, both inspection and quality control are performed by the same department and personnel. In others, they are completely separated and may even have separate data collecting facilities.

INSPECTION PROCEDURES

Because of their effects on the product function, the selection of dimensions, qualities, and appearance factors for any product is primarily a design problem. In many cases the choices are empirical in nature, being based on past experiences, and in some cases are even arbitrary because of the lack of real information on which to make any other kind of choice.

Most dimensions and qualities are subject to wide variability in the manufacturing process, and in some cases may also be very difficult to measure. The desired life expectancy for a product also will usually play an important part in the consideration given to dimensions and qualities needed for satisfactory manufacturing. Because of these factors and the close association between processing and quality control, both the manufacturing and inspection divisions of a manufacturing plant are often consulted before a final determination of quality tolerances. In addition, they are usually the principal decision makers for setting the inspection qualities, quantities, and standards.

The difference in the amount and kind of inspection necessary for a machine tool as compared to a piece of farm equipment is considerable. In the first case, a machine tool would be expected to be rigid, to be free-working with a minimum of friction loss, to have very accurate related surfaces for maintenance of accurate movement, to have long life, and during that period to be able to produce parts accurate within a few ten thousandths of an inch of dimension. These requirements mean that most of the parts of which the machine is constructed must be held within extremely close accuracy limits, and large amounts of inspection are necessary. In the case of the farm machinery, which may be no less important in its own area, the product must be strong, rugged, able to withstand exposure to the elements, and also to function over a long period of time, although the actual hours of use may be relatively few. The farm machinery, however, does not require the relationship accuracies that must exist in the machine tool, so that both the quality and quantity of inspection can be reduced. These differences naturally show up in the cost of the completed equipment.

The meeting of specifications set by the designer is primarily a manufacturing problem. Whether or not the specifications are met is determined by inspection, which may be performed by either operating or specialized personnel. Regardless of his other duties, an inspector at the time he is performing this function may be considered to represent both management and the customer.

Any product is always subject to quality variation, the degree of which will vary in wide ranges depending largely upon the relationship between the product design and the process chosen for its manufacture. The materials of the product, the equipment used, the personnel operating the equipment, and the planned steps by which the manufacturing is carried on are all influencing factors on the quality variation. Inspection is for the purpose of finding these variations, and in many cases aiding in assigning the causes for their existence.

Organization of Inspection. Although certain kinds of inspection are limited to certain phases during the manufacturing processes, inspection of some type, sometimes as simple as casual observation, is needed in every stage of manufacturing of every kind of product. It is, however, customary in many plants to label in general terms the inspection procedures according to the state of the product being examined, as receiving inspection, in-process inspection, and final inspection.

The term *receiving* inspection denotes all the inspections regardless of type that are given to incoming material, including such things as raw materials, speciality items, and subassemblies manufactured under subcontract. In order to cut down transportation and handling, companies making use of large quantities of speciality items or subcontract work frequently perform this kind of inspection in the suppliers plant.

Inspection that is conducted during the time raw material is being converted into a finished product is called *in-process* inspection. The place of inspection is dependent largely upon the degree of examination, and the kind of equipment needed. When only a percentage of the parts produced are inspected, either periodically or in spot checks, the work is usually carried on at the machine. Particularly in small plants, this inspection may be performed by the machine operator himself. When large quantities of product are to be inspected, and when the inspection procedures require specialized equipment, the work is most often done in centralized areas.

Regardless of the amount of other inspection that might be necessary, *first-piece* inspection is common practice. After any equipment setup, tool change, or any action that may influence the quality of the product, the first piece is examined to determine its conformance to specification. This is sometimes a very formal procedure, and in many cases, as in press working where the effect of wear and other factors is small, this may be the only inspection required.

Inspection performed at *final* inspection may include a great variety of work. Visual inspection for appearance (paint, labels, cleanliness, etc.) and completeness (all parts, instruction books, parts list, etc.) is nearly always part of the job. Tests for function, which are sometimes necessary on mechanical goods, may involve elaborate testing procedures requiring much time and adding considerable cost to the overall manufacturing operation. Testing of most aircraft in the final stages would fall in this category.

When the amount of final inspection is large, reduced in-process inspection may be permitted, although this will depend on a number of factors, including the relation of inspection cost to processing cost and the cost of replacement of bad parts from the final assembly.

Quantity of Inspection. The percentage of inspection at any phase of manufacturing will vary widely. When lowest inspection cost is the principal interest, the variation can be from 0 to 100 per cent. When greatest reliability is of interest, 0 per cent would be unlikely, but 100 per cent may also be unlikely because 100 per cent inspection does not always mean 100 per cent reliability due to the effects of fatigue and monotony as well as the psychological and hypnotic effects of continuous detailed work.

With a large portion of manufactured goods, the quantity to be inspected is determined by the use of various sampling plans. These may be used only in those cases where something less than 100 per cent perfect quality will be accepted. In general, the lot size being inspected must be large because of the assumption that the inspected quality will vary according to known statistical laws. Mathematical methods are available for designing a number of sampling plans which take into account the product quality level and the willingness to accept a certain defective part. The necessary sample size is affected by these factors. For any sampling

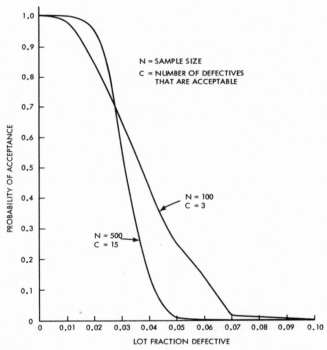

FIG. 26–1. Operating characteristic curves for different sample sizes.

plan to be effective, the sample inspected must be random and truly represent the overall quality of the lot. Before a complete sampling plan can be devised, a decision must be made as to the percentage of defective parts in a lot that would be willingly accepted. Ideally, a sampling plan would accept all good lots and reject all bad lots of parts.

The ideal, however, can be reached only when the sample size becomes 100 per cent and is, in addition, performed without fault as shown in Fig. 26–1. Ideal results are approached when the sample size is increased, so the best sample size will always be a compromise based on the relative values of improved reliability versus greater inspection costs. Accepted sampling plans are essential when inspection cost is high and the cost for replacing defectives is low, when the sampling plan is more efficient than 100 per cent inspection, and in every case where the inspection procedure is destructive.

The operating characteristic curve shown in Fig. 26–2 is a single sampling plan requiring an attribute (quality which is either wholly present or absent) of two hundred randomly selected parts to be compared with its specification. If four or less defective parts are found in the sample, the

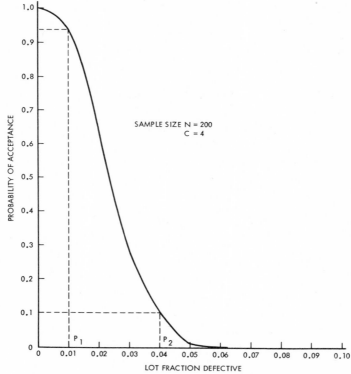

FIG. 26–2. Operating characteristic curve.

entire lot from which it came will be accepted. If more than four defectives are found, the lot will be rejected and likely be sorted for removal of the defectives. In the plan shown the dotted line marked P_1 indicates the so-called "producers risk." If the lot being inspected had only 1 per cent defectives, there would be a 6 per cent chance that this plan would reject the material. The dotted line marked P_2 indicates the *consumer's risk,* which in this case is a 10 per cent chance that a lot with 4 per cent defectives might be accepted. Sampling plans of this type therefore must be designed to be acceptable to both the producer and the consumer.

Process Control Charts.   Another valuable use of statistical mathematics in inspection is for the construction of control charts with limit lines.

Inspection values plotted on the chart will rarely fall outside these lines except when an assignable cause exists. In other words, the variation of points inside the control limits can be from chance causes alone. The data collected for construction of process control charts is in the form of variables rather than attributes. Data collection is therefore more costly, but in most cases considerably more information can be made available from analysis of the data.

In the making of control charts some assumptions are made, which, although they may not be entirely true, can usually be approximated closely enough that the system will work. One of the important assump-

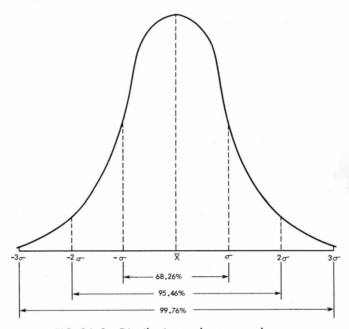

FIG. 26–3.   Distribution under a normal curve.

tions is that variation of the quality being inspected will follow a known frequency distribution. Most often it is assumed that the frequency distribution 99.73 per cent of the measured values from an entire population will probably fall within the limits of plus or minus 3σ from the arithmetical mean. Sigma is the symbol for *standard deviation* which is a measure of the dispersion of the measured values. Similarly, 95.46 per cent of measured values would be expected to fall within $\pm 2\sigma$ limits, and 68.26 per cent within $\pm 1\sigma$.

The construction of a quality control chart usually follows the following kind of procedure. First, the process is examined to ascertain that it is normal, and that all assignable causes have been eliminated so that its operation is stable within the limits of chance variation. Next, an historical record is made by plotting the mean values of a number of samples, the size, frequency, and selection of which have been carefully predetermined after consideration of the process characteristics. These values are placed on two charts, one for averages and one for ranges, and limits calculated for each. If the limits used are plus and minus 3σ, not more than 0.2 per cent of any plotted points would be expected to fall outside these lines. Therefore, whenever a point does fall outside, the process is critically examined for an assignable cause. As the process continues, current samples are plotted and compared with past history to determine that the

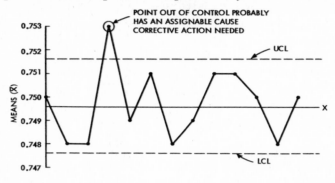

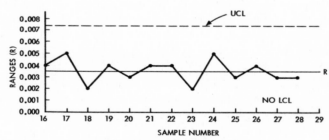

FIG. 26–4. Quality control process chart.

process remains in control. In most processes the mean is controllable by adjustment of the process, but the range can be changed only by finding and eliminating assignable causes.

Although process control charts can be useful for short-run operations under some conditions, their greatest value is in continuing operations in which a minimum number of changes may contribute to variability. The information which can be gathered from control charts can be useful for several purposes. It may be used for determining the overall quality of a product. The data can be useful for matching mating part dimensions with a minimum of waste. Understanding of the statistical variation in a product usually will permit wider tolerance use. Although all the points within the control limits on the mean chart could be in these positions by chance variation, a gradual shift toward one or the other limit can often be interpreted as a trend caused by an assignable reason. For example, gradual tool wear in a cutting operation would cause the average mean value to change gradually. Frequently, the use of process control charts will cause improvement in the processes on which they are used by pointing out possibly correctable variation causes. Analysis of the process itself and correction of faults as they are found will produce gradual improvement in the process history, tending to tighten down on the control limits as they are recalculated. The presence of regularly kept charts in the process control area tends to have a rather large psychological effect on the process operators. Frequently they do a better job merely because the chart is before them. The data that is collected for construction of the control chart is, of course, useful also for inspection acceptance, and often provides more information than would be available from data collected for inspection alone.

PRINCIPLES OF MEASUREMENT

This section on inspection is concerned primarily with dimensions, shapes, finishes, dimensional tolerances, and the dimensional relationship, together with geometric relationships existing between surfaces. Any quality desired in a manufactured product may require inspection to assure its meeting specifications. In the manufacture of hard goods, the greatest amount of inspection time is spent checking those qualities mentioned above. Some important properties such as hardness and strength, together with their testing procedures, have been discussed in earlier chapters.

Dimensional References. When dimensional measurements are being made, a reference point and a measured point always exist. In the case of single dimensions, it usually makes no difference which is which, except in those cases in which one surface is more rigid or more easily accessible and will serve better as a reference point. When a number of dimensions originate from the same point or can be measured from a common point, that point should be used as the reference point; all measurements should be made from it in order to reduce the possibilities of accumulation of error. When a series of dimensions are measured, each dependent upon the previous one, the total possible error is the accumulation of all the individual errors. But if, as shown in Fig. 26–5, each measurement is made to a common reference point, the maximum total error can be only two individual errors for any of the dimensions measured. In those cases where the only practical dimensioning method requires a sequential group of measurements, it is good practice to leave the least important dimension off the drawing, thereby eliminating the argument as to whether the overall dimension or individual dimensions should receive first consideration regarding the holding of tolerances.

Drawing dimensions should always agree as closely as possible with manufacturing and inspection procedures to minimize the need for calculations by machine operators and production personnel. When changes in process cause changes in measurement procedures, action should be taken to correct the working drawings to fit the new methods.

Tolerances. Although it is possible by use of sufficient time and care to work as closely to a given dimension as is desired, it is impossible to manufacture to an exact size. Regardless of the accuracy displayed, it is always possible to choose a finer measuring method which can show

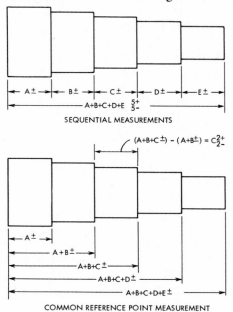

SEQUENTIAL MEASUREMENTS

COMMON REFERENCE POINT MEASUREMENT

FIG. 26–5.   Accumulation of dimensional error.

discrepancies in the dimension. Since working to higher accuracies costs more in money, time, and equipment, it is most economical and practical that dimensions should be permitted to vary within the widest limits for which they can still function properly. This variation is permitted by the use of *tolerances* added to dimensions in such a way that they indicate the permissible variation. Theoretically at least, the designer applies dimensional tolerances as wide as can be safely used. One of the inspector's jobs is to determine whether the product is made within these manufacturing limits.

Manufacturing tolerances may be shown in different ways as indicated in Fig. 26–6. If a dimension is approached in a definite direction by the manufacturing process used, and greater chance of error exists on one side of the basic dimension than on the other, unilateral tolerances are usually displayed, using the dimension that would be reached first as the basic dimension. When no reason exists for error on one side of the basic dimension more than on the other, bilateral tolerances permitting variation in both directions are used. The third method shows both limiting dimensions, and thereby eliminates the need for calculation by production personnel. However, it tends to clutter up the drawings because of its sometimes greater space requirement and the increase of significant numbers.

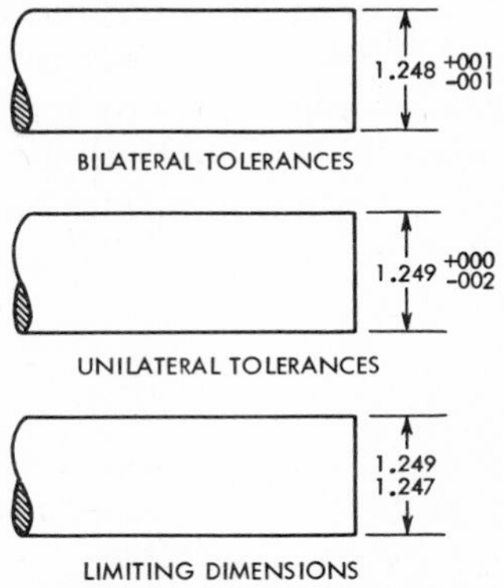

BILATERAL TOLERANCES

1.248 $^{+001}_{-001}$

UNILATERAL TOLERANCES

1.249 $^{+000}_{-002}$

LIMITING DIMENSIONS

1.249
1.247

The majority of dimensions on drawings are not critical and are usually shown without tolerances indicated. However, to prevent complete loss of control, these are usually treated to have *understood* tolerances which may vary in different plants but are usually in the range of ±0.010 to ±0.015 inches.

FIG. 26–6. Methods of showing dimensional limits.

Sources of Measurement Variation. Variation in dimensional measurement comes from a number of sources. Some are common enough that they should be given consideration in the majority of measuring and inspection procedures. Among these are parallax, temperature effects, pressure effects, and human error.

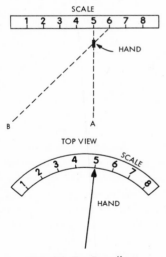

FIG. 26–7. Parallax.

The illusion created by parallax is shown in Fig. 26–7. If the hand swinging over the scale is viewed from Point A, directly in front, measurement five would be observed. If, however, the eye were moved to position B the hand in the same position would indicate a reading of six. This is the illusion that makes it difficult to read a clock correctly when viewing it from an angle. Any measuring or indicating device that has a finite thickness between the indicating member and the reading scale or the work will display an error caused by parallax if used incorrectly. Many meters are constructed with mirrors underneath the indicating hand so that in order to obtain a single view of the hand the eye must be positioned in the only spot where a correct reading can be directly read.

It is well known that temperature variation causes changes of dimension in most materials, causing them to grow larger with increased temperature and smaller as they become colder. Different materials are affected to different degrees by temperature changes, or in other words, have different coefficients of thermal expansion. Many of the manufacturing processes cause temperature changes in the work, in the gaging and measuring equipment, or are concerned with different materials such that measurement problems caused by temperature are significant. The coefficient of thermal expansion for steel is approximately 0.0000065/in./°F. It would not be unusual for a steel disc being machined to a six inch diameter to have its temperature increased during the machining work to 200° above standard temperature of 68°F. If measured while still hot with a gage calibrated for use at standard temperature, an error of almost 0.008 inch would be measurable on the disc when cooled to standard temperature.

$$(200 \times 6.5 \times 10^{-6} \times 6 = 0.0078)$$

Aluminum, for which the coefficient of expansion is approximately 0.000012/in./°F., would under the same conditions be expanded almost twice as much and upon cooling would show an error of over 0.014 inch.

$$(200° \times 12 \times 10^{-6} \times 6 = 0.0144)$$

When using a steel measure or gage on a steel workpiece, little error would be caused if both were at the same temperature (dependent somewhat upon the gage design). However, in the case of the gage and work being of different materials, such as a steel gage on an aluminum part, exact measurement can be made only when both are at standard temperature. For example, if the above aluminum disc and steel gage were both at only 30° above standard temperature, the error in measurement would be almost 0.001.

$$(30 \times 12 \times 10^{-6} \times 6 = 0.00216$$
$$30 \times 6.5 \times 10^{-6} \times 6 = 0.00117$$
$$0.00216 - 0.00117 = 0.00099)$$

For most dimensional measurement some element of the measuring device must make contact with the work surfaces. The effect of the contact pressure will be dependent on the material strength and rigidity of both the work and measuring tool and on the loads applied. Most measuring devices are constructed to use light pressures that only break through oil and dirt films on the surfaces, since contact is often only at a point or along a line until deformation causes sufficient bearing area to carry the applied load. It must be remembered that load can be carried only by a reaction of bending or deformation, so light and repeatable contact pressures are a necessity to accurate dimensional measurement.

One of the most difficult problems to deal with in inspection, as well as all the other phases of manufacturing, is error caused by the human element. Errors from this source are almost uncontrollable except by elimination of the source, and are certainly unpredictable. Inspection procedures making use of any of the human senses (sight, hearing, smell, taste, or touch) are subject to some variation with any individual and usually to large variation between individuals. Sight and touch in particular are frequently used as part of a measuring system. At any time great reliability is required, the procedure should be designed to minimize the effects of the human element.

Basis for Measurement. Measurement of various attributes may be either comparative or absolute. In many cases knowledge of the value of a dimension or other quality is unimportant, and interest is focused on measurement of the difference from some standard. Many kinds of gaging apparatus are designed to show only the nearness or farness of a measurement from a predetermined standard. Other gaging equipment sets the limits within which a dimension must fall to be acceptable, and also does not assign any real value to the measurement. A third type of measurement provides knowledge regarding the real or absolute value of a measurement by comparing the measurement with a known standard. The differential measurements described above can be converted to absolute values by addition or subtraction of the reading with the standard, if its absolute value is known. All absolute measurements use zero as a reference point.

Two measuring systems are commonly used throughout the world. These are the metric and English systems, with the metric being more widespread, but the English being more important to manufacturing in the United States. The metric system is universally used in most scientific applications, but for manufacturing in the United States is limited to a few specialties, mostly items that are related in some way to products manufactured abroad.

Length measurement standards are essential in order that units of measure have any meaning. All length measurements are related to the standard meter which at one time was the distance between two marks on gold buttons placed on a platinum-iridium bar stored in Paris, France. Since the year 1960, a standard meter has been defined as being 1,650,763. 73 wave lengths of light emitted from krypton-86. In 1866, the Congress of the United States defined a legal yard as being 3600/3937 of the length of a meter. From this definition, one inch turns out to be slightly more than 25.4 millimeters. More recently the inch has been defined as exactly 25.4 millimeters. The meter and the inch are therefore primary measurement standards to which all length measurements are related.

The use of uniform length measurement throughout the country is made possible by the use of secondary standards in the form of gage blocks which are used in three ways. Master gage blocks, the most accurate obtainable (guaranteed to be accurate within $\pm.000002$ inch per inch of length), are used only for checking other gage block sets in order that their accuracy may be retained. Other sets of gage blocks, which may be of less original accuracy, are used as references and inspection blocks for the manufacture, calibration, and setting of various measuring devices. A third use applies blocks directly to precision measuring work in shop operations. The more gage blocks are used, the more important it becomes that they be frequently checked against other blocks to prevent inaccuracies from wear and abuse, affecting the accuracy of production.

Gage blocks may be obtained in sets containing from as few as five to over one hundred individual blocks. They are used by selecting blocks of such size as needed, and wrung together to make up a desired dimension. Wringing in this case implies the use of a twisting sliding motion between the blocks which places their extremely flat and smooth faces so close together that they adhere to each other and can be built up to larger dimensions without inaccuracy caused by added space between the contacts.

A tertiary measuring standard is used in manufacturing in the form of gages and measuring devices designed for specific purposes, and in the form of master work parts which can be used for comparative measurements.

INSPECTION EQUIPMENT

The equipment to be described in this section is primarily for dimensional measurements. It all employs some type of comparison, with the principal difference being in the degree of reference to an absolute standard. The steel rule, for example, has a built in reference to zero. A dial indicator has no built in reference and is used mostly for differential measurements, but it can be used for absolute measurement by establishing proper reference. The spring caliper may be used as a gage to establish a dimensional limit, or it can be used to transfer a dimension from a work surface to some measuring device. Measuring tools may be classified as direct reading devices, comparators, or limit gages.

Direct reading devices provide the widest range of measurement of any of the measuring tools but are slower to use than the other types. In general, they require greater skill from the user and are therefore more subject to human error.

Among the most common of the direct reading inspection devices are steel rules and their variations. Steel rules are made in all sizes, from a fraction of an inch long that must be held in special holders, up to several feet in length. They may be calibrated in different ways, depending on the use for which they were intended, and sometimes are calibrated with four different scales on the same rule. Most common for use in the United States are calibrations showing $\frac{1}{64}$, $\frac{1}{32}$, $\frac{1}{16}$, and $\frac{1}{8}$ inch, although in some applications divisions in hundredths are of value. Good quality steel rules are machine divided with the calibration marks accurately placed, but ordinarily cannot be expected to be used with accuracies closer than about $\pm\frac{1}{64}$ inch because of the approach to the limitations of the average human eye.

The steel rule has a number of variations, including the hooked rule which can be held over a corner, caliper rules which have a fixed and sliding jaw to permit setting and easier reading, and depth rules for reaching into recesses and other variations. Some of these are shown in Fig. 26–8.

Vernier calipers are variations of the steel rule that can be read to thousandths of inches by use of a vernier scale built as part of the instrument. The heighth gage is similar to the vernier caliper with the exception that it is mounted on a base to hold it in a position suitable for vertical measurement. Both instruments are calibrated as shown in the insert of Fig. 26–9, with the main scale divided into inches and subdivided into $\frac{1}{10}$ and $\frac{1}{40}$ (0.025) inch. The vernier scale, which slides along adjacent to the main scale, has twenty-five divisions in a length equal to twenty-four divisions of the main scale and furnishes the witness line for reading a

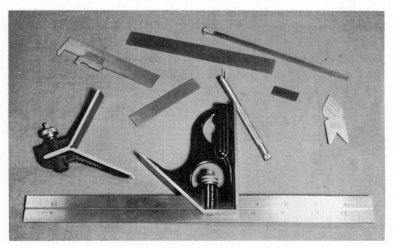

FIG. 26–8. Steel rules.

measurement. Each division on the vernier scale is 0.001 inch shorter than the similar divisions on the main scale, so that for each 0.001 inch of movement between the two, a different line on the vernier scale will line up with one of the marks on the main scale. A measurement reading is accomplished by first reading the full inches, adding the tenths of an inch exposed before the 0 of the vernier scale, adding 0.025 inch for each exposed subdivision and finally adding the number indicated by the mark on the vernier that is in closest alignment with one of the marks on the main scale.

Micrometer Caliper. The micrometer caliper or "mike" shown in Fig. 26–10 is one of the most common measuring instruments used in the manufacturing field. For a precision tool, its construction is relatively simple. A U-shaped frame supports a hardened steel button called an *anvil* on the inside of one end, and a *sleeve, barrel* or *hub* containing a threaded nut on the opposite end. The threaded nut supports threads on a spindle which extends through the sleeve and frame so its flat end can be paired with the anvil to serve as the measuring element. The opposite end of the spindle is attached to a tubular *thimble* that rides over the outside of the sleeve so that when the thimble is turned the spindle thread rotates in the fixed nut, causing the distance between the spindle and anvil to decrease or increase.

The threads of micrometers are the real measuring elements and are precision made, usually being ground in hardened materials. Forty threads per inch cause the thread lead to be $\frac{1}{40}$ inch, or 0.025. A witness line along the side of the micrometer sleeve is divided into ten numbered divisions

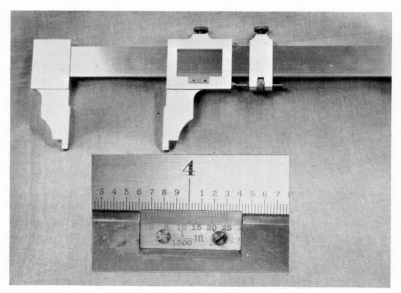

FIG. 26–9. Vernier caliper.

representing four full turns of the micrometer thread, a distance of 0.010 inch. Each one-tenth inch division is subdivided into four smaller divisions, each representing one full turn or 0.025 inch. The bevel of the micrometer thimble is divided into twenty-five equal spaces to enable the user to read fractional turns with the accuracy permitted by 0.001 inch calibration. Some micrometers carry also a vernier calibration consisting of ten marked spaces on the sleeve of the micrometer in a space equal to nine .001 divisions on the thimble. The principle of the vernier is the same as that on the vernier caliper and with proper use allows the micrometer to be read accurately to the nearest 0.0001 inch. Vernier micrometers calibrated to this accuracy are not too commonly used however, since variations in temperature, pressure, and the human element frequently cause errors large enough to make this kind of accuracy impractical.

Most micrometer heads are substantially the same in design, and cover a one inch range. In order to permit wide range measurement, the heads are fitted to frames different in size by one inch increments. The tool is in common enough use in small sizes that the one, two, and three inch micrometers (maximum limits) are usually personal tools of machine operators and mechanics. Larger sizes, usually up to twenty-four inches, although larger than this have been built, are normally supplied from a company tool crib when their use is required. The larger sizes are naturally more difficult to position on work and to adjust with the correct "feel." Thus, frequently, some other device will be used when long dimensions must be accurately measured. Mikes are rugged tools and can stand some abuse, but should be accorded the careful treatment due a precision instrument. With relative ease they can be used for measuring to accuracies well within 0.001 inch; in the case of vernier mikes they can be used within 0.0001 inch if proper consideration is given to temperature and pressure effects.

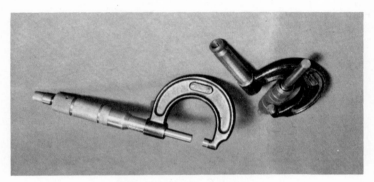

FIG. 26–10. Micrometer.

In addition to the outside micrometer described, the same principles are applied in the making of inside micrometers and depth micrometers for measurements, and to various types of positioning screws for accurate locating type applications. A bench type *supermicrometer* is sometimes used in laboratories and tool rooms for accurate length measurements. This instrument also uses a screw thread for measurement, but is constructed with a heavy frame consisting of a steel bar over $3\frac{1}{2}$ inches in diameter, and incorporating spring loading on the workpiece so that very accurate measuring or contact pressure can be duplicated. The design eliminates practically all of the effects of the human element.

Some commonly used adjustable inspection tools can be set to be used as limit gages, but are more commonly used as dimension transfer devices. Inside calipers have turned out legs to make contact with inside shoulders and holes. Outside calipers have turned in legs for checking across the outside of shoulders or diameters of bar material. Hermaphrodite calipers, consisting of an inside caliper leg combined with a pointed divider leg, are primarily layout tools rather than measuring devices. Telescoping gages are made up of sleeves that can be locked in position to carry an inside dimension such as a hole diameter to a measuring device such as a micrometer.

Angles may be measured in a number of ways, but one of the more precise methods used primarily in the laboratory and tool room is by use of a *sine bar*, illustrated in Fig. 26–11. Sine bars are constructed with accurately ground round buttons either five or ten inches apart. The bar can be positioned with an angular position to match a workpiece. The difference in button heights from the base plane, divided by five for the five inch bar, and by ten for the ten inch bar provides a number which is the sine of the angle of the bar's position in relation to the base. Accurate measurement of the button height is frequently performed by use of gage blocks.

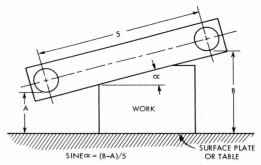

SINE$\propto$ = (B–A)/5

FIG. 26–11.   Sine bar.

Indicating Gages and Comparators.   A second type of inspection device is the indicating gage or comparator which is used for showing deviation from a dimension. By relating the reading to a suitable reference, these gages can provide absolute measure values. These devices require more skill than the direct reading instruments for setup. But once setup, they may be used faster, easier, and frequently with greater accuracy than the direct type. Many also have the advantage of being combinable for multiple measurements, thus providing even greater time savings. Most do, however, have a narrow measuring range for any single setup.

Most indicating gages and comparators are quite sensitive, with high amplification characteristics that may be provided by mechanical, electrical, pneumatic, or optical systems. They are used for comparing with known dimensions, with master workpieces, and for checking parallelism, concentricity, and general conformance to shape.

Dial Indicators.   The majority of mechanical type comparators are of the dial indicator style shown in Fig. 26–12. These are constructed with a spindle which operates a rack gear in contact with a system of gears that turn the indicating hand over a calibrated dial. The use of light return springs to keep backlash from contributing error, and high quality bearing supports provide sensitivity permitting the indicator to be read accurately to within $\frac{1}{10,000}$ inch. The majority of dial indicators are calibrated in thousandths of inches, but many, particularly in the larger diameters where the calibration marks can be better separated, are calibrated in $\frac{1}{10,000}$ inch. The majority of dial indicators operate over ranges from about $\frac{1}{16}$ to $\frac{1}{8}$ inch, but some long range types have been designed to cover as much as one inch. These are constructed with an additional hand to count the multiple revolutions of the main indicating hand.

FIG. 26–12. Dial indicator type snap gage.

The majority of dial indicators are used for measuring dimension differences without regard to absolute values. Many special purpose structures have been designed for supporting dial indicators for different kinds of uses. Some are special attachments designed to permit contact to be made with a surface difficult to reach. Some support a dial indicator in such a way that it may be used for work that would ordinarily be done with a fixed gage. Others hold the indicator so that it can be adjusted over a table where it can be used for making accurate comparison measurement.

The *reed* mechanism shown in Fig. 26–13 is another method for amplifying small motions. One make of comparator gage uses this type mechanism to move a small mirror. A light beam reflected by this mirror to a calibrated scale is in effect a weightless lever which increases the amplification of motion and provides extremely high sensitivity and response, permitting accurate readings in the range of $\frac{1}{100,000}$ inch.

Electrical Gages. Electrical power is used for operation of both comparator type gages and limit gages. In the comparator type, movement of the work contact point of the gage from its zero or set position produces unbalance in the electrical system causing current flow which can be read on a meter calibrated as finely as $\frac{1}{1,000,000}$ inch.

The electrical limit type gage operates by the action of extremely sensitive switches which may be preset to definite dimensions. The switches may then be connected to operate signal lights, buzzers, or controls of gates in high speed sorting operations.

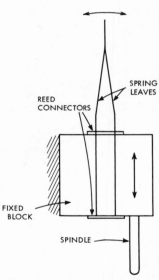

FIG. 26–13. Reed mechanism for movement amplification.

Pneumatic Gages. Air gages for making comparative dimensional measurements are of two types. In the pressure type, a pressure sensing element indicates a dimensional value on a calibrated scale as a result of back pressure built up from restriction of air flow through the gaging head. In the flow type gage an indicator button floats on a column of air in a tapered glass tube, as air at constant pressure flows through a flexible tube and out orifices in the gage head. The gages are usually set with master workpieces or with limit gages which determine the limiting acceptance points.

Air gages are made with different degrees of amplification and sensitivity. Although they are used primarily as limit gages, a strong indication of absolute value is provided by the position of the indicator. Since air gage heads have some clearance with the surfaces they are designed to measure, their life is quite long. They are especially satisfactory for measuring materials that have abrasive characteristics or for use around abrasive processes such as grinding, honing, and lapping.

Optical Comparators. Optical comparators are designed to show a reflected surface picture, or a profile image of a workpiece on a frosted glass screen. This is accomplished by casting light against the surface of the specimen and projecting its reflection through a magnifying lens system onto a mirror, which in turn reflects the image to the glass screen, or by passing light past the edge of the work to show its silhouette or contour. Most comparators permit lens changing to vary the magnification from 10 power to 100 power. The enlarged image on the screen can be measured, observed visually for defects, or compared with enlarged drawings, frequently complete with limiting outlines, for inspection purposes.

The equipment is especially useful for inspection of small complicated shapes that would be difficult to examine carefully or measure by other means. Multiple dimensions and complex shapes can be quickly checked with this device.

Optical Flats. Another method of optical inspection involves the use of optical flats. These are flat, clear discs, usually made of fused quartz, constructed with the two sides as parallel as possible. The principle upon which use of the optical flat is based is interferometry, a word used to indicate light wave interference to produce identifiable light and dark bands as illustrated in Fig. 26–14. Light waves from a monochromatic (single wave length) light source are transmitted through the optical flat which is set at a slight angle on the work surface. Part of the light will be reflected from the lower surface of the optical flat. Another part will pass this surface and continue on to be reflected from the work surface to rejoin the first part as both are reflected toward the observer's eye. Depending on the distances each set of waves travel, some will be in phase and reenforce each other to form bright lines, while others will be out of phase, will interfere, and cancel each other to produce dark bands or "fringes." Interference to form dark fringes will occur as the thickness of the air wedge between the optical flat and the work surface varies by ½ wave lengths. The frequency of bands will therefore depend upon the angle of the flat and the wave lengths of the light being used.

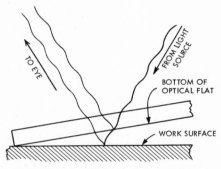

FIG. 26–14.   Light wave interference.

Optical flats may be used for checking flatness of surfaces since any deviation of the work surface being checked from the lower surface of the optical flat results in a pattern of fringe bands. The shape and spacing of the bands can be used to calculate the degree of difference between the surfaces accurately. Optical flats can also be used for making measurements as illustrated in Fig. 26–15. In this case, a one inch working gage block "A" is being compared with a one inch master block "B." Observation of the fringe bands of block "A" in the top view shows three complete bands indicating that if a monochromatic light source of 11.6 microinch ½ wave length (0.0000116) is being used, the optical flat is 3×11.6 or 34.8 microinches higher on one edge than on the other. By simple proportions, it can then be calculated that block A is shorter than block B by 3×34.8 or 104.4 microinches and the height of block A is $1.000000 - 0.000104$ or 0.999896 inch.

Fixed Gages. A third type of inspection tool is the fixed gage, which is set to a limit of a dimension to establish a maximum or minimum value or both limits to enclose the tolerance range. This type gage measures attributes only and provides very little information regarding absolute measurement. Fixed gages are fast to use, and require little skill to produce satisfactory results, so are frequently used as production gages. Most fixed gages are single purpose tools, useful only for the dimension for which they have been set, although some of the standard types are adjustable, and can be changed for other dimensions within a limited range. Fixed gages may be designed to check dimensions, shapes, relationships, or in some cases, combinations of these qualities. Pictured in Fig. 26–16 are some

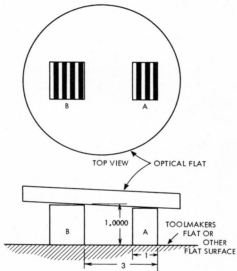

FIG. 26–15.   Work measurement with an
optical flat.

typical fixed gages. Some, such as the plug gages and ring gages, are *go-not go* gages which are made with the two tolerance limits. Others, such as profile gages, are a negative shape of the part to be checked and may or may not be made to both tolerance limits, depending mainly on the importance of the shape and size. Progressive gages, such as a sequential series of increasing diameter plugs come close to providing an absolute measure by dividing the overall tolerance up into a number of smaller increments, thus tying the dimension down to a small range.

Gages, like any other manufactured articles, must be made to tolerances permitting some dimensional variation. These tolerances, naturally, must be smaller than the tolerances for the manufactured part on which the gage is to be used, and are usually held to between 10 and 20 per cent of the part tolerance. Gages must also be designed with some wear allowance so they will not accept bad parts after a short period of use. The wear allowance used is variable depending on the conditions of gage use, the precision of the product being inspected, and the gage life desired. In large operations it is common for two sets of gages to be used. One set called *working gages* is made to the above tolerances and is used by the machine operators to check the product as it is being manufactured. The other set, *inspection gages*, are made to approximately one half this tolerance in order to reduce the chance of rejecting good parts. Where many gages of the same type are used, master gages are sometimes constructed with tolerances 10 per cent of the gage tolerance for checking the gages themselves.

Surface Finish. In addition to conformance to a general geometric pattern, many applications require that a surface have high quality finish. Three kinds of irregularities may occur on a surface. The one most evident is *roughness*, a term used to describe surface irregularities that are

FIG. 26–16. Fixed gages.

relatively close together. Surface roughness is usually a result of machining or other processing procedure which produces finely spaced irregularities. A second surface fault is *waviness* which refers to irregularities of wider spacing than those termed roughness. Waviness may be the result of warping, deflection, or springing while being worked upon, or the result of a tool movement pattern while being cut. The third fault is an irregularity called a flaw or imperfection, which is relatively infrequent and usually randomly located. These consist of such things as scratches, holes, ridges, and cracks.

The quality of some surfaces can play an important part in their function. Both flat and rotating bearing surfaces must usually be relatively smooth to function properly, and often have their maximum roughness quality specified on their drawing. Materials that are likely to be highly stressed in service, particularly repeated or reversed load applications, may need good quality surface finish to reduce chances for fatigue failure. Any surface irregularity or discontinuity may be a point of stress concentration which can serve as a source of fatigue failure. As a precaution, the highly polished wing surfaces for high performance aircraft are frequently covered with a plastic coating for protection against nicks and scratches during manufacture since any marks on the surface might be a source of wing failure during flight.

The effect of surface finish on appearance alone should not be discounted. It is often the case that appearance is the only factor available for making a decision as to whether or not to purchase a product. It should be noted, however, that finish quality and light reflective ability are not necessarily synonymous. A newly finished clean surface with small regularly spaced tool marks, particularly those made in a grinding process, will reflect light to produce a polished appearance. A random pattern of even smaller tool marks, such as might be made in a superfinishing operation, will not reflect light as well but will measure better although appearing to be of lower quality finish.

A close relationship exists between surface finish and linear measurement. Most measuring procedures involve the use of tools or instruments that physically contact the work surface and touch only on the high spots or peaks. A bearing surface might loose these peaks very quickly in use, and the large change of dimension that would occur with a rough surface would cause the original measurement to be meaningless. Good surface finish is certainly called for whenever close tolerances are required.

Surface Finish Measurement. The roughness of a surface is made up of two qualities—the height and depth of irregularities, and the spacing between these. Most measurement methods take both into consideration to some degree without actually defining their relationship. Most surfaces also will show different roughness measurement and characteristics in different directions. Measurements across the *lay* will in general be much higher than those with the lay. Lay is the direction of the predominant surface pattern. For example, a measurement across the lay on a piece turned in a lathe would be taken parallel to the workpiece axis.

Some surface quality measurements depend upon comparison with standard samples displaying measured and known roughnesses. Visual comparison is sometimes satisfactory, but often may not be too accurate because of the effect of dirt, corrosion, and irregularity of pattern on appearance. Accuracy of the comparison can be considerably improved by scraping a fingernail across the surfaces, adding a sense of feel. A visual method of comparing optical projection through a plastic film that has been pressed against the surfaces is also available. A film softened by solvent takes on the surface irregularities and by its refraction effect on the projected light rays causes a third dimension effect on the screen, making accurate comparisons possible.

The majority of accurate surface quality measurements are made with instruments that trace the work surface with a stylus which in traveling over the hills and valleys disturbs an electrical circuit to make a reading possible. With some instruments a pen is actuated to draw a magnified profile of the surface on a moving tape, in addition to a meter reading showing the RMS (root mean square) value of the surface traced. Other instruments show only the meter reading which is the average deviation from the mean surface in microinches RMS.

Surface Specification. The specification of surface quality is indicated on the drawing as shown in Fig. 26–17. A 60 degree check mark is usually placed on the surface to which it refers, although in some cases it may be located on a witness line, or an arrow may be used to indicate the surface. A number representing the maximum permissible roughness is located inside the v of the check mark. On the right side of the check mark is the lay symbol indicating the direction in which measurement should be made, and the width of the maximum permissible roughness. Waviness is shown above a horizontal crossbar on the check mark. Some place on the drawing should be a note indicating whether the roughness value is total height, average height, or average deviation from the mean, either arithmetical or RMS. It is most common to show only maximum value figures, although lower limits also may be indicated whenever of value.

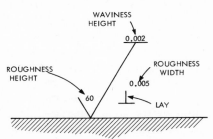

FIG. 26–17. Drafting symbol for surface quality.

Following are the lay symbols used to indicate a direction of measurement for which the figures in the specification apply:

═—parallel to the boundary line of the nominal surface.
⊥—perpendicular to the boundary line of the nominal surface.
X—angular in both directions to the boundary line of the nominal surface.
M—multidirectional.
C—approximately circular relative to the center.
R—approximately radial relative to the center of the nominal surface.

NONDESTRUCTIVE TESTING

As has been pointed out before, any desired product quality is likely to require inspection to determine its conformance to specifications or desired limits. The inspection may be of either the destructive or nondestructive type depending upon the quality being inspected and whether or not an economical, reliable test exists.

Destructive tests are those that destroy the product tested. They must therefore be tests of samples of the product, for 100 per cent inspection would mean total product destruction. The sample size however must be large enough that a high degree of confidence can be placed in the test results, since the somewhat dangerous assumption must be made that the product not tested is similar to and will react the same as that tested. Destructive tests include such varieties as strength tests where material failure must occur to provide a measured value, most chemical and metallurgical tests which require samples of material for examination, and life tests where the product is run to destruction.

Even though destructive, life tests are quite important for many products such as automobile tires, mattresses, and switch gear, since they provide information concerning the combined reaction of all qualities including those affected by materials processing, design, and specifications. Such tests are frequently accelerated by use of exaggerated conditions and elimination of delays which might occur in normal service.

Definition of Nondestructive Testing.   Nondestructive testing is the use of all possible methods of detection and measurement of properties or performance capabilities, of materials, parts, assemblies, structures, and machines, which do not damage or destroy their serviceability. Included by this definition are the dimensional measurements discussed in the first part of this chapter, visual examinations which are used for measurement of many qualities, and other direct nondestructive procedures. Nondestructive testing is most commonly interpreted to mean all tests performed indirectly to determine internal qualities and properties without destruction of the part being examined.

Since most of these tests are indirect, a dangerous assumption exists here in much the same way as it does for destructive testing. The assumption is that true correlation exists between the measured property and the service property being evaluated. This correlation can be established only by performing both destructive and nondestructive tests and analyzing the data correctly on suitable sample sizes.

Nondestructive tests result in an estimation of critical or useful properties by measurement of related, but noncritical properties. Typical of nondestructive test uses are as follows:

1. Identification and sorting of raw material.
2. Checking chemical composition.
3. Detecting variations in structure.
4. Detecting conditions of mechanical stress.
5. Detecting internal voids or discontinuities.
6. Detecting internal inclusions.
7. Detecting surface cracks.
8. Gaging difficult dimensions.
9. Detecting properties or presence of specific materials.

Basic Elements for Nondestructive Tests.   Five basic elements are required for the performance of nondestructive testing, as follows.

1. A suitable probing medium, which may be of mechanical, electrical, magnetic, or chemical nature, capable of transporting energy, matter, or both into the test object.

2. A modification of the probing medium caused by variations in the test object material. The type variations expected might be density change, discontinuity, dimensional differences, and composition variation. The variation of interest must in some way effect the probing medium.

3. A means of detecting changes in the probing medium. Depending upon the probing medium used, various methods of detecting change may be employed. Photographic film may be used for X rays, strain gages for displacement, thermocouples for temperature change, and coils of conducting wire for electrical or magnetic disturbances.

4. A means of recording or indicating signals. Here also, a variety of devices are used depending upon the probing medium, and how it is applied. recording or indicating may make use of electrical or pressure meters, photographs or other picture simulation, graphs and curves, or counters in a variety of types.

5. A means of interpreting the record or signal. As in the case of X ray film, an experienced observer is sometimes essential for interpretation of nondestructive testing results. In other cases, the signal may be such that the result may be automatically put to work as in a feed-back device used to maintain the control of a process.

Nondestructive Tests. A number of nondestructive test procedures make use of these principles. Among the more important is *radiography*, which includes both X ray and gamma ray examination. When fast moving electrons are stopped suddenly by coming in contact with a target, X rays with a wave length dependent on the target material are emitted. Gamma rays, which in general have shorter wave lengths than X rays, are emitted by the disintegration of atomic nuclei. Both are penetrating rays that will be absorbed in proportion to the density of the material through which they pass, so that those reaching the reading device provide a type of picture of the material through which they have come. Most commonly the reading is done with a fluoroscopic screen which is excited to luminescence by the rays or by exposing photographic plates to make a permanent record. Reading can also be accomplished xeroradiographically by the effect of the rays on a statically charged plate which has the ability to hold fine powder particles in proportion to its charge. One of the most recently developed methods for X rays involves the use of a television camera with a special lens permitting closed circuit television to present an enlarged X ray picture. One of the oldest uses for radiography is the examination of materials for internal flaws such as voids, cracks, and inclusions. By making suitable comparisons it is possible to use the procedure also for making some kinds of chemical analysis, metallurgical phase identification, measurement of wall thicknesses, and much other inspection work difficult to do by nondestructive means.

A recently developed inspection tool that is finding wide use in industry is the beta gage. Electrons projected through a moving sheet of steel, paper, or other relatively thin material can be counted on the opposite side to serve as a measure of thickness of the material. This type gage can be connected into the process in such a way as to feed back information for automatic correction of errors in the system.

A number of inspection devices apply electric or magnetic fields to the work material in such a way that variation of properties in the work will disturb the field, permitting comparison with results from known samples. Uniform electric current flow through any conductive material will set up a magnetic field which will be distorted about any crack, inclusion, or discontinuity. Electrical coils passing through this magnetic field can be used to detect these disturbances, and identify faulty locations or parts. By comparison procedures, the sorting of magnetic materials also may be accomplished.

Ferromagnetic materials can be inspected by *magnetic particle* methods. A magnetic field is set up in the work by direct application of electric power, or in some cases, by use of an auxiliary conductor. Fine magnetic powders are then applied to the work, either dry or suspended in liquid. The particles will align themselves with the magnetic field and any disturbances in the field will be evident by observation. In order to detect all flaws, the magnetic field must be set up in at least two directions to be certain that lines of flux will be cut by the discontinuity. Magnetic particle inspection will show up both external faults and internal faults. Interpretation of the surface indication for an internal fault however does require considerable experience and skill on the part of the operator.

The *triboelectric* principle is useful in inspecting for very fine cracks and crazing that occurs with some kinds of products, such as porcelain enamelware. In this process, powdered chalk dust is sprayed through an air gun with a rubber nozzle. Positively charged particles will collect on the surface of the test object in such a manner that cracks, invisible to the eye, will be revealed.

Porcelain enamel, glass coatings, and coatings of many plastics or other nonconductor materials can be tested for pin holes, cracks, and other imperfections by electrical resistance tests. For these, relatively high voltage electric power is applied across the coating. Cracks or holes will be revealed by breakdown and the jumping of an electric spark.

Advantage is taken of capillary action for some types of surface defect inspection. A *penetrant* carrying very fine particles of materials is supplied to the work surface where it will enter any cracks or openings, even those invisible to the eye. After the surface has been wiped clean, some of the penetrant will creep back out of the openings, revealing their presence.

In many cases fluorescent particles are used so that by the use of blacklight the visibility will be greatly improved.

Mechanical vibration is receiving more and more use in the nondestructive field. It has long been known that the tapping of a freely suspended grinding wheel will result in a bell-like tone or ringing sound if the wheel is sound. If the wheel is cracked, however, the result will be a dull sound or a buzz. In the case of a good wheel, mechanical vibration of sonic frequency is a result of resonance of the entire object.

Mechanical vibration at *ultrasonic* frequencies is capable of detecting defects smaller than might be found by radiography and may be used for a wide range of work sizes. In this process, a quartz crystal vibrated by an electronic ultrasonic generator is placed in contact, usually with an oil film to prevent any air insulation, with the work surface. Pulses of vibration are transmitted into the work where they will be reflected back from any discontinuity, hole, inclusion, change of geometry, etc. The same crystal that transmits the vibration picks up the reflected vibrations and converts them to electrical energy which is applied to a cathode ray tube. The tube pictures the applied vibration and all echoes along a time line, so accurate distance to each discontinuity can be readily determined.

Ultrasonic inspection may be used to check most metallic materials for internal flaws but is especially valuable for examining large forgings such as high speed motor, generator, or turbine shafts, and for checking the wall thickness of items like closed end tanks.

QUESTIONS

1. What is the difference between inspection and quality control?
2. How are inspection procedures arranged, with respect to the state of the product being examined?
3. Why is first-piece inspection more important for press working than for machining operations?
4. Why does 100 per cent inspection not guarantee 100 per cent reliability?
5. What are two fundamental requirements before a sampling inspection may be used?
6. In sampling inspection, what are producer's risk and consumer's risk?
7. On control charts what is the difference in meaning attached to variations of the mean and the range?
8. Where a series of dimensions is to be established, how may the accumulation of errors be minimized?
9. What are the common sources of variation in dimensional measurement?
10. When is the effect of temperature variation on measurement of least consequence?
11. What is the conversion factor between metric and English system measurements?
12. What are the three classes of gage blocks and their uses?
13. How does a vernier operate?
14. What is the measuring element of a micrometer?
15. What is a sine bar? Describe its use.
16. What is a reed mechanis?
17. Why do air gage heads have especially long life, even when used on abrasive materials?

18. What fringe pattern would be produced by an optical flat on a convex spherical surface?
19. What are the principal drawbacks of fixed limit gages?
20. What are usual gage tolerances?
21. What is meant by the term lay?
22. What is the principal assumption underlying the use of nondestructive tests?
23. What are the basic elements of any nondestructive test?
24. Why is a single magnetic field insufficient for thorough magnetic particle testing?

REFERENCES FOR ADDITIONAL READING

1. AMERICAN SOCIETY OF TOOL ENGINEERS HANDBOOK COMMITTEE. *Tool Engineers Handbook.* 2d ed. New York: McGraw-Hill Book Co., 1959.
2. AZAROFF, LEONID V. *Introduction to Solids.* New York: McGraw-Hill Book Co., 1960.
3. BAUMEISTER, THEODORE (ed.). *Mechanical Engineers Handbook.* 6th ed. New York: McGraw-Hill Book Co., 1958.
4. BEGEMAN, MYRON L., and AMSTEAD, B. H. *Manufacturing Processes.* 5th ed. New York: John Wiley and Sons, Inc., 1957.
5. CAMPBELL, JAMES S., JR. *Principles of Manufacturing Materials and Processes.* New York: McGraw-Hill Book Co., 1961.
6. CARSON, GORDON B. (ed.). *Production Handbook.* 2d ed. New York: The Ronald Press Co., 1958.
7. CLARK, DONALD S. *Engineering Materials and Processes.* 3d ed. Scranton, Pa.: International Textbook Co., 1959.
8. COONAN, FREDERICK L. *Principles of Physical Metallurgy.* New York: Harper and Bros., 1943.
9. CRANE, EDWARD V. *Plastic Working in Presses.* 3d ed. New York: John Wiley and Sons, Inc., 1944.
10. DEBRUYNE, NORMAN A., and HOUWINK, ROELOF. *Adhesion and Adhesives.* New York: Elsevier Publishing Co., 1951.
11. DEGARMO, E. PAUL. *Materials and Processes in Manufacturing.* 2d ed. New York: The Macmillan Co., 1962.
12. DELVECCHIO, E. J. (ed.). *Resistance Welding Manual.* Resistance Welders Manufacturers Assoc., 1956.
13. DOYLE, LAWRENCE E.; MORRIS, JOE L.; LEACH, JAMES L.; and SCHRADER, GEORGE F. *Manufacturing Processes and Materials for Engineers.* Englewood Cliffs, N.J.: Prentice-Hall, Inc., 1961.
14. DUNCAN, ACHESON J. *Quality Control and Industrial Statistics.* Rev. ed. Homewood, Ill.: Richard D. Irwin, Inc., 1959.
15. DWYER, PAT. *Gates and Risers for Castings.* 3d ed. Cleveland: The Penton Publishing Co., 1949.
16. EARY, DONALD F., and REED, EDWARD A. *Techniques of Pressworking Sheet Metal.* Englewood Cliffs, N.J.: Prentice-Hall, Inc., 1958.
17. GOETZEL, CLAUS G. *Treatise on Power Metallurgy.* New York: Interscience Publishers, 1952.
18. GUY, ALBERT G. *Elements of Physical Metallurgy.* Reading, Mass.: Addison-Wesley, 1959.
19. HEINE, RICHARD W., and ROSENTHAL, PHILIP C. *Principles of Metal Casting.* New York: McGraw-Hill Book Co., 1943.

20. HINMAN, CHAUNCEY W. *Pressworking of Metals.* 2d ed. New York: McGraw-Hill Book Co., 1950.
21. KEHL, ROBERT J. *Principles of Metallographic Laboratory Practice.* New York: McGraw-Hill Book Co., 1943.
22. KYLE, P. E. *The Closed Die Forging Process.* New York: The Macmillan Co., 1954.
23. LINDBERG, ROY A. *Processes and Materials of Manufacture.* Boston: Allyn and Bacon, Inc., 1964.
24. MALLORY, P. R., Co., INC. *Mallory Resistance Welding Data Book.* Indianapolis, 1951.
25. MARIN, JOSEPH. *Mechanical Behavior of Engineering Materials.* Englewood Cliffs, N.J.: Prentice-Hall, Inc., 1962.
26. NIEBEL, BENJAMIN W., and BALDWIN, EDWARD N. *Designing for Production.* Rev. ed. Homewood, Ill.: Richard D. Irwin, Inc., 1963.
27. SCHALLER, GILBERT S. *Engineering Manufacturing Methods.* 2d ed. New York: McGraw-Hill Book Co., 1959.
28. SOCIETY OF CHEMICAL INDUSTRY. *Adhesion and Adhesives, Fundamentals and Practice.* New York: John Wiley and Sons, Inc., 1954.
29. THE SOCIETY OF PLASTICS INDUSTRY, INC. *Plastics Engineering Handbook.* New York: Reinhold Publishing Corp., 1960.
30. TAYLOR, HOWARD F.; FLEMINGS, MERTON C.; and WULFF, JOHN. *Foundry Engineering.* New York: John Wiley and Sons, Inc., 1959.
31. UDIN, HARRY; FUNK, EDWARD R.; and WULFF, JOHN. *Welding for Engineers.* New York: John Wiley and Sons, Inc., 1954.
32. UHLIG, HERBERT H. (ed.). *Corrosion Handbook.* New York: John Wiley and Sons, Inc., 1948.
33. UNITED STATES STEEL CORPORATION. *The Making, Shaping and Treating of Steel.* 1957.
34. WILSON, FRANK W. (ed.). *Fundamentals of Tool Design.* American Society of Tool and Manufacturing Engineers. Englewood Cliffs, N.J.: Prentice-Hall, Inc., 1962.

Index

This book has been set on the Linotype in 10 point Janson, leaded 2 points, and 9 point Janson, leaded 1 point. Chapter numbers and titles are in 14 and 18 point Medium Extended. The size of the type page is 27 by 47 picas.